AS / Year 1 Physics

The Complete Course for OCR A

So, you've decided to study AS (or A-Level) Physics — excellent choice. From now on, admiring strangers will approach you in the street, wanting to shake your hand and quiz you on the wave-particle duality of light.

The path you've chosen won't be easy, but this brilliant CGP book will help you stay ahead throughout the course. It's packed with in-depth explanations, realistic exam practice, top advice on Maths Skills and practicals... and more!

It even includes a free Online Edition to read on a PC, Mac or tablet.

CGP

How to get your free Online Edition

Go to **cgpbooks.co.uk/extras** and enter this code...

0569 6805 4961 2939

This code will only work once. If someone has used this book before you, they may have already claimed the Online Edition.

Contents

Introduction

How Science Works

Module 1

Module 2

Module 3

How to use this book

Learning Objectives

- These tell you exactly what you need to learn, or be able to do, for the exam.
- There's a specification reference at the bottom that links to the OCR A specification.

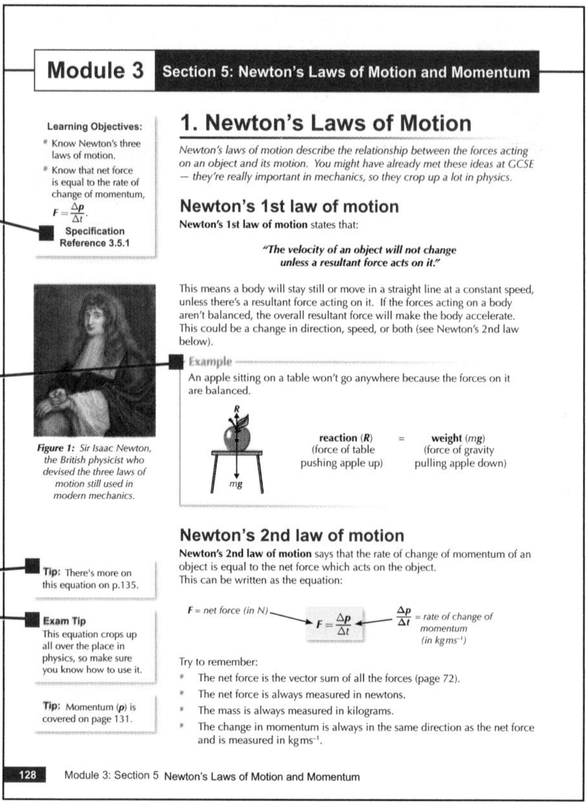
Module 3 Section 5: Newton's Laws of Motion and Momentum

Learning Objectives:
- Know Newton's three laws of motion.
- Know that net force is equal to the rate of change of momentum, $F = \frac{\Delta p}{\Delta t}$.

Specification Reference 3.5.1

1. Newton's Laws of Motion

Newton's laws of motion describe the relationship between the forces acting on an object and its motion. You might have already met these ideas at GCSE — they're really important in mechanics, so they crop up a lot in physics.

Newton's 1st law of motion

Newton's 1st law of motion states that:

"The velocity of an object will not change unless a resultant force acts on it."

This means a body will stay still or move in a straight line at a constant speed, unless there's a resultant force acting on it. If the forces acting on a body aren't balanced, the overall resultant force will make the body accelerate. This could be a change in direction, speed, or both (see Newton's 2nd law below).

Figure 1: Sir Isaac Newton, the British physicist who devised the three laws of motion still used in modern mechanics.

Example

An apple sitting on a table won't go anywhere because the forces on it are balanced.

reaction (*R*) (force of table pushing apple up) = weight (*mg*) (force of gravity pulling apple down)

Newton's 2nd law of motion

Newton's 2nd law of motion says that the rate of change of momentum of an object is equal to the net force which acts on the object. This can be written as the equation:

$$F = \frac{\Delta p}{\Delta t}$$

F = net force (in N); $\frac{\Delta p}{\Delta t}$ = rate of change of momentum (in kg ms^{-2})

Tip: There's more on this equation on p.135.

Exam Tip: This equation crops up all over the place in physics, so make sure you know how to use it.

Tip: Momentum (*p*) is covered on page 131.

Try to remember:
- The net force is the vector sum of all the forces (page 72).
- The net force is always measured in newtons.
- The mass is always measured in kilograms.
- The change in momentum is always in the same direction as the net force and is measured in kg ms^{-1}.

128 Module 3: Section 5 Newton's Laws of Motion and Momentum

Examples

These are here to help you understand the theory.

Tips and Exam Tips

There are tips throughout the book to help with all sorts of things, including exam tips to do with answering exam questions.

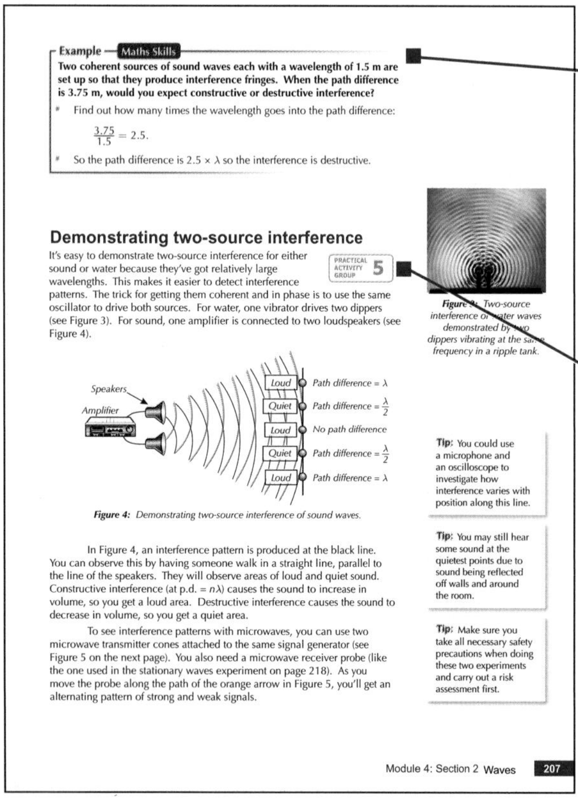
Example — Maths Skills

Two coherent sources of sound waves each with a wavelength of 1.5 m are set up so that they produce interference fringes. When the path difference is 3.75 m, would you expect constructive or destructive interference?

- Find out how many times the wavelength goes into the path difference: $\frac{3.75}{1.5} = 2.5$.
- So the path difference is 2.5 × λ so the interference is destructive.

Demonstrating two-source interference

PRACTICAL ACTIVITY GROUP 5

It's easy to demonstrate two-source interference for either sound or water because they've got relatively large wavelengths. This makes it easier to detect interference patterns. The trick for getting them coherent and in phase is to use the same oscillator to drive both sources. For water, one vibrator drives two dippers (see Figure 3). For sound, one amplifier is connected to two loudspeakers (see Figure 4).

Figure 3: Two-source interference of water waves demonstrated by two dippers vibrating at the same frequency in a ripple tank.

Speakers, Amplifier; Loud — Path difference = λ; Quiet — Path difference = λ/2; Loud — No path difference; Quiet — Path difference = λ/2; Loud — Path difference = λ

Figure 4: Demonstrating two-source interference of sound waves.

In Figure 4, an interference pattern is produced at the black line. You can observe this by having someone walk in a straight line, parallel to the line of the speakers. They will observe areas of loud and quiet sound. Constructive interference (at p.d. = *n*λ) causes the sound to increase in volume, so you get a loud area. Destructive interference causes the sound to decrease in volume, so you get a quiet area.

To see interference patterns with microwaves, you can use two microwave transmitter cones attached to the same signal generator (see Figure 5 on the next page). You also need a microwave receiver probe (like the one used in the stationary waves experiment on page 218). As you move the probe along the path of the orange arrow in Figure 5, you'll get an alternating pattern of strong and weak signals.

Tip: You could use a microphone and an oscilloscope to investigate how interference varies with position along this line.

Tip: You may still hear some sound at the quietest points due to sound being reflected off walls and around the room.

Tip: Make sure you take all necessary safety precautions when doing these two experiments and carry out a risk assessment first.

Module 4: Section 2 Waves 207

Maths Skills

There's a range of maths skills you could be expected to apply in your exams. Examples that show these maths skills in action are marked up like this. There's also a maths skills section at the back of the book.

Practical Activity Groups

If you're doing the A-level Physics course you'll need to show you've mastered some key practical skills in your Practical Endorsement. Information on the skills you need and opportunities to apply them are marked up throughout the book.

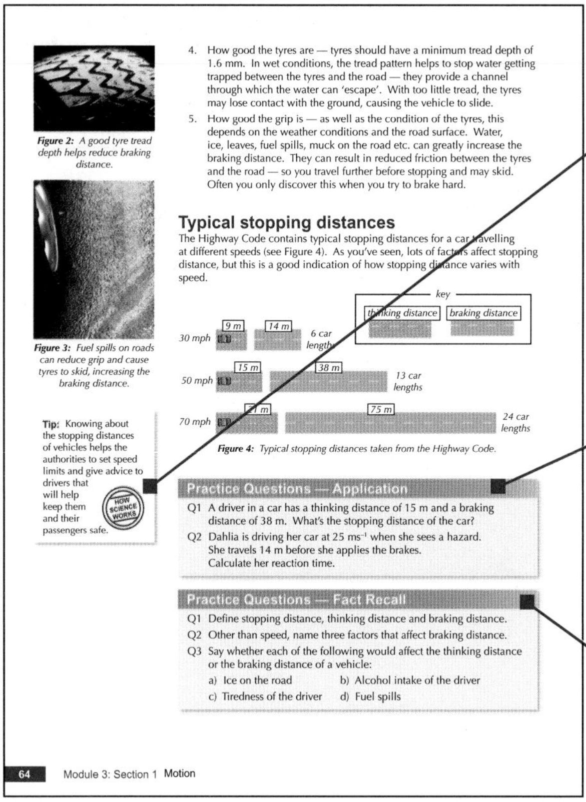

Figure 2: A good tyre tread depth helps reduce braking distance.

Figure 3: Fuel spills on roads can reduce grip and cause tyres to skid, increasing the braking distance.

Tip: Knowing about the stopping distances of vehicles helps the authorities to set speed limits and give advice to drivers that will help keep them and their passengers safe.

4. How good the tyres are — tyres should have a minimum tread depth of 1.6 mm. In wet conditions, the tread pattern helps to stop water getting trapped between the tyres and the road — they provide a channel through which the water can 'escape'. With too little tread, the tyres may lose contact with the ground, causing the vehicle to slide.
5. How good the grip is — as well as the condition of the tyres, this depends on the weather conditions and the road surface. Water, ice, leaves, fuel spills, muck on the road etc. can greatly increase the braking distance. They can result in reduced friction between the tyres and the road — so you travel further before stopping and may skid. Often you only discover this when you try to brake hard.

Typical stopping distances

The Highway Code contains typical stopping distances for a car travelling at different speeds (see Figure 4). As you've seen, lots of factors affect stopping distance, but this is a good indication of how stopping distance varies with speed.

Figure 4: Typical stopping distances taken from the Highway Code.

Practice Questions — Application

Q1 A driver in a car has a thinking distance of 15 m and a braking distance of 38 m. What's the stopping distance of the car?

Q2 Dahlia is driving her car at 25 ms⁻¹ when she sees a hazard. She travels 14 m before she applies the brakes. Calculate her reaction time.

Practice Questions — Fact Recall

Q1 Define stopping distance, thinking distance and braking distance.

Q2 Other than speed, name three factors that affect braking distance.

Q3 Say whether each of the following would affect the thinking distance or the braking distance of a vehicle:
a) Ice on the road
b) Alcohol intake of the driver
c) Tiredness of the driver
d) Fuel spills

64 Module 3: Section 1 Motion

How Science Works

- You need to know about How Science Works. There's a section on it at the front of the book.
- How Science Works is also covered throughout the book wherever you see this symbol.

HOW SCIENCE WORKS

Practice Questions — Application

- Annoyingly, the examiners expect you to be able to apply your knowledge to new situations — these questions are here to give you plenty of practice at doing this.
- All the answers are in the back of the book (including any calculation workings).

Practice Questions — Fact Recall

- There are a lot of facts you need to learn — these questions are here to test that you know them.
- All the answers are in the back of the book.

Exam-style Questions

- Practising exam-style questions is really important — you'll find some at the end of each section.
- They're the same style as the ones you'll get in the real exams — some will test your knowledge and understanding and some will test that you can apply your knowledge.
- All the answers are in the back of the book, along with a mark scheme to show you how you get the marks.

Exam Help

There's a section at the back of the book stuffed full of things to help with your exams.

Glossary

There's a glossary at the back of the book full of useful words — perfect for looking up key words and their meanings.

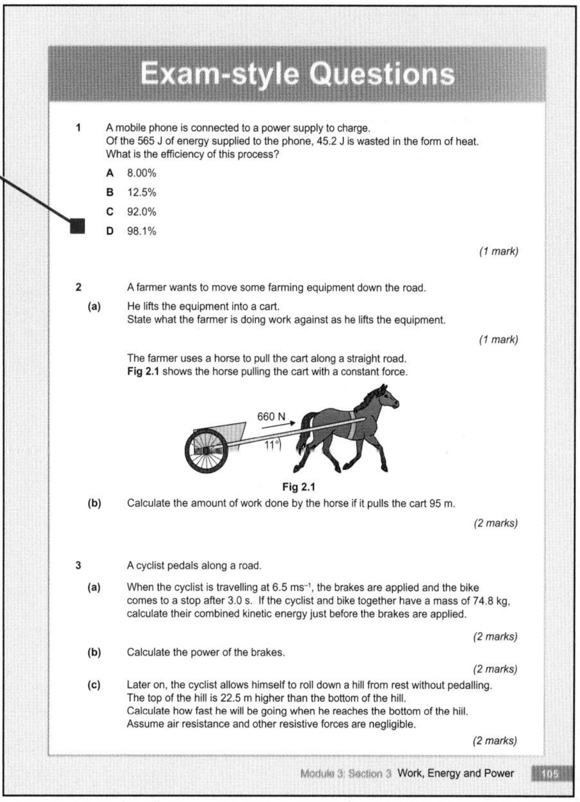

Exam-style Questions

1 A mobile phone is connected to a power supply to charge. Of the 565 J of energy supplied to the phone, 45.2 J is wasted in the form of heat. What is the efficiency of this process?
A 8.00%
B 12.5%
C 92.0%
D 98.1%
(1 mark)

2 A farmer wants to move some farming equipment down the road.
(a) He lifts the equipment into a cart. State what the farmer is doing work against as he lifts the equipment.
(1 mark)
The farmer uses a horse to pull the cart along a straight road. Fig 2.1 shows the horse pulling the cart with a constant force.

Fig 2.1

(b) Calculate the amount of work done by the horse if it pulls the cart 95 m.
(2 marks)

3 A cyclist pedals along a road.
(a) When the cyclist is travelling at 6.5 ms⁻¹, the brakes are applied and the bike comes to a stop after 3.0 s. If the cyclist and bike together have a mass of 74.8 kg, calculate their combined kinetic energy just before the brakes are applied.
(2 marks)
(b) Calculate the power of the brakes.
(2 marks)
(c) Later on, the cyclist allows himself to roll down a hill from rest without pedalling. The top of the hill is 22.5 m higher than the bottom of the hill. Calculate how fast he will be going when he reaches the bottom of the hill. Assume air resistance and other resistive forces are negligible.
(2 marks)

Module 3: Section 3 Work, Energy and Power 105

Published by CGP

Editors:
Sarah Armstrong, Emily Garrett, Duncan Lindsay, Andy Park, Frances Rooney, Charlotte Whiteley and Sarah Williams.

Contributors:
Tony Aldridge, Jane Cartwright, Peter Cecil, Mark Edwards, Barbara Mascetti, John Myers and Andy Williams.

ISBN: 978 1 78294 790 5

With thanks to Ian Francis for the proofreading.
With thanks to Ana Pungartnik for the copyright research.

Printed by Elanders Ltd, Newcastle upon Tyne.
Clipart from Corel®

The Scientific Process

Science tries to explain how and why things happen. It's all about seeking and gaining knowledge about the world around us. Scientists do this by asking questions and suggesting answers, and then testing them to see if they're correct — this is the scientific process.

Developing and testing theories

A **theory** is a possible explanation for something. Theories usually come about when scientists observe something and wonder why or how it happens. Scientists also sometimes form a **model** too — a simplified picture or representation of a real physical situation. Scientific theories and models are developed and tested in the following way:

- Ask a question — make an observation and ask why or how whatever you've observed happens.
- Suggest an answer, or part of an answer, by forming a theory or a model.
- Make a **prediction** or **hypothesis** — a specific testable statement, based on the theory, about what will happen in a test situation.
- Carry out tests — to provide evidence that will support the hypothesis or refute it (help to disprove it).

Tip: A theory is only scientific if it can be tested.

Tip: The results of one test can't prove that a theory is true — they can only suggest that it's true. They can however disprove a theory — show that it's wrong.

Example

Question: What is the nature of light?

Theory: Light is a wave.

Hypothesis: If light is a wave, it will exhibit interference effects, and be diffracted when it passes through a small enough gap.

Test: Shine light from a single source through two side-by-side narrow slits in a piece of card. If light is a wave, it will diffract as it passes through each slit. The diffracted waves from each slit will then interfere with each other when they meet. This constructive and destructive interference will produce an interference pattern of a series of bright and dark fringes. If this pattern is observed, then light has shown diffraction and interference effects, and must be a wave. This is known as Young's double slit experiment — see p.209.

Communicating results

The results of testing a scientific theory are published — scientists need to let others know about their work. Scientists publish their results in scientific journals. These are just like normal magazines, only they contain scientific reports (called papers) that use scientific terminology, instead of the latest celebrity gossip.

Scientific reports are similar to the lab write-ups you do in school. And just as a lab write-up is reviewed (marked) by your teacher, reports in scientific journals undergo **peer review** before they're published. The report is sent out to peers — other scientists who are experts in the same area.

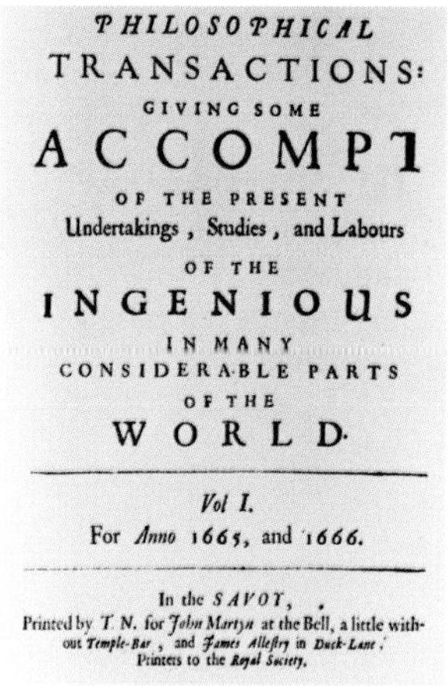
PHILOSOPHICAL
TRANSACTIONS:
GIVING SOME
ACCOMPT
OF THE PRESENT
Undertakings, Studies, and Labours
OF THE
INGENIOUS
IN MANY
CONSIDERABLE PARTS
OF THE
WORLD.
Vol I.
For Anno 1665, and 1666.
In the SAVOY,
Printed by T. N. for John Martyn at the Bell, a little without Temple-Bar, and James Allestry in Duck-Lane, Printers to the Royal Society.

Figure 1: *The first British scientific journal, 'Philosophical Transactions of the Royal Society', published in 1665.*

Tip: Scientific research is often funded by companies who have a vested interest in its outcomes. Scientists are ethically obliged to make sure that this does not bias their results.

The other scientists go through it bit by bit, examining the methods and data, and checking it's all clear and logical. Thorough evaluation allows decisions to be made about what makes a good methodology or experimental technique. Individual scientists may have their own ethical codes (based on their humanistic, moral and religious beliefs), but having their work scrutinised by other scientists helps to reduce the effect of personal bias (either deliberate or accidental) on the conclusions drawn from the results.

When the report is approved, it's published. This makes sure that work published in scientific journals is of a good standard. But peer review can't guarantee the science is correct — other scientists still need to reproduce it. Sometimes mistakes are made and bad work is published. Peer review isn't perfect but it's probably the best way for scientists to self-regulate their work and to publish quality reports.

Validating theories

Other scientists read the published theories and results, and try to test the theory themselves in order to validate it (back it up). This involves:

- Repeating the exact same experiments.
- Using the theory to make new predictions and then testing them with new experiments.

Examples

- In 1989, two scientists claimed that they'd produced 'cold fusion' (the energy source of the Sun but without the high temperatures). If it was true, it would have meant cheap energy for the world forever. However, other scientists just couldn't reproduce the results, so the theory of 'cold fusion' couldn't be validated.
- In the 1900s a study was published linking exposure to ionising radiation with an increased risk of cancer. After this, many more studies were conducted all over the world that found similar results, and so validated the conclusion of the first study.

Tip: Once an experimental method is found to give good evidence it becomes a <u>protocol</u> — an accepted method to test that particular thing that all scientists can use.

How do theories evolve?

If multiple experiments show a theory to be incorrect then scientists either have to modify the theory or develop a new one, and start the testing again. If all the experiments in all the world provide good evidence to back a theory up, the theory is thought of as scientific 'fact' (for now) — see Figure 2. But it will never become totally indisputable fact. Scientific breakthroughs or advances could provide new ways to question and test the theory, which could lead to new evidence that conflicts with the current evidence. Then the testing starts all over again... And this, my friend, is the tentative nature of scientific knowledge — it's always changing and evolving.

Tip: Sometimes data from one experiment can be the starting point for developing a new theory.

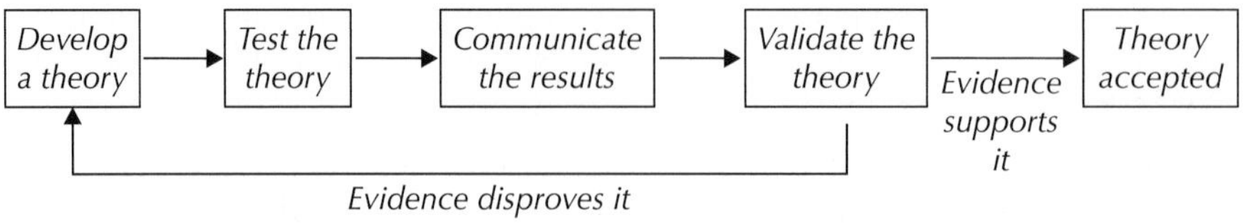

***Figure 2:** Flow diagram summarising the scientific process.*

Example

The structure of the atom

It took years and years for the current model of the atom to be developed and accepted.

Dalton's theory in the early 1800s, that atoms were solid spheres, was disputed by the results of Thomson's experiments at the end of that century. As a result, Thomson developed the 'plum pudding' model of the atom, which was later proven wrong by Rutherford's alpha-scattering experiments in 1909. Rutherford's 'nuclear model' has since been developed and modified further to create the currently accepted model of the atom we use today — but scientists are still searching for more accurate models.

Collecting evidence

1. Evidence from lab experiments

Results from controlled experiments in laboratories are great. A lab is the easiest place to control **variables** so that they're all kept constant (except for the one you're investigating). This means you can draw meaningful conclusions.

Tip: There's more about variables and drawing conclusions from lab experiments on pages 5-6 and 19-20.

Example

The speed of a trolley down a ramp

If you're investigating how the angle of a ramp affects the speed of a trolley travelling down it, you have to keep everything but the angle of the ramp constant. This means controlling things like the mass of the trolley, the distance travelled down the ramp and the surface of the ramp. Otherwise there's no way of knowing if it's the change in angle that's affecting the speed, or some other changing variable.

2. Investigations outside the lab

There are things you can't study in a lab. And outside the lab, controlling the variables is tricky, if not impossible.

Example

Does living near power lines increase the risk of developing certain cancers?

You could compare the number of cancer cases in a group of people who live near power lines to a group of people who don't. But there are always differences between groups of people. The best you can do is to have a well-designed study using matched groups — choose two groups of people (those who live near power lines and those who don't) that are as similar as possible (same mix of ages, same mix of diets etc.). But you still can't rule out every possibility.

Figure 3: *Studies are ongoing to determine if there is a link between proximity to power lines and the risk of cancer.*

Science and decision making

Scientific knowledge is used by society (that's you, me and everyone else) to make decisions — about the way we live, what we eat, what we drive, etc. All sections of society use scientific evidence to make decisions, e.g. politicians use it to devise policies and individuals use science to make decisions about their own lives.

Tip: Don't get mixed up — it's not the scientists who make the decisions, it's society. Scientists just produce evidence to help society make the decisions.

Example

X-rays are used in dentistry to see images of the teeth inside the human body. They're used to monitor dental health, including seeing when adult teeth or wisdom teeth are coming through.

However, science has found a link between exposure to X-rays and increased risk of cancer. To minimise this risk, there are restrictions on when X-ray images of a patient's mouth can be taken (e.g. not during pregnancy), and how often. As a result, patients don't tend to have X-ray images taken as part of their standard check-ups, unless there is a strong medical reason to do so.

Factors affecting decision making

The scientific evidence we have can be overshadowed by other influences such as personal bias and beliefs, public opinion, and the media.

Tip: People's perception of risk also affects how they make decisions. For example, people may underestimate the risk of things with long-term harmful effects that aren't immediately seen.

Economic factors

Society has to consider the cost of implementing changes based on scientific conclusions. Sometimes it decides the cost outweighs the benefits.

Example

Building new power plants that use renewable energy resources helps to reduce our contribution to global warming but it costs money. Sometimes the cost of building a new plant is just too much for the government to justify it, especially when government money could be put to more immediate use in, for example, the NHS or schools.

Tip: Economic factors just mean anything to do with money, and social factors just mean anything to do with people.

Social factors

Decisions affect people's lives — sometimes people don't want to follow advice, or are strongly against some recommendations.

Examples

- Exposure to UV radiation from tanning beds can lead to cancer. Scientists recommend that people don't use tanning beds, but shouldn't we be able to choose whether we want to use them or not?
- People may not want new wind farms to be built in certain locations, as they believe that the turbines spoil the view.

Figure 4: *Wind farms are often built at sea to reduce the impact on people.*

Environmental factors

Some scientific research and breakthroughs might affect the environment. Not everyone thinks the benefits are worth the possible environmental damage.

Example

Hydroelectricity requires the building of a dam. This often destroys the habitats of plants and animals, so many think that other renewable energy resources should be used instead.

1. Planning an Experiment

You have to do practical work in class as part of your course. You'll be asked about it in exams too, so you need to know how to plan the perfect experiment.

Designing an experiment

PRACTICAL ACTIVITY GROUP 11

HOW SCIENCE WORKS

Before you start planning an experiment, you need to be clear about what you're trying to find out. You might be asked to design a physics experiment to investigate something or answer a question. It could be a lab experiment that you've seen before, or something applied, like deciding which building material is best for a particular job. Either way, you'll be able to use the physics you know from your course and the skills in this topic to figure out the best way to investigate the problem.

Planning experiments

Planning an experiment properly helps to make your results valid, accurate and precise (see p.18). There's plenty of info on the next few pages, but here's a summary of how you go about it...

- Make a prediction or hypothesis — you need to come up with an idea (or question) based on a theory. This is what you'll be trying to prove (or answer) with an experiment.
- Think about the aims of the experiment and identify the independent, dependent and control variables (see below).
- Select appropriate equipment (see next page) that will give you accurate and precise results.
- Do a risk assessment and plan any safety precautions (see p.8).
- Decide what data to collect and how you'll do it (p.9).
- Write out a clear and detailed method — it should be clear enough that anyone could follow it and repeat your experiment exactly.
- Carry out tests — to provide evidence that will support the prediction or refute it.

Variables

You probably know this all off by heart but it's easy to get mixed up sometimes. So here's a quick recap.

A **variable** is a quantity that has the potential to change, e.g. mass. There are two types of variable commonly referred to in experiments:

Independent variable — the thing that you change in an experiment.

Dependent variable — the thing that you measure in an experiment.

Learning Objectives:

- Know how to design experiments, including how to solve problems set in a practical context.
- Be able to identify variables that must be controlled, where appropriate.
- Be able to select appropriate units for measurements.
- Know how to use a wide range of practical apparatus and techniques correctly.
- Be able to evaluate whether an experimental method is appropriate to meet the expected outcomes.

Specification References 1.1.1 and 1.1.2

Tip: There's lots more about how hypotheses are created and the scientific process in How Science Works on pages 1-4.

Tip: Time is <u>always</u> an independent variable.

Tip: For more on potentiometers see page 173.

Example

You could investigate the effect of varying the potential difference across a filament lamp on the current flowing through it using the circuit shown in Figure 1 below:

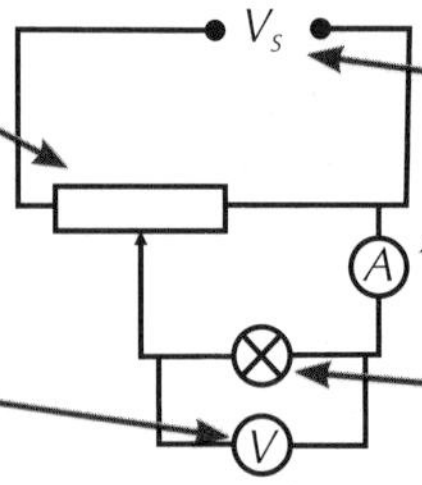

Potentiometer — to alter the potential difference supplied to the filament lamp from 0 V to the source voltage, V_s.
V_s
Power supply.
Ammeter — to measure the current flowing through the filament lamp.
A
Filament lamp.
Voltmeter — to measure the potential difference.
V

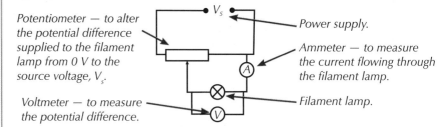

Figure 1: *Circuit diagram for measuring the current flowing through a filament lamp.*

- The independent variable will be the potential difference supplied to the lamp.
- The dependent variable will be the current flowing through the lamp.

Apart from the independent and dependent variables, all other variables should stay the same during your experiment. These are known as **control variables**. If control variables are not kept the same, you can't tell whether or not the independent variable is responsible for any changes in your dependent variable, so your results won't be valid (page 18). Control variables that are likely to change during your experiment should be measured to check that they are constant throughout the experiment.

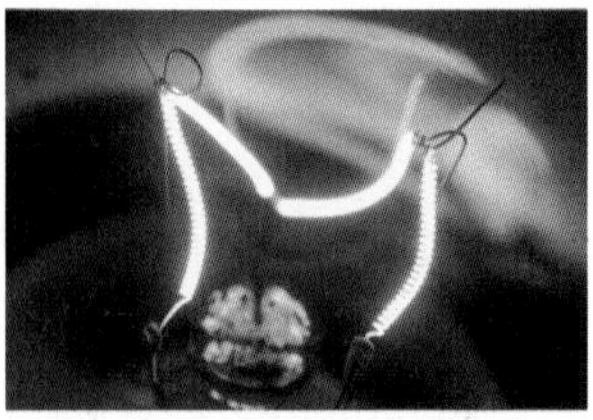

Figure 2: *The filament in a bulb is designed to heat up, so it should be allowed to cool in between repeats to make the experiment a fair test.*

Example cont.

So for the circuit experiment above, the control variables include the length of the connecting leads, the filament bulb used and the temperature of the circuit wires. To keep the temperature constant, you might use small potential differences (and currents) to stop the circuit wires heating up during the experiment, and allow the filament to cool between repeats.

Apparatus and techniques

Before you start, make sure you're measuring things using appropriate units. To choose the correct units, you need to think about what scale your measurements of the independent and dependent variables are likely to be on (e.g. millimetres or metres, milliseconds or hours) and how you're going to analyse the results later.

Example

If you're measuring time, it might be better to use seconds rather than minutes — when you come to processing your results, it'll be easier to work with a result of 73 seconds than a result of 1.217 minutes.

Think about the range you plan on taking measurements over too — e.g. if you're measuring the effect of increasing the force on a spring, you need to know whether you should increase the force in steps of 1 newton, 10 newtons or 100 newtons. Sometimes, you'll be able to estimate what effect changing your independent variable will have, or sometimes a **pilot experiment** might help. In a pilot experiment, the apparatus is set up as it will be used in the actual experiment, and the independent variable is varied to see (roughly) how much the dependent variable changes.

Example

A student is investigating the extension of a test wire using the apparatus in Figure 3. She will add weights to the wire and measure its extension using the marker and the ruler.

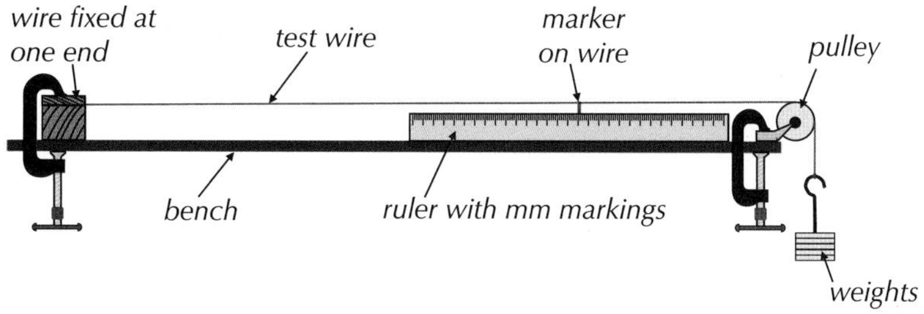

Figure 3: *Experimental set-up for investigating the extension of a test wire.*

She decides to do a pilot experiment to decide on the increments in which she should add weights to the test wire. She is aiming to find out how much weight needs to be added to cause the marker on the wire to move a measurable distance along the ruler that can be clearly recorded, but won't bring the wire close to the point at which it will snap.

Tip: There's more on using this apparatus on page 117.

Tip: The extension being measured here is very small, so you need a long piece of wire for the change to be noticeable. The wire is too long to suspend vertically from a clamp, which is why the pulley is more suitable here.

Tip: Measuring a distance that is small compared to the resolution of your equipment will lead to a high percentage error in your measurements — see page 16.

Considering your measurements before you start will also help you choose the most appropriate apparatus and techniques for the experiment. You want to pick the apparatus that will give you the best results. Make sure you know how to use all the instruments and equipment you've come across in class and can carry out all the techniques too.

Examples

- If you're measuring the length of a spring that you're applying a force to, you might need a ruler. If you're measuring the diameter of a wire, you'd be better off with some callipers.
- If you're measuring a time interval, you could use a stopwatch. If the time is really short (for example if you're investigating acceleration due to gravity of an object as it falls to the floor), you might need something more sensitive, like light gates (see page 59).

Tip: Remember — part of choosing your apparatus and planning your technique will involve thinking about safety precautions. This should all be covered in your risk assessment (see next page).

Make sure you perform all techniques carefully and that any apparatus is set up correctly — this will help to minimise errors which would affect your results. E.g. if you're measuring a length, make sure your eye is level with the ruler when you take the measurement.

Figure 4: *Goggles should be used in most experiments to protect the eyes from any moving objects, snapping wires, chemicals and other dangers.*

Identifying risks

HOW SCIENCE WORKS

You'll be expected to show that you can identify any risks and hazards in an experiment. You'll need to take appropriate safety measures depending on the experiment. For example, for anything involving lasers you'll probably need to wear special laser goggles.

Evaluating experiment designs

HOW SCIENCE WORKS

If you need to evaluate an experiment design, whether it's your own or someone else's, you need to think about the following things:

- Does the experiment actually test what it sets out to test?
- Is the method clear enough for someone else to follow?
- Apart from the independent and dependent variables, is everything else going to be properly controlled?
- Are the apparatus and techniques appropriate for what's being measured? Will they be used correctly?
- Will the method give precise results? E.g. are repeat measurements going to be taken in order to calculate a mean value (see page 17)?
- Is the experiment going to be conducted safely?

Exam Tip
Examiners love getting you to suggest improvements to methods — e.g. how a method could be improved to make the results more precise, so make sure you know how to design a good experiment.

Practice Question — Application

Q1 A student is investigating how the angle of a ramp, θ, affects the final velocity of a trolley as it travels 1 m down the ramp. He measures the velocity at the bottom of the ramp using a light gate. The student assumes the friction acting on the trolley is negligible. He sets up the following apparatus:

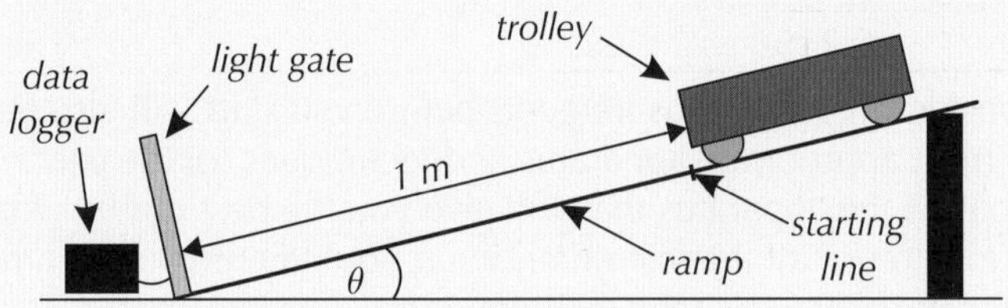

a) Name the independent and dependent variables in this investigation.

b) Name one variable in this investigation that the student should keep the same.

Tip: The light gate is a suitable piece of apparatus to use in this experiment as it can measure the instantaneous velocity of the trolley as it is accelerating. This is not possible with a stopwatch.

Practice Questions — Fact Recall

Q1 Why is it important to make sure the control variables don't change during an experiment?

Q2 State what is meant by a pilot experiment, and explain why they are used.

Q3 Give three things that must be considered when evaluating an experimental method.

2. Recording and Processing Data

Time to find out how to record your data correctly, and how to do maths-y things with your data like calculating means. The fun doesn't end...

Tables of data

You need to make a table to write your results in. You should include:

- Space for your independent variable and your dependent variable. You should specify the units in the headers, not within the table itself.
- Space to repeat each measurement at least three times to reduce random error and make sure your final results are more precise (see p.17), and to spot anomalous results (p.10).
- Space for any results from data processing you need to do, e.g. calculating the mean from repeats (see the next page), or calculating speed from measurements of distance and time. (Your table shouldn't include your workings, just the results from your calculations.)

Your table should have the independent variable in the first column, and the dependent variable in the columns next to that. Any results from data processing should be in the furthest right-hand column(s). Figure 1 is the sort of table you might end up with when you investigate the effect of potential difference (p.d.) on current.

P.d. /V	Current / A Run 1	Current / A Run 2	Current / A Run 3	Mean current / A (to 3 s.f.)
0.0	0.000	0.000	0.000	**0.000**
1.0	0.104	0.105	0.102	**0.104**
2.0	0.150	0.151	0.149	**0.150**
3.0	0.188	0.187	0.187	**0.187**
4.0	0.219	0.220	0.193	**0.220**

Figure 1: *Table of results showing the effect of p.d. on current through a resistor.*

Most of the time, you'll be recording numerical values, known as **quantitative data**. Occasionally, you may have to deal with data that can be observed but not measured with a numerical value. This is known as **qualitative data** (see Figure 2). It's still best to record this kind of data in a table to keep your results organised, but the layout may be a little different.

Rounding to significant figures

When using your data in further calculations you need to consider significant figures. The first significant figure of a number is the first digit that isn't a zero. The second, third and fourth significant figures follow on immediately after the first (even if they're zeros).

Example — Maths Skills

0.6074976 rounds to **0.61** to **2 s.f.** and to **0.607** to **3 s.f.**

When you're doing calculations using measurements given to a certain number of significant figures, you should give your answer to the lowest number of significant figures that was used in the calculation.

The lowest number of significant figures in the calculation is used because the fewer digits a measurement has, the less accurate it is. Your answer can only be as accurate as the least accurate measurement in the calculation.

Learning Objectives:

- Be able to record and present observations and data in an appropriate format.
- Understand the terms 'qualitative results' and 'quantitative results'.
- Be able to use significant figures appropriately.
- Be able to process experimental results.
- Be able to use appropriate mathematical skills to process quantitative data.
- Be able to identify anomalies in experimental measurements.

Specification References 1.1.2 1.1.3 and 1.1.4

Tip: You should give all of your data to the number of decimal places that you measured to — e.g. 0.000 A, not just 0 A.

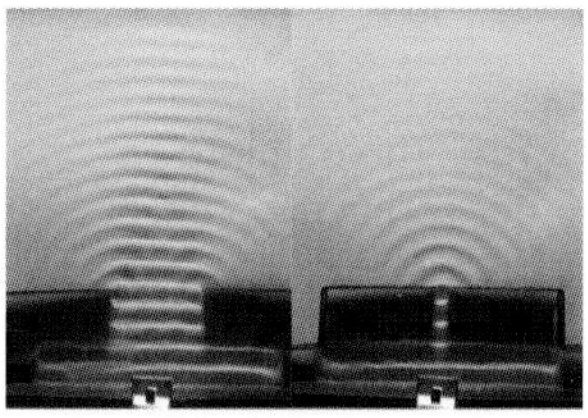

Figure 2: *Measuring how the diffraction of water waves varies with gap width will involve recording qualitative data.*

Exam Tip
You shouldn't give your answer to too few significant figures. So if the lowest number of significant figures in a calculation is 3, then you shouldn't give your answer to 1 or 2 significant figures. You could lose a mark in the exam if you do this.

Example — Maths Skills

For the calculation: $1.2 \div 1.85 = 0.648648648...$

1.2 is given to 2 s.f. and 1.85 is given to 3 s.f., so the answer should be given to 2 s.f.: $1.2 \div 1.85 =$ **0.65 (to 2 s.f.)**

Calculating a mean

For many experiments, you'll need to calculate the arithmetic **mean** (average) of some repeated measurements:

$$\text{arithmetic mean (average) of a measurement} = \frac{\text{sum of your repeated measurements}}{\text{number of measurements taken}}$$

Watch out for **anomalous results**. These are ones that don't fit in with the other values and are likely to be wrong. They're usually due to experimental errors, such as making a mistake when measuring (see page 29). You should ignore anomalous results when you calculate averages.

Tip: Just because you ignore anomalous results in your calculations, you shouldn't ignore them in your write-up. Try to find an explanation for what went wrong so that it can be avoided in future experiments.

Example — Maths Skills

Look at the table in Figure 1 again — the current at 4.0 V in Run 3 looks like it might be an anomalous result. It's much lower than the values in the other two runs. It could have been caused by the filament lamp being hotter at the end of Run 3 than it was at the end of the first two runs.

The anomalous result should be ignored to calculate the average:

With anomalous result: $(0.219 + 0.220 + 0.193) \div 3 = 0.211$ (to 3 s.f.)

Without anomalous result: $(0.219 + 0.220) \div 2 = 0.220$ (to 3 s.f.)

So the average current at 4.0 V should be 0.220 A (rather than 0.211 A).

Practice Questions — Application

Q1 Calculate the following, giving your answer to the correct number of significant figures:

a) 4.53×3.142 b) $0.315 \div 0.025$

Q2 A scientist carries out an investigation to find the force constant of a spring. She adds different masses to the spring, then records the weight of the masses and the spring's extension. Her results are shown in the table below. Complete the table by calculating the mean extension of the spring for each weight.

Tip: There's more on this spring experiment on page 109.

Weight / N	*Extension / cm*			
	Trial 1	*Trial 2*	*Trial 3*	*Mean*
2.0	2.9	3.2	3.1	
4.0	5.8	8.6	5.9	
6.0	8.4	8.4	8.5	

Practice Questions — Fact Recall

Q1 What is meant by quantitative data?

Q2 What is an anomalous result?

3. Presenting Results

When you're planning an experiment, you need to think about the best way to present your results. It all depends on what sort of data you've got...

Learning Objective:

- Be able to plot suitable graphs from experimental results, including selecting and labelling axes with appropriate scales, quantities and units.

Specification Reference 1.1.3

Types of data

1. Discrete data

You get discrete data by counting. E.g. the number of weights added to the end of a spring would be discrete (see Figure 1). You can't have 1.25 weights. That'd be daft. Shoe size is another good example of a discrete variable — only certain values are allowed.

There are lots of ways to present discrete data, depending on what other data sets you've recorded. Scatter graphs (p.12) and bar charts are often used.

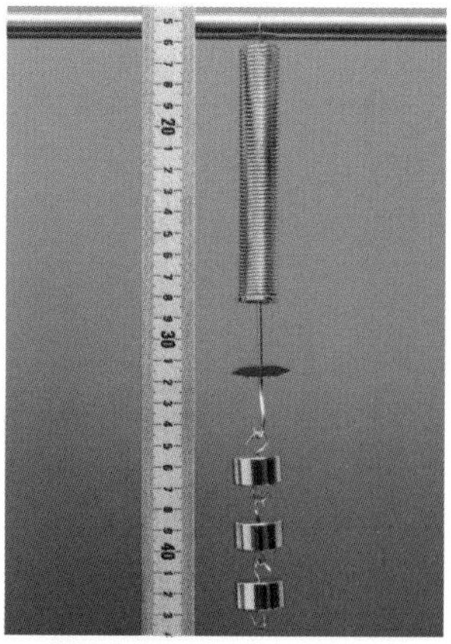

Figure 1: *The number of weights added to a spring is discrete data. The spring's extension is continuous data.*

2. Continuous data

A continuous variable can have any value on a scale. For example, the extension of a spring or the current through a circuit. You can never measure the exact value of a continuous variable.

The best way to display two sets of continuous data is a line graph or a scatter graph (see page 12).

3. Categoric data

A categoric variable has values that can be sorted into categories. For example, types of material might be brass, wood, glass or steel.

If one of your data sets is categoric, a pie chart or a bar chart is often used to present the data — see Figure 2.

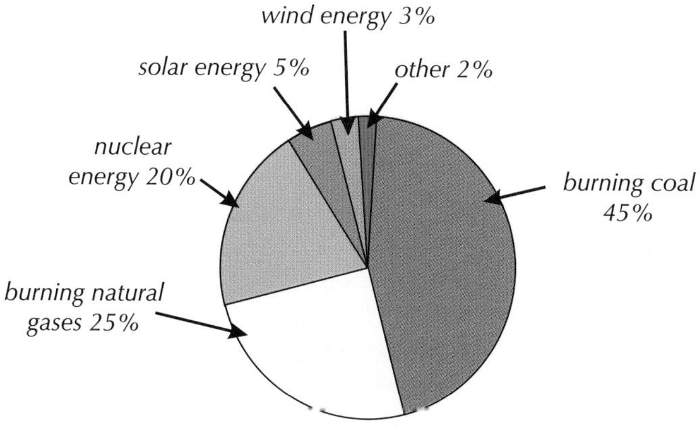

Figure 2: *Categoric data of different types of energy production in a particular country presented on a pie chart.*

4. Ordered (ordinal) data

Ordered data is similar to categoric, but the categories can be put in order. For example, if you classify frequencies of light as 'low', 'fairly high' and 'very high' you'd have ordered data.

A bar chart is often used if one of your data sets is ordered — see Figure 3.

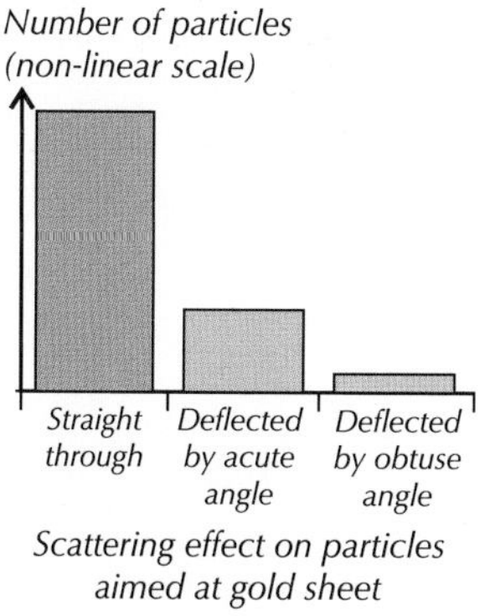

Figure 3: *Ordered data of particle scattering effects presented on a bar chart.*

Tip: Axes increments should go up in sensible amounts that are easy plot, like 1s, 2s, 0.1s, etc. You shouldn't ever use awkward increments like 3s or 7s as any intermediate points between those labels would be very tricky to plot or read.

Tip: You should make sure the scale is labelled with numbers regularly, e.g. at least every three large squares.

Scatter graphs

You can plot discrete or continuous data on a scatter graph. These are useful for spotting any correlation between two variables (see the next page). Usually, the independent variable goes on the *x*-axis and the dependent variable goes on the *y*-axis. Both axes should be labelled clearly, with the quantity and units. The scales used should be sensible (i.e. they should go up in sensible steps, and should spread the data out over the full graph rather than bunching it up in a corner). If you need to use your graph to measure something, select units for your axes that will let you do this easily (e.g. by measuring the gradient or the intercept, see pages 14 and 15).

Plot your points using a sharp pencil, to make sure they're as accurate as possible. You need to draw a line of best fit for your results. Around half the data points should be above the line, and half should be below it (you should ignore anomalous results). Depending on the data, the line of best fit might be straight or curved.

Example — Maths Skills

An experiment is carried out to see how the acceleration of a trolley is dependent on the force acting on it. The results are shown in the graph.

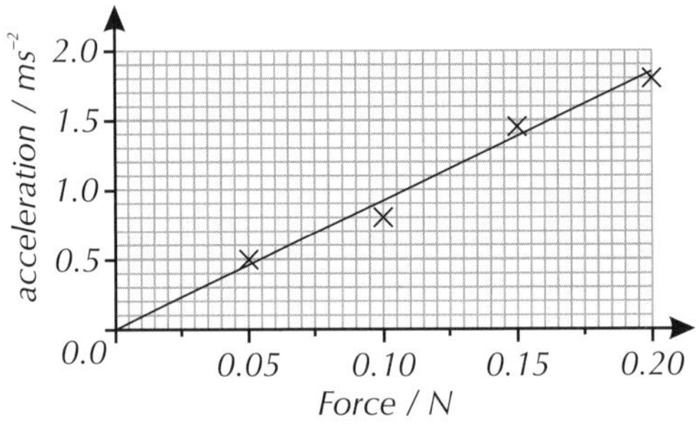

- The force is the independent variable and so is on the *x*-axis.
- The acceleration is the dependent variable and so is on the *y*-axis.
- The line of best fit is a straight line, with 2 points above the line and 2 points below it.

Example — Maths Skills

- In the graph on the right, the points show that the velocity is increasing at an increasing rate over time.
- So a curved line of best fit is drawn.

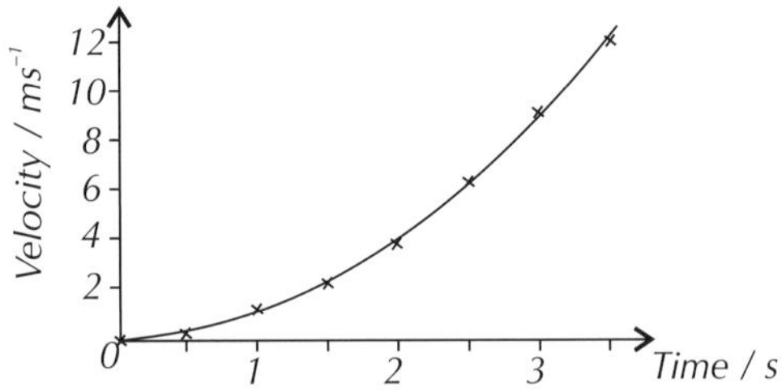

Practice Question — Application

Q1 A car is accelerating along a road. A computer connected to the car measures the velocity of the car every 2.5 s. The results are shown in the table below. Plot a suitable graph for the data.

Time / s	0.0	2.5	5.0	7.5	10.0	12.5	15.0
Velocity / mph	0.0	12.8	22.4	29.0	33.3	35.8	37.0

Practice Questions — Fact Recall

Q1 Give one way that categoric data can be presented in results.

Q2 Which variable usually goes on the *x*-axis of a scatter graph?

4. Analysing Results

Now you've got your data, you can use your results to describe what happened in the experiment. You can also use your results to calculate more quantities.

Learning Objectives:

- Be able to analyse and interpret qualitative and quantitative experimental results.
- Be able to use appropriate mathematical skills for analysis of quantitative data.
- Be able to interpret suitable graphs from experimental results, including by taking measurements of gradients and intercepts.

Specification Reference 1.1.3

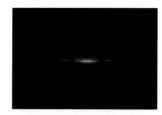

Qualitative data

Analysing qualitative data is a bit more wordy than analysing quantitative data. You need to be able to talk about what your results are showing.

Example

An experiment is carried out to see the diffraction patterns produced by shining a laser through a slit in a piece of card. The size of the slit is varied to see the effect on the diffraction pattern.
A sketch of the results are shown below.

Slit = 0.02 mm | Slit = 0.04 mm | Slit = 0.06 mm

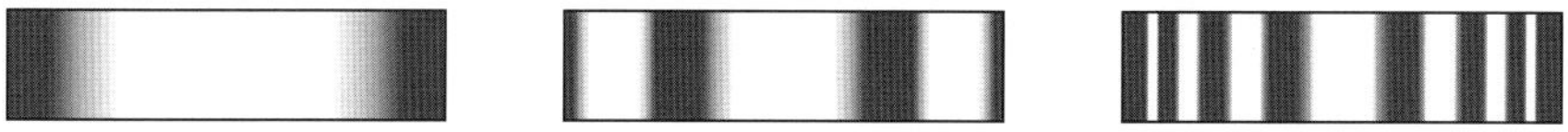

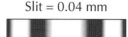

From these results you can see that as the slit gets wider, the pattern gets narrower — there are more fringes in a given area.

Figure 1: The diffraction pattern produced when a laser is shone through a slit. *There's more on diffraction patterns on p.205.*

Scatter graphs and correlation

HOW SCIENCE WORKS

Correlation describes the relationship between two variables — usually the independent one and the dependent one. Data can show positive correlation, negative correlation or no correlation (see Figure 2).

Positive correlation
As one variable increases, the other also increases.

Negative correlation
As one variable increases, the other decreases.

No correlation
There is no relationship between the variables.

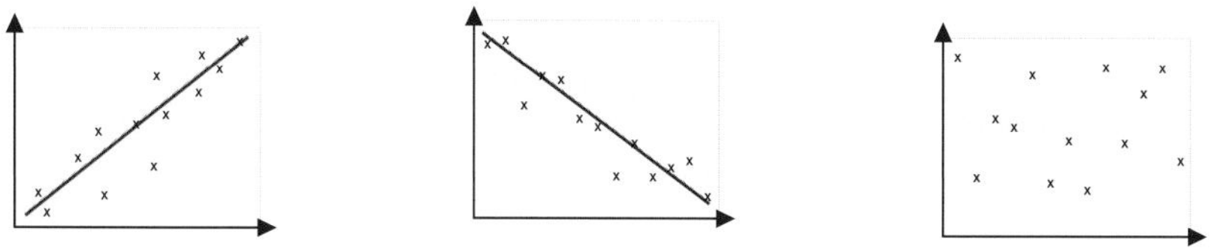

Figure 2: Scatter graphs showing positive, negative and no correlation.

Tip: You have to be very careful when drawing conclusions from data like this because a correlation between two variables doesn't always mean that a change in one variable causes a change in the other. There's more on this on page 20.

Linear graphs

If you plot two variables that have a linear relationship, you'll get a straight line of best fit. The equation of a straight line is $y = mx + c$, where m = gradient (slope of the line) and c = y-intercept. This means you can use your graph to work out certain values, and the relationship between your variables.

Proportionality

If you plot two variables against each other and get a straight line that goes through the origin, the two variables are **directly proportional**. The y-intercept, c, is 0, so the equation of the straight line is $y = mx$ where m is a constant. The constant of proportionality, m, is the gradient of the graph.

You can show two variables as being directly proportional using the symbol $\propto$. For example $x \propto y$ means that x is directly proportional to y.

Example — Maths Skills

Current and potential difference are directly proportional for ohmic conductors. You can see this by using the circuit in Figure 3. Use the variable resistor to decrease (or increase) the resistance in small equal steps. This changes the amount of current flowing through the ohmic conductor. Take readings of current through it and potential difference across it at each step. Once you have all the data, plot a graph of I against V (Figure 4). The graph you'll get is a straight line going through the origin — so current and potential difference are directly proportional.

Tip: For more on this experiment see page 155.

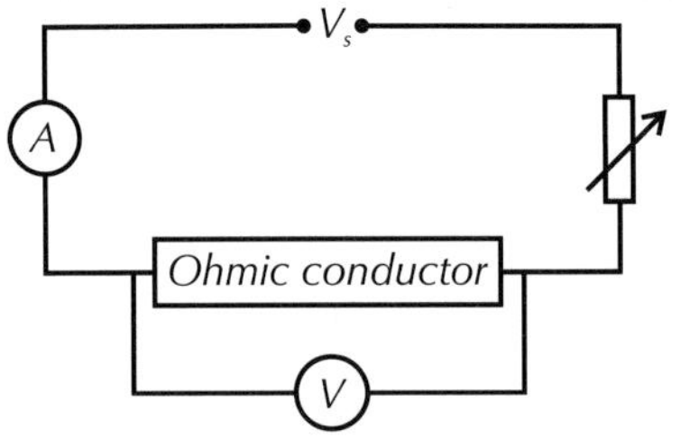

Figure 3: *Circuit for showing the proportional relationship between I and V for an ohmic conductor.*

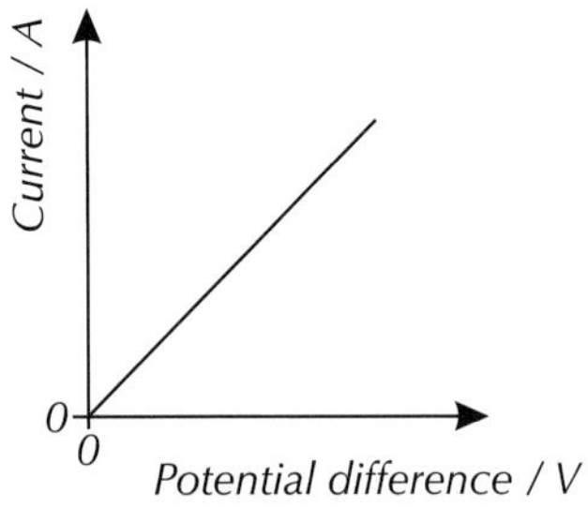

Figure 4: *An I-V graph for an ohmic conductor.*

Finding the gradient and *y*-intercept

If you've plotted a linear graph, you can read the gradient and *y*-intercept straight off it. This means you can work out certain quantities from your graph. You can find the gradient of the straight-line graph using:

$$\text{Gradient} = \frac{\text{Change in } y}{\text{Change in } x}$$

You should draw a triangle to help you find the gradient of a line. Make it as big as possible — it should take up more than half of the line, and use values you can easily read from the graph.

Example — Maths Skills

Returning to the example of the ohmic conductor above, you can use the I-V graph to calculate the resistance of the component:

- I and V are directly proportional, so $I = kV$, where k is a constant.
- You know from $V = IR$ that $I = \frac{1}{R}V$.
- $I = \frac{1}{R}V$ is the equation of a straight line where $y = I$, $x = V$, $m = \frac{1}{R}$ and $c = 0$.
- You can work out $\frac{1}{R}$ from the graph — it's the gradient.

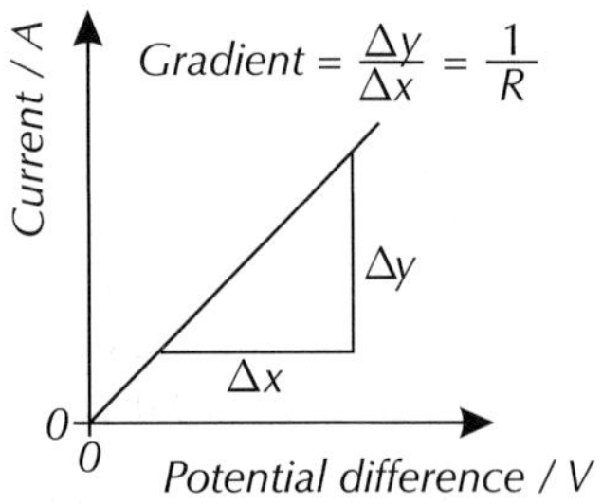

Figure 5: *Using an I-V graph to work out the resistance of an ohmic conductor.*

Tip: To find R, just calculate the inverse of $\frac{1}{R}$ found from the graph.

Tip: The gradient of an I-V graph like this is <u>only</u> equal to $\frac{1}{R}$ if the graph is a straight line through the origin (which is only true for ohmic conductors — see page 152).

Example — Maths Skills

The solid line in the graph in Figure 6 shows how the maximum kinetic energy of the photoelectrons from a metal surface varies with the frequency of the light shining on it. You can use a graph like this to find the value of the work function of the metal (ϕ) by extending the graph back to the y-axis.

Rearranging the equation $hf = \phi + KE_{max}$ gives $KE_{max} = hf - \phi$. Since h and ϕ are constants, $KE_{max} = hf - \phi$ is just the equation of a straight line (in the form: $y = mx + c$). You can just read ϕ from the graph — it's the intercept on the vertical axis. You'll just need to continue the line back to the y-axis to find the intercept, then the value of the y-intercept will be $-\phi$.

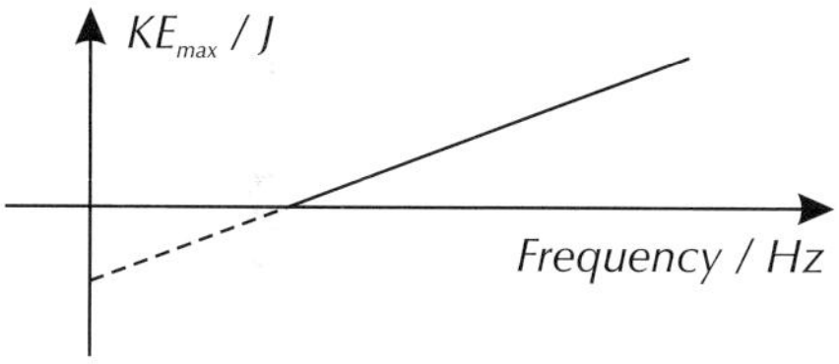

Figure 6: *You can extend the line on a graph to find the y-intercept.*

Tip: For more on work functions, see page 230.

Tip: Here, $y = KE_{max}$, $m = h$, x = frequency and $c = -\phi$.

Tip: If you were to calculate the gradient, you should get h, Planck's constant.

Non-linear relationships

Linear graphs are really easy to work with, but some variables won't produce a straight line if you plot them against each other. You can sometimes change what you plot on the axes so that you get one though.

For example, say two variables are inversely proportional, then $y = \frac{k}{x}$, where k is a constant. If you plot y against x, you'll get a curved graph which shoots off to infinity (Figure 7). It's not very easy to work out the value of k from this graph, but if you plot y against $\frac{1}{x}$ you'll get a lovely straight line (Figure 8) with a constant gradient of k that goes through the origin. This is because the graph plotted is $y = k\left(\frac{1}{x}\right)$, which is just the equation of a straight line in form $y = mx + c$, where $m = k$ and $x = \frac{1}{x}$ (and $c = 0$).

If you want to find the gradient of a point on a curved line of best fit, you can draw a tangent to the curve at that point and then find the gradient of the tangent (see p.248).

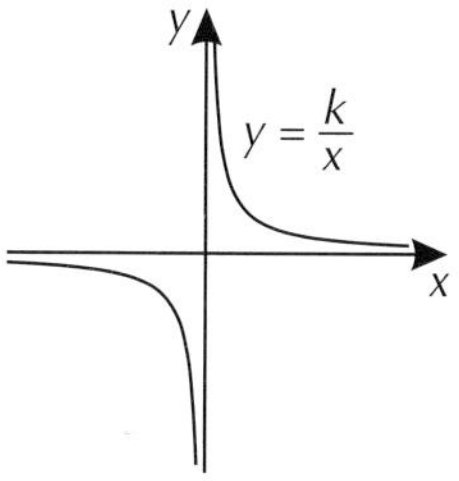

Figure 7: *An inverse proportionality relationship between x and y.*

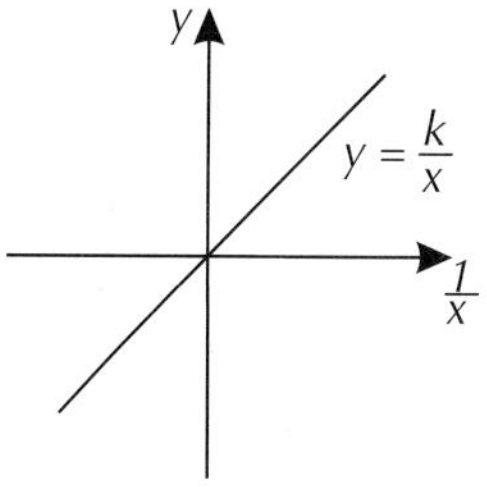

Figure 8: *If $y = \frac{k}{x}$, plotting y against $\frac{1}{x}$ gives a straight line through the origin.*

Practice Question — Application

Q1 A student wants to find the internal resistance of a cell. He sets up a series circuit containing the cell and a variable resistor. He varies the resistance of the variable resistor and records the current through and the potential difference (p.d.) across the cell. A graph of his results is shown on the right.

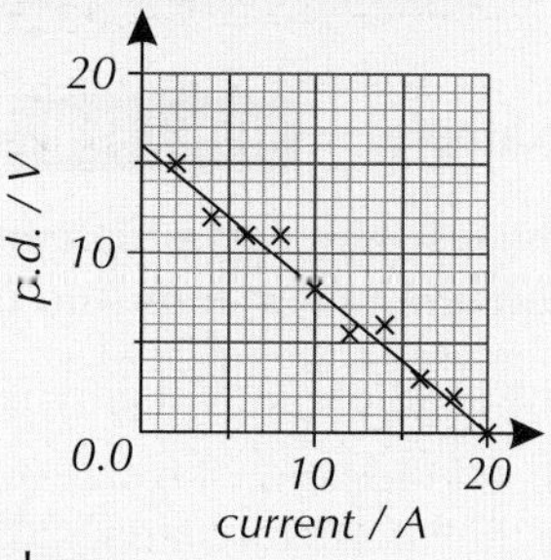

a) State what type of correlation the graph shows.

The graph illustrates the relation $V = \varepsilon - Ir$.

b) Determine ε, the e.m.f. of the cell.

c) Calculate r, the internal resistance of the cell.

Tip: This experiment is shown on page 166.

Learning Objectives:

- Understand precision and accuracy of measurements and data, including margins of error, percentage errors and uncertainties in apparatus.
- Understand how to evaluate results.
- Be able to refine experimental designs by suggesting improvements to the procedures and apparatus.
- Be able to identify the limitations in experimental procedures.
- Be able to draw conclusions.

Specification Reference 1.1.4

Figure 1: *This thermometer measures to the nearest °C. Any measurement you take using it will have an uncertainty of ± 0.5 °C.*

Tip: There's more about different types of errors and how to do calculations with uncertainty on pages 29 and 30 .

Tip: Take a look at page 10 for a reminder on the mean.

5. Evaluating and Drawing Conclusions

You need to be able to evaluate your results and draw conclusions from them. You also need to be able to evaluate and draw conclusions from other people's data — which is what you're likely to be asked to do in the exams.

Uncertainty

When you're evaluating your results, it's often a good idea to talk about the uncertainty in your data — in other words, the amount of error there might be. The results you get from an experiment won't be completely perfect — there'll always be a degree of uncertainty in your readings or measurements due to limits in the sensitivity of the apparatus you're using. Say you measure the temperature of a beaker of water with an analogue thermometer. You might think you've measured its temperature as 21 °C, but at best you've probably measured it to be 21 ± 0.5 °C. And that's without taking into account any other errors that might be in your measurement.

If you measure a length of something with a ruler, you actually take two measurements, one at each end of the object you're measuring. There is an uncertainty in each of these measurements. E.g. a length of 17.0 cm measured using a mm ruler will have an uncertainty of 0.05 + 0.05 = ± 0.1 cm (page 30).

The ± bit gives you the range in which the true value (the one you'd really like to know) probably lies. For the length above, 17 ± 0.1 cm tells you the true length is very likely to lie in the range of 16.9 to 17.1 cm. The maximum difference between your value and the true value (here 0.1 cm) is sometimes called the **margin of error**.

The smaller the uncertainty in a result or measurement, the smaller the range of possible values the result could have and the more precise your data can be. There are two measures of uncertainty you need to know about:

Absolute uncertainty — the total uncertainty for a measurement.

Percentage error — the uncertainty given as a percentage of the measurement.

Example — Maths Skills

The resistance of a filament lamp is given as 5.0 ± 0.4 Ω. Give the absolute uncertainty and the percentage error for this measurement.

The absolute uncertainty is 0.4 Ω.

To get the percentage error, just convert this to a percentage of the lamp's resistance: (0.4 ÷ 5.0) × 100 = 8%

The uncertainty on a mean of repeated results is equal to half the range of the results. E.g. say the repeated measurement of a current gives the results 0.5 A, 0.3 A, 0.3 A, 0.3 A and 0.4 A. The range of these results is 0.5 – 0.3 = 0.2 A, so the uncertainty on the mean current would be ± 0.1 A.

Reducing uncertainty

There are a few different ways you can reduce the uncertainty in your results:

Repeating and averaging

One of the easiest things you can do is repeat each measurement several times. The more repeats you do, and the more similar the results of each repeat are, the more precise the data.

By taking an average (mean) of your repeated measurements (see p.10), you will reduce the random error in your result. The more measurements you average over, the less random error you're likely to have. Repeating also allows you to check your data for any anomalous results (see p.10).

Tip: Precision and errors are covered on pages 18 and 29.

Using appropriate equipment

You can also cut down the uncertainty in your measurements by using the most appropriate equipment. The smallest possible uncertainty in a measurement is usually taken to be ± half the smallest interval that the measuring instrument can measure. A micrometer scale has smaller intervals than a millimetre ruler, so by measuring a wire's diameter with a micrometer instead of a ruler, you instantly cut down the random error in your experiment.

Computers and data loggers can often be used to measure smaller intervals than you can measure by hand and reduce random errors, e.g. timing an object's fall using a light gate rather than a stopwatch. You also get rid of any human error that might creep in while taking the measurements.

There's a limit to how much you can reduce the random uncertainties in your measurements, as all measuring equipment has a **resolution** — the smallest change in what's being measured that can be detected by the equipment. The resolution of the equipment is an example of a limitation of an experiment (see the next page).

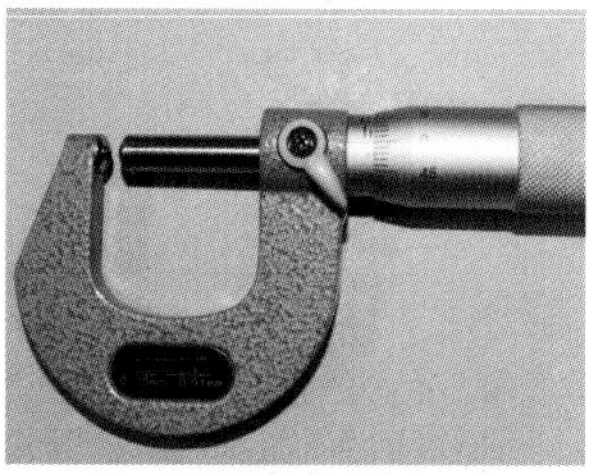

Figure 2: *A micrometer is very precise, it gives readings to within 0.01 mm.*

Tip: A data logger (or data recorder) is an electronic device that can record data over time using a sensor. They can sometimes be connected to a computer.

Significant figures and uncertainty

You always have to assume the largest amount of uncertainty in data.

Whether you're looking at experimental results or just doing a calculation question in an exam, you must round your results to the same number of significant figures as the given data value with the fewest significant figures. Otherwise you'd be saying there is less uncertainty in your result than in the data used to calculate it.

If no uncertainty is given for a value, the number of significant figures a value has gives you an estimate of the uncertainty. The assumed uncertainty is half the increment of the last significant figure that the value is given to.

Example — Maths Skills

2 N only has 1 significant figure, so without any other information you know this value must be 2 ± 0.5 N — if the value was less than 1.5 N it would have been rounded to 1 N (to 1 s.f.), if it was 2.5 N or greater it would have been rounded to 3 N (to 1 s.f.).

Evaluations

Before you can make any conclusions, you'll need to evaluate your results to see how convincing they are. You need to be careful about what words you use — precise, valid and accurate may all sound similar, but they all say different things about your results.

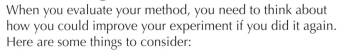

Figure 3: *Newton's famous experiment to show that white light is made up of a spectra of colours has been reproduced by scientists and students all over the world. The results are now accepted.*

Tip: It's possible for results to be precise but not accurate, e.g. a balance that weighs to 1/1000th of a gram will give precise results, but if it's not calibrated properly the results won't be accurate.

1. Precise results

The smaller the amount of spread of your data from the mean, the more precise it is. Precision depends on the amount of random error (p.29) in your readings. A precise result is one that is repeatable and reproducible.

- **Repeatable results** — Results are repeatable if you can repeat an experiment multiple times and get the same results.
- **Reproducible results** — Results are reproducible if someone else can recreate your experiment using different equipment or methods, and get the same results you do.

2. Valid results

A valid result answers the original question using precise data. If you don't keep all variables apart from the ones you're testing constant, you haven't only tested the variable you're investigating — the results aren't valid.

3. Accurate results

An accurate result is really close to the true answer.
You can only comment on how accurate a result is if you know the true value of the result. So you can't assess the accuracy of a result if your measuring something that's unknown or has never been measured before.

Evaluating methods

When you evaluate your method, you need to think about how you could improve your experiment if you did it again. Here are some things to consider:

- Is there anything you could have done to make your results more precise or accurate? Could you do anything to prevent random or systematic errors (p.29)?
- Were the results valid? If not, could you fix this, e.g. by changing the data you're collecting?
- Were there any limitations in your method (see below)?
- Did you take enough measurements to be confident in spotting any anomalies? Should you have taken measurements more frequently?
- Could you have reduced the uncertainty in your results, e.g. by using more sensitive apparatus or equipment?

Experimental limitations

An experiment will always have limitations — this is anything that will affect the overall results. You need to be able to identify the limitations for any experiment (e.g. the resolution of the equipment used, see p.17).

Example

A student needs to measure the length of a piece of wire to use in an experiment. She does this using a ruler that can measure to the nearest millimetre. She measures it to be 9.8 cm. The length of the wire could actually be 9.8127563 cm. But the measurement is limited by the resolution of the ruler.

Other limitations include uncontrollable external variables that contribute to the data.

Example

A student sets up the apparatus as shown to see how varying the angle of the ramp (θ) affects the acceleration of the trolley on the ramp. The acceleration of the trolley is due to gravity, and the student therefore assumes it is constant.

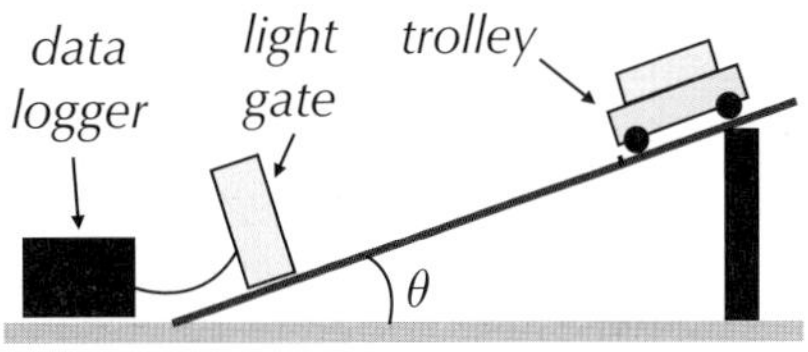

The main limitation in this experiment is the friction acting on the trolley due to the ramp and the air. The friction will increase as the speed of the trolley increases, which means the acceleration of the trolley on the ramp will not be constant. You can reduce the amount of friction acting on the trolley by using a smooth ramp and making the trolley more streamlined, but it is not possible to remove the effects of friction completely.

Tip: For more on the dependence of friction on speed see page 83.

Drawing conclusions

HOW SCIENCE WORKS

A conclusion explains what the data shows. You can only draw a conclusion if your data supports it. Your conclusion should be limited to the circumstances you've tested it under — if you've been investigating how the current flowing through a resistor changes with the potential difference across it, and have only used potential differences between 0 and 6 V, you can't claim to know what would happen if you used a potential difference of 100 V, or if you used a different resistor.

You also need to think about how much you can believe your conclusion, by evaluating the quality of your results (see previous page). If you can't believe your results, you can't form a strong conclusion.

Tip: Whoever funds the research (e.g. an engineering company) for an investigation may have some influence on what conclusions are drawn from the results, but scientists have a responsibility to make sure that the conclusions they draw are supported by the data.

Example

The stress of a material X was measured at strains of 0.002, 0.004, 0.006, 0.008 and 0.010. Each strain reading had an error of 0.001. All other variables were kept constant, and the results are shown on the right.

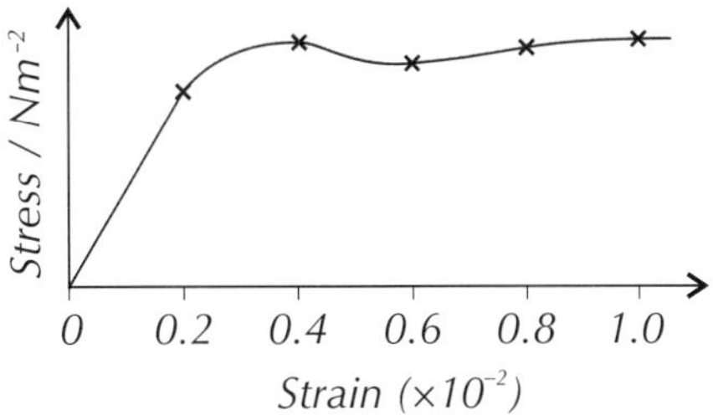

A science magazine concluded from this data that material X's yield point is at a strain of 0.005. This could be true — but the data doesn't support this. Because strain increases of 0.002 at a time were used and the stress at in-between strains wasn't measured, you can't tell where the yield point is from the data. All you know is that the yield point is somewhere between 0.004 and 0.006, as the stress drops between these values.

Also, the graph only gives information about this particular experiment. You can't conclude that the yield point would be in this range for all experiments — only this one. And you can't say for sure that doing the experiment at, say, a different constant temperature, wouldn't give a different yield point.

You must also consider the error in the strain readings. The error in each reading is 0.001, which gives a percentage uncertainty of 50% for the lowest strain reading. This means the results might not be accurate.

Tip: For more on interpreting stress-strain graphs see pages 120-123.

Tip: Taking more readings in an experiment can allow you to make stronger conclusions. If a measurement had been taken at a strain of 0.005 here, you'd have been able to say more about where the yield point was. It's also good to do a pilot experiment (p.7) to get an idea of roughly where the yield point is before you start.

Correlation and cause

Your data may show a correlation between two variables, but the change in one may not be causing the change in the other. Both changes might be caused by a third variable.

Example

Some studies have found a correlation between exposure to the electromagnetic fields created by power lines and certain ill health effects. So some people argue that this means we shouldn't live close to power lines, or build power lines close to homes. But it's hard to control all the variables between people who live near power lines and people who don't. Ill health in people living near power lines could be affected by many lifestyle factors or even genetics. Also, people living close to power lines may be more likely to believe that any ill health they suffer is due to the EM fields from the power lines if they are aware of the studies.

Tip: Remember — if you don't know the uncertainty of the apparatus used to measure a value, you can use the number of significant figures of the value to work out its uncertainty.

Practice Questions — Application

Q1 a) What is the uncertainty of a mass balance that measures masses to the nearest 0.2 g?

b) What is the percentage error of a measurement of 50 g made with the mass balance in part a)?

Q2 A student is investigating the potential difference across a lamp. He measures the potential difference across the lamp 5 times whilst the current is 5.2 A. His results are shown in the table.

Repeat 1	*Repeat 2*	*Repeat 3*	*Repeat 4*	*Repeat 5*
3.4 V	*3.6 V*	*4.0 V*	*3.9 V*	*3.6 V*

a) What is the uncertainty of the value for current?

b) Calculate the mean potential difference and its uncertainty.

Q3 A student is carrying out an experiment to find the resistivity of a wire by measuring its resistance at different lengths. She measures the resistance of the wire every 10 cm, from 10 cm to 60 cm. She uses a millimetre ruler to measure the length and diameter of the wire. She stops her experiment halfway through, and continues with it later the same day when the temperature of the room has dropped. She then plots a graph of wire length against resistance and uses the gradient to find the wire's resistivity.

a) Comment on the validity of her experiment.

b) Give two ways she could improve her experiment.

Practice Questions — Fact Recall

Q1 What is the percentage error of a measurement?

Q2 Give two ways of reducing uncertainty in an experiment.

Q3 What is the meaning of the terms precision and accuracy?

Section Summary

Make sure you know...

- How to design experiments in order to investigate something or answer a question.
- How to solve problems in a practical context by starting with a prediction or hypothesis.
- How to identify the different types of variables in an experiment, including independent, dependent and control variables.
- That control variables must stay the same throughout an experiment.
- How to select the units that data should be recorded in.
- How and when to use different practical apparatus and techniques.
- How to evaluate an experimental method, including whether the experiment will answer the original question and whether the experiment will be valid.
- How to correctly record data in tables.
- That all the measurements of one variable should be recorded to the same number of decimal places.
- What is meant by quantitative data and what is meant by qualitative data.
- What significant figures are and how many significant figures a value should be given to.
- How to calculate the arithmetic mean of the results of repeated measurements.
- What an anomaly is and how to identify one in a set of results.
- How to choose the correct way to present data depending on what the data is.
- How to plot scatter graphs, including choosing the right scales and units for the axes.
- How to draw a line of best fit on a scatter graph.
- How to analyse the results of data that is either qualitative or quantitative.
- That the equation of a linear graph is $y = mx + c$, where m is the gradient and c is the y-intercept.
- How to calculate the gradient and y-intercept of a scatter graph of results, and how to work out what these values represent in an experiment.
- How to find the uncertainty in a measurement from the resolution of the apparatus used.
- What the terms margin of error, absolute uncertainty and percentage error mean.
- That taking more repeats in an experiment or using more appropriate apparatus can reduce the uncertainty of the results.
- How to find the uncertainty of a value based on the number of significant figures it has been given to.
- The terms precision, repeatable, reproducible, valid and accurate and what they mean.
- How to evaluate an experiment and be able to comment on how an experiment could be improved if it was repeated.
- How to identify limitations in an experimental method.
- How to draw conclusions from an experiment based on the evidence available.
- That a correlation between two variables doesn't necessarily mean there is a causal relation between them.

Exam-style Questions

1 The equation that relates final velocity ($\mathbf{v}$), initial velocity ($\mathbf{u}$), acceleration ($\mathbf{a}$) and displacement ($\mathbf{s}$) is $\mathbf{v}^2 = \mathbf{u}^2 + 2\mathbf{as}$.

A graph is plotted for an object moving with a constant acceleration, with $\mathbf{v}^2$ on the y-axis and $\mathbf{s}$ on the x-axis. Which of the following is equal to the acceleration of the object?

A The square root of the y-intercept of the graph.

B The y-intercept of the graph.

C The gradient of the graph multiplied by 2.

D The gradient of the graph divided by 2.

(1 mark)

2 A student wants to find how the resistance of a thermistor varies with temperature. They set up the circuit shown in **Fig. 2.1**.

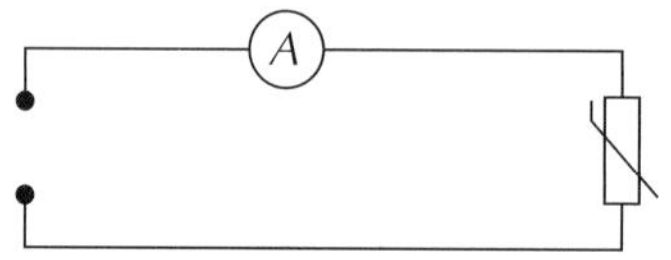

Fig. 2.1

The thermistor is then placed in a beaker of hot water that contains a thermometer. The thermometer has 1 °C graduations. The student then records the current through the thermistor for each 20 °C temperature drop of the water. She will use her results and the potential difference of the power supply to calculate the resistance of the thermistor. She repeats the experiment 6 times. Her results are shown in **Fig. 2.2**.

Temperature / °C	*Current / A*						
	Run 1	*Run 2*	*Run 3*	*Run 4*	*Run 5*	*Run 6*	*Mean*
90	5.3	5.5	5.2	5.2	5.3	5.3	5.3
70	3.1	3.3	3.3	3.0	3.1	2.9	3.1
50	1.9	1.8	2.8	2.0	2.0	2.1	

Fig. 2.2

a) Calculate the percentage uncertainty for the temperature reading of 90 °C.

(2 marks)

b) Calculate the mean value for the current when the water's temperature was 50 °C. Include the uncertainty of this value in your answer.

(3 marks)

c)* Evaluate the student's experiment. In your answer, you should include suggestions for how the student could improve her experiment.

(6 marks)

* The quality of your response will be assessed in this question.

Module 2 Foundations of Physics

1. Quantities and Units

For absolutely everything in Physics, you need to make sure your values are in the correct units. The next few pages show you the correct units for the most common quantities, as well as how to use prefixes with them.

Learning Objectives:

- Know that physical quantities have a numerical value and a unit.
- Know the Système Internationale (S.I.) base quantities and their units – mass (kg), length (m), time (s), current (A), temperature (K), amount of substance (mol).
- Know derived units of S.I. base units.
- Be able to check the homogeneity of physical equations using S.I. base units.
- Understand units listed in this book.
- Know prefixes and their symbols and be able to use them to indicate decimal submultiples or multiples of units – pico (p), nano (n), micro (μ), milli (m), centi (c), deci (d), kilo (k), mega (M), giga (G), tera (T).

Specification Reference 2.1.2

S.I. units

A **physical quantity** is something that you can measure. Every physical quantity has a numerical value and a unit. Each time you measure something, or do a calculation, you need to give the correct units of the quantity.

You might need to convert quantities into the right units before using a formula. The Système International (S.I.) includes a set of **base units** from which lots of others are derived. There are seven base units in this system, but you only need to know these six:

Quantity	*S.I. base unit*	*Symbol*
Length	*metre*	*m*
Mass	*kilogram*	*kg*
Time	*second*	*s*
Current	*ampere*	*A*
Temperature	*kelvin*	*K*
Amount of a substance	*mole*	*mol*

Figure 1: *Quantities and their S.I. base units.*

Homogeneity of units

The units in any equation must always be equivalent (in terms of S.I. base units) on both sides. This is called **homogeneity of units**. You can use this rule to work out **S.I. derived units** — other units derived from the S.I. base units.

For example, density is found using $\rho = \frac{m}{V}$. The unit of mass, m, is kilograms, kg. The unit of volume, V, is the unit of length (m) cubed, m^3. So density, ρ, is in 'kilograms per metre-cubed', $kg\,m^{-3}$.

Example — Maths Skills

Show that the S.I. derived unit for speed is ms^{-1}.

You know that speed = distance ÷ time

Distance is a length, so its S.I. base unit is the metre, m. The base unit of time is the second, s.

To find the unit for speed, just put the units for distance and time into the equation for speed: $m \div s = ms^{-1}$.

The S.I. derived units you need to know will be covered throughout the book.

Figure 2: Alessandro Volta, the man after whom the 'volt' was named. All of the derived S.I. units in Figure 3, and some of the base units in Figure 1, are named after famous physicists.

Tip: You don't need to remember all of the combinations of units in the last column of Figure 3. If you need them, you're better working them out using the formulas you know.

All S.I. derived units can be expressed purely in terms of S.I. base units. But some S.I derived units have their own names and symbols. Here are some of examples of these S.I. derived units that you'll come across quite often:

Quantity	*S.I. derived unit*	*Symbol*	*Written in S.I. base units*
Energy, work, heat	*joule*	*J*	kgm^2s^{-2}
Resistance	*ohm*	*Ω*	$kgm^2s^{-3}A^{-2}$
Potential difference, e.m.f.	*volt*	*V*	$kgm^2s^{-3}A^{-1}$
Charge	*coulomb*	*C*	*As*
Force, weight	*newton*	*N*	$kgms^{-2}$
Power	*watt*	*W*	kgm^2s^{-3}
Pressure, stress	*pascal*	*Pa*	$kgm^{-1}s^{-2}$
Frequency	*hertz*	*Hz*	s^{-1}

Figure 3: *Quantities and their S.I. derived units.*

You can also use the homogeneity of units to help you to check your working if you have to combine or rearrange equations.

Examples — Maths Skills

Rearrange $P = I^2R$ for I. Check the homogeneity of your answer.

Rearrange $P = I^2R$ to get: $I = \sqrt{\frac{P}{R}}$

To check the units are the same on both sides, substitute the units for each quantity into the equation, then cancel down:

I is current in amperes, P is power in watts, or kgm^2s^{-3}, and R is resistance in ohms, or $kgm^2s^{-3}A^{-2}$.

$$A = \sqrt{\frac{\cancel{kg}\cancel{m^2}\cancel{s^{-3}}}{\cancel{kg}\cancel{m^2}\cancel{s^{-3}}A^{-2}}} = \sqrt{\frac{1}{A^{-2}}} = \sqrt{A^2} = A$$

There are only amperes left on both sides of the equation, so the equation is homogeneous.

For an object moving with uniform acceleration, $v = u + at$ and $s = \frac{1}{2}(u + v)t$.
Combine these equations to get an equation for s in terms of u, v and a. Check the homogeneity of your answer.

Rearrange $v = u + at$ to get: $t = \frac{v - u}{a}$

Then substitute this into $s = \frac{1}{2}(u + v)t \Rightarrow s = \frac{1}{2}(u + v)\left(\frac{v - u}{a}\right)$

Then simplify the equation: $s = \frac{1}{2a}(v^2 - u^2)$

Again, substitute the units for each quantity into the equation and cancel down (you can ignore any numbers, e.g. the 2):

s is a length in metres, v and u are velocities in ms^{-1} and a is acceleration in ms^{-2}.

$$m = \frac{1}{ms^{-2}}((ms^{-1})^2 - (ms^{-1})^2) = \frac{1}{\cancel{m}\cancel{s^{-2}}}(m^{\cancel{2}}\cancel{s^{-2}} - m^{\cancel{2}}\cancel{s^{-2}}) = m$$

There are only metres left on both sides of the equation, so the equation is homogeneous.

Prefixes

Physical quantities come in a huge range of sizes. **Prefixes** are scaling factors that let you write very big or small numbers without having to put everything in standard form (p.241). Again, the Système International (S.I.) defines some standard prefixes. The S.I. prefixes that you need to know are:

Prefix	Multiple of unit
pico (p)	1×10^{-12}
nano (n)	1×10^{-9}
micro (μ)	1×10^{-6}
milli (m)	$0.001\ (1 \times 10^{-3})$
centi (c)	$0.01\ (1 \times 10^{-2})$
deci (d)	$0.1\ (1 \times 10^{-1})$
kilo (k)	$1000\ (1 \times 10^{3})$
mega (M)	1×10^{6}
giga (G)	1×10^{9}
tera (T)	1×10^{12}

Figure 4: *Common S.I. prefixes.*

Prefixes can tell you the order of magnitude of a quantity. This gives you a rough idea of the quantity's size, which is useful if you're using it to estimate another value. For example, a length of 1 m is 3 orders of magnitude greater than a length of 1 mm.

Example — Maths Skills

Convert 0.247 megawatts into kilowatts.

$1\text{ MW} = 1 \times 10^6\text{ W}$ and $1\text{ kW} = 1 \times 10^3\text{ W}$

So the scaling factor to move between MW and kW is:

$(1 \times 10^6) \div (1 \times 10^3) = 1 \times 10^3$

So $0.247\text{ MW} = 0.247 \times 1 \times 10^3\text{ kW} = 247\text{ kW}$.

If you need to convert between prefixes for area or volume, be very careful. For example, you could be asked to convert from m^2 to cm^2. In this case it's not enough to multiply the quantity by 1×10^2, you would need to multiply the quantity by $(1 \times 10^2)^2$.

It's the same for converting between volumes, for example from nm^3 to mm^3, you would multiply by $(1 \times 10^{-6})^3$ and not just by 1×10^{-6}.

Example — Maths Skills

Convert 0.083 m³ into cm³.

$1\text{ cm} = 1 \times 10^{-2}\text{ m}$, so the scaling factor between m and cm is $1 \div (1 \times 10^{-2}) = 1 \times 10^2$.

So to convert from m^3 to cm^3, multiply by $(1 \times 10^2)^3$.

$0.083 \times (1 \times 10^2)^3 = 83\ 000\text{ cm}^3$

Tip: The S.I. base unit kilogram, kg, is the only one that already has a prefix. Most of the time you'll need to convert into kg to do a calculation, not g.

Figure 5: *A coulombmeter measuring in nC. Often, measured values will already have a prefix, defined by the apparatus, so make sure you check before recording anything.*

Tip: If you get confused with converting between prefixes, it might be easier to first convert to the unit without a prefix and then convert to the new prefix. So for this example, you'd multiply 0.247 by 1×10^6 first to change the quantity into W. Then you'd divide by 1×10^3 to convert the quantity into kW.

Tip: When converting, you should check your answer is sensible. A centimetre is smaller than a metre, so there are more of them in a given value. So if you're converting from m to cm (or m^3 to cm^3) the number should get bigger.

You need to have a rough idea of the size of each S.I. base unit and S.I. derived unit in this book, as well as prefixes, so that you can estimate quantities using them. There's more about estimating quantities on the next page.

Practice Questions — Application

Q1 A wave has a frequency of 0.3 THz.
State the frequency of the wave in Hz.

Q2 The momentum of an object is found using $\boldsymbol{p} = m\boldsymbol{v}$, where $\boldsymbol{p}$ is the momentum, m is the object's mass and $\boldsymbol{v}$ is the velocity of the object. Find the S.I. derived unit of momentum.

Practice Questions — Fact Recall

Q1 What is the S.I. unit of temperature?

Q2 Give two S.I. derived units.

Q3 Give the multiple of the unit for the following prefixes:

a) pico

b) centi

c) mega

2. Making Estimates

Estimates are a just informed guesses. They're a good way to check your calculations and to make sure your experiments are correct too.

Learning Objective:

- Be able to make estimates of physical quantities listed in this book.

Specification Reference 2.1.1

Estimating values

Estimating values can be tricky, especially for random situations you're not likely to come across in real life. The easiest thing to do is to compare the situation with one you are more familiar with. Figure 1 shows some typical values for things you come across in everyday life.

	Typical value
Mass of a person	*70 kg*
Mass of a car	*1500 kg*
Height of a man	*1.8 m*
Walking speed	*1.5 ms^{-1}*

Figure 1: *Common values for everyday situations.*

Tip: Lots of everyday speeds are given in miles per hour (mph) instead of metres per second, which can make estimates difficult. To (roughly) change from mph to ms^{-1}, divide the value by two. E.g. a car travelling at 60 mph travels at roughly 30 ms^{-1}.

Example — **Maths Skills**

A cyclist goes for a ride. Estimate the kinetic energy of a cyclist as he travels at a constant, typical speed.

The equation for kinetic energy is $E_k = \frac{1}{2}m\boldsymbol{v}^2$.

E_k is kinetic energy, m is mass and $\boldsymbol{v}$ is velocity.

So you need to make an estimate of the cyclist's total mass and velocity.

Using information from Figure 1, the mass of a person is 70 kg and walking speed is about 1.5 ms^{-1}.

The mass of a road bike is roughly 10 kg.

A cyclist probably travels at around 10 mph, or 5 ms^{-1}.

Substitute these estimates into the equation:

$$E_k = \frac{1}{2}m\boldsymbol{v}^2 = \frac{1}{2} \times (70 + 10) \times 5^2 = \frac{1}{2} \times 80 \times 25 = 1000 \text{ J}$$

So the kinetic energy of the cyclist is about 1000 J.

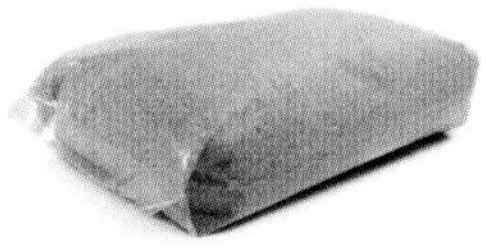

Figure 2: *Common objects that have a mass of 1 kg are a large bag of sugar and a litre bottle of water.*

Tip: There are a few ways you could estimate the cyclist's speed. If you think you have a good idea, you can just use that as an estimate, but if you're struggling, you could try comparing cycling to walking, or driving at 30 mph.

You can also use estimates to quickly check that you've not made mistakes during a calculation.

Example — **Maths Skills**

A handbag costs £5.22 to make. It is sold for £29.99.
Calculate the profit made if 8 handbags are sold.

Profit for one = £29.99 – £5.22 = £24.77

Total profit = £24.77 × 8 = £198.16

Using estimates, you can quickly check if this number is roughly correct:

Profit for one is roughly £30 – £5 = £25,

Total profit is roughly £25 × 8 = £200

The two answers are very close, so £198.16 is probably correct.

Tip: It will depend on the question, but most estimates should be rounded to 1 significant figure.

Making predictions

You may also be asked to use estimates to make predictions about how the outcome of an experiment would change, were one of the variables to change.

Examples

The equipment used in Figure 3 is used to measure the speed of sound, *v*.

The tuning fork creates a sound wave at a set frequency, *f*.

The distance between the fork and the water is increased until the wave reaches its first point of resonance. At this point the distance is equal to one quarter of the wavelength.

An error is made whilst measuring this distance. The actual distance is smaller than the value that has been recorded.

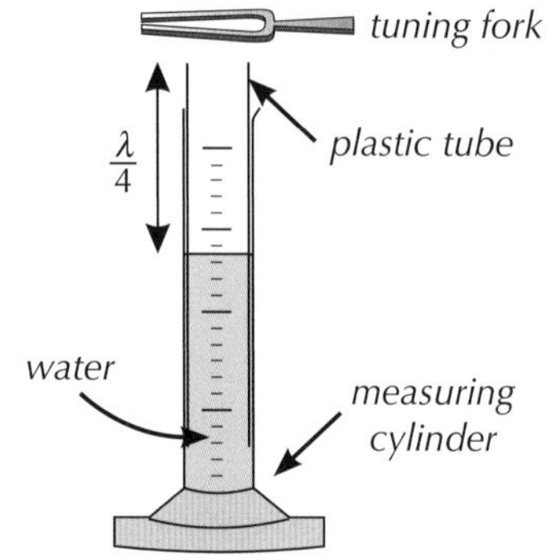

Figure 3: *Set-up used for finding the speed of sound.*

Discuss how this error will affect the result of the experiment.

This error will mean that the actual value of the wavelength of the sound wave will be smaller than the result of the experiment. As $v = f\lambda$, this will also mean that the actual value of the speed of sound will be smaller than that calculated.

The resistivity of a wire is investigated. The diameter of the wire is measured and its cross-sectional area calculated. Its resistance for given lengths is recorded, and a graph of resistance against length is produced. An error is made whilst recording the diameter of the wire. The diameter recorded is smaller than the actual value.

Discuss how this will affect the results of the experiment.

Cross-sectional area, $A = \pi r^2 = \pi\left(\frac{\text{diameter}}{2}\right)^2$

So if the actual value of the diameter is larger than the recorded value, the actual cross-sectional area is larger too.

Resistivity, ρ, is equal to $\frac{RA}{L}$. So if the actual value of A is larger than that calculated from the results, the actual resistivity of the wire is higher than the value that will be calculated.

Tip: There's more about this experiment on page 219.

Tip: Resistivity is covered in more detail on page 148.

Practice Questions — Application

Q1 Estimate:

a) The height of a two-storey house.

b) The gravitational potential energy of a child 3 m above the ground in a tree. (Gravitational potential energy = mass of object × g × height of object above ground, where $g = 9.81\ \text{ms}^{-2}$.)

Q2 The force acting on a ball as it is kicked is investigated. The ball's mass, its change in velocity and the time taken to change velocity are measured. This is used to calculate the force acting on the ball. The change in the ball's velocity is incorrectly measured. The actual value is larger than the one recorded. Describe how this would affect the calculated value of the force acting on the ball.
(Acceleration = change in velocity ÷ time; Force = mass × acceleration)

Tip: If you're struggling with Q1a) think about how high a room is, compared to the height of a person.

3. Errors and Uncertainties

Scientists always have to include the uncertainty of a result, so you can see the range the actual value probably lies within. Dealing with error and uncertainty is an important skill — you need to make sure that you know and try to minimise the uncertainty of your experimental results.

Learning Objectives:

- Understand systematic errors (including zero errors) and random errors in measurements.
- Know how errors affect precision and accuracy.
- Be able to calculate absolute and percentage uncertainties when data are combined by addition, subtraction, multiplication, division and raising to powers.
- Be able to calculate percentage difference.

Specification Reference 2.2.1

Types of error

Every measurement you take has an experimental uncertainty (see page 16), caused by two types of error:

Random errors

Random errors cause readings to be spread about the true value due to the results varying in an unpredictable way. They affect precision (see page 18).

They can just be down to noise, or because you're measuring a random process such as nuclear radiation emission. You can get random errors in any measurement and you can't completely prevent them, no matter how hard you try.

If you measured the length of a wire 20 times, the chances are you'd get a slightly different value each time, e.g. due to your head being in a slightly different position when reading the scale. It could be that you just can't keep controlled variables exactly the same throughout the experiment. Or it could just be the wind was blowing in the wrong direction at the time.

Example

You could investigate the force constant (see page 106) of a particular rubber band using the apparatus in Figure 1.

The force constant of the rubber band increases with temperature. If the surrounding temperature changes, it could introduce a random error.

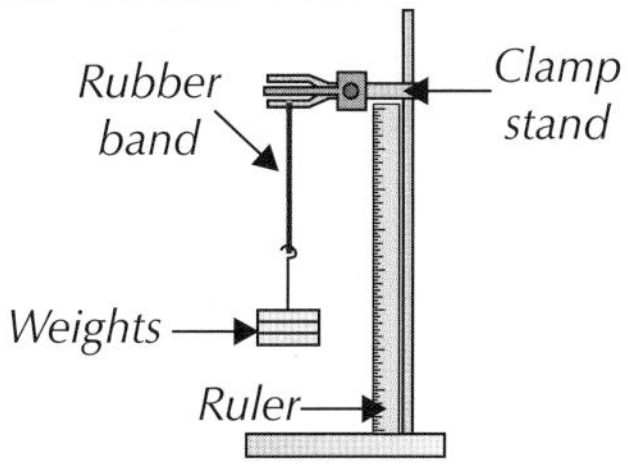

***Figure 1:** An experiment to find the force constant of a rubber band.*

Tip: All sorts of things are affected by temperature, from the properties of a material to the current flowing in a circuit.

Using more sensitive apparatus can reduce the size of random errors, which makes your results more precise. Repeating your experiment and taking an average (mean) of your repeated measurements (see page 10) will also reduce the effect of random error. The more measurements you average over, the less effect random error is likely to have in your final result.

Systematic errors

Systematic errors usually cause each reading to be different to the true value by the same amount i.e. they shift all of your measurements. They affect the accuracy of your results (see page 18).

You usually get systematic errors because of the environment, the apparatus you're using or your experimental method, e.g. using an inaccurate clock, repeated identical mistakes in measurements, etc.

The problem is often that you don't know systematic errors are there. You've got to spot them first to have any chance of correcting for them. They're annoying, but there are things you can do to reduce them if you manage to spot them (see next page).

If you suspect a systematic error, you should repeat the experiment with a different technique or apparatus and compare the results.

Tip: A newton meter that always measures values 1 N greater than they should be will shift all your results up by 1 N — this would introduce a systematic error due to the apparatus used.

Example — continued

Look back at the investigation of the force constant on the previous page (see Figure 1). If the ruler is not correctly lined up to the top of the piece of rubber, all the extension measurements would be shifted by the same amount. This would introduce a systematic error due to your experimental method.

You can **calibrate** your apparatus by measuring a known value. If there's a difference between the measured and known value, you can use this to correct the inaccuracy of the apparatus, and so reduce your systematic error.

Calibration can also reduce **zero errors** (caused by the apparatus failing to read zero when it should do, e.g. when no current is flowing through an ammeter) which is a type of systematic error.

Tip: To calibrate a set of scales you could weigh a 10.0 g mass and check that it reads 10.0 g. If these scales are precise to the nearest 0.1 g, then you can only calibrate to within 0.05 g. Any measurements taken will have an uncertainty of ± 0.05 g.

Combining uncertainties

When you do calculations involving values that have an uncertainty, you have to combine the uncertainties to get the overall uncertainty for your result.

Adding or subtracting

When you're adding or subtracting data you add the absolute uncertainties (p.16).

Tip: Be very careful. Even if you subtract the data, you add the uncertainties (combining uncertainties should always make the uncertainty increase).

Example — Maths Skills

A wire is stretched from 0.3 ± 0.1 cm to 0.5 ± 0.1 cm. Calculate the extension of the wire.

First subtract the lengths without the uncertainty values:

$$0.5 - 0.3 = 0.2 \text{ cm}$$

Then find the total uncertainty by adding the individual absolute uncertainties:

$$0.1 + 0.1 = 0.2 \text{ cm}$$

So, the wire has been stretched 0.2 ± 0.2 cm.

Multiplying or dividing

When you're multiplying or dividing data, you add the percentage uncertainties, p.16.

Tip: Don't forget to convert all the uncertainties to percentages before you combine by multiplying or dividing — see page 16 for how.

Example — Maths Skills

A force of 15 ± 3% N is applied to a stationary object which has a mass of 6.0 ± 0.3 kg. Calculate the acceleration of the object and state the percentage uncertainty in this value.

First calculate the acceleration without uncertainty:

$$\boldsymbol{a} = \boldsymbol{F} \div m = 15 \div 6.0 = 2.5 \text{ ms}^{-2}$$

Next, calculate the percentage uncertainty in the mass:

$$\% \text{ uncertainty in } m = \frac{0.3}{6.0} \times 100 = 5\%$$

Add the percentage uncertainties in the force and mass values to find the total uncertainty in the acceleration:

Total uncertainty = 3% + 5% = 8%

So, the acceleration = 2.5 ± 8% ms^{-2}

Raising to a power

When you're raising data to a power, you multiply the percentage uncertainty by the power.

Tip: You're given the area of a circle as πr^2 in the data and formulae booklet.

Example — Maths Skills

The radius of a circle is r = 40 ± 2.5% cm. What will the percentage uncertainty be in the area of this circle, i.e. πr^2?

The radius will be raised to the power of 2 to calculate the area.

So, the percentage uncertainty will be 2.5% × 2 = 5%

Percentage difference

If you know the true value of what you're investigating you can measure the accuracy of your result using **percentage difference**. This is the difference between your experimental value and the accepted value, expressed as a percentage of the accepted value.

Tip: Be careful to not confuse this with percentage uncertainty.

$$\text{percentage difference} = \frac{\text{experimental value} - \text{accepted value}}{\text{accepted value}} \times 100$$

Tip: 'Accepted' means that the value is currently believed to be true by the scientific community as it has lots of evidence supporting it. It is sometimes called the true value.

Example — Maths Skills

The speed of light in a vacuum is 299 792 458 ms^{-1}.
In an experiment, it is measured to be 299 790 000 ms^{-1}.
What is the percentage difference of these results?
Give your answer to 2 significant figures.

$$\text{percentage difference} = \frac{\text{experimental value} - \text{accepted value}}{\text{accepted value}} \times 100$$

$$= \frac{299\,790\,000 - 299\,792\,458}{299\,792\,458} \times 100$$

$$= -0.000008199... \times 100 = -0.00082\% \text{ (to 2 s.f.)}$$

Tip: The sign of the percentage difference shows you if the experimental value was too big or too small.

Practice Questions — Application

Q1 The speed, v, of a sound wave is found using $v = f\lambda$. In an experiment, the frequency, f, is measured to be 125 ± 1% Hz. The wavelength, λ, is measured to be 2.72 ± 1.5% m. Calculate the speed of the sound wave and the percentage uncertainty in this value.

Q2 The length, L, of each side of a cube is 4.0 ± 0.05 cm. Calculate the volume of the cube and the percentage uncertainty in this value.

Practice Questions — Fact Recall

Q1 Give one way to reduce:

a) random errors

b) systematic errors

Q2 Describe how to find the uncertainty in the result of adding two pieces of data that both have an uncertainty.

Q3 State the equation you would use to calculate the percentage difference. Explain what percentage difference shows.

4. Graphical Representations of Uncertainties

Learning Objectives:

- Understand and use graphical treatment of errors and uncertainties, including absolute and percentage uncertainties.
- Recall the conventions used for labelling graph axes and table columns.
- Be able to draw lines of best fit and worst lines.

Specification References 2.1.2 and 2.2.1

You can show the uncertainties in your data on any graphs that you plot. These graphs can be used to see both the uncertainty in each measurement, as well as to calculate the uncertainty in your final result.

Error bars

Most of the time, you work out the uncertainty in your final result using the uncertainty in each measurement you make. When you're plotting a graph, you show the uncertainty in each measurement by using error bars to show the range the point is likely to lie in. You can have error bars for both the dependent and the independent variable.

Example — **Maths Skills**

The error in measuring the extension of material *X* can be found using the error bars in the graph below.

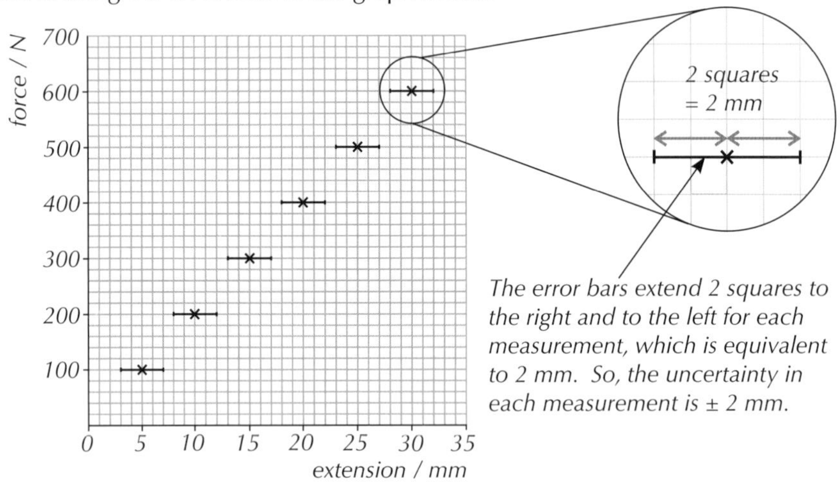

force / N
700
600
500
400
300
200
100
0
5
10
15
20
25
30
35
extension / mm
2 squares
= 2 mm
The error bars extend 2 squares to the right and to the left for each measurement, which is equivalent to 2 mm. So, the uncertainty in each measurement is ± 2 mm.

Figure 1: *A graph of force against extension for material X.*

Trial	Length ± 5% / m
1	0.80
2	0.81
3	0.80

Figure 2: *If the uncertainty is the same for all values in a table, it's sometimes written in the table heading instead of by each value. Look out for this when drawing graphs or using data from a table.*

Whenever you're drawing a graph, make sure you follow the conventions covered on page 12. Make sure that the axes of graphs are written in the form "quantity / unit". The same is also true for table headings — see Figure 2.

Measuring uncertainty of final results

Normally when you draw a graph you'll want to find the gradient or intercept. You can find the uncertainty in that value by using **worst lines**.

Draw a line of best fit for your data and use this to calculate your result. Then, draw lines of best fit which have the maximum and minimum possible slopes for the data and still go through all of the error bars. These are the worst lines for your data.

Tip: Your line of best fit (page 12) should always go through all of the error bars.

For example, you can calculate k, the force constant of the object being stretched, from the gradient of the graph in Figure 3 — here it's about 20 000 Nm^{-1}. The the pink and blue lines in Figure 3 are the worst lines for your data.

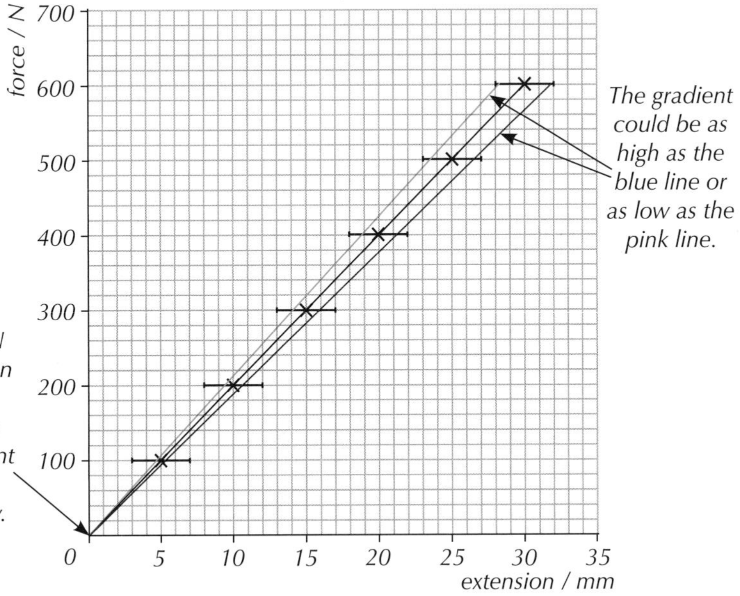

force / N
700
600
500
400
300
200
100
0
5
10
15
20
25
30
35
extension / mm
The gradient could be as high as the blue line or as low as the pink line.
When the force is 0 N the extension is 0 mm — this is a measurement with no uncertainty.

Figure 3: *The maximum and minimum slopes possible through the error bars.*

Calculate the worst gradient — the gradient of the slope that is furthest from the gradient of the line of best fit. In Figure 3, the gradient of the blue line is about 21 000 Nm^{-1} and the gradient of the pink line is about 19 000 Nm^{-1}, so you can use either.

The uncertainty in the gradient is given by the difference between the best gradient (of the line of best fit) and the worst gradient — here it's 1000 Nm^{-1}. So this is the uncertainty in the value of the force constant. For this object, the force constant is 20 000 ± 1000 Nm^{-1} (or 20 000 Nm^{-1} ± 5%).

Similarly, the uncertainty in the y-intercept is just the difference between the best and worst intercepts (although there's no uncertainty in Figure 3 since the best and worst lines both go through the origin).

Tip: Be careful — sometimes error bars are calculated using a set percentage of uncertainty for each measurement, and so will change depending on the measurement.

Tip: If a point doesn't have an error bar (like the origin in Figure 3) you should treat it as you would a normal point whilst drawing a line of best fit. The worst lines you draw should go through or near to it.

Practice Question — Application

Q1 The table below shows the temperature of a beaker of water as it is heated over time.

Time / s	Temperature / °C
0	21 ± 1
30	28 ± 1
60	35 ± 1
90	43 ± 1
120	50 ± 1

a) Draw a temperature-time graph for the water.

b) Calculate the gradient of the graph.
State the uncertainty in your answer.

5. Scalars and Vectors

Vectors are quantities with both a size and a direction. You need to be able to add them to find a resultant vector or split them into components.

Learning Objectives:

- Understand the difference between scalar and vector quantities.
- Be able to add and subtract vectors.
- Be able to use a vector triangle to determine the resultant of any two coplanar vectors.
- Be able to resolve a vector into two perpendicular components; $F_x = F\cos\theta$; $F_y = F\sin\theta$.

Specification Reference 2.3.1

The difference between scalars and vectors

- A **scalar** quantity has no direction — it's just an amount of something, like the mass of a sack of potatoes.
- A **vector** quantity has magnitude (size) and direction — e.g. the velocity of a car is its speed and direction.

You need to know some examples of scalar and vector quantities — like the ones given in the table below.

Scalars	Vectors
length/distance, speed, mass, temperature, time, energy	displacement, velocity, force (including weight), acceleration, momentum

Finding the resultant vector

Adding or subtracting two or more vectors is called finding the **resultant vector**. There are two ways of doing this you need to know about.

For both methods, you should start by drawing a diagram. Draw the vectors 'tip to tail'. If you're doing a vector subtraction, draw the vector you're subtracting with the same magnitude but pointing in the opposite direction.

Finding resultant vectors using scale diagrams

You can find the resultant vector of any two vectors by drawing a **scale drawing** of them 'tip-to-tail' and then measuring the length and angle of the resultant vector on the diagram.

Example — Maths Skills

A man walks 3.0 m on a bearing of 055° then 4.0 m east. Find the magnitude and direction (to the nearest degree) of his displacement, s.

Start by drawing a scale diagram for how far the man walked using a ruler and a protractor:

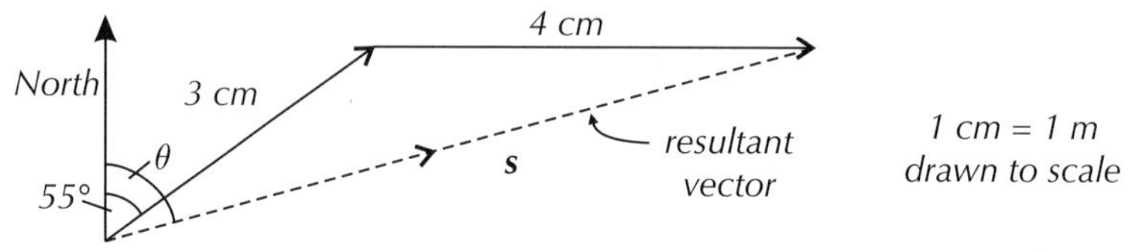

Then just measure the missing side with a ruler and the missing angle with a protractor: **s** = 6.7 cm and θ = 75° (to the nearest degree).

So, using the scale from the drawing, the man's displacement is 6.7 m, on a bearing of 075°.

Tip: A bearing is a three digit angle measured clockwise from north in degrees.

Tip: You could also calculate this using the sine and cosine rules — see page 253.

Tip: The man has walked 7 m in total, but his displacement is less than 7 m. Displacement gives the position relative to the start point (see page 41).

Finding resultant vectors using trigonometry

If two vectors are perpendicular to each other, like in Figure 1, you can calculate the size and angle of the resultant vector using trigonometry, by drawing a vector triangle.

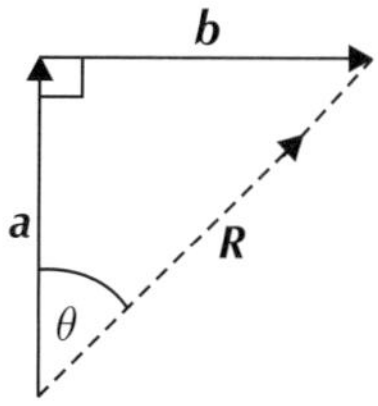

Figure 1: *A right-angled triangle representing two vectors '**a**' and '**b**', and the resultant vector '**R**'.*

Tip: Printed vectors are normally bold (***a***). When they're handwritten, you normally write them underlined ($\underline{a}$) or with an arrow above them ($\vec{a}$).

You can calculate the size of the resultant vector ***R*** using the formula:

$$R = \sqrt{a^2 + b^2}$$

Tip: This is from Pythagoras' theorem. You might remember this from GCSE maths.

You can calculate the size of the angle θ in degrees using the formula:

$$\theta = \tan^{-1}\left(\frac{b}{a}\right)$$

Tip: *a* and *b* are the sizes of vectors ***a*** and ***b*** respectively.

For any right-angled triangle where you know two sides, you can work out the size of an angle with one of the formulas below. A handy way to remember them is SOH CAH TOA (see page 252).

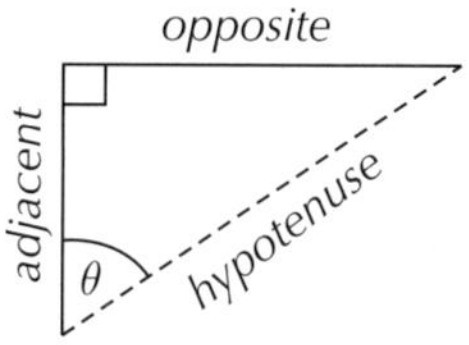

$$\sin\theta = \frac{opp}{hyp} \qquad \cos\theta = \frac{adj}{hyp} \qquad \tan\theta = \frac{opp}{adj}$$

Figure 2: *SOH CAH TOA for a right-angled triangle.*

Figure 3: *Boats won't just travel in a straight line if they try to sail straight across a river — there is a force on the boat from the river. So it will experience a resultant force that makes it travel on a longer path.*

Example — Maths Skills

A remote-controlled aeroplane flies with a driving force of 63 N east while being pushed north by the wind by a 36 N force. What is the resultant force on the aeroplane?

Start by sketching a diagram:

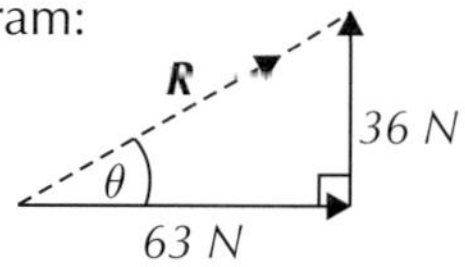

Then find R:

$R = \sqrt{63^2 + 36^2} = 72.5603... = 73$ N (to 2 s.f.)

Then find θ:

$\theta = \tan^{-1}\frac{36}{63} = 29.744... = 30°$ (to 2 s.f.)

So the resultant force ***R*** is a 73 N force, 30° anticlockwise from east.

Tip: You may be given angles in degrees or radians. Make sure you know how to change your calculator between the two.

Resolving vectors into components

Tip: The components are normally horizontal and vertical. If you're working with an object on an inclined plane, it might be easier to use components that are parallel and at right angles to the plane (see next page).

Resolving vectors is the opposite of finding the resultant — you start from the resultant vector and split it into two components at right angles to each other. You're basically working backwards from the examples on pages 34 and 35.

Resolving is dead useful because two perpendicular components of a vector don't affect each other. This means you can deal with the two directions completely separately. When you have to add another vector that affects only one of the components, you can just ignore the other.

Resolving a vector into horizontal and vertical components

The components of a vector are perpendicular to each other, so they form a right-angled triangle with the vector.

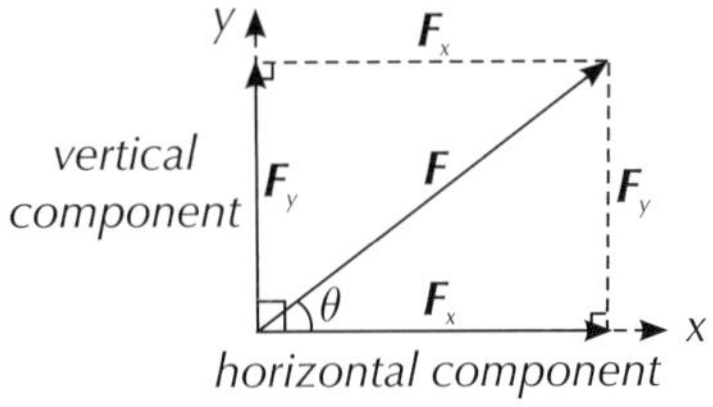

Figure 4: *The vector* ***F*** *and its horizontal component* $\boldsymbol{F}_x$ *and vertical component* $\boldsymbol{F}_y$.

You just need to use a bit of trigonometry to find the components of the vector in each direction:

Tip: This uses SOH CAH TOA as well (p.35).

Tip: In these formulae, θ is measured from the horizontal.

You get the horizontal component $\boldsymbol{F}_x$ like this:

$$\cos\theta = \frac{\boldsymbol{F}_x}{\boldsymbol{F}}$$

$$\boldsymbol{F}_x = \boldsymbol{F}\cos\theta$$

...and the vertical component $\boldsymbol{F}_y$ like this:

$$\sin\theta = \frac{\boldsymbol{F}_y}{\boldsymbol{F}}$$

$$\boldsymbol{F}_y = \boldsymbol{F}\sin\theta$$

Example — Maths Skills

A hot air balloon is travelling at a velocity of 5.0 ms⁻¹ at an angle of 60.0° up from the horizontal. Find the vertical and horizontal components of its velocity.

First, sketch a diagram:

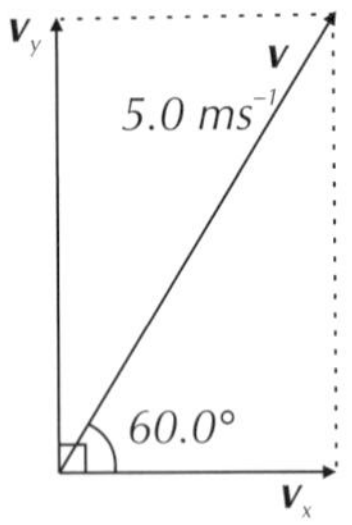

The horizontal component $\boldsymbol{v}_x$ is:

$$\boldsymbol{v}_x = \boldsymbol{v}\cos\theta = 5.0\cos 60.0° = 2.5\ \text{ms}^{-1}$$

The vertical component $\boldsymbol{v}_y$ is:

$$\boldsymbol{v}_y = \boldsymbol{v}\sin\theta = 5.0\sin 60.0° = 4.3301... = 4.3\ \text{ms}^{-1}\ \text{(to 2 s.f.)}$$

Exam Tip
$\cos 60° = \sin 30° = 0.5$. Remembering this may save time in the exam.

Resolving a vector on a slope

You should always resolve vectors in the directions that make the most sense for the situation you're dealing with. If you've got an object on a slope, choose your directions along the slope and at right angles to it.

Tip: Turning the paper to an angle can help you see what's going on better in vector problems on a slope.

Exam Tip
Examiners like to call a slope an 'inclined plane'.

Example — Maths Skills

An apple with a weight of 1.5 N is at rest on a slope inclined at 29° to the horizontal, as shown in Figure 5. Find the component of its weight that acts along the slope.

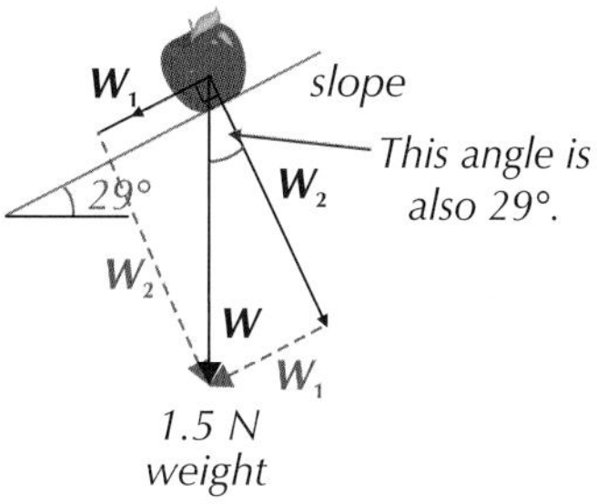

Figure 5: *An apple with a weight of 1.5 N at rest on a slope.*

This time, instead of resolving the vector into vertical and horizontal components, you're resolving it into components parallel and perpendicular to the slope ($\boldsymbol{W}_1$ and $\boldsymbol{W}_2$).

To find $\boldsymbol{W}_1$, use $opp = \sin\theta \times hyp$

$$\Rightarrow \boldsymbol{W}_1 = \sin 29° \times 1.5 = 0.7272...$$
$$= 0.73 \text{ N (to 2 s.f.)}$$

Tip: Weight always acts vertically downwards (see page 69).

Tip: Angle rules were used to work out that the angle between $\boldsymbol{W}$ and $\boldsymbol{W}_2$ was 30° too.

Resolving vectors to find the resultant

Resolving vectors also gives you another way to find the resultant vector of two vectors that aren't at right angles to each other. Resolve the vectors into their horizontal and vertical components, and add up the vertical and horizontal components separately. Then you just need to combine the two to get the resultant vector. It can be a lot less fiddly than drawing accurate scale diagrams.

Tip: You'll need to resolve forces when it comes to projectile motion on page 46.

Example — Maths Skills

Two forces, *A* and *B*, are pulling on a block, shown to the right. *A* has a magnitude of 15 N and acts at 30° to the horizontal. *B* has a magnitude of 10 N and acts at 60° to the horizontal. Calculate the resultant force on the block to 2 significant figures.

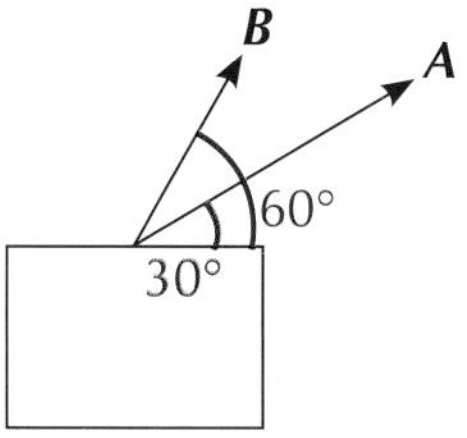

For force $\boldsymbol{A}$:

$\boldsymbol{A}_x = \boldsymbol{A}\cos\theta = 15\cos 30°$
$\boldsymbol{A}_y = \boldsymbol{A}\sin\theta = 15\sin 30°$

For force $\boldsymbol{B}$:

$\boldsymbol{B}_x = \boldsymbol{B}\cos\phi = 10\cos 60°$
$\boldsymbol{B}_y = \boldsymbol{B}\sin\phi = 10\sin 60°$

The resultant horizontal component (F_x) is:
$\boldsymbol{F}_x = \boldsymbol{A}_x + \boldsymbol{B}_x = 15\cos 30° + 10\cos 60° = 17.990...$ N

And the resultant vertical component (F_y) is:
$\boldsymbol{F}_y = \boldsymbol{A}_y + \boldsymbol{B}_y = 15\sin 30° + 10\sin 60° = 16.160...$ N

Then using Pythagoras' theorem (page 35), the size of the resultant vector, R, is:

$$R = \sqrt{F_x^2 + F_y^2} = \sqrt{17.990...^2 + 16.160...^2} = 24.1827... \text{ N}$$

The angle between $\boldsymbol{R}$ and the horizontal is:

$$\psi = \tan^{-1}\left(\frac{\boldsymbol{F}_y}{\boldsymbol{F}_x}\right) = \tan^{-1}\left(\frac{16.160...}{17.990...}\right) = 41.93°$$

So the resultant force on the block is 24 N (to 2 s.f.) acting at 42° (to 2 s.f.) to the horizontal.

Tip: θ, ϕ and ψ are all Greek letters that can be used to represent different angles.

Tip: Be careful if your forces are acting in opposite directions — when you find the resultant components you'll end up taking away instead of adding. In these cases, it's always good to mark the direction you've chosen as positive on any diagrams you use.

Practice Questions — Application

Q1 Without drawing a scale diagram, find the magnitude and direction of a paper plane's resultant velocity ***v***, from its horizontal and vertical components, shown below.

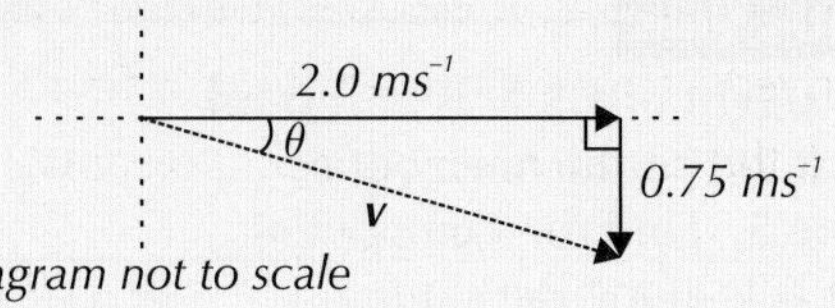

Diagram not to scale

Q2 Without drawing a scale diagram, find the horizontal and vertical components of this force.

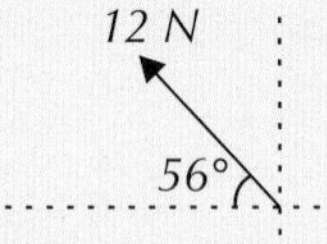

Diagram not to scale

Q3 Use a scale diagram to find magnitude and direction of the resultant force produced by a 2.9 N force north and a 4.1 N force east.

Q4 A brick with a weight of 20.0 N is on a slope at 25° to the horizontal.

a) Find the component of the brick's weight that acts down the slope.

b) Find the size of the normal contact force exerted on the brick by the slope.

Q5 Two children are pulling on a toy. The forces exerted on the toy are shown below. Calculate the resultant force, including the angle at which it acts to the horizontal, on the toy.

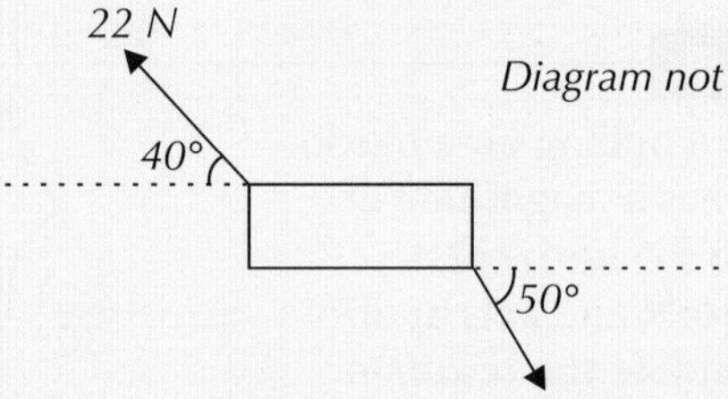

Diagram not to scale

Tip: The normal contact force due to an object's weight acts perpendicular to the surface. It is equal in size to the component of the weight applied to the surface, but acts in the opposite direction.

Tip: For question 5, it's easiest to choose upwards as the positive vertical direction and to the left to be the positive horizontal direction.

Practice Questions — Fact Recall

Q1 What's the difference between a scalar and a vector?

Q2 What name is given to a vector formed by adding vectors together?

Section Summary

Make sure you know...

- That all physical quantities have a numerical value and a unit.
- The Système International base quantities and their units.
- The units derived from S.I. base units, including any units covered in this book.
- How to check the homogeneity of equations using S.I. base units.
- The prefixes for units and their meanings.
- How to estimate the sizes of physical quantities covered in this book.
- How to make predictions of how changes in, or incorrect recordings of, a variable will affect the results of an experiment.
- The meaning of the terms random error, systematic error and zero error.
- How the effect of errors on an experiment can be reduced.
- How errors affect the precision and accuracy of results.
- How to calculate and plot the absolute and percentage uncertainties in a result.
- That when adding or subtracting data that has uncertainties, the uncertainty of the result is found by adding together the absolute uncertainties of the data.
- That when multiplying or dividing data that has uncertainties, the uncertainty of the result is found by adding together the percentage uncertainties of the data.
- That when raising data that has an uncertainty to a power, the uncertainty of the result is found by multiplying the percentage uncertainty by the power.
- That the percentage difference is a way of measuring the accuracy of a result.
- How to calculate the percentage difference of a result.
- How to use error bars to represent the uncertainty in a measurement.
- That axes of graphs and headings of tables should be written in the form "quantity / unit".
- The meaning of the term 'worst line'.
- How to use worst lines to calculate the uncertainty in a result.
- The difference between scalar and vector quantities.
- Examples of both scalar and vector quantities.
- How to add and subtract vectors using a scale drawing.
- How to use trigonometry to find a resultant vector of two perpendicular vectors.
- How to resolve a vector into two components at right angles to each other.

Exam-style Questions

1 An *I-V* graph for a resistor is shown below.

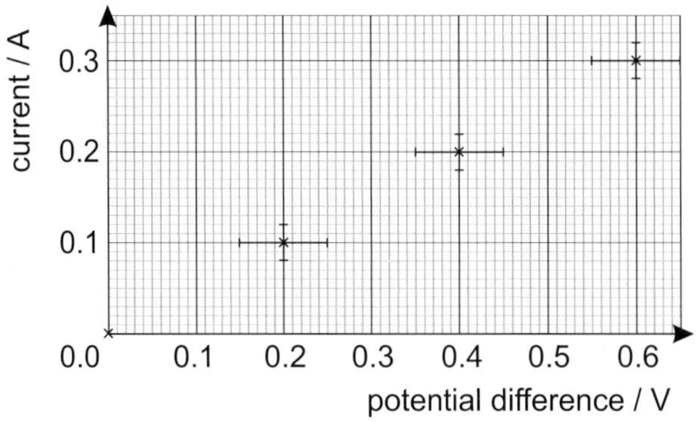

What is the percentage uncertainty in the measurement of 0.4 V?

A 0.05%

B 0.1%

C 5%

D 12.5%

(1 mark)

2 A box of books is sliding down a frictionless slope inclined at 30.0° to the horizontal. The weight of the box of books is 15 ± 0.5 N.

(a) Calculate the size of the component of the box's weight that acts down the slope. Calculate the percentage uncertainty in this value.

(3 marks)

(b) More books are added to the box. A 23 N force is then applied to the box. This force acts parallel to the horizontal. It produces a 3.0 N resultant force up the slope. Calculate the new weight of the box.

(3 marks)

3 A student investigates the force constant of a spring, by measuring the extension of the spring for different stretching forces.

(a) The student realises that the mass balance he has been using has caused a zero error. State whether this is a type of random or systematic error, and describe the difference between systematic and random errors.

(2 marks)

(b) The spring was extended linearly by 3.0 ± 0.05 cm when a force of 60 ± 5 N was applied to it. Calculate the force constant of the spring and the uncertainty in this value. Use the equation: force = force constant × extension.

(4 marks)

1. Constant Acceleration

There's a set of famous equations that you can use to work out an object's displacement, acceleration and starting and finishing velocity. These equations work for an object in uniform acceleration, and are really useful in physics.

Displacement, velocity and acceleration

You won't get far in physics without coming across **speed**, **displacement**, **velocity** and **acceleration**. Displacement, velocity and acceleration are all vector quantities (page 34), so the direction matters.

Speed — How fast something is moving, regardless of direction.

Displacement — How far an object's travelled from its starting point in a given direction.

Velocity — The rate of change of an object's displacement (its speed in a given direction).

Acceleration — The rate of change of an object's velocity.

During a journey, the **average speed** is just the total distance covered divided by the total time elapsed. The speed of an object at any given point in time is known as its **instantaneous speed**.

The constant acceleration equations

There are four main equations that you use to solve problems involving uniform (constant) acceleration. You need to be able to use them, but you don't have to know how they're derived — it's just shown here to help you learn them. The equations use 5 different letters:

s — displacement (in m) u — initial velocity (in ms^{-1})

v — final velocity (in ms^{-1}) a — acceleration (in ms^{-2}) t — time (in s)

- Acceleration is the rate of change of velocity. From this you get:

  $a = \frac{(v - u)}{t}$ so $v = u + at$ ①

- Displacement = average velocity × time.
  If acceleration is constant, the average velocity is just the average of the initial and final velocities, so:

  $s = \frac{1}{2}(u + v)t$ ②

- Substitute the expression for v from equation 1 into equation 2 to give:

  $s = \frac{1}{2}(u + u + at)t = \frac{1}{2}(2ut + at^2) \Rightarrow$ $s = ut + \frac{1}{2}at^2$ ③

Learning Objectives:

- Understand what is meant by the terms displacement, instantaneous speed, average speed, velocity and acceleration.
- Be able to use the equations of motion for constant acceleration in a straight line:
  $v = u + at$
  $s = \frac{1}{2}(u + v)t$
  $s = ut + \frac{1}{2}at^2$
  $v^2 = u^2 + 2as$

Specification References 3.1.1 and 3.1.2

Tip: Acceleration could mean a change in speed or direction or both — since velocity is speed in a given direction.

Figure 1: *All objects fall through a vacuum with the same acceleration (g). There's more on this on pages 43-45.*

Tip: These equations are sometimes called 'suvat equations'.

- You can derive the fourth equation from equations 1 and 2:

Use equation 1 in the form: $\mathbf{a} = \dfrac{(\mathbf{v} - \mathbf{u})}{t}$

Multiply both sides by **s**, where: $\mathbf{s} = \frac{1}{2}(\mathbf{u} + \mathbf{v})t$

This gives: $\mathbf{as} = \dfrac{(\mathbf{v} - \mathbf{u})}{t} \times \frac{1}{2}(\mathbf{u} + \mathbf{v})t$

The *t*'s on the right cancel, so: $2\mathbf{as} = (\mathbf{v} - \mathbf{u})(\mathbf{v} + \mathbf{u})$

$= \mathbf{v}^2 - \mathbf{uv} + \mathbf{uv} - \mathbf{u}^2$

so: $\mathbf{v}^2 = \mathbf{u}^2 + 2\mathbf{as}$ ④

Example — Maths Skills

A mouse runs 10 m as it accelerates uniformly from 1.5 ms⁻¹ to 3.5 ms⁻¹. Calculate the mouse's acceleration.

First of all, write out what you know:

$\mathbf{s} = 10$ m
$\mathbf{u} = 1.5$ ms^{-1}
$\mathbf{v} = 3.5$ ms^{-1}
$\mathbf{a} = ?$

Choose the equation with only one unknown quantity.
So you need to use: $\mathbf{v}^2 = \mathbf{u}^2 + 2\mathbf{as}$

Substitute the values into the equation, then rearrange to find acceleration.

$$3.5^2 = 1.5^2 + (2 \times \mathbf{a} \times 10) \Rightarrow \mathbf{a} = \frac{12.25 - 2.25}{20} = 0.5 \text{ ms}^{-2}$$

Examples — Maths Skills

A car accelerates steadily from rest at a rate of 4.2 ms⁻² for 6.0 seconds. Calculate its final speed.

As always, start by writing down what you know:

$\mathbf{u} = 0$ ms^{-1}
$\mathbf{a} = 4.2$ ms^{-2}
$t = 6.0$ s
$\mathbf{v} = ?$

Then choose the right equation... $\mathbf{v} = \mathbf{u} + \mathbf{a}t$

$\mathbf{v} = 0 + (4.2 \times 6.0) = 25.2 = 25$ ms^{-1} (to 2 s.f.)

Calculate the distance travelled in 6.0 seconds.

$\mathbf{u} = 0$ ms^{-1}
$\mathbf{v} = 25.2$ ms^{-1}
$\mathbf{a} = 4.2$ ms^{-2}
$t = 6.0$ s
$\mathbf{s} = ?$

You can use: $\mathbf{s} = \frac{1}{2}(\mathbf{u} + \mathbf{v})t$
⇓
$\mathbf{s} = \frac{1}{2}(0 + 25.2) \times 6.0$
$= 75.6$ m
$= 76$ m (to 2 s.f.)

or: $\mathbf{s} = \mathbf{u}t + \frac{1}{2}\mathbf{a}t^2$
⇓
$\mathbf{s} = 0 + (\frac{1}{2} \times 4.2 \times 6.0^2)$
$= 75.6$ m
$= 76$ m (to 2 s.f.)

Tip: You can use either $\mathbf{s} = \frac{1}{2}(\mathbf{u} + \mathbf{v})t$ or $\mathbf{s} = \mathbf{u}t + \frac{1}{2}\mathbf{a}t^2$ to find the distance travelled, but it's safer to use $\mathbf{s} = \mathbf{u}t + \frac{1}{2}\mathbf{a}t^2$ because it doesn't rely on previously calculated values.

Practice Questions — Application

Q1 A cat runs with uniform acceleration from rest to 10 ms^{-1} in 20 s. What's its displacement after this time?

Q2 The brakes are applied to a train travelling at 25 ms^{-1} and it takes 18 s to stop with uniform deceleration. What is its deceleration?

Q3 An electric tram sets off from rest and travels 103 m in 9.2 seconds. Calculate its acceleration during this time, assuming it was uniform.

Tip: Deceleration is the same as negative acceleration.

Practice Questions — Fact Recall

Q1 What is a) the velocity of an object? b) the acceleration of an object?

Q2 What are the 4 'suvat equations' for constant acceleration?

2. Acceleration Due To Gravity

If you drop a ball (or anything else heavier than air) from a height, it accelerates towards the ground due to gravity. If no other forces act on the ball (like air resistance) the ball is said to be in 'free fall'.

Learning Objectives:
- Know that an object in free fall experiences an acceleration of $\mathbf{g}$.
- Be able to use the equations of motion for constant acceleration in a straight line for bodies falling in a uniform gravitational field without air resistance.
- Know and be able to use techniques and procedures to determine the acceleration of free fall, such as using a trapdoor and electromagnet arrangement (PAG1).

Specification Reference 3.1.2

What is free fall?

Free fall is when there's gravity acting on an object and nothing else. It's defined as the motion of an object undergoing an acceleration of '$\mathbf{g}$'. You need to remember:

- Acceleration is a vector quantity — and '$\mathbf{g}$' acts vertically downwards.
- The magnitude of '$\mathbf{g}$' is usually taken as 9.81 ms^{-2}, though it varies slightly at different points on the Earth's surface.
- The only force acting on an object in free fall is its weight.
- Objects can have an initial velocity in any direction and still undergo free fall as long as the force providing the initial velocity is no longer acting.

'$\mathbf{g}$' is also used for gravitational field strength, where $\mathbf{g} = 9.81$ Nkg^{-1} (p.69). If you break down Nkg^{-1} into S.I. units, they are actually the same as ms^{-2}, so it's the same '$\mathbf{g}$'.

Free fall and the equations of motion

You need to be able to work out speeds, distances and times for objects moving vertically in a uniform gravitational field with an acceleration of $\mathbf{g}$. As $\mathbf{g}$ is a constant acceleration you can use the equations of motion. But because $\mathbf{g}$ acts downwards, you need to be careful about directions. To make it clear, there's a sign convention: upwards is positive, downwards is negative.

- $\mathbf{g}$ is always downwards, so it's usually negative.
- t is always positive.
- $\mathbf{u}$ and $\mathbf{v}$ can be either positive or negative.
- $\mathbf{s}$ can be either positive or negative.

Tip: Make sure you learn these conventions — remember that direction is important when using vectors.

Tip: See pages 41 and 42 for the equations of motion.

Case 1: No initial velocity

This means an object is just falling — initial velocity $\mathbf{u} = 0$.
Acceleration $\mathbf{a} = \mathbf{g} = -9.81$ ms^{-2}. Hence the equations of motion become:

$$\mathbf{v} = \mathbf{g}t \qquad \mathbf{v}^2 = 2\mathbf{g}\mathbf{s}$$

$$\mathbf{s} = \frac{1}{2}\mathbf{g}t^2 \qquad \mathbf{s} = \frac{1}{2}\mathbf{v}t$$

Case 2: An initial velocity upwards

This means it's projected up into the air. The equations of motion are just as normal, but with $\mathbf{a} = \mathbf{g} = -9.81$ ms^{-2}.

Case 3: An initial velocity downwards

This is like case 2 — the equations of motion are as normal with $\mathbf{a} = \mathbf{g} = -9.81$ ms^{-2}.

Figure 1: *A ball bearing that is falling vertically is assumed to be in free fall. This is because they are small and quite streamlined, so any air resistance acting on them is assumed to be negligible. This makes them useful for free fall experiments (see the next page).*

Examples — Maths Skills

A tile falls from a roof 25 m high. Calculate its speed when it hits the ground.

As before, start by writing out what you know:

$s = 25$ m
$u = 0$ ms^{-1} (since the tile's stationary to start with)
$g = 9.81$ ms^{-2}
$v = ?$

We want to find v, we know s and g, and the tile has no initial velocity. So use $v^2 = 2gs$:

$v^2 = 2 \times 9.81 \times 25$
$v^2 = 490.5$
$\Rightarrow\ v = \sqrt{490.5} = 22.147... = 22$ ms^{-1} (to 2 s.f.)

Alex throws a stone upwards. She throws it with an initial velocity of 4.00 ms^{-1}. What is the maximum height reached by the stone?

You know $u = 4.00$ ms^{-1}, $v = 0$ ms^{-1} and $a = g = -9.81$ ms^{-2}
You need to find s.

Use $v^2 = u^2 + 2as$, $s = (v^2 - u^2) \div 2a$

$s = (0^2 - 4.00^2) \div (2 \times -9.81)$
$= 0.81549...$ m
$= 0.815$ m (to 3 s.f.)

Tip: Here, all of the values we're interested in act downwards, so we can define downwards as the positive direction, so all the vector quantities are positive.

Tip: Acceleration due to gravity acts against the motion of the stone, so it's negative here.

Determining *g* using free fall

PRACTICAL ACTIVITY GROUP 1

One method you can use to determine the acceleration due to gravity g using free fall involves dropping a ball bearing onto a trap door using an electromagnet. You can carry out the experiment by following these steps:

- Set up the equipment shown in Figure 2.

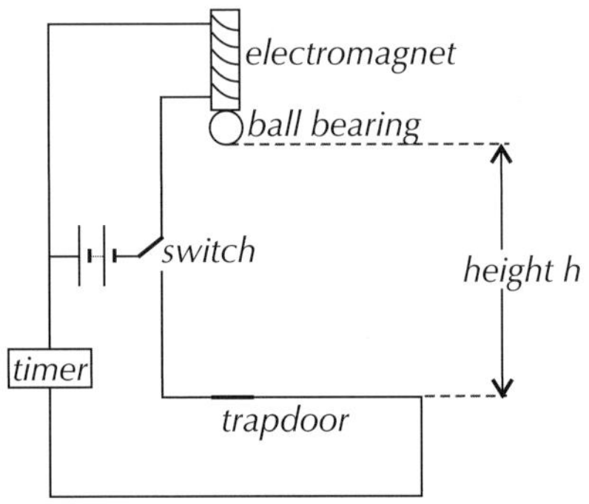

Figure 2: *Circuit diagram for an experiment to determine* ***g*** *using free fall.*

- Measure the height h from the bottom of the ball bearing to the trapdoor.
- Flick the switch to simultaneously start the timer and disconnect the electromagnet, releasing the ball bearing.
- The ball bearing falls, knocking the trapdoor down and breaking the circuit — which stops the timer. Record the time t shown on the timer.
- Repeat this experiment three times and average the time taken to fall.

Tip: Whether you use this experiment or another method, be sure you are working safely. Do a risk assessment before you start.

Tip: You could reduce the error in your measurement of h by using a set square to make sure your eye is level with the ruler.

- To calculate **g** from the results, rearrange the equation $h = \frac{1}{2}\mathbf{g}t^2$ (page 43) to get $\mathbf{g} = 2h \div t^2$, where t is the time measured by the timer and h is the height that the ball bearing has fallen.
- Repeat this experiment for several different heights. Calculate a value of **g** for each height.
- Average the values of **g** for each of the heights to find your final value of **g**.

Identifying and reducing errors

The most significant source of random error in this experiment will be in the measurement of h. Using a ruler, you'll have an uncertainty of about ±1 mm.

Using a small and heavy ball bearing means you can assume air resistance is so small you can ignore it.

Using this kind of mechanism to automatically release and time the ball bearing's fall means you can measure times with a smaller uncertainty than if you tried to drop the ball and time the fall using a stopwatch.

If you were to do this by hand, you'd get a larger uncertainty due to human reaction times (it will take you a fraction of a second to press the buttons on the stopwatch). But there may still be a small systematic error if there is a delay in the switch or timing mechanism.

Exam Tip
You could also measure **g** using light gates. Drop the ball between two light gates that are a known distance apart (h), and use the light gates to measure the velocity at each gate ($\mathbf{u}$ and $\mathbf{v}$). You can then use the equation $\mathbf{v}^2 = \mathbf{u}^2 + 2\mathbf{g}h$ (from the equation on page 42) to find **g**.

Tip: If you need to buff up on your practical skills, head over to pages 5-22.

Exam Tip
Unless you're given the value of **g** in an exam question, you should assume it has a value of 9.81 ms^{-2}.

Practice Questions — Application

Q1 A ball is dropped from the top of a cliff and takes 6.19 s to hit the ground. Assuming there's no air resistance, how tall is the cliff?

Q2 A spanner is dropped from a height of 6.83 m. Assuming there's no air resistance, how fast will it be going when it hits the ground?

Q3 Give two ways errors can be reduced when carrying out an experiment to determine the value of **g** by measuring the length of time an object takes to fall a set distance.

Practice Questions — Fact Recall

Q1 What's the only force present in free fall motion?

Q2 a) Describe an experiment you could do to obtain data that you could use to determine the value of **g**.

b) Explain how you can use your results to find **g**.

Learning Objectives:

- Understand the independence of the vertical and horizontal motion of a projectile.
- Understand and be able to perform calculations involving the two-dimensional motion of a projectile with constant velocity in one direction and constant acceleration in a perpendicular direction.

Specification Reference 3.1.3

Exam Tip
If you're doing AS or A Level Maths, you'll probably cover projectiles in mechanics.

Exam Tip
"Assume the [object] acts as a particle and there is no air resistance" means you don't need to worry about any forces other than the one caused by gravity (weight).

Tip: v_h is the horizontal velocity and s_h is the horizontal displacement.

Tip: Resolving vectors was covered on pages 36-37.

3. Projectile Motion

Objects such as a thrown ball or a bullet leaving a gun have projectile motion. They follow a curved path and experience free fall. The key thing here is to treat the horizontal and vertical parts of motion separately.

Projectile motion

Any object given an initial velocity and then left to move freely under gravity is a projectile. In **projectile motion**, the horizontal and vertical components of the object's motion are completely independent. Projectiles follow a curved path because the horizontal velocity remains constant, while the vertical velocity is affected by the acceleration due to gravity, $\boldsymbol{g}$.

Example — Maths Skills

A cannon ball is fired horizontally with a velocity of 120 ms⁻¹ from 1.5 m above the ground. How long does it take to hit the ground, and what is its change in horizontal displacement in this time? Assume the cannon ball acts as a particle, the ground is horizontal and there is no air resistance.

Start with the vertical motion — it's constant acceleration under gravity:

You know $\boldsymbol{u} = 0$ (no vertical velocity at first), $\boldsymbol{s} = -1.5$ m and $\boldsymbol{a} = \boldsymbol{g} = -9.81$ ms^{-2}. You need to find t.

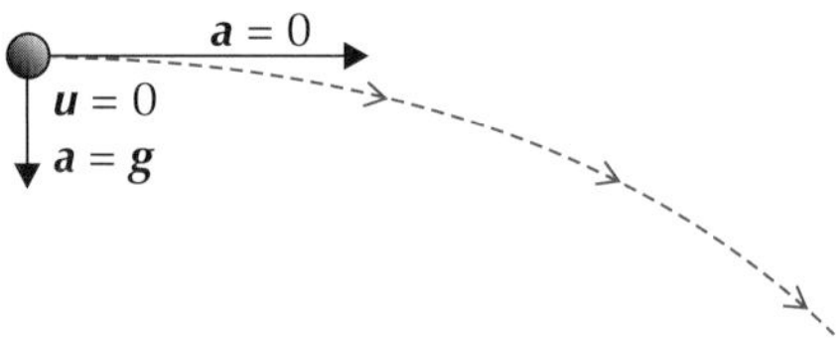

Use $\boldsymbol{s} = \frac{1}{2}\boldsymbol{g}t^2 \Rightarrow t = \sqrt{\frac{2\boldsymbol{s}}{\boldsymbol{g}}} = \sqrt{\frac{2 \times -1.5}{-9.81}} = 0.5530...$ s

So the ball hits the ground after 0.55 seconds (to 2 s.f.).

Then do the horizontal motion:

The horizontal motion isn't affected by gravity or other forces, so it moves at a constant speed. This means you can just use velocity = $\frac{\text{displacement}}{\text{time}}$.

Now $\boldsymbol{v}_h = 120$ ms^{-1}, $t = 0.5530...$ s and $\boldsymbol{a} = 0$. You need to find $\boldsymbol{s}_h$.

$\boldsymbol{s}_h = \boldsymbol{v}_h t = 120 \times 0.5530... = 66.36... = 66$ m (to 2 s.f.)

Projectile motion at an angle

If something's projected at an angle (like, say, a javelin) you start off with both horizontal and vertical velocity. This can make solving problems trickier.

To solve this kind of problem, you need to use this method:

- Resolve the initial velocity into horizontal and vertical components.
- Use the vertical component to work out how long it's in the air and/or how high it goes.
- Use the horizontal component to work out how far it goes in the horizontal direction while it's in the air.

Example — Maths Skills

A javelin is thrown with a velocity of 21 ms^{-1} at an angle of 45° to the ground from a height of 1.8 m. How far does the javelin travel? Assume the javelin acts as a particle, the ground is horizontal and there is no air resistance.

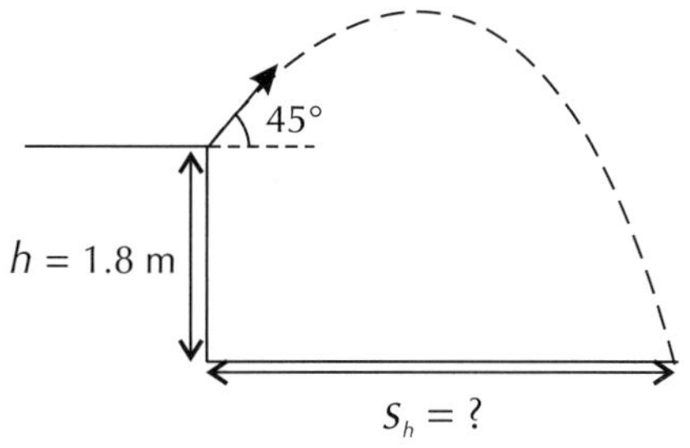

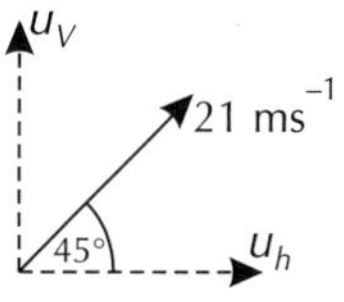

Start by resolving the velocity into horizontal and vertical components:

$u_h = \cos 45° \times 21 = 14.84...$ ms^{-1}

$u_v = \sin 45° \times 21 = 14.84...$ ms^{-1}

Then find how long it's in the air for — start by finding v_v. The javelin starts from a height of 1.8 m and finishes at ground level, so use $s = -1.8$ m:

$v_v^2 = u_v^2 + 2gs_v \Rightarrow v_v = \sqrt{14.84...^2 + 2\times(-9.81)\times(-1.8)} = -15.99...$ ms^{-1}

Then find the time it stays in the air:

$s_v = \frac{(u_v + v_v)}{2} \times t \Rightarrow t = \frac{s_v}{(u_v + v_v)} \times 2 = \frac{-1.8}{14.84... - 15.99...} \times 2 = 3.144...$ s

Now you can work out how far it travels horizontally in this time:

$s_h = u_h t = 14.84... \times 3.144... = 46.68... = 47$ m (to 2 s.f.)

Figure 1: *The only thing carrying a javelin forwards after it's been thrown is the initial horizontal velocity given to it by the thrower.*

Tip: v_v is negative because the javelin is travelling downwards when it lands.

Practice Questions — Application

Q1 A gun fires a bullet at 502 ms^{-1} horizontally. If the gun was held 1.61 m above the ground, how far will the bullet travel? Assume there's no air resistance and the ground is horizontal.

Q2 A catapult hurls a rock from ground level at 25 ms^{-1}, 60.0° to the horizontal. Assuming there's no air resistance and that the ground is horizontal, calculate:

a) The amount of time the rock stays in the air.

b) How far away from the catapult the rock will land.

Q3 A golf ball is hit at 12.1 ms^{-1} at an angle of 31.5° above the horizontal from a podium 4.20 m above the surface of the ground. Calculate the maximum height above the ground reached by the ball. Assume there's no air resistance and the ground is horizontal.

Figure 2: *A bullet acts as a projectile in free fall after leaving the gun (if you ignore air resistance).*

Practice Questions — Fact Recall

Q1 What's free fall motion called when the object is given an initial velocity?

Q2 What should you do if you need to use the equations of uniform acceleration on an object that has an initial velocity at an angle to the horizontal, in order to find the horizontal distance travelled?

4. Displacement-Time Graphs

Learning Objectives:

- Be able to plot displacement-time graphs.
- Understand graphical representations of displacement, speed, velocity and acceleration on displacement-time graphs.
- Know that the gradient of an object's displacement-time graph gives the velocity of the object.

Specification Reference 3.1.1

Displacement-time graphs show an object's position relative to its starting point over a period of time. They're useful because they can be used to describe an object's motion as well as find its velocity at a given point.

Plotting displacement-time graphs

You need to be able to plot **displacement-time graphs** for moving objects. The suvat equations from page 41 can be used to work out values to plot. Displacement is plotted on the y-axis and time on the x-axis.

Example — Maths Skills

Plot a displacement-time graph for a panther who accelerates constantly from rest at 2.0 ms^{-2} for 5.0 seconds.

You want to find **s**, and you know that:

$\boldsymbol{a} = 2.0\ \text{ms}^{-2}$
$\boldsymbol{u} = 0\ \text{ms}^{-2}$

Use $\boldsymbol{s} = \boldsymbol{u}t + \frac{1}{2}\boldsymbol{a}t^2$ to find values of t and **s** to plot on the graph.
If you substitute in $\boldsymbol{u}$ and $\boldsymbol{a}$, this simplifies to:

$$\boldsymbol{s} = (0 \times t) + (\tfrac{1}{2} \times 2.0t^2)$$
$$= t^2$$

Now pick values of t between 0 and 5.0 seconds and work out **s** at those points with $\boldsymbol{s} = t^2$: ...then plot the graph:

t (s)	s (m)
0.0	0.0
1.0	1.0
2.0	4.0
3.0	9.0
4.0	16.0
5.0	25.0

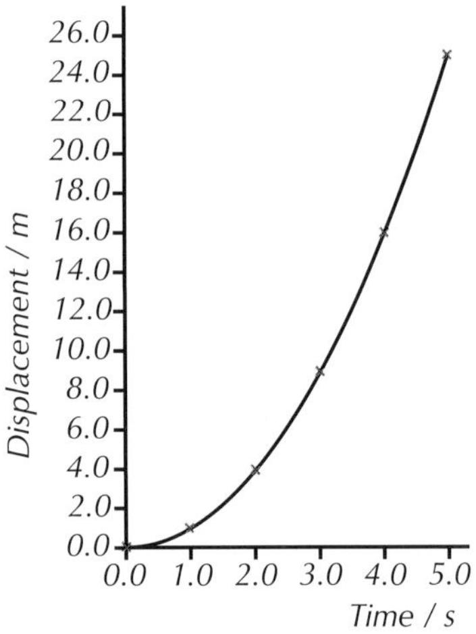

Tip: Try to use time intervals that make plotting the graph easier. In this example, using intervals of 1 second gives you 6 points to plot, which is enough for a neat curve.

Figure 1: *GPS and displacement-time graphs can be used to track a sea turtle's movement between mating seasons.*

Acceleration on displacement-time graphs

The gradient of a displacement-time graph shows velocity. Acceleration is the rate of change of velocity (see page 41), so on a displacement-time graph, acceleration is the rate of change of the gradient.

A graph of displacement against time for an accelerating object always produces a curve. If the object's accelerating at a uniform rate, then the rate of change of the gradient will be constant. Acceleration is shown by a curve with an increasing gradient (like the one in the example above). Deceleration is shown by a curve with a decreasing gradient.

Changing the acceleration of the panther in the example on the previous page would change the gradient of the displacement-time graph like this:

Tip: You could use spreadsheet modelling to plot the s-t graph for the panther. See pages 249-250 for more.

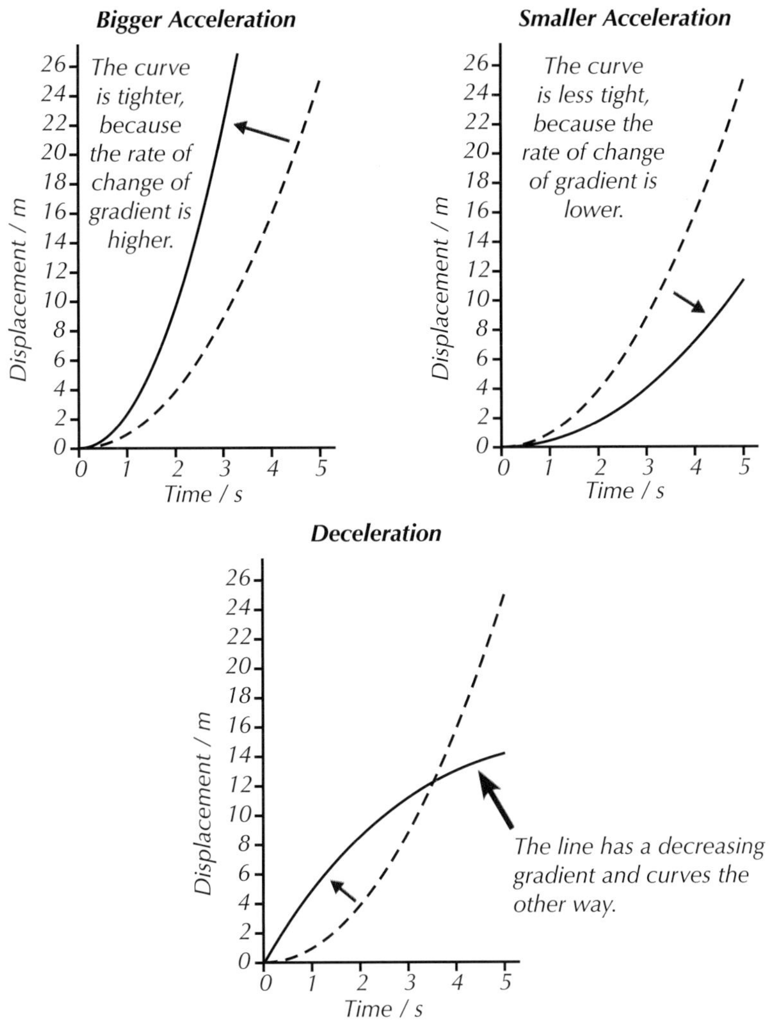

Bigger Acceleration
The curve is tighter, because the rate of change of gradient is higher.
Displacement / m
Time / s
Smaller Acceleration
The curve is less tight, because the rate of change of gradient is lower.
Displacement / m
Time / s
Deceleration
The line has a decreasing gradient and curves the other way.
Displacement / m
Time / s

Figure 2: *The effect of changing the acceleration on the gradient of a displacement-time graph.*

Tip: Note that in the case of deceleration, the panther must have been already moving at $t = 0$. Otherwise its displacement would be negative.

Finding the velocity

When velocity is constant (but not zero), the displacement-time graph is a diagonal straight line. As you saw on the previous page, the gradient of a displacement-time graph shows velocity. This is because velocity is defined as:

$$\text{velocity} = \frac{\text{change in displacement}}{\text{time taken}} \quad \text{or:} \quad \boldsymbol{v} = \frac{\Delta s}{\Delta t}$$

On the graph, this is $\frac{\text{change in } y}{\text{change in } x} = \frac{\Delta y}{\Delta x}$, i.e. the gradient.

Tip: If a section of a displacement-time graph is horizontal (gradient = 0), the object's velocity is zero — it's not moving.

Tip: A negative gradient means the object's moving in a negative direction.

Example — Maths Skills

The graph below shows a car's displacement over time. What's the car's velocity between 0 and 6 seconds?

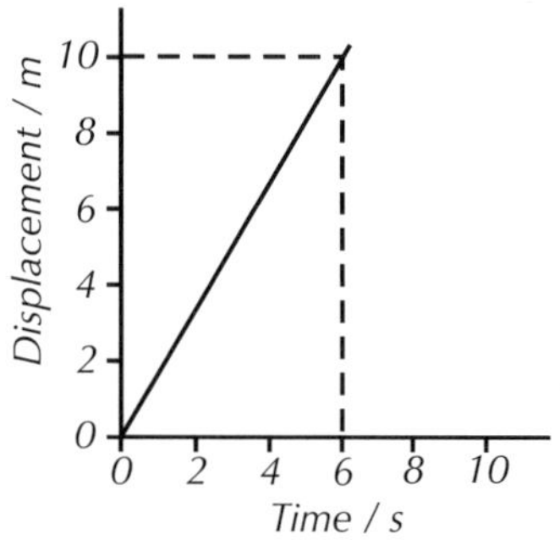

To work out the velocity, find the change in displacement and the change in time during the period given in the question:

$$v = \frac{\Delta y}{\Delta x} = \frac{10 - 0}{6 - 0} = \frac{10}{6} = 1.666... = 1.7\ \text{ms}^{-1}\ \text{(to 2 s.f.)}$$

Tip: Although it might seem pointless subtracting zero, the section of the graph you're working with won't always start at 0.

Velocity and curved displacement-time graphs

If the gradient isn't constant (i.e. if it's a curved line), it means the object is accelerating and the velocity is constantly changing.

An object's instantaneous velocity is just its velocity at a particular moment in time. To find the instantaneous velocity at a certain point, you need to draw a **tangent** to the curve at that point to find its gradient.

Figure 3: A displacement-time graph of a runner during a race can be used to work out their velocity at any point in the race.

Example — Maths Skills

The graph below shows the displacement of a ball rolling down a slope over time. Find its velocity at 5.5 s.

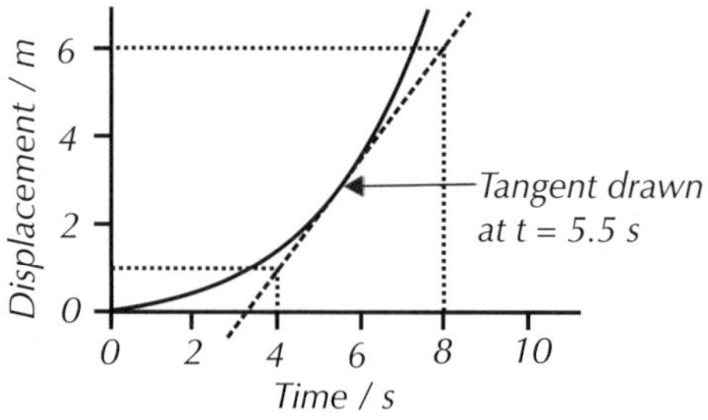

Start by drawing a tangent to the curve at 5.5 s (this has been done already). You can then draw horizontal and vertical lines from the tangent to the axes to find values for Δy and Δx.

$$v = \frac{\Delta y}{\Delta x} = \frac{6 - 1}{8 - 4} = \frac{5}{4} = 1.25\ \text{ms}^{-1}$$

The average velocity is just the total change in displacement of the object divided by the total time taken. You can ignore any variations in acceleration and velocity, you just need the time and total displacement.

Example — **Maths Skills**

The graph below shows the displacement of a model railway train along a straight track over time. Calculate the average velocity of the train during the time period shown on the graph.

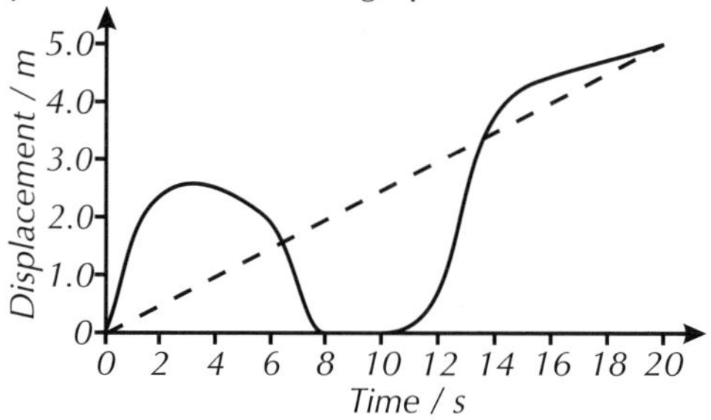

average velocity = total change in displacement ÷ time taken

= 5.0 ÷ 20 = 0.25 ms^{-1}

Practice Questions — Application

Q1 Use the data in the table below to plot a displacement-time graph.

t (s)	s (m)
2	6
2.5	7.5
3.5	10.5
5	15
7	21
8	24

Q2 The graph below shows the displacement of a cyclist during a journey. Describe what's happening in parts a), b), c) and d).

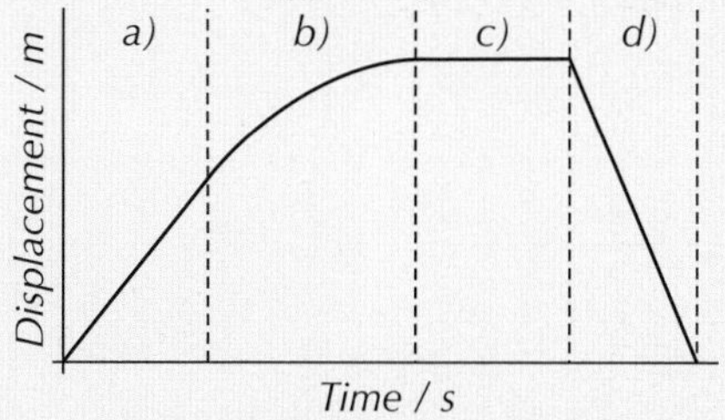

Figure 4: *The graph in Q2 might describe a cyclist's displacement as they go up and down a hill.*

Q3 A rocket accelerates at a constant rate from rest to 100.0 ms^{-1} in 5.0 s. Plot a displacement-time graph for the rocket during this time.

Tip: Start by finding the rocket's acceleration.

Q4 a) Use the data in the table below to plot a displacement-time graph.

t (s)	s (m)
0.0	0.0
1.0	1.5
2.0	6.0
3.0	13.5
4.0	24.0
5.0	37.5

b) Use your graph to find the velocity of the object at 3.0 s?

Figure 5: *The displacement-time graph for a bus is likely to show a non-uniform acceleration as it makes frequent stops.*

Practice Questions — Fact Recall

Q1 What kind of motion does a curved displacement-time graph show?

Q2 What kind of motion does a straight line on a displacement-time graph show?

Q3 What does the rate of change of gradient on a displacement-time graph represent?

Q4 What value can be calculated using the tangent on the distance-time graph below?

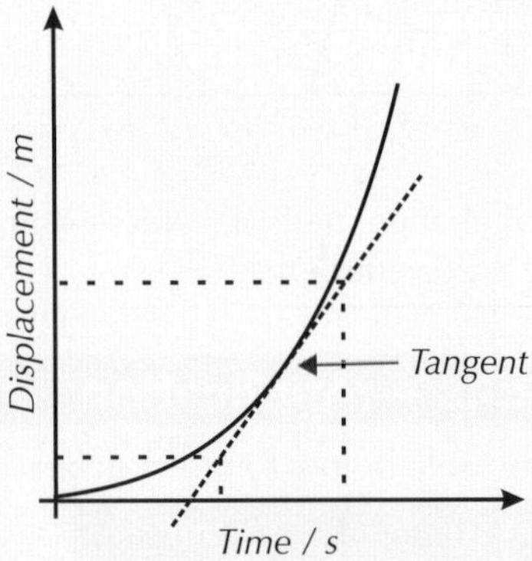

Q5 What is the difference between average and instantaneous velocity?

Q6 How would you calculate the average velocity of an object moving with non-uniform acceleration using a displacement-time graph?

5. Velocity-Time Graphs

Velocity-time graphs show, as the name suggests, an object's velocity over time. As with displacement-time graphs, their shape can be used to find out about an object's movement at different points in time.

Finding the acceleration

The gradient of a **velocity-time graph** tells you the acceleration, since:

$$\text{acceleration} = \frac{\text{change in velocity}}{\text{time taken}} \quad \text{or:} \quad \boldsymbol{a} = \frac{\Delta \boldsymbol{v}}{\Delta t}$$

Uniform acceleration is always a straight line. The steeper the gradient, the greater the acceleration.

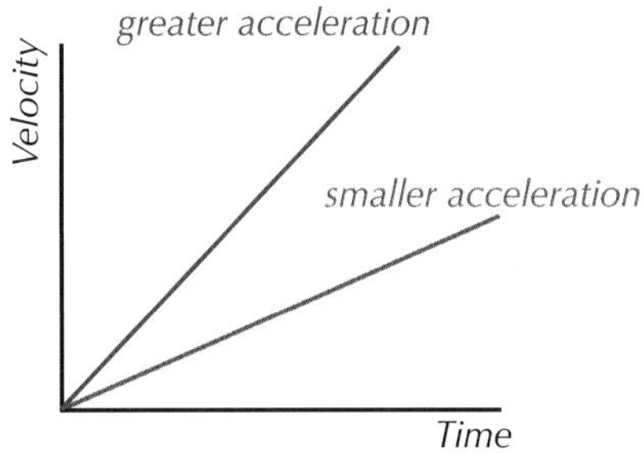

Figure 1: *A velocity-time graph showing the gradients of two different accelerations.*

Example — Maths Skills

A lion walks at 1.5 ms^{-1} for 4.0 s and then accelerates uniformly at a rate of 2.5 ms^{-2} for 4.0 s. Plot this information on a velocity-time graph.

Start by finding the lion's velocity at intervals between 0 and 8 s — it's 1.5 ms^{-1} for the first 4 seconds, then it increases by 2.5 ms^{-1} every second.

t (s)	v (ms^{-1})
0.0 – 4.0	1.5
5.0	4.0
6.0	6.5
7.0	9.0
8.0	11.5

Then just plot a graph with time on the x-axis and velocity on the y-axis:

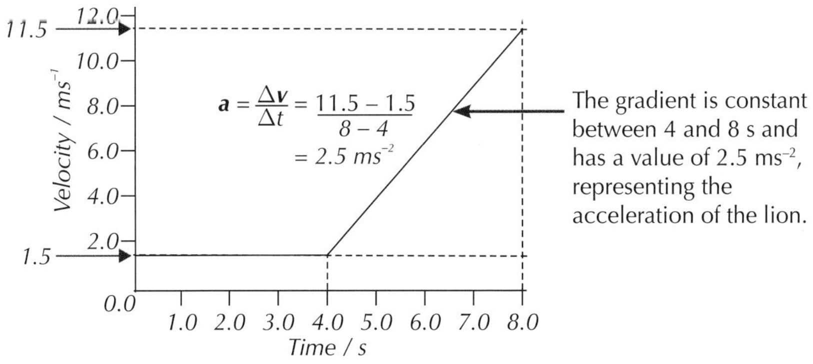

Learning Objectives:

- Understand graphical representations of displacement, speed, velocity and acceleration on velocity-time graphs.
- Be able to plot velocity-time graphs.
- Know that the gradient of an object's velocity-time graph gives the acceleration of the object.
- Know that the area under an object's velocity-time graph gives the displacement of the object.

Specification Reference 3.1.1

Tip: The equation for a straight line is $y = mx + c$. You can rearrange the acceleration equation into the same form, getting $\boldsymbol{v} = \boldsymbol{u} + \boldsymbol{a}t$. So on a linear $\boldsymbol{v}$-t graph, acceleration, $\boldsymbol{a}$, is the gradient (m) and the initial speed, $\boldsymbol{u}$, is the y-intercept (c).

Tip: In questions like this you could use the equations of motion to find the object's velocity at various times — in a similar way to the displacement-time graph example on page 48.

Finding displacement

A speed-time graph is very similar to a velocity-time graph. The big difference is that velocity-time graphs can have negative regions to show something travelling in the opposite direction.

Tip: When the ball slows down and starts falling, its velocity will become negative but its speed will start increasing again.

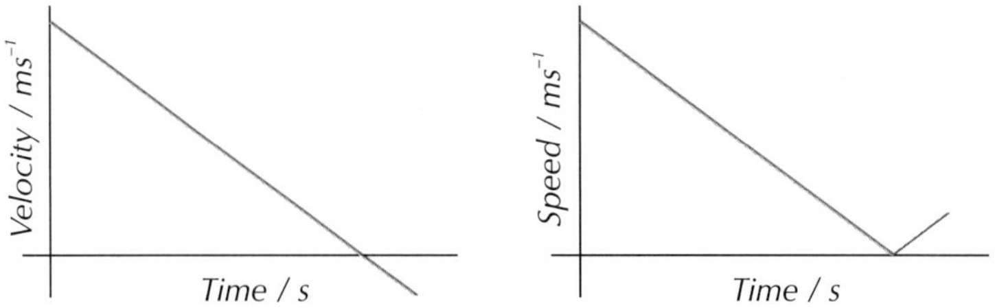

Figure 2: *The velocity-time and speed-time graphs for a ball being thrown up into the air.*

Tip: For velocity-time graphs, the areas under any negative parts of the graph count as 'negative areas', as they show the object moving the opposite way to whichever direction you took as being positive.

The area under a velocity-time graph represents the displacement of an object, as displacement, **s**, of an object with uniform acceleration can be found using:

$$\mathbf{s} = \tfrac{1}{2}(\boldsymbol{u} + \boldsymbol{v})t = \text{average velocity} \times \text{time}$$

You can find the total distance travelled by an object using:

$$\text{distance travelled} = \text{average speed} \times \text{time}$$

Therefore the area underneath a speed-time graph is the distance travelled.

Tip: The examples below show the link between these equations and the area under a speed-time or velocity-time graph.

Examples — **Maths Skills**

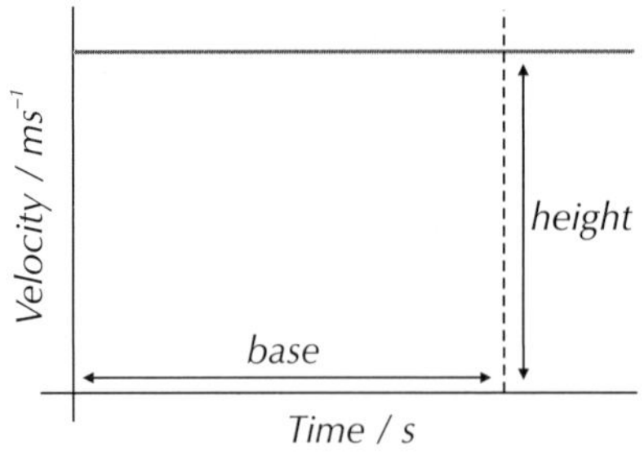

Figure 3: *The displacement for a rectangular velocity-time graph is just base × height.*

Average velocity = $\tfrac{1}{2}(\boldsymbol{u} + \boldsymbol{v})$

But velocity is constant, so $\boldsymbol{u} = \boldsymbol{v}$.

So average velocity = $\dfrac{\boldsymbol{v} + \boldsymbol{v}}{2} = \boldsymbol{v}$

= final velocity

Area under graph
= base × height
= final velocity × time
= average velocity × time
= displacement

Tip: Remember, $\boldsymbol{u}$ is initial velocity and $\boldsymbol{v}$ is final velocity.

Tip: Here, displacement is the same as distance travelled because the velocity-time graph has no negative parts.

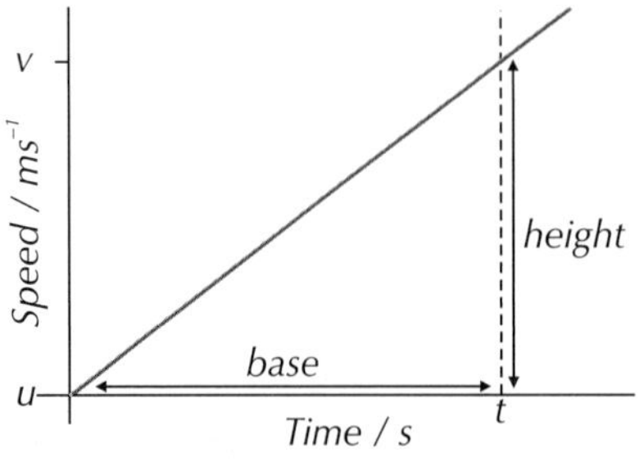

Figure 4: *The distance travelled for a triangular speed-time graph is ½ × base × height.*

Average speed = $\tfrac{1}{2}(u + v)$

But $u = 0$, so average speed = $\dfrac{v}{2}$

Area under graph
= ½ × base × height
= ½ × time × final speed
= $\tfrac{1}{2} \times t \times v$
= $\dfrac{v}{2} \times t$
= average speed × time
= distance travelled

Example — Maths Skills

A racing car accelerates uniformly from rest to 40.0 ms^{-1} in 10.0 s. It maintains this speed for a further 20.0 s before coming to rest by decelerating at a constant rate over the next 15.0 s. Draw a velocity-time graph for this journey and use it to calculate the total distance travelled by the racing car.

Start by drawing the graph and then splitting it up into sections:

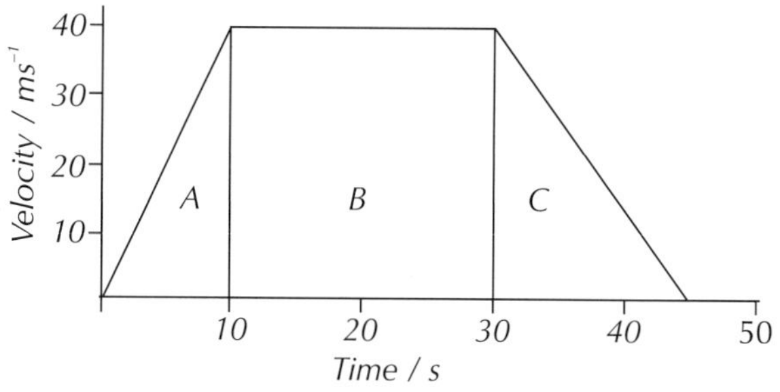

Calculate the area of each section and add the three results together.

A: Area = ½ × base × height = ½ × 10.0 × 40.0 = 200 m

B: Area = base × height = 20.0 × 40.0 = 800 m

C: Area = ½ × base × height = ½ × 15.0 × 40.0 = 300 m

Total distance travelled = 200 + 800 + 300 = 1300 m

Tip: Remember, uniform acceleration and deceleration are shown by straight lines on a velocity-time or speed-time graph.

Tip: If the ***v-t*** graph is on a grid, you could also work out the area under the graph by counting how many squares make up the area. Multiplying the value of each square by the number of squares will give you the displacement.

Example — Maths Skills

A ball is dropped from table-height so it bounces vertically. It bounces twice before someone catches it. The ball's motion while it bounces is shown on the *v-t* graph below. Calculate how high the ball rebounds on the first bounce.

Before you try and calculate anything, make sure you understand what each part of the graph is telling you about the ball's motion.

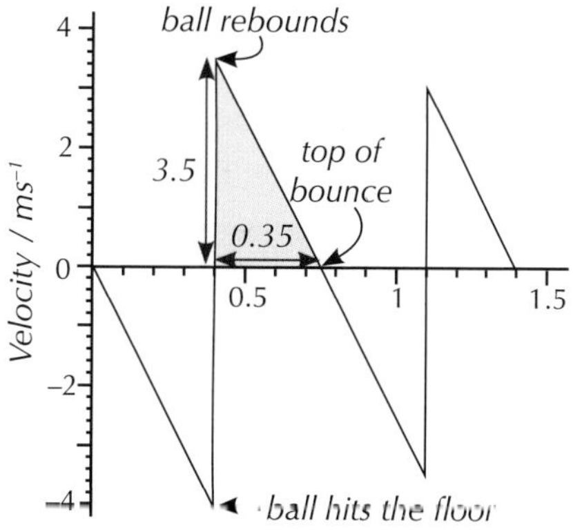

1. When the ball is first dropped, the velocity of the ball is negative — so downwards is the negative direction.
2. The points where the ball hits the floor are shown by the vertical straight lines on the graph — the ball's speed remains roughly the same, but its direction (and velocity) changes the instant it hits the floor.
3. The points where the ball's velocity is zero show where the ball reaches the top of a bounce before starting to fall downwards.

The height of the first bounce is the area under the graph between the time the ball first rebounds from the floor and the time it reaches the top of the bounce.

displacement = area under graph

= (3.5 × 0.35) ÷ 2 = 0.6125 = 0.61 m (to 2 s.f.)

Figure 5: *When a ball bounces, it changes the direction in which it is travelling, so the sign of its velocity changes.*

Tip: The maximum velocity decreases with each bounce because some of the ball's kinetic energy is transferred into other forms when it hits the ground. This means the height of each bounce also decreases.

Tip: The straight, diagonal lines show that there is constant deceleration under gravity — see page 43.

Practice Question — Application

Q1 The graph below shows the velocity of a car over 10 seconds. Use the graph to find the displacement of the car in this time.

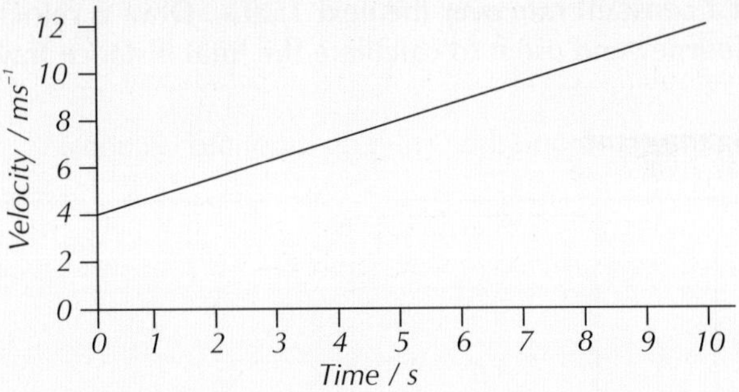

Tip: To find the area of a non-standard shape, try splitting it into two easier shapes (e.g. a rectangle and a triangle).

Non-uniform acceleration

If the acceleration is changing, the gradient of the velocity-time graph will also be changing — so you won't get a straight line. Increasing acceleration is shown by an increasing gradient — like in curve ① below. Decreasing acceleration is shown by a decreasing gradient — like in curve ② below.

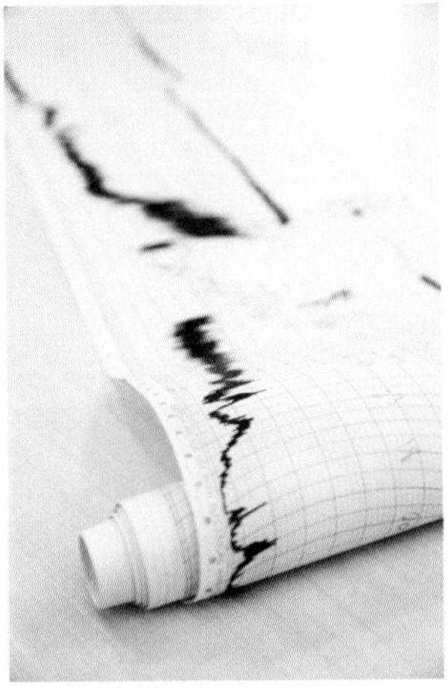

Figure 6: A speed-time graph of wind during a hurricane.

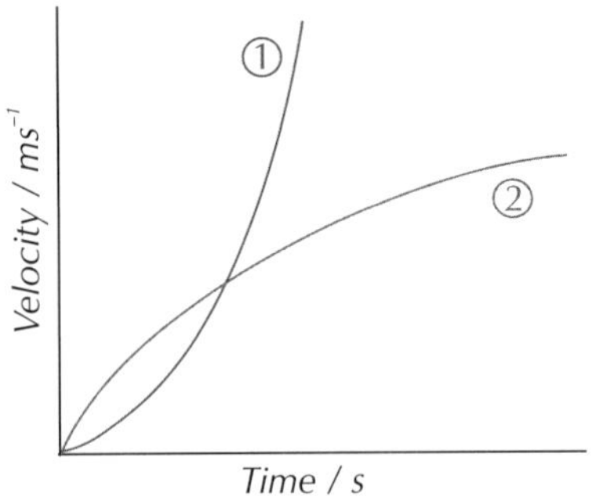

Figure 7: *Non-uniform acceleration on a velocity-time graph.*

For graphs like this, you can find the acceleration of an object at a particular point by drawing a tangent to the curve at that point and finding its gradient.

Example — Maths Skills

Find the acceleration shown by the velocity-time graph below at 60 seconds.

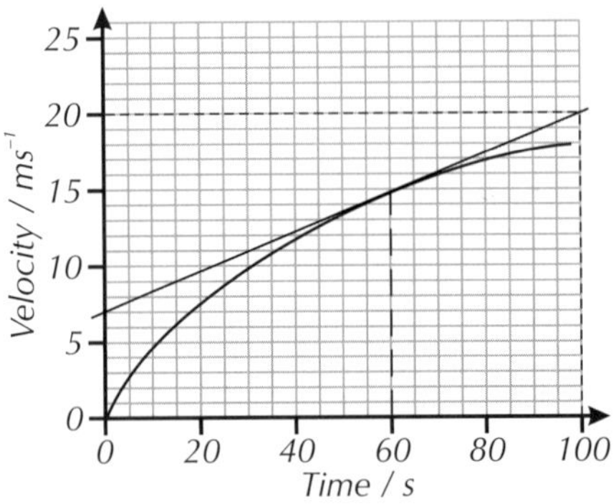

First draw a tangent to the curve at 60 seconds.

Then find the gradient of the tangent: gradient = $\frac{\Delta y}{\Delta x} = \frac{20-7}{100-0} = 0.13$ ms^{-2}

Displacement on non-linear velocity-time graphs

As our velocity-time graph is no longer a simple straight line, we have to use methods to estimate the area under the curve.

If the graph is on squared paper, an easy way to do this is just count the squares under the curve (see p.246). Another way is to split the curve up into trapeziums, calculate the area of each one and then add them all up.

Exam Tip

The counting the squares method is useful, but it can be time consuming. If the graph you're given has lots of small squares, it might be quicker to split the area up into trapeziums and find the area of those instead. Otherwise, block out larger squares — e.g. in the graph below you know there are 100 small squares in a big square.

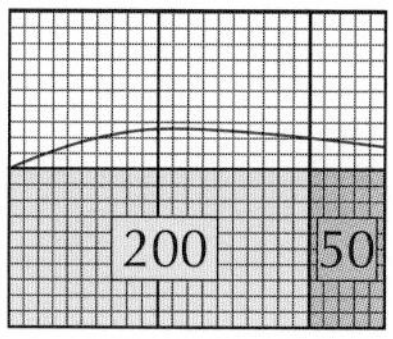

Example — Maths Skills

A car decreases its acceleration as it approaches 13 ms^{-1}. Estimate its displacement between 0 and 3 seconds from the velocity-time graph.

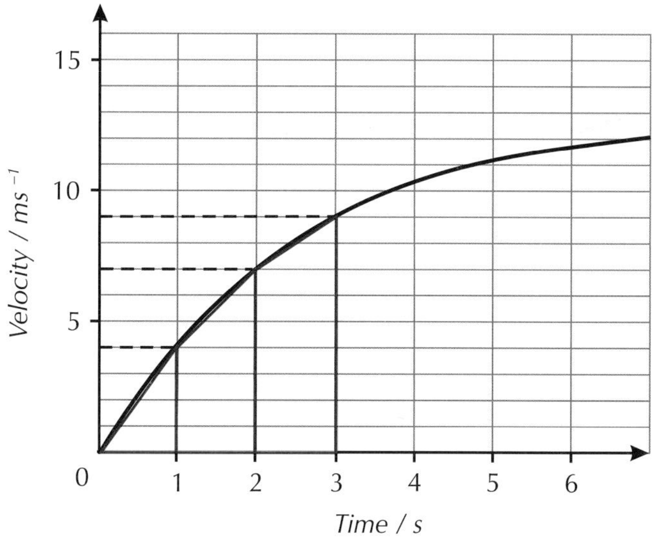

Split the area under the curve up into trapeziums and a triangle.

0-1 s — estimate the area with a triangle.
The height of the triangle is 4.
The base of the triangle is 1.

$$A = \frac{1}{2}(1 \times 4) = 2\,\text{m}$$

1-2 s — estimate the area using a trapezium.

$$\text{Area} = \frac{1}{2}(a + b)h$$

a is the length of the first side, $a = 4$
b is the length of the second side, $b = 7$
h is the width of each strip, so $h = 1$

$$A = \frac{1}{2}(4 + 7) \times 1 = 5.5\,\text{m}$$

2-3 s — trapezium, $a = 7$, $b = 9$, $h = 1$

$$A = \frac{1}{2}(7 + 9) \times 1 = 8\,\text{m}$$

Now add the areas together — Total area = 2 + 5.5 + 8 = 15.5 m

The estimated overall displacement of the car is 15.5 m = **16 m (to 2 s.f.)**

Tip: If you did this by counting the squares (or rectangles in this case), each rectangle represents 1 m. There are 15.5 rectangles under the graph between 0 and 3 s, so you get 15.5 m, the same answer as the trapezium method.

Practice Questions — Application

Q1 a) A cyclist goes down a hill with increasing acceleration.
Use the table below to plot a velocity-time graph of the cyclist.

t (s)	v (ms^{-1})
0	0
1	1
2	4
3	9
4	16

b) Use the graph to find the acceleration at 2 seconds.

Q2 The acceleration of a car is being tested on a test-track. The graph below is the velocity-time graph for the car during the test.

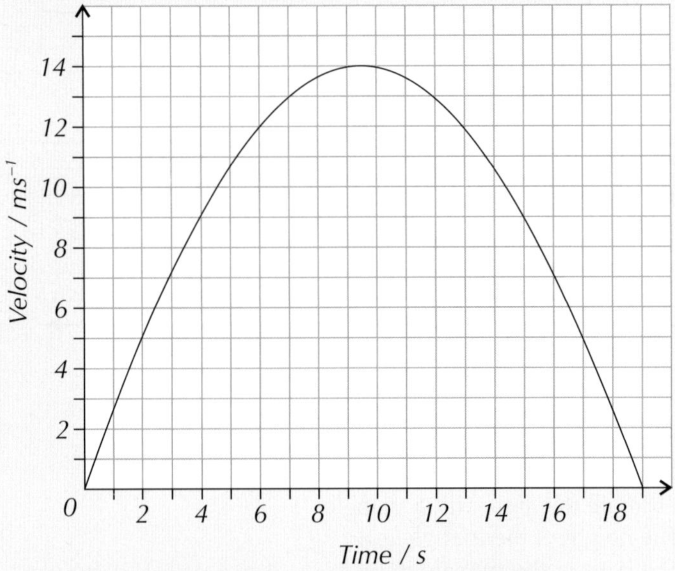

Estimate the total distance travelled during the test.

Practice Questions — Fact Recall

Q1 What does the gradient of a velocity-time graph tell you?

Q2 How is uniform acceleration shown on a velocity-time graph?

Q3 What does the area under a velocity-time graph tell you?

Q4 How is non-uniform acceleration shown on a velocity-time graph?

6. Investigating Motion

PRACTICAL ACTIVITY GROUP 1

If you want to do some experiments involving motion, you need to know the ins and outs of the apparatus you'll be using to make measurements. You need to make sure you know the best ways to measure the basic values.

Learning Objective:

- Know and understand techniques and procedures to investigate the motion and collisions of objects (PAG1).

Specification Reference 3.1.2

Light gates

A light gate sends a beam of light from one side of the gate to a detector on the other side. When something passes through the gate, the beam of light is interrupted. The light gate (along with some computer software) measures how long the beam was interrupted for.

Light gates are often used to find the velocity or acceleration of an object. To find the velocity of an object, the length of the interrupting object should be input into the software. The software then uses velocity = length of object ÷ interruption time to calculate the velocity. To find the acceleration, the object needs to interrupt the beam twice, for example by attaching a piece of card in the shape of a 'U' to the top of the object. The software uses the difference in the velocity of the two sections of the card to calculate the acceleration (page 41).

Light gates are particularly useful because they give a much lower uncertainty than other methods of timing, like stopwatches. This is because the system doesn't rely on human reaction times and judgement.

***Figure 1**: The beam of light in a light gate being interrupted by a piece of card attached to a trolley.*

Example

An experiment you can do using light gates involves a trolley rolling down a ramp.

For example, you can investigate how the distance a trolley has rolled affects its speed using the set-up shown in Figure 2.

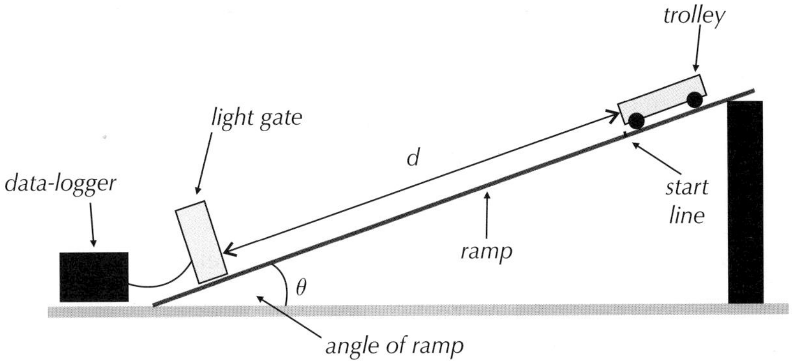

***Figure 2**: The experimental set-up for an investigation into the motion of a trolley as it travels down a ramp.*

- Measure the length of the trolley.
- Mark a start line on the ramp to make sure the trolley always starts from the same position.
- Measure the distance from the chosen start line to the light gate, *d*.

Tip: You could also do this experiment with an air track and a glider. The air track creates a cushion of air that the glider sits on (similar to the puck in air hockey), which reduces the friction in the experiment to almost nothing.

Tip: Remember, you need to carry out a risk assessment before you start any experiments.

- Place the trolley on the ramp and line it up with the start line. Let go of it so its initial velocity, ***u***, is 0.
- The data logger will record the time taken for the trolley to pass through the light gate and calculate the velocity of the trolley as it passes through the gate.
- Change the starting position of the trolley, so *d* is varied.

Repeat this experiment for each distance 3 times and average the recorded velocities to reduce the error in your final result.

Figure 3: *A ticker timer being used to measure the speed of a trolley travelling down a ramp.*

Tip: For slow speeds, the dots may be very close together, so you may want to measure across e.g. five dots, and then calculate the time elapsed for five dots.

Ticker timers

Ticker timers are used to measure the speed of an object. A length of paper tape (ticker tape) is fed through the ticker timer and attached to the object whose speed you want to measure (see Figure 3). The ticker timer creates dots on the tape at regular time-intervals (e.g. every tenth of a second). As the object moves, a line of dots is created on the ticker tape. The further apart two consecutive dots are, the further the object has travelled in a set time, and the faster the object is moving.

You can calculate the speed of the object at a certain point by measuring the distance between two consecutive dots and dividing it by the time elapsed. You can find the acceleration by calculating the change in speed between two pairs of dots and then dividing this by the time elapsed between the two pairs of dots. The further apart the pairs of dots, the lower the percentage error in your calculation (page 16). If you know that the acceleration isn't constant, you can use three consecutive dots as your two pairs of dots. This will give the acceleration of the object at that point.

Ticker timers are generally a bit trickier to get your head around than light gates. They don't come with handy software that does the calculations for you, and it can be difficult to match parts of the ticker tape to specific sections of the object's journey.

Figure 4: *You should use a tripod, or a similar support, to keep your video camera level and still.*

Video techniques

For a light gate to work, the object you're measuring the motion of has to pass completely through the light gate. So, if you want to measure the speed immediately before and after an event, such as in a collision, then light gates aren't suitable. In these situations, you can use video equipment to find speed.

Set up a video camera so it can record the event you're investigating. Make sure the video camera is filming the object from the side (perpendicular to the object's motion) and that there is a distance scale of some kind (e.g. a metre rule) within shot and alongside the path of the object.

Once you have filmed the event, you can use computer software to view your video frame by frame. Pick a point of reference on the metre stick and count how many frames it takes the object to pass that point.

If you know how many frames per second the video is shot at (the frame rate of the video), you can calculate the time taken (t) for the whole object to pass that point. You can then use this time and the length (l) of the object to calculate its velocity using these equations:

$$\text{Time taken for the object to pass the point} = \text{Number of gaps between frames for an object to pass the point} \times \frac{1 \text{ second}}{\text{Frame rate of camera}}$$

$$\text{velocity} = \frac{l}{t}$$

l = length of object

t = time taken for object to pass a point

This method is particularly useful when investigating collisions, such as how the velocity of an object before a collision affects its velocity after the collision.

Figure 5: *Images like this one are made by filming an action with a high frame-rate, and then combining the frames into a single picture.*

Example — **Maths Skills**

The set-up shown in Figure 6 is used to investigate the velocity of a trolley before and after it hits a wall. A video camera that records at 20 frames per second is used to record the experiment.

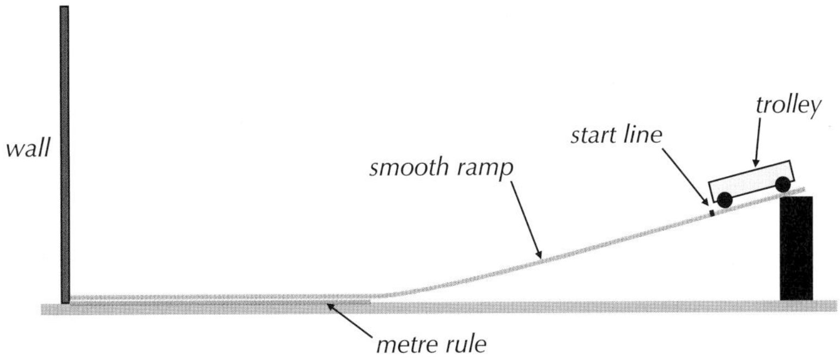

Figure 6: *The experimental set-up for an investigation into the motion of a trolley as it collides with a wall.*

Tip: Being able to do experiments involving collisions is particularly useful when it comes to investigating conservation of momentum (p.131).

Figure 7 shows three consecutive video frames of the trolley after it collides with the wall.
Calculate the velocity of the trolley from the results in Figure 7.

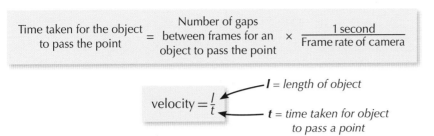

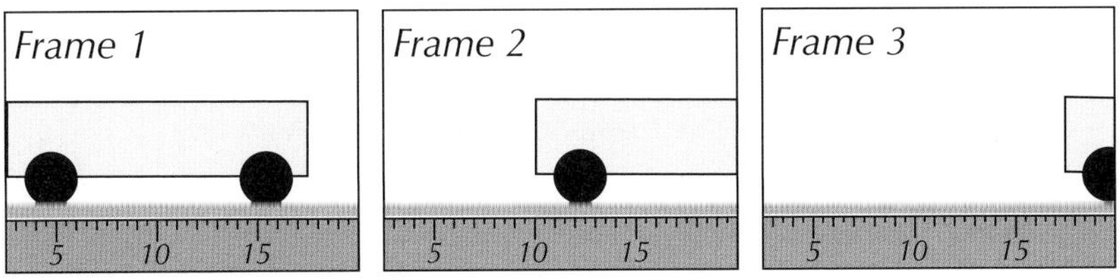

Figure 7: *Three consecutive frames of footage of the trolley moving along after it has hit the wall. The values on the metre rule are in centimetres.*

Tip: You could also have a trolley colliding with another, stationary trolley. This is to investigate how the speed of the moving trolley affects the speed of both trolleys after the collision.

From Frame 1, you can see that the total length of the trolley is 15 cm.

To find the speed of the trolley, you need to find out how long it takes the trolley to pass a certain point.

For these frames, a good reference point is 17.5 cm.

It took three frames for the trolley to pass 17.5 cm, so there are 2 gaps between the frames.

$$\text{Time taken for the trolley to pass the point} = \text{Number of gaps between frames for the trolley to pass the point} \times \frac{1 \text{ second}}{\text{Frame rate of camera}}$$

$$= 2 \times \frac{1}{20} = 0.10 \text{ s}$$

Now calculate the velocity from the length of the trolley, l, and the time taken, t.
$l = 15$ cm $= 0.15$ m,
$t = 0.10$ s

$$\text{velocity} = \frac{l}{t} = \frac{0.15}{0.10} = 1.5 \text{ ms}^{-1}$$

Tip: Remember to make sure all your variables are in the right units before you stick them into an equation.

ICT and data-loggers

A fairly standard piece of kit that is used for motion experiments in industry is an ultrasound position detector. This is a type of data-logger that automatically records the distance of an object from the sensor several times a second. If you attach one of these detectors to a computer with graph-drawing software, you can get real-time displacement-time and velocity-time graphs.

The main advantages of data-loggers over traditional methods are:

- The data is more accurate — you don't have to allow for human reaction times.
- Automatic systems have a much higher sampling rate than humans — ultrasound position detectors can take a reading ten times every second.
- You can see the data displayed in real time.

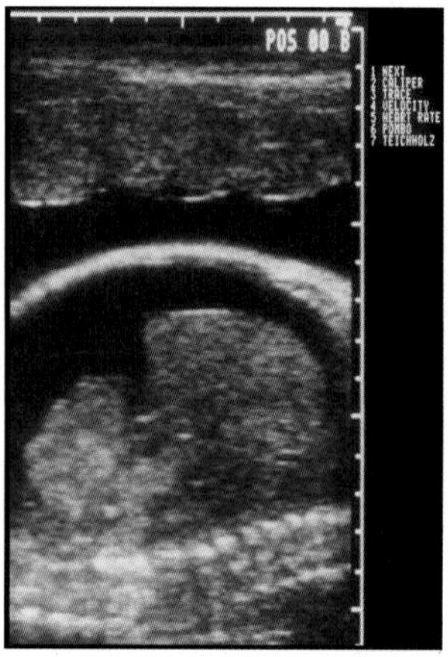

Figure 8: *Ultrasound position tracking is used to obtain medical images in real time.*

Practice Question — Application

Q1 A student is investigating the speed of a trolley using a ticker timer. The ticker timer makes 2 dots per second. The student cuts out the part of the ticker tape they are interested in, which is shown below.

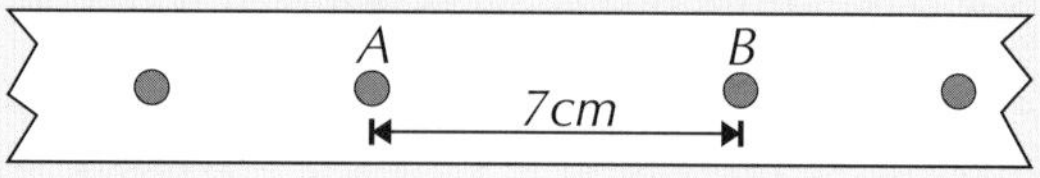

Calculate the speed of the trolley between points A and B.

Practice Questions — Fact Recall

Q1 State and explain one advantage of using a light gate, instead of a stopwatch, to make time measurements.

Q2 A student wants to know how the velocity of a trolley changes after it hits a wall. Describe an experiment they could do to investigate this. Your answer should include a description of how measurements are taken and analysed.

7. Stopping Distances

Stopping distances are important — awareness of them can make the difference between crashing and not. Stopping distance is split into thinking distance and braking distance, and different factors affect each.

Learning Objective:

- Know and be able to explain the terms: reaction time, thinking distance, braking distance and stopping distance.

Specification Reference 3.1.2

Stopping distance

In an emergency (e.g. a hazard ahead in the road), a driver may perform an emergency stop. This is where maximum force is applied by the brakes in order to stop the car in the shortest possible distance. The longer it takes to perform an emergency stop, the higher the risk of crashing into whatever's in front.

The total **stopping distance** of a vehicle is the distance covered in the time between the driver first spotting a hazard and the vehicle coming to a complete stop. The total stopping distance is the sum of the thinking distance and the braking distance.

stopping distance = thinking distance + braking distance

- The **thinking distance** is the distance the vehicle travels during the driver's **reaction time** (the time between seeing a hazard and applying the brakes).
- The **braking distance** is the distance the vehicle travels after the brakes are applied until it comes to a complete stop, as a result of the braking force.

Many factors affect your total stopping distance — and you can break it down into thinking distance and braking distance to look at the factors that affect each of these.

Thinking distance

You can calculate the thinking distance using:

thinking distance = speed × reaction time

So thinking distance is affected by two main factors:

1. How fast you're going — whatever your reaction time, the faster you're going, the further you'll go in that time.
2. How quick to respond you are, i.e. your reaction time — this can be affected by tiredness, illness, drugs, alcohol and a lack of concentration.

Figure 1: *Tiredness can increase reaction times, so some roads have signs reminding motorists to take regular breaks and to not drive whilst tired.*

Braking distance

Braking distance depends on the braking force, friction between the tyres and the road, the mass and the speed. It is affected by:

1. How fast you're going — the faster you're going, the further you travel before you stop.
2. The mass of the car — the larger the mass of the car, the smaller the deceleration for a given braking force (p.72), and so the further it will travel before stopping.
3. How good your brakes are — all brakes must be checked and maintained regularly. Worn or faulty brakes won't be able to apply as much force as well-maintained brakes and could let you down catastrophically just when you need them the most, i.e. in an emergency.

Figure 2: A good tyre tread depth helps reduce braking distance.

Figure 3: Fuel spills on roads can reduce grip and cause tyres to skid, increasing the braking distance.

Tip: Knowing about the stopping distances of vehicles helps the authorities to set speed limits and give advice to drivers that will help keep them and their passengers safe.

4. How good the tyres are — tyres should have a minimum tread depth of 1.6 mm. In wet conditions, the tread pattern helps to stop water getting trapped between the tyres and the road — they provide a channel through which the water can 'escape'. With too little tread, the tyres may lose contact with the ground, causing the vehicle to slide.
5. How good the grip is — as well as the condition of the tyres, this depends on the weather conditions and the road surface. Water, ice, leaves, fuel spills, muck on the road etc. can greatly increase the braking distance. They can result in reduced friction between the tyres and the road — so you travel further before stopping and may skid. Often you only discover this when you try to brake hard.

Typical stopping distances

The Highway Code contains typical stopping distances for a car travelling at different speeds (see Figure 4). As you've seen, lots of factors affect stopping distance, but this is a good indication of how stopping distance varies with speed.

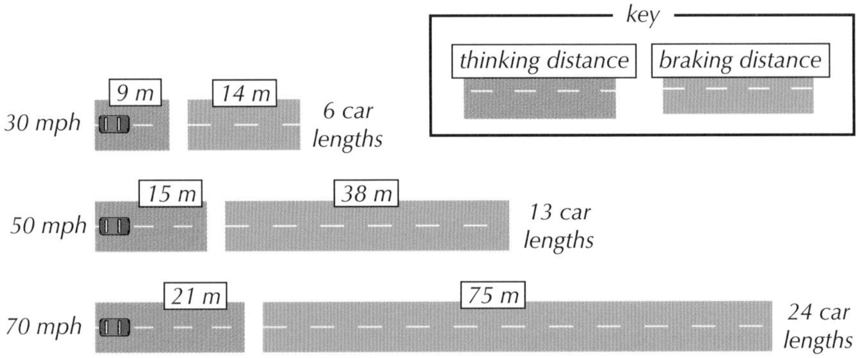

Figure 4: Typical stopping distances taken from the Highway Code.

Practice Questions — Application

Q1 A driver in a car has a thinking distance of 15 m and a braking distance of 38 m. What's the stopping distance of the car?

Q2 Dahlia is driving her car at 25 ms^{-1} when she sees a hazard. She travels 14 m before she applies the brakes. Calculate her reaction time.

Practice Questions — Fact Recall

Q1 Define stopping distance, thinking distance and braking distance.

Q2 Other than speed, name three factors that affect braking distance.

Q3 Say whether each of the following would affect the thinking distance or the braking distance of a vehicle:

a) Ice on the road b) Alcohol intake of the driver

c) Tiredness of the driver d) Fuel spills

Section Summary

Make sure you know...

- That speed is how fast something is moving, regardless of its direction.
- That displacement is how far an object has travelled from its starting point in a given direction.
- That velocity is the rate of change of displacement and acceleration is the rate of change of velocity.
- That the average speed of an object is the total distance travelled by the object divided by the total time taken.
- That the instantaneous speed of an object is the speed of an object at a given point in time.
- The equations of motion for uniform acceleration and when to use them.
- What is meant by free fall and that all objects in free fall have the same acceleration due to gravity, $\mathbf{g}$.
- That $\mathbf{g}$ is directed vertically downwards and has a magnitude of 9.81 ms^{-2}.
- How to use the equations of motion for all objects in free fall.
- How to determine the value of $\mathbf{g}$ using a free fall method.
- That the vertical and horizontal components of projectile motion are independent.
- How to use the equations of uniform acceleration to solve problems that include projectile motion.
- How to plot a displacement-time graph.
- How to use a displacement-time graph to describe the motion of an object.
- How to calculate velocity from the gradient of a displacement-time graph.
- How to plot a velocity-time graph.
- How to use a velocity-time graph to describe the motion of an object.
- How to calculate acceleration from the gradient of a velocity-time graph.
- How to calculate displacement from the area under a velocity-time graph.
- How to estimate the area under a non-linear velocity-time graph.
- Some techniques you can use to investigate the motion and collisions of objects, including the use of light gates, data-loggers, ticker timers and video recordings and analysis.
- That the stopping distance of a vehicle is the total distance travelled between a driver seeing a hazard and the vehicle coming to a complete stop.
- That the stopping distance is the sum of the thinking distance and braking distance.
- That the reaction time of a driver is the time between the driver seeing a hazard and applying the brakes.
- That the thinking distance is the distance travelled during a driver's reaction time.
- That the braking distance is the distance travelled after the brakes are applied until the vehicle comes to a complete stop.
- How thinking distance depends upon the speed of the vehicle and the driver's reaction time and how it is affected by factors such as drug use and tiredness.
- How braking distance can be affected by factors such as the speed and mass of the vehicle, the weather, road conditions and the conditions of the brakes and tyres, and the implications for safety in an emergency.

Exam-style Questions

1 A student is investigating the value of $\boldsymbol{g}$. She drops a ball bearing so that it falls vertically through a light gate. The initial speed of the ball bearing is 0 ms^{-1}. Which of the following sets of measurements will allow her to calculate $\boldsymbol{g}$?

A Only the final speed of the ball bearing.

B Only the time taken for the ball bearing to reach the light gate.

C Only the distance between the ball bearing's starting point and the light gate, and time taken for the ball bearing to reach the light gate.

D Only the distance between the ball bearing's starting point and the light gate, and the mass of the ball bearing.

(1 mark)

2 A man is driving a car at a speed of 18.0 ms^{-1} when he makes an emergency stop. His reaction time during the emergency stop is 0.45 s. The car travels 24.9 m after he applies the brakes. What is the stopping distance of the vehicle?

A 8.1 m.

B 16.8 m.

C 24.9 m.

D 33.0 m.

(1 mark)

3 A tennis ball is dropped from a height and is in free fall. The speed of the ball when it reaches the ground is 3.80 ms^{-1}. What height was the tennis ball dropped from?

A 19.4 cm

B 73.6 cm

C 136 m

D 147 m

(1 mark)

4 A student throws a tennis ball at an angle of 60.0° to the horizontal, with an initial velocity of 2.50 ms^{-1}. How far does the ball travel horizontally in 3.00 s? You can assume that the ball does not reach the ground during this time and that air resistance is negligible.

A 6.50 m

B 1.25 m

C 13.0 m

D 3.75 m

(1 mark)

5 A student wears a smart watch as she walks to the bus stop. Later, she uses the information to plot a displacement-time graph of her walk.
The graph is shown in **Fig. 5.1**.

Fig. 5.1

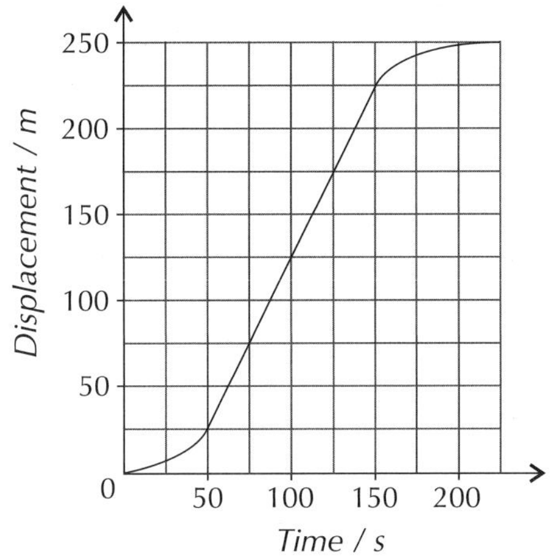

(a) Describe the student's motion through the course of her journey.

(2 marks)

(b) Calculate the student's average velocity for her entire journey.

(2 marks)

6 A student is investigating how the velocity of a trolley at the bottom of a ramp (***v***) changes when it is released from rest at different starting points on the ramp (***s***). They use the set-up shown in **Fig. 6.1**. Their results are shown in **Fig. 6.2**.

Fig. 6.1

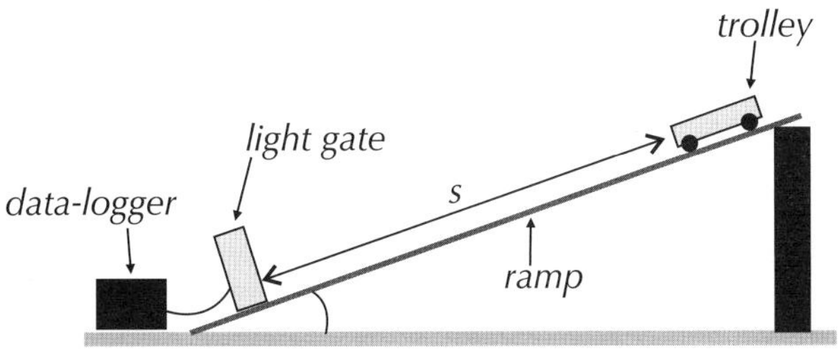

Fig. 6.2

distance travelled down the ramp / m	*final velocity / ms⁻¹*
0.20	1.22
0.40	1.73
0.60	2.12
0.80	2.45
1.00	2.74
1.20	3.00

(a) Plot a graph of final velocity squared against distance travelled down the ramp using the results in **Fig. 6.2**. Draw a line of best fit.

(2 marks)

(b) The student assumes that friction and air resistance on the trolley are negligible. The acceleration is therefore constant acceleration due to gravity. Use your graph to calculate the acceleration of the trolley down the ramp.

(3 marks)

7 **Fig. 7.1** shows the velocity-time graph for the motion of a cyclist during a 20 second time trial. The cyclist travels in a straight line during this time.

Fig. 7.1

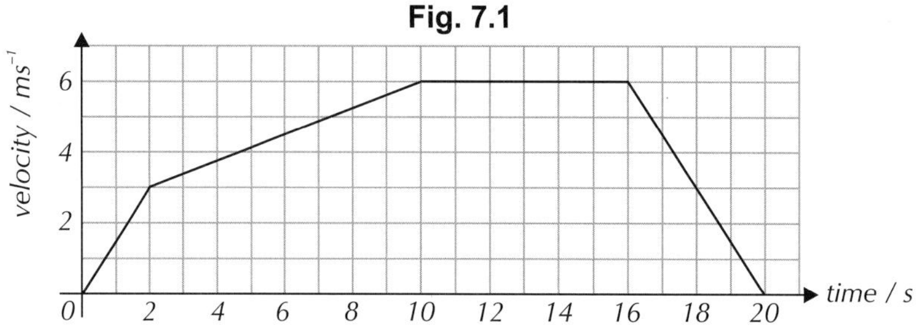

(a) Find the cyclist's displacement at the end of the 20 seconds shown.

(2 marks)

(b) Find the acceleration of the cyclist during the last 4 s of the time trial.

(2 marks)

(c) During a later bike ride, the cyclist allows herself to roll down a hill without pedalling. She starts at the top of the hill at rest. The road down the hill is 22.5 m long. The cyclist undergoes a constant acceleration of 3.40 ms^{-2} as she travels down the hill. Calculate how fast she will be going when she reaches the bottom of the hill. Assume air resistance and other resistive forces are negligible.

(2 marks)

The cyclist throws a water bottle with a velocity of 6.50 ms^{-1}, from a height of 1.31 m and at 29.0° above the horizontal, as shown in **Fig. 7.2**.

Fig. 7.2

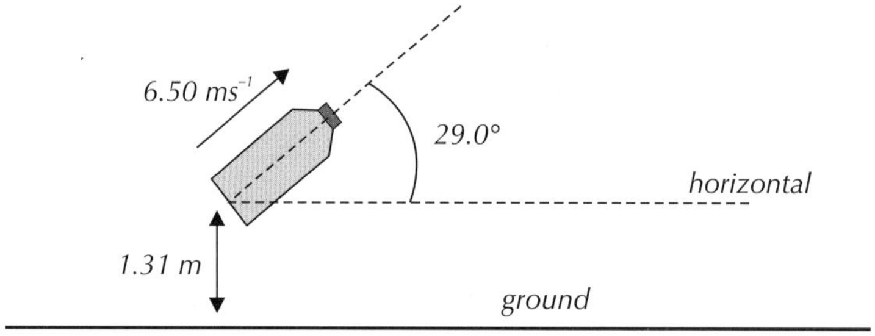

(d) Calculate the vertical component of the velocity of the bottle when it hits the ground.

(2 marks)

(e) Calculate how long the bottle will take to hit the ground.

(2 marks)

1. Mass, Weight and Force Basics

Before diving into how forces affect an object's motion, take some time to refresh your memory of the basics...

Learning Objectives:
- Know what is meant by the weight of an object.
- Know that the newton (N) is the unit of force.
- Know and be able to use the equation $W = mg$.
- Understand what is meant by the centre of mass and centre of gravity of an object.
- Know how to experimentally determine the centre of gravity of an object.
- Know what is meant by the terms normal contact force, tension, friction and upthrust.
- Understand and be able to draw free-body diagrams.

Specification References 3.2.1 and 3.2.3

Mass and weight

The **mass** of an object is the amount of 'stuff' (or matter) in it. It's measured in kg. The greater an object's mass, the greater its resistance to a change in velocity (called its inertia). The mass of an object doesn't change if the strength of the gravitational field changes.

Weight is a force. It's measured in newtons (N), like all forces. Weight is the force experienced by a mass due to a gravitational field. The weight of an object does vary according to the size of the gravitational field acting on it.

Weight is given by the equation:

$$W = mg$$

W = weight (in N)
m = mass (in kg)
g = gravitational field strength (in N kg^{-1})

Tip: g is usually taken as $-9.81\ \text{N kg}^{-1}$ because it acts downwards.

Figure 1 shows an example of how mass and weight vary for different values of g.

Name	Quantity	Earth ($g = 9.81\ \text{Nkg}^{-1}$)	Moon ($g = 1.6\ \text{Nkg}^{-1}$)
Mass	Mass (scalar)	150 kg	150 kg
Weight	Force (vector)	1471.5 N	240 N

Figure 1: *The mass and weight of an object on the Earth and on the Moon.*

Example — Maths Skills

An astronaut has a mass of 85.0 kg. What would his weight be on Mars, where the value of g is 3.75 Nkg^{-1}?

$W = mg$
$= 85.0 \times 3.75 = 318.75 = 319$ N (to 3 s.f.)

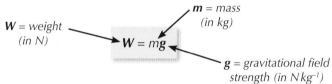

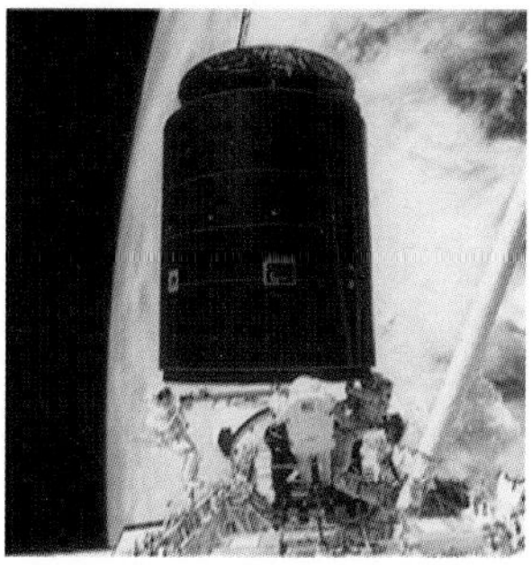

Figure 2: *The value of* **g** *decreases as you move away from a planet — which is important for satellite calculations.*

Centre of mass

The **centre of mass** (or **centre of gravity**) of an object is the single point that you can consider its whole weight to act through (whatever its orientation). The object will always balance around this point, although in some cases the centre of mass falls outside the object. For a uniform regular solid, the centre of mass is at the centre of the object.

***Figure 3:** The centres of mass of three objects.*

Finding the centre of gravity by experiment

You can find the centre of gravity of a flat object using a simple experiment:

- Hang the object freely from a point (e.g. one corner).
- Draw a vertical line downwards from the point of suspension — use a plumb bob to get your line exactly vertical.
- Hang the object from a different point, and draw another vertical line.
- The centre of gravity is where the two lines cross.

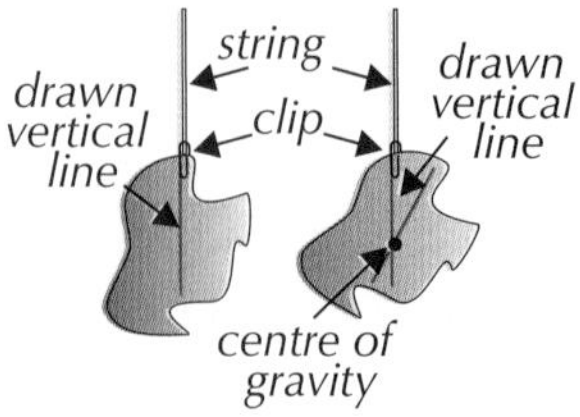

***Figure 4:** The experimental set-up for finding the centre of gravity of a flat object.*

Tip: A plumb bob is just a piece of string or thread with a weight on the end of it, that hangs perfectly vertical.

Types of forces

In addition to weight, you need to know some other common types of forces.

1. **Normal contact force** (or **reaction force**) — if an object exerts a force on a surface, the surface exerts an equal but opposite force on the object. The force acts normal (perpendicular) to the surface.
2. **Tension** — if a string is pulled tight, tension is the force pulling equally on the objects at either end of the string.
3. **Friction** — if an object is moving, it usually has a friction force acting on it in the opposite direction to motion.
4. **Upthrust** — if an object is submerged (or partially submerged) in a fluid, it experiences an upwards force called upthrust (see page 88).

Examples

- Normal contact force:
  The man pushes on the wall with a force of 300 N. The wall 'pushes back' with a normal contact force of 300 N.

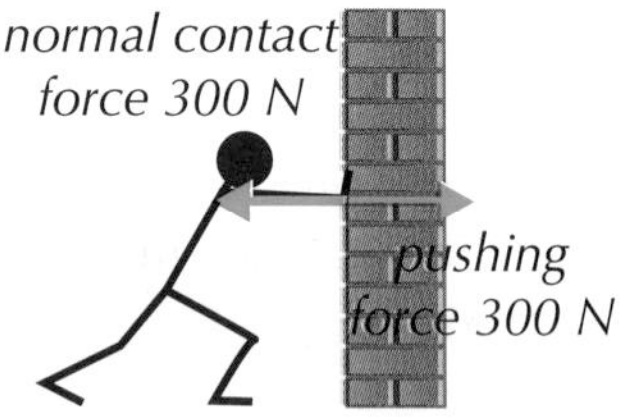

- Tension:
  A pulling force of 80 N is applied to each side of the rope. A tension force acts at each end of the rope to balance these forces.

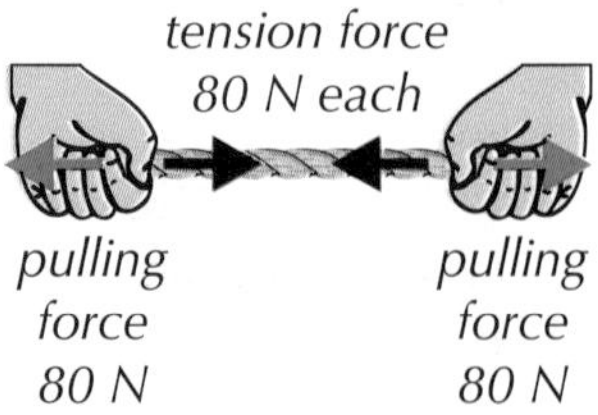

- Friction:
  The car is moving at a constant speed. The 900 N driving force is balanced by a friction force of 900 N.

Tip: The normal contact force always acts at right angles to the surface. For example, an object on a slope will have a normal contact force (***R***) acting on it perpendicular to the slope. Its magnitude is equal to the component of its weight (***W***) that is perpendicular to the surface.

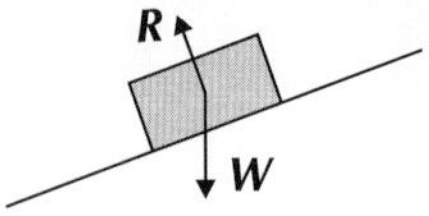

- Upthrust:
  The beach ball is floating in a pool of water. The weight of the beach ball acts downwards. It is balanced by a force of upthrust from the water.

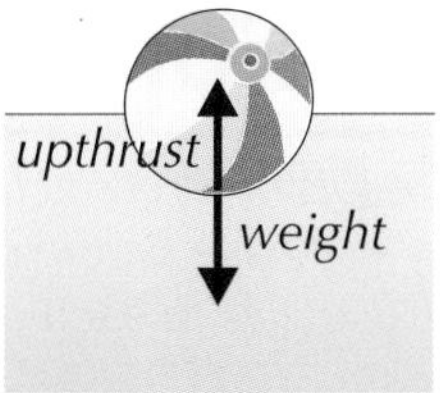

Free-body diagrams

A **free-body diagram** shows a single body on its own and the forces acting on it. The diagram should include all the forces that act on the body, but not the forces it exerts on the rest of the world.

Remember, forces are vector quantities (p.34), so the arrows should show the direction of the forces, and be labelled with the size of the force.

Gravity pulls the satellite downwards towards Earth.

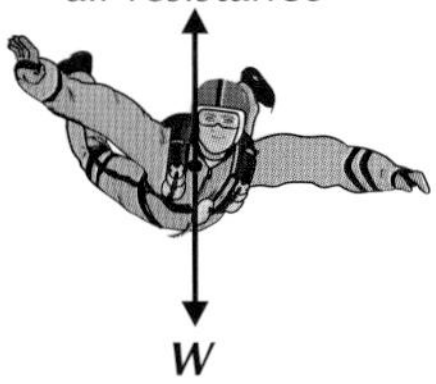

Gravity pulls man down, air resistance pushes man up.

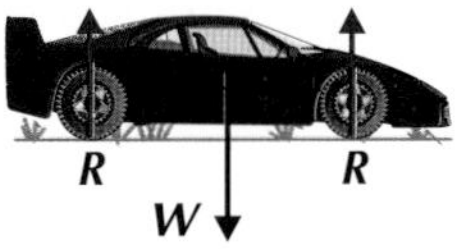

Gravity pulls car down. Earth pushes car up (normal contact force, R).

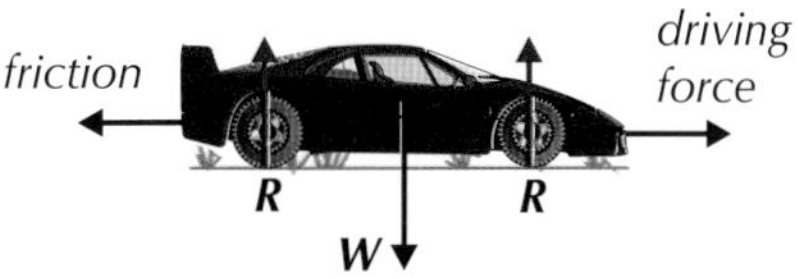

Engine pushes car forward. Friction pulls car backwards. Gravity pulls car down. Earth pushes car up.

Figure 5: *Some free-body diagrams.*

Tip: All the forces in the diagrams in Figure 5 are coplanar — they're all in the same plane. You'll only need to deal with coplanar forces.

Practice Questions — Application

Q1 An object has a weight of 7.75 N on Pluto, where $\mathbf{g} = 0.620$ N kg^{-1}. Calculate the mass of the object.

Q2 A coconut with a weight of 11.4 N is falling from a tree. It experiences a 4.65 N force of air resistance. Draw a free-body diagram for the coconut.

Practice Questions — Fact Recall

Q1 Give the equation for weight.

Q2 What is the centre of mass of an object?

Q3 Where is the centre of gravity of a uniform, regular solid?

Q4 Give the name of the upwards force experienced by an object which is submerged (or partially submerged) in a fluid.

Q5 What is the name given to a diagram showing all of the forces acting on an object, but none of the forces it exerts on its surroundings?

Learning Objectives:

- Know and be able to use the equation ***F*** = *m****a*** (net force = mass × acceleration).
- Be able to solve problems involving one- and two-dimensional motion under a constant force.

Specification Reference 3.2.1

2. Net Forces

If you have lots of forces acting on an object, it can be tricky to see what effect they will have on the object's motion, especially if the forces are acting at awkward angles to each other. Step forward net forces...

Net force and acceleration

The **net force** (or **resultant force**) on an object is the sum of all of the forces acting on the object, accounting for their relative directions. An object can only accelerate (change speed, change direction, or both — see page 41) if a non-zero net force is acting on it. In other words, a net force is needed for an object to accelerate.

The acceleration of an object is proportional to the net force acting on it. This can be written as the well-known equation:

$$\mathbf{F} = m\mathbf{a}$$

F = *net force (in N)*
m = *mass (in kg)*
a = *acceleration (in ms^{-2})*

Tip: From this equation, 1 N = 1 kg ms^{-2}. This is the definition of a newton. ***F*** = *m****a*** is a special case of Newton's Second Law (see page 128).

The acceleration given by this equation is always in the same direction as the net force used to calculate it.

Example — Maths Skills

A 14 kg box is on the floor. A man pushes the box so that a resultant force of 1.2 N is acting on it. Calculate the initial acceleration of the box.

Rearrange ***F*** = *m****a*** for acceleration:

$\mathbf{a} = \mathbf{F} \div m = 1.2 \div 14 = 0.08571... = 0.086$ ms^{-2} (to 2 s.f.)

Why do all objects fall at the same rate?

Consider two balls dropped at the same time, ball 1 being heavy and ball 2 being light. Then use the equation above to find their acceleration:

Tip: This only works if you ignore air resistance.

Example — Maths Skills

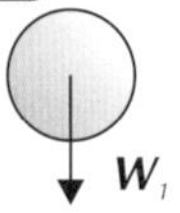

mass = m_1

resultant force = $\mathbf{F}_1$

acceleration = $\mathbf{a}_1$

By Newton's second law:

$$\mathbf{F}_1 = m_1\mathbf{a}_1$$

Ignoring air resistance, the only force acting on the ball is weight, given by $\mathbf{W}_1 = m_1\mathbf{g}$ (where $\mathbf{g}$ = gravitational field strength = 9.81 Nkg^{-1}).

So: $\mathbf{F}_1 = m_1\mathbf{a}_1 = \mathbf{W}_1 = m_1\mathbf{g}$

So: $m_1\mathbf{a}_1 = m_1\mathbf{g}$, then m_1 cancels out to give $\mathbf{a}_1 = \mathbf{g}$

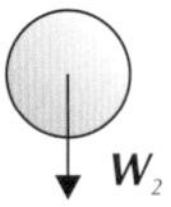

mass = m_2

resultant force = $\mathbf{F}_2$

acceleration = $\mathbf{a}_2$

By Newton's second law:

$$\mathbf{F}_2 = m_2\mathbf{a}_2$$

Ignoring air resistance, the only force acting on the ball is weight, given by $\mathbf{W}_2 = m_2\mathbf{g}$ (where $\mathbf{g}$ = gravitational field strength = 9.81 Nkg^{-1}).

So: $\mathbf{F}_2 = m_2\mathbf{a}_2 = \mathbf{W}_2 = m_2\mathbf{g}$

So: $m_2\mathbf{a}_2 = m_2\mathbf{g}$, then m_2 cancels out to give $\mathbf{a}_2 = \mathbf{g}$

In other words, the acceleration is independent of the mass. It makes no difference whether the ball is heavy or light.

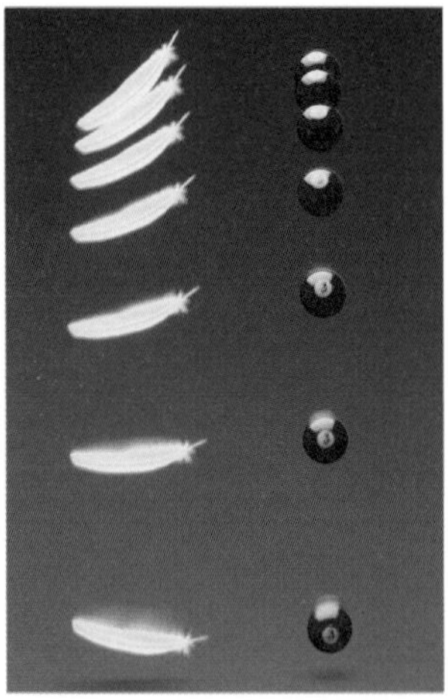

Figure 1: *In a vacuum with no air resistance, a feather will fall at the same rate as a heavy ball.*

Finding the net force

For one-dimensional problems, where all the forces are acting along the same line, you can find the net force by simply adding the forces together.

Tip: If the net force acting on an object acts along the line of motion of the object, the object will keep moving in the same direction and will either speed up or slow down (see p.128).

Example — Maths Skills

Figure 2 shows the forces acting on a firework rocket shortly after it is fired into the air. Calculate the net force acting on the firework.

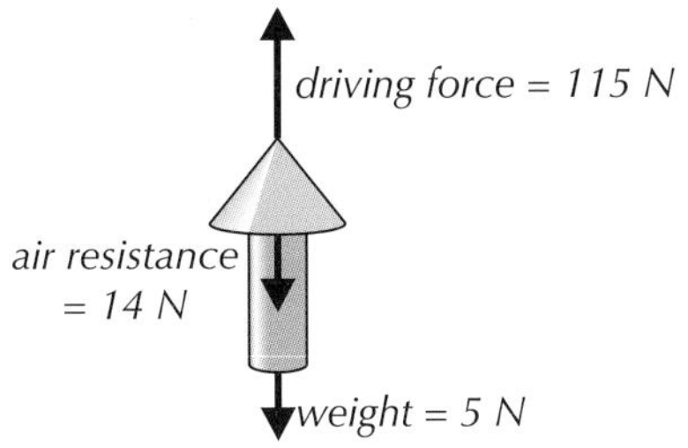

***Figure 2**: The forces acting on a firework rocket.*

Let up be positive, and down be negative.
Add all the forces together to find the net force.

Net force = 115 N + (–14 N) + (–5 N)
= 115 N – 19 N
= 96 N

So the net force is 96 N upwards.

For two-dimensional problems, with two forces acting at an angle to each other, you can find the net force by drawing a vector triangle. Draw the forces as vector arrows tip-to-tail, then draw in the third side to represent the net force (as shown on page 34).

You can then use trigonometry, such as Pythagoras' theorem (p.252) or the sine and cosine rules (p.253), to calculate the net force.

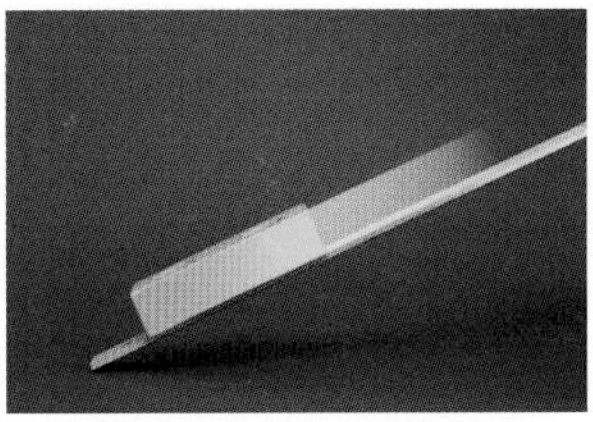

***Figure 3**: A block accelerating down a slope. It experiences a force of weight directly downwards, a normal contact force perpendicular to the slope, and a force of friction directed up the slope. This results in an overall net force down the slope.*

Example — Maths Skills

Two children are making a snowman. They roll a snowball along the ground. Child A applies a force of 5.0 N northwards, child B exerts a force of 2.0 N eastwards. You can assume no friction acts on the snowball. Find the net force on the snowball.

Draw the forces as vector arrows, touching tip-to-tail, then complete the triangle by drawing a net force arrow, ***R***.

By Pythagoras' theorem:

$\boldsymbol{R}^2 = 5.0^2 + 2.0^2$,

so $\boldsymbol{R} = \sqrt{29} = 5.4$ N (to 2 s.f.)

Use the tangent function to find the angle θ.

$\tan\theta = \frac{2.0}{5.0}$

so $\theta = \tan^{-1} 0.4$

$= 22°$ (to 2 s.f.)

So the net force is 5.4 N at an angle of 22° from north.

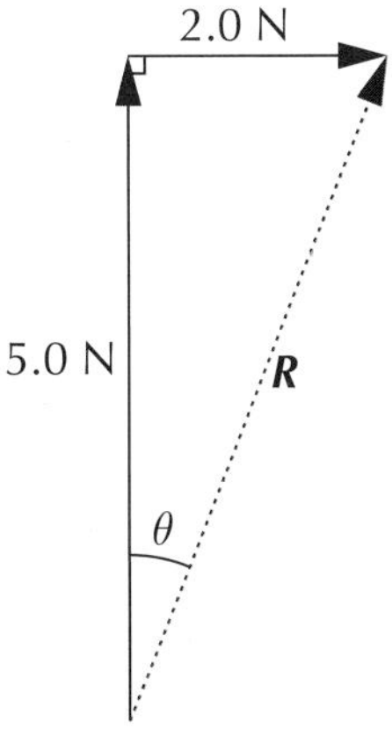

Tip: You need to use the sine and cosine rules when the forces aren't perpendicular.

Tip: Remember, a bearing is just the number of degrees clockwise from north.

Tip: When using the sine and cosine rules, you need to make sure the sides and angles of your triangle are labelled correctly. See page 253 for a full explanation of how to do this.

Tip: You could also work this out by drawing a really accurate scale drawing (see p.34).

Example — Maths Skills

Child A and child B are rolling a second snowball along the ground. Child A applies a force of 4.7 N eastwards, and child B exerts a force of 3.2 N at a bearing of 052°. You can assume no friction acts on the snowball. Find the net force on the snowball.

Draw the forces as vector arrows, touching tip-to-tail, then complete the triangle by drawing a net force arrow, ***R***.

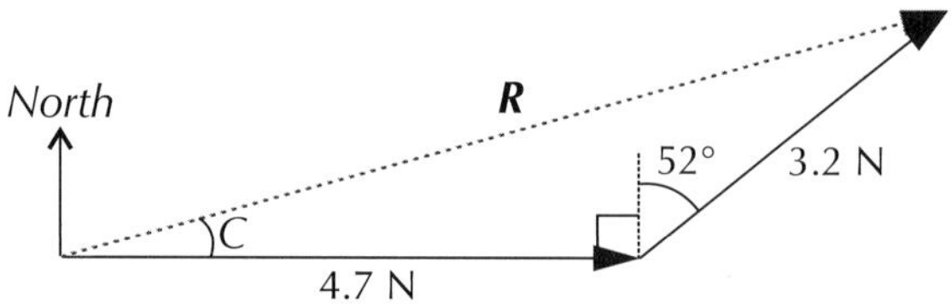

To find the size of ***R***, use the cosine rule:

$a^2 = b^2 + c^2 - 2bc\cos(A)$

where $a = \boldsymbol{R}$, $b = 4.7$, $c = 3.2$, and $A = 52 + 90 = 142°$. So:

$\boldsymbol{R} = \sqrt{4.7^2 + 3.2^2 - (2 \times 4.7 \times 3.2 \times \cos(142°))} = 7.48554... = 7.5 \text{ N (to 2 s.f.)}$

To find angle C, use the sine rule:

$$\frac{c}{\sin(C)} = \frac{a}{\sin(A)}$$

$$C = \sin^{-1}\left(\frac{\sin(142°)}{7.48554...} \times 3.2\right) = 15.25...°$$

To find the angle of ***R*** from north, subtract C from 90°.

Angle of ***R*** from north = 90 – 15.25...

= 74.74... = 75° (to 2 s.f.)

So, the net force is 7.5 N at an angle of 75° from north.

Practice Questions — Application

Q1 Calculate the net force acting on a 24.1 kg object that has an acceleration of 3.5 ms^{-2}.

Q2 A net force of 18 N is acting on a toy car. It has an acceleration of 29 ms^{-2}. What is the mass of the toy car?

Q3 Below is the free-body diagram of a cyclist cycling along a road while experiencing a cross-wind.

a) Calculate the net force on the cyclist. Give the direction as a clockwise angle from east.

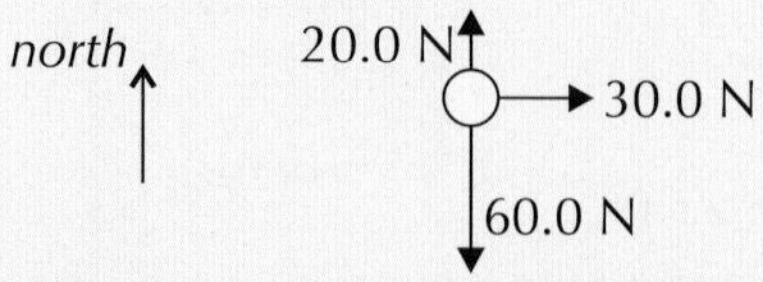

b) The cyclist and bicycle have a total mass of 89.0 kg. Calculate the magnitude of their acceleration.

Practice Question — Fact Recall

Q1 What is meant by the net force acting on an object?

Q2 Define the variables and their units in the equation $\boldsymbol{F} = ma$.

3. Equilibrium

Time to find out how you can solve force problems for objects that are in equilibrium. Have a quick flick back to pages 34-38 — the vectors stuff will be pretty handy here.

Learning Objectives:
- Understand how an object can be in equilibrium while under the action of forces.
- Know the conditions for equilibrium of three coplanar forces.
- Be able to use triangles of forces to solve problems involving equilibrium.

Specification Reference 3.2.3

Forces in equilibrium

If an object is in **equilibrium**, all the forces acting on it are balanced and cancel each other out. In other words, there's no net force on an object in equilibrium, so it isn't accelerating.

When only two forces act on an object, the object is in equilibrium if they're equal and opposite. If there are three forces acting on an object, there are two ways you can go about solving equilibrium problems:

Triangle of forces

Forces acting on an object in equilibrium form a closed loop when you draw them to scale and tip-to-tail. For the case of three coplanar forces, this will form a triangle of forces.

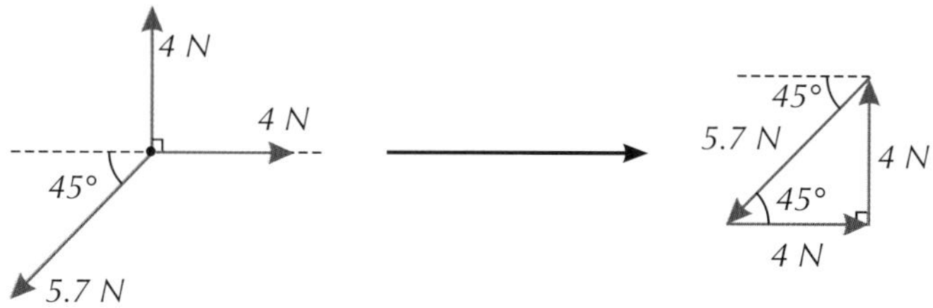

***Figure 1:** Three balanced force vectors shown acting from a point and in a triangle of forces.*

Tip: An object in equilibrium (i.e. not accelerating) is either at rest or moving with a constant velocity (p.128).

Tip: You could do this for any number of coplanar forces. As long as the vector arrows, drawn to scale and tip-to-tail, form a closed shape, the object is in equilibrium.

Example — Maths Skills

Figure 2 shows all the forces acting on a particle. Given that the particle is in equilibrium, find the magnitude of the missing force *P*.

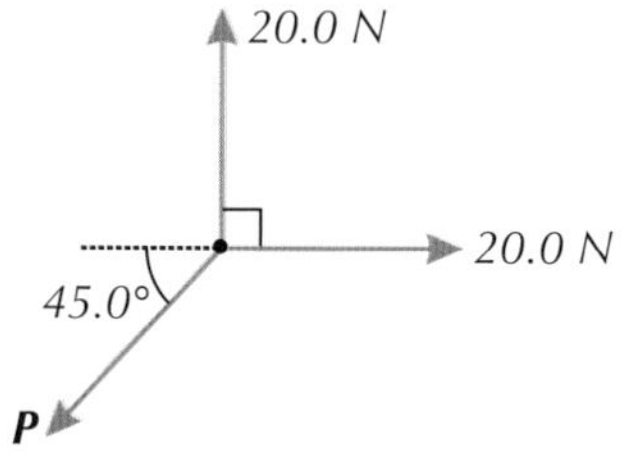

***Figure 2:** Three balanced forces acting on a particle.*

The particle is in equilibrium, so the forces will form a triangle of forces when drawn to scale and tip-to-tail.

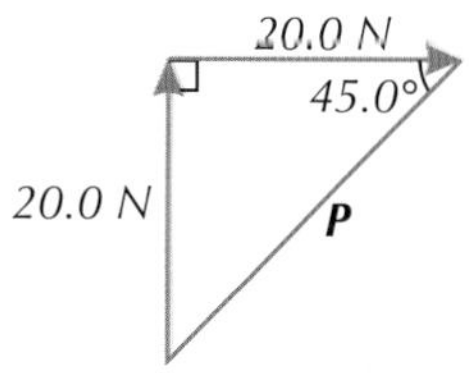

This means you can use trigonometry to find the magnitude of the force, *P*.

$$\cos 45.0° = \frac{20.0}{P}$$

$$P = \frac{20.0}{\cos 45.0°} = 28.2842... = 28.3 \text{ N (to 3 s.f.)}$$

Tip: Remember, the magnitude of a vector is its size (without the direction), see page 34.

***Figure 3:** These rocks are in a state of equilibrium — all the forces on them must cancel out for them to be balanced. This is true for all balanced objects.*

Resolving forces in two perpendicular directions

You saw how to resolve vectors into perpendicular components on page 36, and it's no different for the forces acting on objects in equilibrium. If an object is in equilibrium, the sum of the components in each direction must be equal to zero. To find the components of each force in a direction, just use trigonometry:

Tip: When you're resolving forces, remember that the force being resolved is always the hypotenuse.

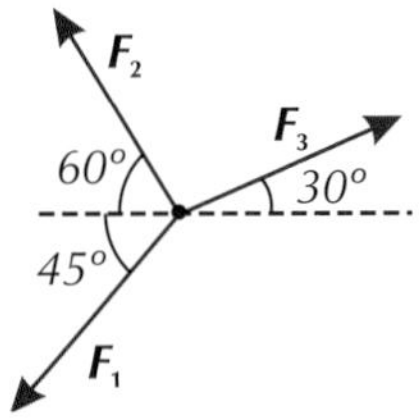

Tip: Remember, the direction matters with forces, so forces in the negative direction have a negative value. In this case, the negative directions are down and to the left.

↑ Vertical components

$-\sin 45° \times F_1$

$\sin 60° \times F_2$

$\sin 30° \times F_3$

→ Horizontal components

$-\cos 45° \times F_1$

$-\cos 60° \times F_2$

$\cos 30° \times F_3$

Figure 4: *Three forces acting at a point, and their horizontal and vertical components.*

Example — Maths Skills

Figure 5 shows all the forces on a particle in equilibrium. Find the magnitude of the missing force *Q*.

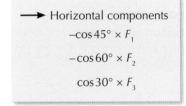

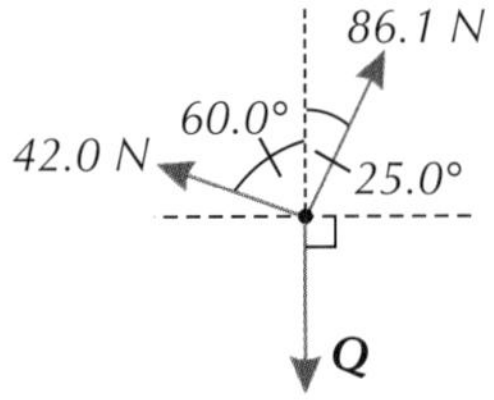

Figure 5: *The forces acting on a particle in equilibrium.*

The missing force ***Q*** acts vertically downwards. So for the particle to be in equilibrium, the magnitude of the force, *Q*, must equal the sum of the vertical components of the other two forces.

Vertical component of 42.0 N force = $42.0 \cos 60.0°$
Vertical component of 86.1 N force = $86.1 \cos 25.0°$

So, $Q = 42.0 \cos 60° + 86.1 \cos 25.0°$
$= 21.0 + 78.033...$
$= 99.033...$
$= 99.0$ N (to 3 s.f.)

Tip: The horizontal component of a vertical vector is zero, and vice versa. Since you're told the object is in equilibrium, you don't need to worry about the horizontal components.

Tip: You could also use the cosine rule to answer this question (see page 253).

Practice Questions — Application

Q1 Show with a triangle of forces that an object is in equilibrium if only these forces are acting on it: 12 N acting east, 5 N north, 13 N at 23° anticlockwise from west.

Q2 The three forces shown below are in equilibrium. Find the magnitude of the unknown force ***F***.

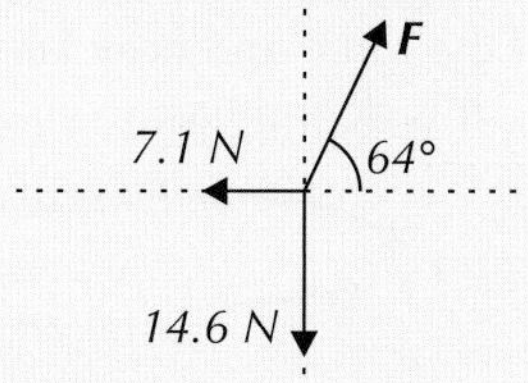

Q3 The diagram below shows the forces acting on a box on a slope. The box is in equilibrium. Calculate the size of force ***F***.

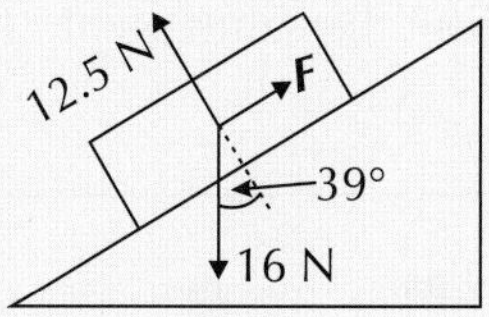

Practice Questions — Fact Recall

Q1 What is the size of the net force acting on an object in equilibrium?

Q2 What is meant by 'resolving a force'?

Learning Objectives:

- Be able to calculate the moment of a force about a point.
- Know the principle of moments and use it to solve problems involving moments.
- Know what is meant by a couple.
- Be able to calculate the torque of a couple.
- Understand how an object can be in equilibrium while under the action of torques.

Specification Reference 3.2.3

Tip: The perpendicular distance means the distance along a line that makes a right angle with the line of action of the force (i.e. the shortest possible distance between the pivot and the line in which the force acts).

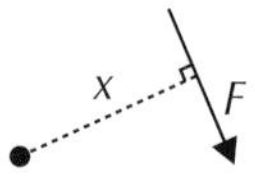

Tip: The symbol Σ means "the sum of".

Tip: Remember, for regular, symmetrical objects, the centre of mass is at the centre of the object. So in the first example on this page it can be assumed that the centre of mass of the seesaw is above the pivot, and so the moment of its weight is zero.

4. Moments and Torques

A moment is the turning effect of a force around a point. Two moments of equal size acting parallel to each other are called a couple.

Moments and turning effects

A **moment** is the turning effect of a force around a turning point. The moment of a force depends on the size of the force and how far the force is applied from the turning point (or **pivot**). It is defined as:

$$M = Fx$$

M = moment of a force (in Nm)

F = size of force (in N)

x = perpendicular distance between the line of action of the force and the turning point (in m)

The **principle of moments** states that for a body to be in equilibrium, the sum of the clockwise moments about any point equals the sum of the anticlockwise moments about the same point. If the moments aren't balanced, the object will turn.

Example — Maths Skills

Two children sit on a seesaw as shown on the right. An adult balances the seesaw at one end. Find the size and direction of the force, F, that the adult needs to apply to do this.

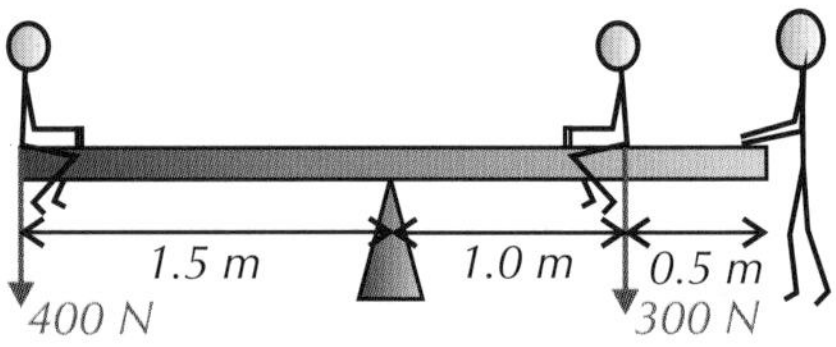

Take moments about the turning point. In equilibrium,

$$\Sigma \text{ anticlockwise moments} = \Sigma \text{ clockwise moments}$$
$$400 \times 1.5 = (300 \times 1.0) + 1.5F$$
$$600 = 300 + 1.5F$$
$$F = \frac{600 - 300}{1.5} = 200 \text{ N downwards}$$

We know the force acts downwards because that's the direction required to produce a clockwise moment.

Centre of mass and moments

When calculating moments, you may also need to consider any turning effects due to the weight of the object that's turning. The line of action of the weight is drawn from the object's centre of mass (see page 69). If the centre of mass is directly over the pivot, there will be no resultant moment in either direction, so you can ignore the weight of the object in your moment calculations. However, if this isn't the case, then you do need to consider the weight.

Example — Maths Skills

A regular, symmetrical plank of wood with a weight of 15 N is in equilibrium, as shown below. Calculate the magnitude of the force, F.

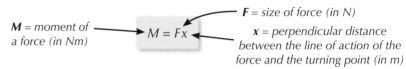

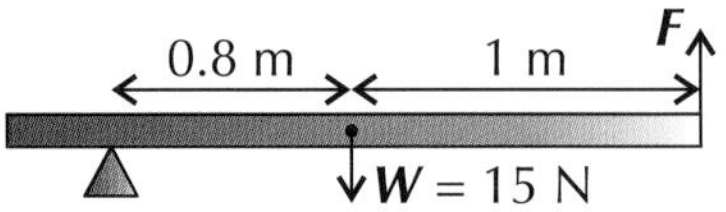

$$\Sigma \text{ anticlockwise moments} = \Sigma \text{ clockwise moments}$$
$$15 \times 0.8 = F \times 1.8$$
$$F = \frac{15 \times 0.8}{1.8} = 6.66... = 7 \text{ N (to 1 s.f.)}$$

An object will topple over if the line of action of its weight falls outside its base area. This is because a resultant moment occurs, whose turning force causes the object to fall.

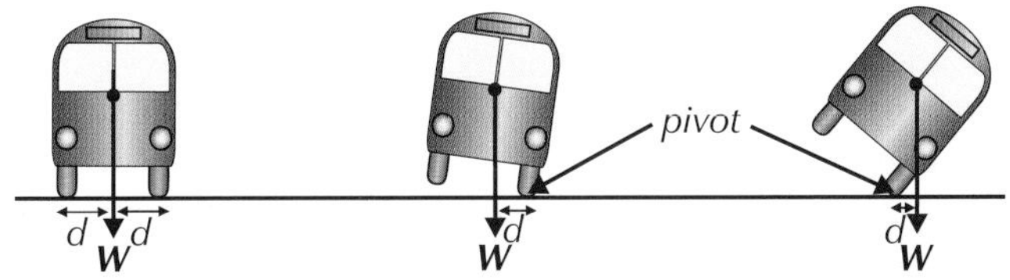

pivot
d
d
W
d
W
d
W
No resultant moment. Bus is stable and stationary.
Net anticlockwise moment about pivot. Bus will rotate to the left and sit back upright.
Net clockwise moment about pivot. Bus will rotate to the right and fall over.

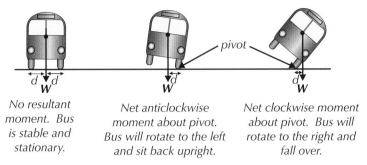

Figure 1: *Moments acting on a bus at different angles of tilt.*

Figure 2: *Cranes need a wide, heavy base to stop them toppling.*

The higher the centre of mass, and the smaller the base area, the less stable the object will be. An object will be very stable if it has a low centre of mass and a wide base area.

This is used a lot in design — for example, racing cars have a wide base area and a low centre of mass to prevent them from toppling over on fast corners.

Moments in levers

In a **lever**, an effort force acts against a load force by means of a rigid object rotating around a pivot. Levers are really useful in situations where you need a larger turning effect. Examples include spanners, wheelbarrows and scissors. They increase the distance from the pivot a force is applied, so you need less force to get the same moment. You can use the principle of moments to answer lever questions.

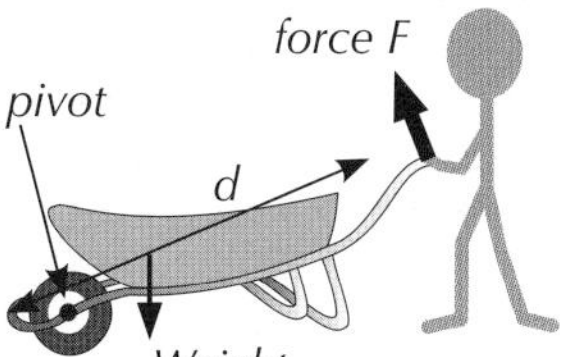

force F
pivot
d
Weight

Figure 3: *A wheelbarrow is a type of lever used to reduce the force needed to lift a heavy load.*

Example — Maths Skills

Find the size of the force exerted by the biceps in holding a bag of gold still. The bag of gold weighs 100 N and the forearm weighs 20 N.

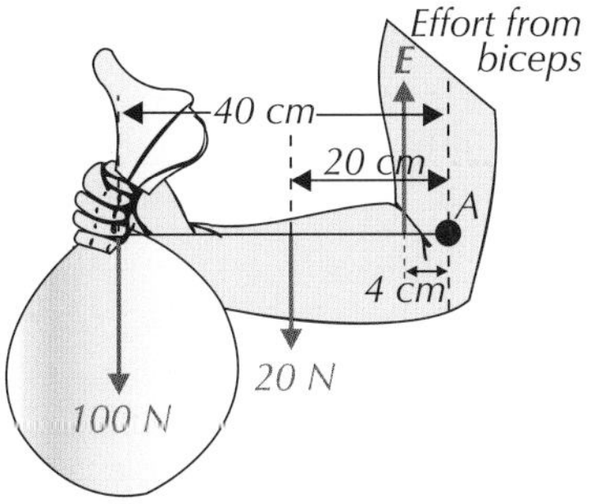

Effort from biceps
E
40 cm
20 cm
A
4 cm
20 N
100 N

Figure 4: *A biceps muscle providing the clockwise moment needed to balance the anticlockwise moments.*

Take moments about A. In equilibrium:

$$\sum \text{anticlockwise moments} = \sum \text{clockwise moments}$$

$$(100 \times 0.4) + (20 \times 0.2) = 0.04E$$

$$40 + 4 = 0.04E$$

$$E = \frac{40 + 4}{0.04} = 1100 = 1000 \text{ N (to 1 s.f.)}$$

Figure 5: *Spanners are a type of lever. They have long handles for larger turning effects.*

Forces on supports

If an object is being held up by supports (e.g. chair legs, car tyres, etc.), the force acting on each support won't always be the same. The closer the object's centre of mass is to a support, the stronger the force on the support. It's all to do with the principle of moments — the anticlockwise and clockwise moments must be equal. So a support closer to the centre of mass will experience a larger force.

Exam Tip
Make sure you understand why different amounts of force can act on different supports, as you might be asked about it in the exam.

Example — Maths Skills

A plank with a weight of 40 N is resting on two supports 3 m and 1 m from the plank's centre of mass. Find the upwards force provided by each support.

Start by treating one of the supports as the pivot and finding how much force is needed to balance the moments provided by the weight of the plank:

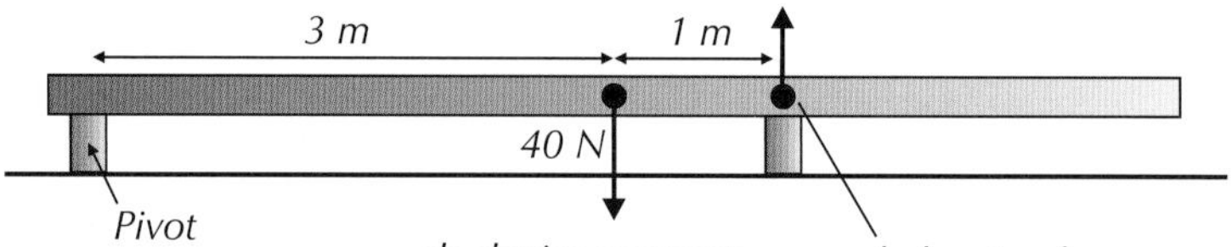

Then do the same, treating the other support as the pivot:

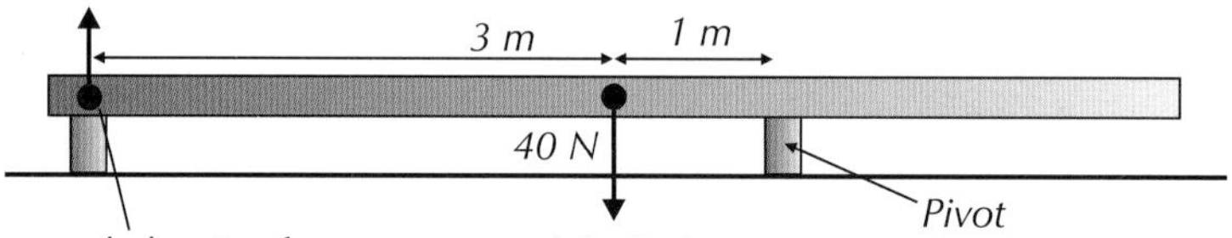

So the support furthest from the centre of mass provides 10 N of force, while the support closest to the centre of mass provides 30 N of force.

Tip: The balancing force is found by rearranging $M = Fx$ to $F = M \div x$.

Tip: This is the force the supports experience too. It's Newton's third law — see p.129 for more on this.

Couples and torque

A **couple** is a pair of forces of equal size which act parallel to each other, but in opposite directions. A couple doesn't cause any resultant linear force, but does produce a turning effect. This type of turning effect is called a **torque**. The size of this torque depends on the size of the forces and the distance between them.

Tip: Couples are coplanar — they act in the same plane.

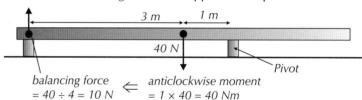

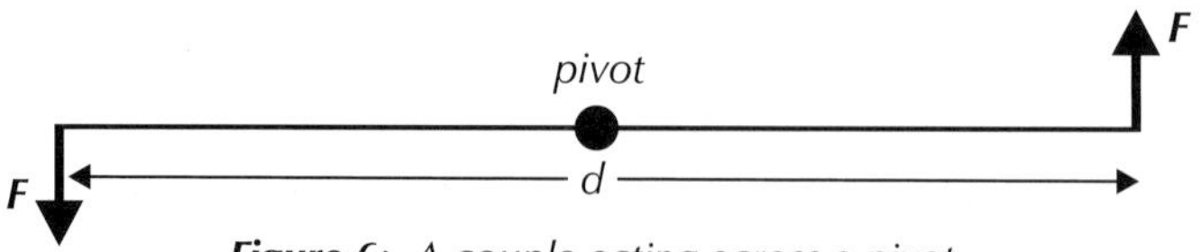

Figure 6: *A couple acting across a pivot.*

You can derive a formula for torque from the equation for moments, $M = Fx$ (p.78). In Figure 6, you can see that each force of the couple is providing a moment in the same direction, equal to:

$$M = F \times \frac{d}{2}$$

Torque, T, is the sum of the moments provided by the couple, so:

$$T = (F \times \frac{d}{2}) + (F \times \frac{d}{2}) = Fd$$

This gives the equation:

$$T = Fd$$

T = torque of a couple (in Nm)

F = size of one of the forces (in N)

d = perpendicular distance between the lines of action of the forces (in m)

Tip: Remember, the two forces in a couple have the same magnitude as each other.

Example — Maths Skills

A cyclist turns a sharp right corner by applying equal but opposite forces of 25 N to the ends of the handlebars. The length of the handlebars is 0.60 m. Calculate the torque applied to the handlebars.

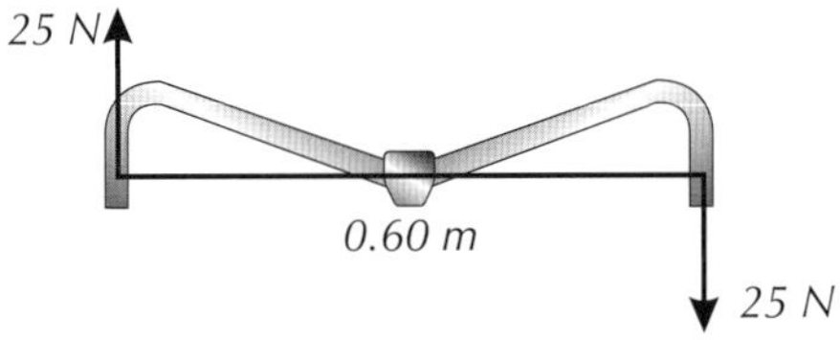

Figure 7: *Turning force being applied across bicycle handlebars.*

$T = F \times d$

$= 25 \times 0.60 = 15$ Nm

Tip: Remember... for couples you need to use the perpendicular distance between the forces, not the distance between the one force and the pivot.

Like with the principle of moments, for an object to be in equilibrium, the clockwise torques have to equal the anticlockwise torques.

Example — Maths Skills

A torque of 120 Nm is applied to turn a revolving door. Two people apply a couple to the door to stop it moving. They are each stood 1.2 m from the pivot. Calculate the size of the force, *F*, applied by each person.

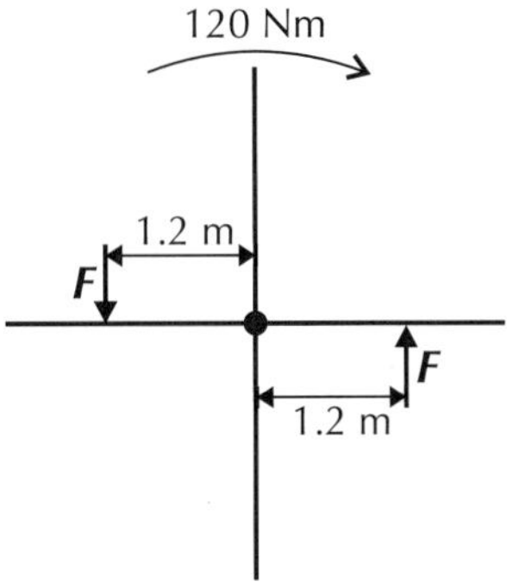

In order for the door to not be moving, it must be in equilibrium.

So the anticlockwise torque supplied by the people must equal the clockwise torque. So, anticlockwise torque = 120 Nm.

The distance between the two forces of the couple = 1.2 + 1.2 = 2.4 m

Rearrange the torque equation for force:

$$F = \frac{T}{d} = \frac{120}{2.4} = 50 \text{ N}$$

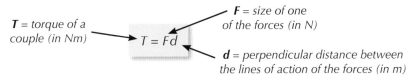

Figure 8: *An oil worker applying a torque to a tap on an oil pipeline.*

Practice Questions — Application

Q1 Find the moment provided by a force of 73.1 N acting at a perpendicular distance of 0.25 m from a pivot.

Q2 The diagram below shows two children on a seesaw. If the child on the left stays where they are, how far from the pivot should the child on the right sit to balance the seesaw?

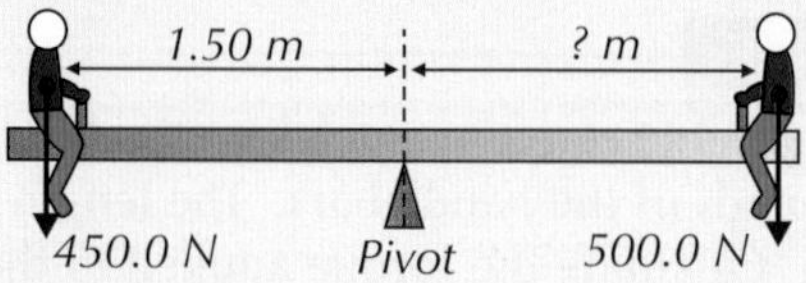

Q3 The diagram below shows a loaded trailer of mass 24 000 kg.

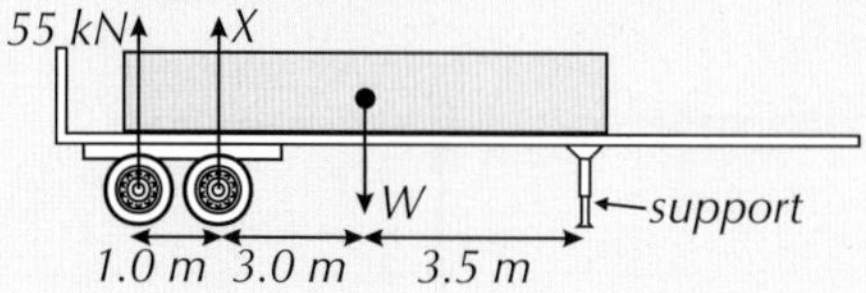

a) Calculate the moment of the trailer's weight about the support.

b) Calculate the upward force *X* acting on the right-hand wheel.

Q4 An airtight chamber is kept shut by a release wheel with a diameter of 0.35 m. The release wheel won't open unless a torque of at least 50.0 Nm is applied across it. What's the minimum force that, when applied to both sides of the wheel, will open the chamber door?

Tip: Remember, for an object to be balanced, the total clockwise moments on the object must be equal to the total anticlockwise moments on the object.

Practice Questions — Fact Recall

Q1 What is a moment?

Q2 What name is given to a pair of forces of equal size which act parallel to each other, in opposite directions?

5. Drag and Terminal Velocity

When an object moves, it feels a resistive force called friction (or drag for a fluid) that opposes its motion. When the friction forces equal the driving forces, the object stops accelerating and reaches its terminal velocity.

Learning Objectives:

- Know what is meant by friction.
- Know that drag is the frictional force experienced by an object travelling through a fluid.
- Know the factors that affect the drag acting on an object travelling through air.
- Know what is meant by terminal velocity.
- Understand the motion of an object falling in a uniform gravitational field in the presence of drag.
- Know and be able to carry out techniques and procedures to determine terminal velocity in fluids (PAG1).

Specification References 3.2.1 and 3.2.2

Friction

Friction is a force that opposes motion. There are two main types of friction — contact friction and fluid friction.

Contact friction happens between solid surfaces (which is what we usually mean when we just use the word 'friction').

'Fluid' is a word that means either a liquid or a gas — something that can flow. Fluid friction is known as **drag**, or fluid resistance or air resistance. Three things affect fluid friction:

- The force depends on the **viscosity** (thickness) of the fluid.
- The force increases as the speed increases. For simple situations it's directly proportional (see page 13), but you don't need to worry about the mathematical relationship.
- The force depends on the size and shape of the object moving through it. The larger the area pushing against the fluid, the greater the resistance force.

There are three things you need to remember about frictional forces:

- They always act in the opposite direction to the motion of the object.
- They can never speed things up or start something moving.
- They convert kinetic energy into heat.

Terminal velocity

Terminal velocity happens when frictional forces equal the driving force. An object will reach a terminal velocity at some point if there's a driving force that stays the same all the time, and a frictional or drag force (or collection of forces) that increases with speed.

There are three main stages to reaching terminal velocity:

Example

The car accelerates from rest using a constant driving force.

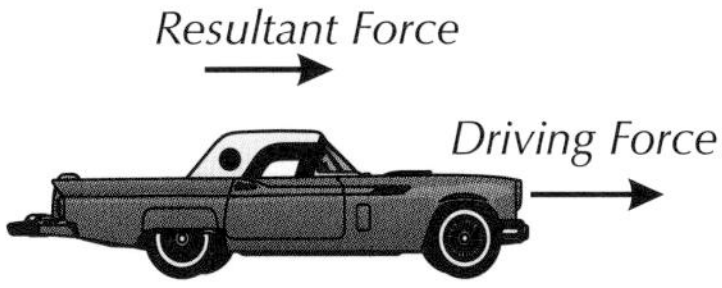

As the speed increases, the resistance forces increase (because of things like turbulence). This reduces the resultant force on the car and hence reduces its acceleration.

Eventually the car reaches a speed at which the resistance forces are equal to the driving force. There is now no resultant force and no acceleration, so the car carries on at a constant speed.

Exam Tip
You don't need to know about turbulence or why resistive forces increase in the exam.

Motion graphs for terminal velocity

You need to be able to recognise and sketch the graphs for velocity against time and acceleration against time for the terminal velocity situation.

Exam Tip
These graphs might come up in the exam, so make sure you get lots of practice with them — try shutting the book and sketching them from memory.

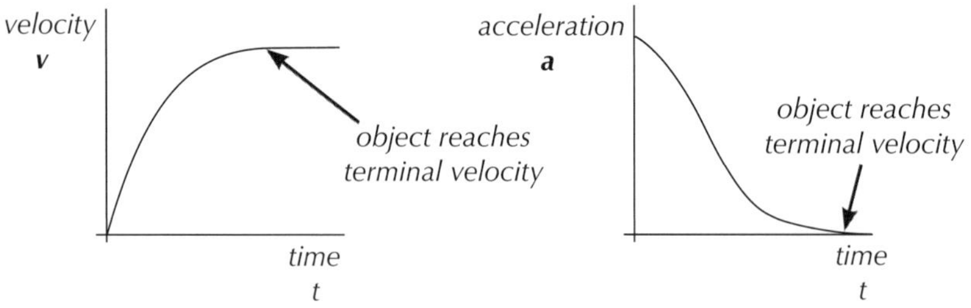

Figure 1: *The velocity-time and acceleration-time graphs for an object reaching terminal velocity.*

Terminal velocity of a parachutist

When something starts falling through air in a uniform gravitational field, its weight causes it to accelerate. The weight of the object is a constant force acting downwards. Air resistance is a frictional force opposing this motion, which increases with speed. So before a parachutist opens the parachute, exactly the same thing happens as with the car:

Example

A skydiver leaves a plane and will accelerate until the air resistance equals his weight.

He will then be travelling at a terminal velocity. But the terminal velocity of a person in free fall is too great to land safely — so he needs to increase the upwards force of air resistance, to slow him down to a lower speed.

Before reaching the ground he will open his parachute, which immediately increases the air resistance so it is now bigger than his weight.

This slows him down until his speed has dropped enough for the air resistance to be equal to his weight again. This new terminal velocity is small enough to survive landing.

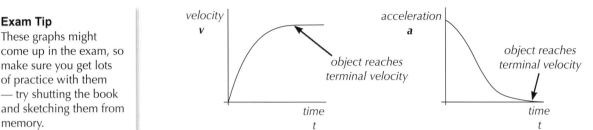

Figure 2: *A parachute increases the drag acting on a skydiver, so they hit the ground at a slower speed.*

Velocity-time graph for a parachutist

The velocity-time graph for this situation is a bit different, because you have a new terminal velocity being reached after the parachute is opened:

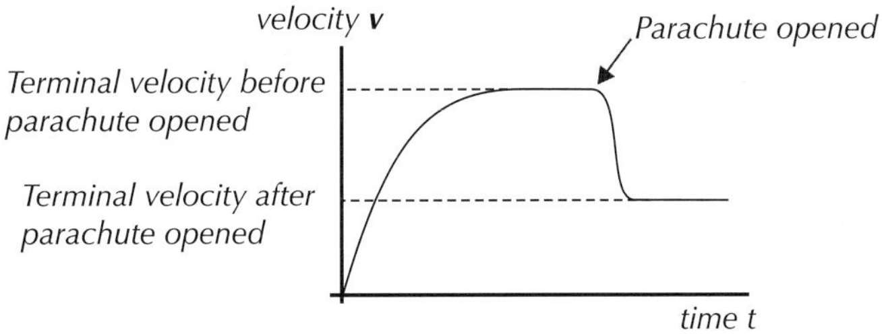

Figure 3: *The velocity-time graph for a skydiver who releases his parachute after reaching terminal velocity.*

Tip: If you need a reminder about velocity-time graphs, go to pages 53-58.

Investigating terminal velocity

PRACTICAL ACTIVITY GROUP 1

Things falling through any fluid will reach a terminal velocity (if it falls for long enough). You can calculate the terminal velocity of a ball bearing in a viscous (thick) liquid (e.g. wallpaper paste) by setting up an experiment like this:

- Put elastic bands around the tube of viscous liquid at fixed distances from the top of the tube (measured with a ruler). Then drop a ball bearing into the tube, and use a stopwatch to record the time at which it reaches each band.
- Repeat this a few times to reduce the effect of random errors on your results, using a strong magnet to remove the ball bearing from the tube.
- Calculate the times taken by the ball bearing to travel between consecutive elastic bands and calculate an average for each reading. Use the average times and the distance between bands to calculate the average velocity between each pair of elastic bands.
- You should find that the average velocity increases at first, then stays constant — this is the ball bearing's terminal velocity in the viscous liquid used.
- Use your average velocity data to plot a graph of velocity against time. Draw a smooth curve and use it to estimate the terminal velocity.

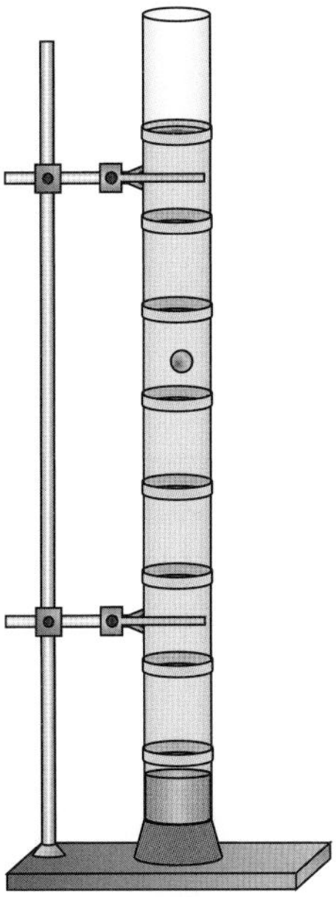

Figure 4: *A possible set-up for an investigation into terminal speed in a viscous liquid.*

Tip: If you do this experiment, be sure to think about how you'd do it safely — do a full risk assessment before you start, and be extra careful not to spill slippery liquids on the floor.

Tip: You might be asked to draw force diagrams as the ball bearing falls. Remember that the forces are balanced when the ball reaches terminal velocity.

Factors that affect terminal velocity

You can change parts of your experiment to see what effect they have on terminal velocity and the time taken to reach terminal velocity.
For example you could:

- Change the liquid — the terminal velocity will be lower in more viscous (thicker) liquids because the drag is greater. Try mixing water into wallpaper paste and see by how much the terminal velocity increases when the drag is lower.
- Change the size of the ball. What happens if the ball is larger? Or smaller?

Figure 5: *Crude oil being poured into a beaker. Crude oil has a higher viscosity than water, so an object falling through it would reach a lower terminal velocity than if it was falling through water.*

- Change the shape of the thing you are dropping.
  The drag force will be greater on less streamlined shapes.
- Change the mass of the thing you are dropping, while keeping the size the same (this might be a bit tricky). You should find that heavier objects reach a faster terminal velocity because a greater drag force is needed to balance the extra weight. (Remember, objects with different masses only fall at the same rate if drag is ignored — p.72.)

Tip: Falling into water has a similar effect on the ball's velocity to opening a parachute.

Practice Questions — Application

Q1 A ball is dropped above a cylinder of water. It falls through the air and lands in the water after 1.2 seconds. It then reaches a terminal velocity after 4.2 seconds. Its motion is shown by the graph below.

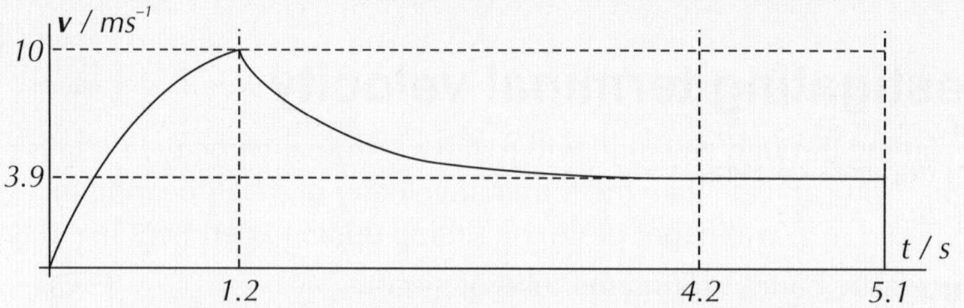

a) Describe the ball's acceleration from when it's dropped to when it reaches the bottom of the cylinder (at 5.1 seconds).

b) Sketch a velocity-time graph for the same ball if it were dropped straight into the water (without falling through air first). Include the ball's terminal velocity in your sketch.

Q2 Explain how air resistance affects the maximum speed of a car.

Practice Questions — Fact Recall

Q1 What is meant by friction and drag?

Q2 In what direction does a frictional force act?

Q3 What can you say about the frictional forces and the driving forces acting on an object when it reaches terminal velocity?

Q4 Which of these graphs shows the velocity-time graph for an object falling through air and reaching a terminal velocity?

a) 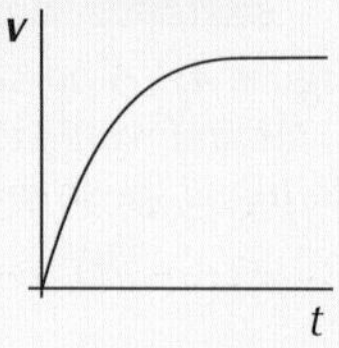

b) 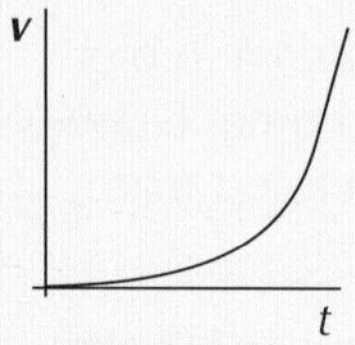

c) 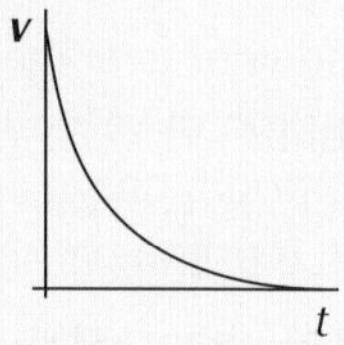

Q5 How does a skydiver reduce his or her terminal velocity?

Q6 Sketch and label the equipment a student could use to investigate the terminal velocity of a ball bearing in a viscous fluid.

6. Density, Pressure and Upthrust

Density is a property that all materials have, and different materials have different densities. The greater the density of a fluid, the greater the pressure an object will experience when it is submerged within it.

Learning Objectives:

- Know what is meant by the density of a material.
- Be able to use the formula $\rho = \frac{m}{V}$.
- Know what is meant by pressure and be able to use the equation $p = \frac{F}{A}$ for solids, liquids and gases.
- Be able to use the equation $p = h\rho g$ to calculate pressure.
- Understand what is meant by the upthrust on an object in a fluid.
- Know and understand Archimedes' principle.

Specification Reference 3.2.4

What is density?

Density is a measure of the 'compactness' of a substance. It relates the mass of a substance to how much space it takes up. The density of a material is its mass per unit volume:

$$\rho = \frac{m}{V}$$

ρ = *density in* $kg\,m^{-3}$; m = *mass in kg*; V = *volume in* m^3

If you're given mass in g and volume in cm^3, you can work out the density of an object in $g\,cm^{-3}$ ($1\ g\,cm^{-3} = 1000\ kg\,m^{-3}$). The density of an object depends on what it's made of. The density of a material doesn't vary with size or shape.

Example — Maths Skills

Aluminium has a density of 2.7 $g\,cm^{-3}$.
Calculate the volume of a 460 g solid object made out of aluminium.

Rearrange the formula $\rho = \frac{m}{V}$ to get $V = \frac{m}{\rho}$.

Substitute $m = 460$ g and $\rho = 2.7\ g\,cm^{-3}$ into the rearranged equation to find the volume of the object.

$$V = \frac{460}{2.7} = 170.37... = 170\ cm^3 \text{ (to 2 s.f.)}$$

What is pressure?

Pressure is the amount of force applied per unit area. It is measured in pascals (Pa), which are equivalent to newtons per square metre ($N\,m^{-2}$). You can calculate the pressure over an area for a solid, liquid or gas using:

$$p = \frac{F}{A}$$

p = *pressure (in Pa)*; F = *force (in N)*; A = *area (in* m^2*)*

Tip: Make sure you know how to find the area of some basic shapes (e.g. rectangles, triangles, circles, etc). You may need to calculate the area of a surface to calculate the pressure.

Example — Maths Skills

A triangular-based pyramid stands on a table. It has a mass of 2.5 kg, and its base has an area of 62 cm^2. Calculate the pressure (in pascals) exerted on the table by the pyramid.

Pressure is give by: $p = \frac{F}{A}$

First, calculate the force exerted by the pyramid.

The force from the pyramid is equal to its weight. So:

$F = mg = 2.5 \times 9.81 = 24.525$ N

Convert its base area to m^2: $A = 62 \div 10\,000 = 6.2 \times 10^{-3}\ m^2$

So, $p = \frac{24.525}{6.2 \times 10^{-3}} = 3955.64...\ \text{Pa} = 4000\ \text{Pa (to 2 s.f.)}$

Fluid pressure

When an object is inside a fluid, particles of the fluid collide with the object. These collisions exert a force on the surface of the object, and hence a pressure is exerted on the object by the fluid. This pressure depends on the density of the fluid, and how deep the object is within the fluid.

A denser fluid will have more particles in a given volume. This means there are more particles that are able to collide — which means more collisions and a larger total force exerted. So the pressure exerted by the fluid is higher.

As depth increases, the number of particles above that point increases. The weight of these particles adds to the pressure experienced at that point, so fluid pressure increases with depth.

The pressure acting on an object due to a fluid can be calculated from the depth of the object in the fluid (h), the density of the fluid (ρ) and the gravitational field strength (g).

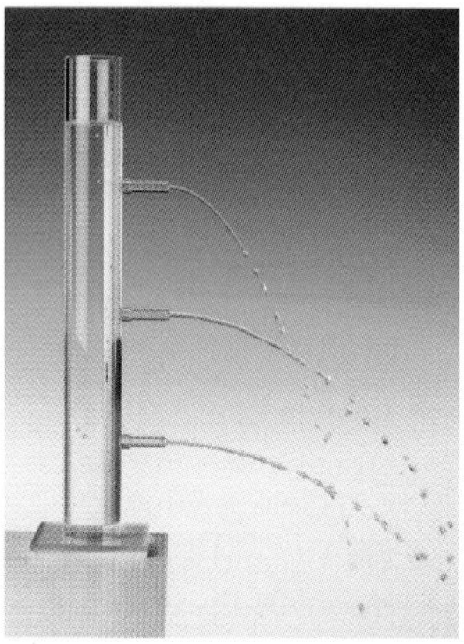

Figure 1: Water emerges out of each spout at different speeds. The deeper the spout, the faster the water spurts out, due to the greater fluid pressure.

$$p = h\rho g$$

p = pressure (in Pa)

g = gravitational field strength (in $N kg^{-1}$)

h = depth (in m)

ρ = density (in $kg m^{-3}$)

Example — Maths Skills

An ice cube is partially submerged in a glass of water. The bottom face of the ice cube is at a depth of 3 cm. The density of water is 1 000 kg m^{-3}. Calculate the pressure acting on the bottom of the ice cube due to the water.

$h = 3$ cm $= 0.03$ m

$\rho = 1\,000$ kg m^{-3}

$g = 9.81$ N kg^{-1}

$p = h\rho g$

$= 0.03 \times 1\,000 \times 9.81$

$= 294.3$ Pa $= 300$ Pa (to 1 s.f.)

Upthrust

Upthrust is an upwards force that fluids exert on objects that are completely or partially submerged in the fluid. It's caused because the top and bottom of a submerged object are at different depths. Consider the cuboid in Figure 2.

- Since $p = h\rho g$, there is a difference in pressure, which causes an overall upwards force known as upthrust.
- The force acting on the top of the body due to the fluid is $F_1 = pA = h_1\rho gA$, where A is the surface area of a face of the cube.
- The force acting on the bottom of the body due to the fluid is $F_2 = pA = h_2\rho gA$
- So the net force (upthrust) acting on the body is:

$$\text{upthrust} = (h_2 - h_1)\rho gA$$

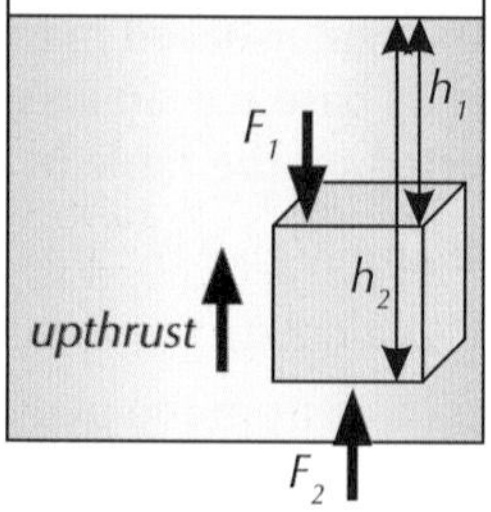

Figure 2: Diagram of an object experiencing upthrust.

Tip: Remember, when you're using the upthrust equation, you need to make sure your units are correct. Since you'll be using $g = 9.81$ N kg^{-1}, density needs to be in kg m^{-3}, distances need to be in m and areas need to be in m^2.

Archimedes' principle says that when a body is completely or partially immersed in a fluid, it experiences an upthrust equal to the weight of the fluid it has displaced. This is because:

$$(h_2 - h_1)\rho g A = V\rho g = mg = W$$

The average density of an object determines whether it floats or sinks. An object will float on a fluid if it has a lower density than the fluid. This is because the object will only displace a volume of water that weighs as much as the object does. This volume of water is lower than the volume of the object (because of the difference in their densities), so the object will only be partially immersed. At this point, the upthrust balances the weight of the object, and it floats.

If an object is more dense than the fluid, the water it displaces will always weigh less than the object itself. This means the upthrust will always be less than the weight of the object, and so the object will sink.

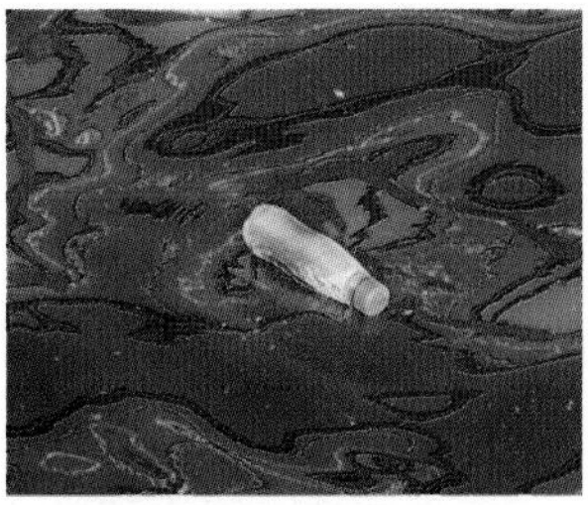

Figure 3: *Oil floats on water because it has a lower density. The bottle floats because the average density of the bottle and the air inside it combined is lower than the density of the water.*

Example

Submarines make use of upthrust to dive underwater and return to the surface. To sink, large tanks are filled with water to increase the weight of the submarine so that it exceeds the upthrust. To rise to the surface, the tanks are filled with compressed air to reduce the weight so that it's less than the upthrust.

Figure 4: *A submarine changes its weight in order to move up and down in the water.*

Practice Questions — Application

Q1 Find the density of an object with a mass of 360 kg and a volume of 0.45 m^3.

Q2 The air pressure inside an inflated basketball is 159 000 Pa. The total force acting on the inner surface of the basketball is 26 500 N. Calculate the inner surface area of the basketball.

Q3 A solid aluminium cylinder has a volume of 9.1×10^{-4} m^3. Aluminium has a density of 2700 $kg\,m^{-3}$. What is the mass of the cylinder?

Q4 An orange has a mass of 0.15 kg and a radius of 4.0 cm. Show that it has a density of approximately 560 $kg\,m^{-3}$.

Q5 A uniform cylinder is submerged in water. The radius of the cylinder is 5.00 cm. The top of the cylinder is at a depth of 65.0 cm, and the bottom of the cylinder is at a depth of 76.0 cm. The density of water is 1.00 $g\,cm^{-3}$. Calculate the upthrust on the cylinder.

Tip: The volume of a sphere is $V = \frac{4}{3}\pi r^3$.

Tip: Remember, 1 $g\,cm^{-3}$ = 1000 $kg\,m^{-3}$.

Practice Questions — Fact Recall

Q1 State the equation for density. Define any symbols that you use.

Q2 An object is submerged in water, and displaces an amount of water. What is the upthrust on the object equal to?

Q3 State how the densities of a solid object and fluid must differ for the object to float when it is placed in the fluid.

Section Summary

Make sure you know...

- That weight is the force experienced by an object with mass due to a gravitational field.
- That the unit of force is the newton, N.
- How to use the equation $\boldsymbol{W} = m\boldsymbol{g}$ to make calculations involving weight.
- That the centre of mass (or centre of gravity) of an object is the point where the weight of an object can be considered to act from.
- That for a uniform regular solid, its centre of gravity is at the centre.
- How to perform an experiment to determine the centre of gravity of a flat object.
- What is meant by the normal contact force, tension, friction and upthrust.
- That a free-body diagram shows all the forces acting on an object, but none of the forces it exerts on other objects.
- How to draw free-body diagrams.
- That the net force on an object is the sum of all the forces acting on the object.
- The equation $\boldsymbol{F} = m\boldsymbol{a}$ and how to use it in calculations involving net force and acceleration.
- How to calculate a net force acting on an object for one- and two-dimensional motion.
- That if all forces acting on an object cancel each other out, the object is in equilibrium.
- That if three coplanar forces are acting on an object in equilibrium, the forces can be drawn as a closed triangle of forces.
- How to resolve forces into perpendicular components.
- How to calculate the moment of a force about a point using the equation $M = Fx$.
- That the principle of moments states that for an object to be balanced, the sum of all clockwise moments acting on the object must equal the sum of all anticlockwise moments acting on it.
- That a couple is a pair of equal sized forces that applies a turning effect to an object.
- How to calculate the torque of a couple using the equation $T = Fd$.
- That for an object to be in equilibrium, the torques acting on it must balance.
- That drag is a form of friction which acts against the motion of an object moving through a fluid.
- That an object is travelling at its terminal velocity when the driving forces and frictional forces acting on it are balanced.
- How different factors affect the air resistance acting on an object, such as its speed, size and shape.
- How an object reaches terminal velocity, in terms of the forces acting on it.
- How to sketch and interpret velocity-time and acceleration-time graphs for an object reaching terminal velocity.
- That an object falling in a uniform gravitational field in the presence of drag will eventually reach a terminal velocity.
- How to perform an experiment to determine the terminal velocity of an object in a fluid.
- That density is a measure of the compactness of a substance.
- How to use the equation $\rho = \frac{m}{V}$ to make calculations involving density.
- That pressure is the force exerted on a surface per unit area.
- How to use the equation $p = \frac{F}{A}$ to find pressure in problems involving solids, liquids and gases.
- How to use the equation $p = h\rho g$ to find the pressure exerted on a surface due to the fluid it's in.
- How to calculate the upthrust exerted on an object by a fluid.
- That Archimedes' principle states that the upthrust on an object that is fully or partially submerged in a fluid is equal to the weight of the fluid displaced by the object.

Exam-style Questions

1 An object that weighs 29.43 N on Earth has a weight of 26.61 N on Venus.
What is the gravitational field strength on Venus?

A 9.04 N kg^{-1}

B 0.90 N kg^{-1}

C 8.87 N kg^{-1}

D 9.81 N kg^{-1}

(1 mark)

2 Which of the following statements about air resistance on a moving object is/are true?

1 Air resistance is independent of the size and shape of the object.

2 Air resistance increases as the velocity of the object increases.

3 Air resistance is smaller for objects with a lower mass.

A Only statement 2 is true.

B Only statements 1 and 2 are true.

C Only statements 1 and 3 are true.

D All of the statements are true.

(1 mark)

3 Which of the following statements regarding equilibrium is true?

A A body in equilibrium has no forces acting on it.

B A body in equilibrium cannot accelerate.

C A body cannot be in equilibrium if it is under the action of more than one moment.

D A body that is changing direction is in equilibrium.

(1 mark)

4 The diagrams below show couples of forces being applied to four identical taps.
The taps are drawn to scale. Which tap is experiencing the largest torque?

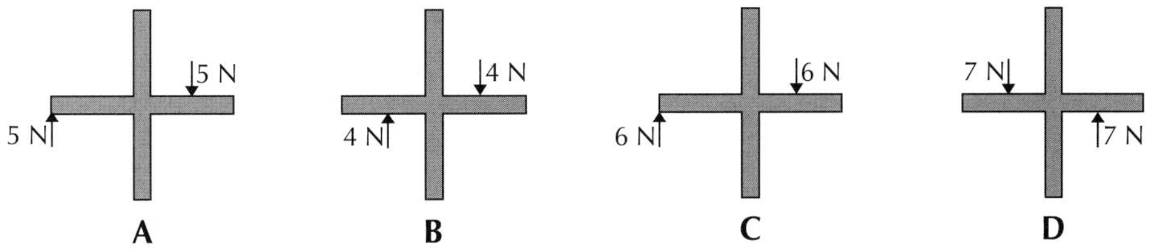

(1 mark)

5 A student is investigating the properties of an unknown liquid, X.

(a) The student wants to investigate the terminal velocity of a ball bearing as it travels through liquid X. Describe an experiment that the student could perform to investigate this.

(3 marks)

The student then pours 450 cm^3 of liquid X into a beaker, and weighs it. The mass of the full beaker is 862 g. The empty beaker has a mass of 250 g.

(b) Calculate the density of liquid X. Give your answer in $g\,cm^{-3}$.

(2 marks)

(c) The student places an apple into liquid X. The apple floats in the liquid. The bottom of the apple is at a depth of 4.0 cm below the surface. Calculate the pressure due to liquid X acting on the bottom of the apple.

(2 marks)

(d) The apple has a mass of 185 g. Calculate the upthrust on the apple.

(2 marks)

6 A dinghy is at rest on water. It is then pulled through water by two constant forces, as shown in **Fig. 6.1**. A resistive force, ***F***, acts against the dinghy's motion.

Fig. 6.1

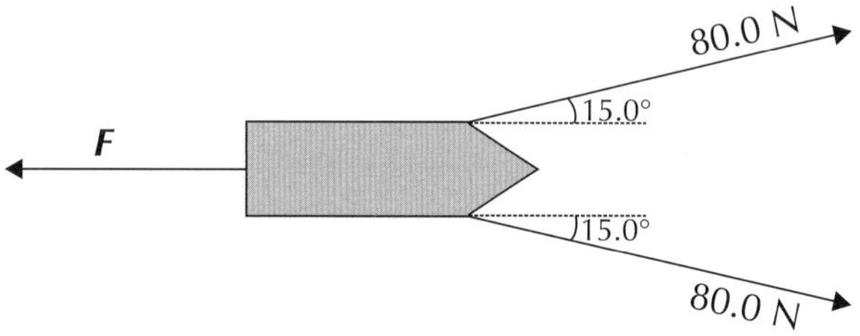

(a) After a period of time, the dinghy reaches terminal velocity. Describe how the dinghy reaches terminal velocity.

(3 marks)

(b) Sketch the velocity-time graph for the dinghy, starting from rest until it reaches terminal velocity.

(1 mark)

(c) Calculate the size of force ***F*** when the dinghy is at terminal velocity.

(2 marks)

(d) Once the dinghy is travelling at terminal velocity, the two 80.0 N forces are removed. The mass of the dinghy is 83.2 kg. Calculate the deceleration of the dinghy immediately after the 80.0 N forces are removed.

(2 marks)

7 A truck is used to carry rocks. The truck has a weight of 21 000 N and is 4.75 m long. When it's carrying no load the centre of mass is 1.3 m from the centre of the front wheels and 2.4 m from the centre of the rear wheels. The truck is shown in **Fig. 7.1**.

Fig. 7.1

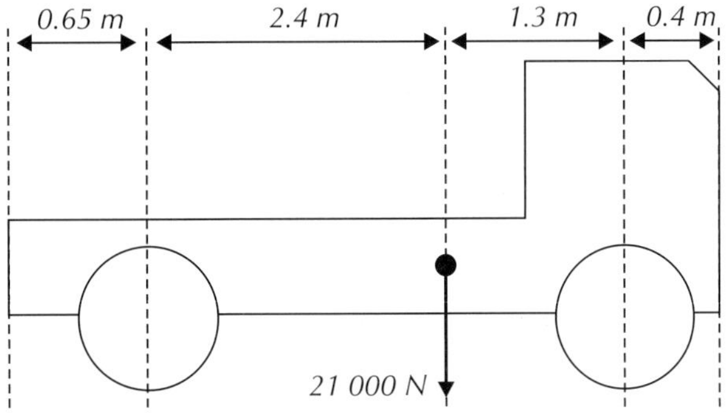

(a) Define the moment of a force about a point or pivot.

(1 mark)

(b) State and explain which set of wheels, front or back, will exert a greater upwards force on the truck when the truck is carrying no load.

(2 marks)

(c) A rock is placed on the very edge of the back of the truck, and the front wheels remain on the ground but no longer feel any force from the truck. Calculate how much the rock weighs.

(2 marks)

8 A student is investigating the centre of gravity of objects.

(a) Define the centre of gravity of an object.

(1 mark)

Fig. 8.1 shows a flat toy parrot.

Fig. 8.1

(b) Describe an experiment the student could perform to find the centre of gravity of the toy parrot.

(3 marks)

(c) Cranes are tall structures used to move heavy objects on construction sites. Describe the features the base of a crane must have and explain why these features are needed.

(3 marks)

Module 3 Section 3: Work, Energy and Power

1. Work and Power

Learning Objectives:

- Understand the concept of work done by a force.
- Know that the transfer of energy is equal to work done.
- Be able to define the unit joule.
- Be able to calculate the work done by a force moving an object, including when the force is at an angle to the direction of motion, using $W = Fx\cos\theta$.
- Know that power is the rate of doing work.
- Be able to calculate power using $P = \frac{W}{t}$.
- Be able to define the unit watt.
- Be able to derive $P = Fv$ and know how to use it.

Specification References 3.3.1 and 3.3.3

You'll have met work and power at GCSE. In physics, they have specific meanings, and they can be calculated with a set of equations.

What is work?

Work is done whenever energy is transferred — they are just two ways of saying the same thing. Here are some examples of work being done:

Activity	Work done against	Final energy form
Lifting up a box.	*Gravity*	*Gravitational potential energy*
Pushing a chair across level floor.	*Friction*	*Heat*
Pushing two magnetic north poles together.	*Magnetic Force*	*Magnetic energy*
Stretching a spring.	*Stiffness of spring*	*Elastic potential energy*

Figure 1: *A table showing examples of work being done and the final energy form for each activity.*

Usually you need a force to move something because you're having to overcome another force. The thing being moved has **kinetic energy** while it's moving, which is transferred to other forms of energy when the movement stops.

The word 'work' in physics means the amount of energy transferred from one form to another when a force causes a movement of some sort. It's measured in **joules** (J).

Figure 2: *When you strike a match, work is done against friction to produce heat.*

Calculating work done

When a car tows a caravan, it applies a force to the caravan to move it to where it's wanted. The force and the displacement of the caravan are in the same direction. To find out how much work has been done, you need to use the equation:

$$W = Fx$$

W *= work done in J*
F *= force causing motion in N*
x *= displacement in m*

- Work is the energy that's been changed from one form to another — it's not necessarily the total energy. E.g. moving a book from a low shelf to a higher one will increase its gravitational potential energy, but it had some gravitational potential energy to start with. Here, the work done would be the increase in gravitational potential energy, not the total gravitational potential energy.
- Remember the displacement needs to be measured in metres — if you have displacement in cm or km, you need to convert it to metres first.

Tip: Have a look at page 25 for more on unit prefixes.

- The force will be a fixed value in any calculations, either because it's constant or because it's the average force.
- The equation assumes that the direction of the force is in the same direction and along the same line as the movement.
- The equation gives you the definition of the joule (symbol J): 'One joule is the work done when a force of 1 newton moves an object through a distance of 1 metre'.

Forces at an angle

Sometimes the direction of movement of an object is different from the direction of the force acting on it. In this case you need to find the component of the force that acts in the direction of the movement.

Because you only need to worry about the component of the force in the direction of the motion, you only ever need to resolve it in that direction. In general for a force at an angle to the direction of motion, you can find the work with this equation:

Tip: Remember force is a vector, so you can resolve it into components (see page 36).

$$W = Fx\cos\theta$$

W = *work done in J*

F = *force causing motion in N*

x = *displacement in m*

θ = *angle at which the force acts from the direction of motion*

Example — Maths Skills

A girl pulls a sledge with a force of 51.9 N for 100.0 m. The string she uses to pull the sledge is at an angle of 19.3° to the ground. Calculate the work she does in pulling the sledge over this distance.

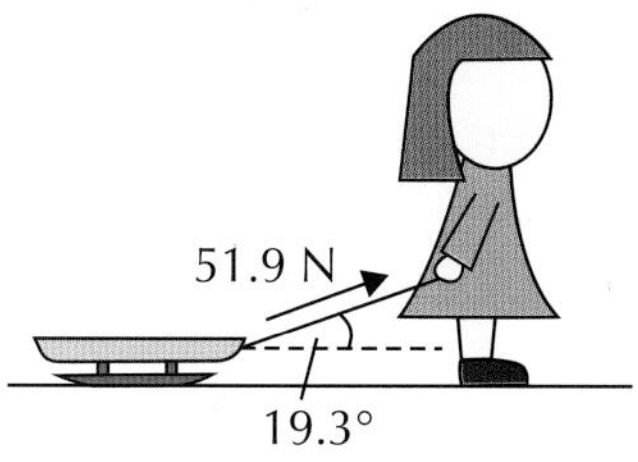

To calculate the work done in a situation like the one above, you need to consider the horizontal and vertical components of the force. The only movement is in the horizontal direction. This means the vertical component of the force is not causing any motion (and hence not doing any work) — it's just balancing out some of the weight, meaning there's a smaller reaction force.

The horizontal component of the force is causing the motion, so to calculate the work done, this is the only force you need to consider. So resolving the force to find the horizontal component (F_x) we get:

$F_x = 51.9 \times \cos 19.3° = 48.98...\ \text{N}$

$\Rightarrow W = F_x \times x = 48.98... \times 100.0 = 4898.32... = 4900\ \text{J}$ (to 3 s.f.)

If the force and displacement are in the same direction, then $\theta = 0$, and $\cos\theta = 1$. This means $W = Fx$, which you saw on the previous page.

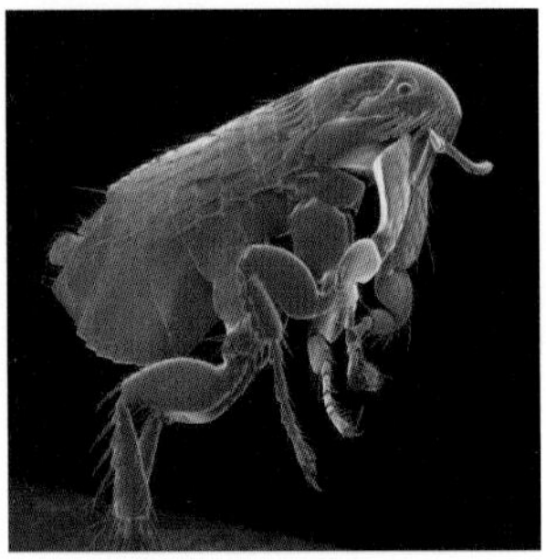

Figure 3: A flea's legs transfer a small amount of energy, but in a very short time — this makes them very powerful.

Power and work

Power means many things in everyday speech, but in physics it has a special meaning. Power is the rate of doing work — in other words it is the amount of energy transferred from one form to another per second.

You calculate the power from this equation:

$$P = \frac{W}{t}$$

P *= power in W*, ***W*** *= work done in J*, ***t*** *= time in s*

The **watt** (symbol W) is defined as a rate of energy transfer equal to 1 joule per second (Js^{-1}). Make sure you learn this definition.

Moving objects

Sometimes, for a moving object, it's easier to use another version of the power equation. It's derived like this:

- You know $P = \frac{W}{t}$.
- You also know $W = \boldsymbol{Fx}$, which gives $P = \frac{\boldsymbol{Fx}}{t}$.
- But $\boldsymbol{v} = \frac{\boldsymbol{x}}{t}$, which you can substitute into the above equation to give:

$$P = \boldsymbol{Fv}$$

P *= power in W*, ***F*** *= force causing the motion in N*, ***v*** *= velocity in* ms^{-1}

Exam Tip
You'll be given this equation in your exam data and formulae booklet.

It's easier to use this if you're given the velocity in the question. Learn this equation as a shortcut to link power and speed.

Example — Maths Skills

A car is travelling at a speed of 10.0 ms⁻¹ and is kept going against the frictional force by a driving force of 525 N in the direction of motion. Find the power supplied by the engine to keep the car running.

Use the shortcut $P = \boldsymbol{Fv}$, which gives:

$P = 525 \times 10.0 = 5250$ W

If the force and motion are in different directions, you can replace ***F*** with ***F***$\cos\theta$ to get:

$$P = \boldsymbol{Fv}\cos\theta$$

θ *= angle at which the force acts from the direction of motion*

Exam Tip
This equation doesn't appear in your data and formulae booklet. Make sure you know how to find the power of a moving object when the force isn't in the direction of the object's motion.

Practice Questions — Application

Q1 John pushes a desk 2.81 m across a flat floor. If he pushes with a steady force of 203 N, how much work does he do?

Q2 A car operating at a power of 60.1 kW is travelling at a steady 34.7 ms^{-1}. How much force is being provided by the engine?

Q3 Alan pulls a desk 1.39 m across the floor by pulling a rope attached to it at 13.1° to the horizontal. If he pulls with a steady force of 371 N, how much work does he do?

Q4 A child is pulling a cart along by a string at 15.2° to the horizontal. The child is pulling with a constant force of 83.1 N and the cart is moving horizontally at 2.99 ms^{-1}. What is the power of the child?

Q5 The diagram below shows a tractor pulling a plough with a constant force.

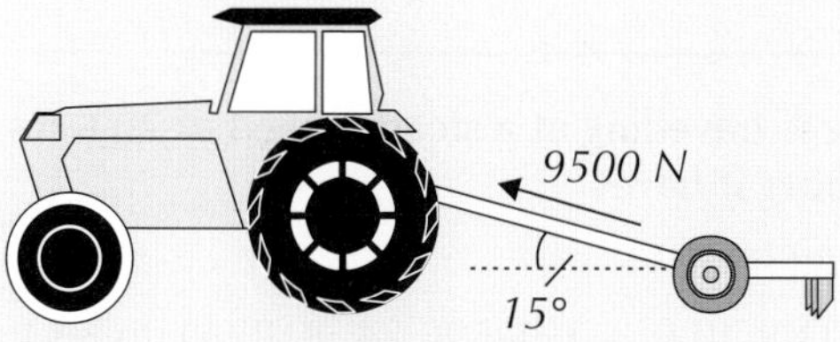

It does 980 kJ of work pulling the plough the length of a field.

a) If it takes the tractor 22 seconds to pull the plough the length of the field, what is the tractor's power?

b) Calculate the length of the field.

Tip: It's a good idea to draw a diagram of the set-up before you start calculating — it usually helps to clear things up a bit.

Practice Questions — Fact Recall

Q1 What's transferred when work is done?

Q2 What is the definition of the joule?

Q3 Power is the rate of doing what?

Q4 What's the equation for finding the power of a moving object?

2. Kinetic Energy and Gravitational Potential Energy

Learning Objectives:

- Know and be able to derive $E_k = \frac{1}{2}mv^2$ and use it to calculate the kinetic energy of an object.
- Know and be able to derive $E_p = mgh$ and use it to calculate the gravitational potential energy of an object in a uniform gravitational field.

Specification Reference 3.3.2

You've probably come across kinetic energy and gravitational potential energy before, but don't assume you know it all. This time you could be asked to derive the equations in the exam.

Kinetic energy

Kinetic energy is the energy of anything moving. You can calculate it for a moving object using this equation:

$$E_k = \frac{1}{2}mv^2$$

E_k = *kinetic energy in J*

m = *mass in kg*

v = *speed in ms*$^{-1}$

Example — Maths Skills

A car with a mass of 903 kg is travelling at a steady speed of 20.6 ms^{-1}. How much kinetic energy does it have?

Just put the numbers into the equation:

$$E_k = \frac{1}{2}mv^2 = \frac{1}{2} \times 903 \times 20.6^2 = 191\ 598.54 = 192 \text{ kJ (to 3 s.f.)}$$

Tip: A kilojoule (kJ) is equal to 1000 joules (J).

To derive this equation you need to think about an object undergoing a change in kinetic energy. When the kinetic energy of an object increases, work is done on the object. Similarly, when the object's kinetic energy decreases, work is done by the object. Work done is equal to energy transferred so the work done is equal to the change in kinetic energy of the object:

Tip: Remember work done, $W = \boldsymbol{Fx}$ (p.94).

$$E_k = \boldsymbol{Fx}$$

You also know that $\boldsymbol{F} = m\boldsymbol{a}$ (p.72) and $\boldsymbol{a} = \frac{\boldsymbol{v} - \boldsymbol{u}}{t}$ so:

$$\boldsymbol{F} = m\left(\frac{\boldsymbol{v} - \boldsymbol{u}}{t}\right)$$

And from page 41, $\boldsymbol{x}$ (displacement) can be written:

$$\boldsymbol{x} = \frac{(\boldsymbol{u} + \boldsymbol{v})}{2}t$$

Substituting these two into the E_k equation gives:

Exam Tip
Make sure you understand this derivation. It could bag you some easy marks in the exam.

$$E_k = m \times \frac{(\boldsymbol{v} - \boldsymbol{u})}{t} \times \frac{(\boldsymbol{u} + \boldsymbol{v})}{2} \times t$$

Cancelling the 't's and expanding the brackets:

$$E_k = \frac{1}{2}m(\boldsymbol{v} - \boldsymbol{u})(\boldsymbol{u} + \boldsymbol{v})$$
$$= \frac{1}{2}m(\boldsymbol{v}^2 + \boldsymbol{uv} - \boldsymbol{uv} - \boldsymbol{u}^2)$$
$$= \frac{1}{2}m(\boldsymbol{v}^2 - \boldsymbol{u}^2)$$
$$= \frac{1}{2}m\boldsymbol{v}^2 - \frac{1}{2}m\boldsymbol{u}^2$$

The kinetic energy of an object is the kinetic energy compared to when the object is at rest, i.e. when $\boldsymbol{u} = 0$ and the object has no kinetic energy. Substituting $\boldsymbol{u} = 0$ into the equation above gives you:

$$E_k = \frac{1}{2}mv^2$$

Tip: You only need the magnitude, not the direction, of $\boldsymbol{v}$ in this equation.

Gravitational potential energy

Gravitational potential energy is the energy something has due to its position in a gravitational field. The greater the height of the object, the greater its gravitational potential energy.

You normally want to find the change in an object's gravitational potential energy, E_p, which you can work out using the equation:

$$E_p = mgh$$

$\boldsymbol{E_p}$ = change in gravitational potential energy in J

$\boldsymbol{h}$ = change in height in m

$\boldsymbol{m}$ = mass in kg

$\boldsymbol{g}$ = gravitational field strength in Nkg^{-1}

To derive this equation, use the idea that the gravitational energy gained is equal to the work done in moving the object a distance h upwards:

$$E_p = W = \boldsymbol{F} \times h$$

The force that work is done against is the force of gravity, which is equal to $m\boldsymbol{g}$ (see p.69). So:

$$E_p = \boldsymbol{F} \times h = m\boldsymbol{g}h$$

This equation only works when $\boldsymbol{g}$ is constant. This is known as a uniform field. You can assume g is constant close to the Earth's surface.

Tip: Remember, $\boldsymbol{g}$ is equal to 9.81 Nkg^{-1} on Earth, but can be very different elsewhere, see p.69. So an object could have a different gravitational potential energy on another planet even if it's at the same height above the surface.

Example — Maths Skills

A man with a mass of 82.5 kg climbs up a cliff and gains 28.5 kJ of gravitational potential energy. Calculate how high the man climbed.

You can rearrange $E_p = m\boldsymbol{g}h$ to get $h = \frac{E_p}{m\boldsymbol{g}}$

Then just put the numbers in:

$$h = \frac{28\,500}{82.5 \times 9.81} = 35.214... = 35.2 \text{ m (to 3 s.f.)}$$

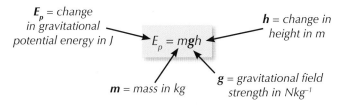

*Figure 1: An astronaut can jump much higher on the moon than they could on Earth by doing same amount of work. This is because g is lower on the moon (p.69) so for a given E_p, h will be bigger (since E_p= m**g**h).*

Practice Questions — Application

Q1 A child with a mass of 32.4 kg jumps 0.285 m into the air. Calculate how much gravitational potential energy she has gained at the top of her jump.

Q2 A 770 kg helicopter descends from a height of 890 m above the ground to a height of 760 m. Calculate the gravitational potential energy that the helicopter loses during this descent.

Q3 A bus is travelling along a road at a speed of 16 ms^{-1}. Calculate the mass of the bus if it has 150 kJ of kinetic energy.

Practice Questions — Fact Recall

Q1 When does an object have kinetic energy?

Q2 When does an object gain gravitational potential energy?

3. Conservation of Energy

You'll no doubt have already met the idea that energy can be transferred from one type to another. Some energy transfers are useful, but others aren't.

Learning Objectives:

- Be able to recall the principle of conservation of energy.
- Understand what is meant by the efficiency of a mechanical system and be able to use the equation for efficiency.
- Be able to apply knowledge of energy in different forms to transfer and conservation problems, including exchanges between gravitational potential energy and kinetic energy.

Specification References 3.3.1, 3.3.2 and 3.3.3

The principle of conservation of energy

The **principle of conservation of energy** states that:

> Energy cannot be created or destroyed. Energy can be transferred from one form to another but the total amount of energy in a closed system will not change.

Whenever energy is converted from one form to another, some is always 'lost'. It's still there (i.e. it's not destroyed) — it's just not in a form you can use.

Example

Not all the energy input into a motor is converted to useful energy (e.g. kinetic energy) — it's not destroyed, but it is converted to less useful forms of energy.

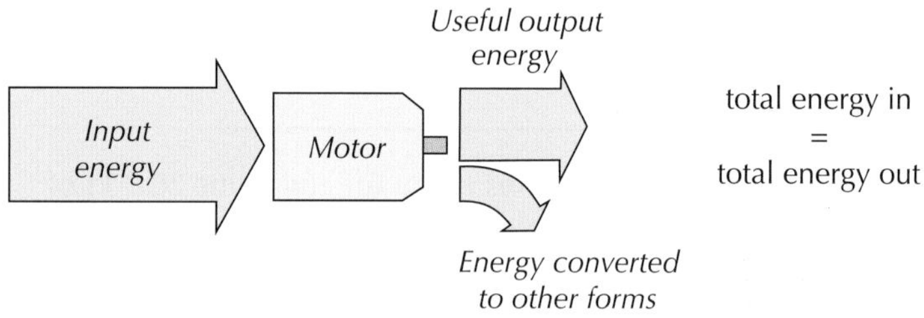

Figure 1: *The input energy is equal to the useful energy output + energy converted to other forms.*

Most often, energy is lost as heat — computers and TVs are always warm when they've been on for a while. No device, except possibly a heater, transfers all energy to useful energy — some energy is always lost as heat. (You want heaters to give out heat, but in other devices the heat loss isn't useful.) Often the heat that is lost is caused by friction.

Energy can be lost in other forms too, such as sound — the important thing is the lost energy isn't in a useful form and you can't get it back.

You can talk about how well energy is transferred in terms of **efficiency**. It's a measure of how much of the input energy is transferred usefully by a mechanical system. The more useful energy you get out of a machine for what you put into it, the more efficient it is. You can use the following equation to calculate efficiency as a percentage:

$$\text{efficiency} = \frac{\text{useful output energy}}{\text{total input energy}} \times 100$$

Exam Tip
Luckily you can normally assume that friction is zero in exam questions (unless stated otherwise).

Tip: To get efficiency as a decimal, just use the first part of the equation and don't multiply by 100.

Example — Maths Skills

A meat grinder has a useful energy output of 725 J when making minced meat. If its efficiency is 89.1%, work out the total input energy.

You know that: $\text{efficiency} = \frac{\text{useful output energy}}{\text{total input energy}} \times 100$

Which you can rearrange to:

$$\text{total input energy} = \text{useful output energy} \div \frac{\text{efficiency}}{100}$$

Then total input energy $= 725 \div \frac{89.1}{100} = 813.69... = 814$ J (to 3 s.f.)

Exam Tip
Some questions will be kind and give you the useful output energy — others will tell you how much is wasted. You just have to subtract the wasted energy from the total input energy to find the useful output energy.

Transfers between kinetic and gravitational potential energy

The principle of conservation of energy nearly always comes up when you're doing questions about changes between kinetic and gravitational potential energy.

Often when an object moves, energy is being transferred from one type to another. For example, kinetic energy can be transferred to gravitational potential energy by doing work, and vice versa.

Figure 2: Rollercoasters transfer gravitational potential energy to kinetic energy and vice versa.

Examples

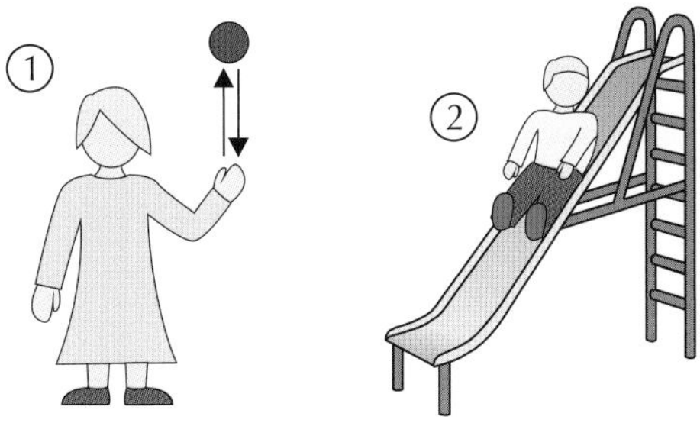

***Figure 3:** Some examples of energy transfers between kinetic and potential energy.*

1. As Becky throws the ball upwards, kinetic energy is converted into gravitational potential energy. When it comes down again, that gravitational potential energy is converted back into kinetic energy.
2. As Dominic goes down the slide, gravitational potential energy is converted into kinetic energy.

In real life there are also frictional forces — in the example above, not all of Dominic's gravitational potential energy would be transferred to kinetic energy. Some would be lost due to frictional forces.

You're usually told to ignore friction in exam questions — this means that in the examples above you can assume that the sum of the kinetic and gravitational potential energy is constant. So for a falling object with no air resistance, the gain in kinetic energy is equal to the loss in gravitational potential energy:

$$\frac{1}{2}mv^2 = mgh$$

Exam Tip
You could be given a graph showing the variation of gravitational potential energy (E_p) and kinetic energy (E_k) with distance or time for an object — remember, the sum of E_p and E_k should remain constant if there are no frictional forces.

You need to be able to use this rule to solve problems. The classic example is the simple pendulum. In a simple pendulum, you assume that all the mass is in the bob at the end.

Example — Maths Skills

A simple pendulum has a mass of 700 g and a length of 50 cm (both correct to 2 significant figures).
It is pulled out to an angle of 30.0° from the vertical.

(a) Find the gravitational potential energy stored in the pendulum bob relative to its lowest point.

You can work out the increase in height, h, of the end of the pendulum using trigonometry.

Start by drawing a diagram:

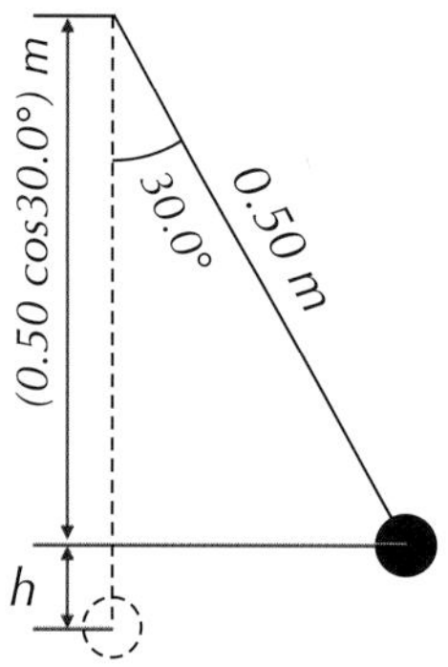

Gravitational potential energy

$= mgh$

$= 0.70 \times 9.81 \times (0.50 - 0.50\cos 30.0°)$

$= 0.460...$

$= 0.46$ J (to 2 s.f.)

Tip: $0.50\cos 30.0°$ is the vertical side of the triangle formed when the pendulum swings, so the change in height is 0.50 (original height) – $0.50\cos 30.0°$ (new height).

(b) The pendulum is released. Find the maximum speed of the pendulum bob as it passes through the vertical position.

To find the maximum speed, assume no air resistance, then use $mgh = \frac{1}{2}mv^2$.

So $\frac{1}{2}mv^2 = 0.460....$ Rearrange to find v:

$$v = \sqrt{\frac{2 \times 0.460...}{0.70}} = 1.1464... = 1.1 \text{ ms}^{-1} \text{ (to 2 s.f.)}$$

OR cancel the ms and rearrange to give:

$v^2 = 2gh$

$= 2 \times 9.81 \times (0.50 - 0.50\cos 30.0°) = 1.3142...$

$\Rightarrow v = \sqrt{1.3142...} = 1.1464... = 1.1 \text{ ms}^{-1}$ (to 2 s.f.)

Exam Tip
You could be asked to apply this stuff to just about anything in the exam. Rollercoasters are an exam favourite.

Practice Questions — Application

Q1 Find the useful energy output of a 20.0% efficient engine with an energy input of 2900 J.

Q2 An apple falls from a tree and accelerates uniformly to a velocity of 7.8 ms^{-1} before it hits the ground. Assuming there is no air resistance, calculate the height the apple fell from.

Q3 a) How much gravitational potential energy does a falcon with a mass of 650 g lose when it dives 103 m?

b) As it dives, 95% of its gravitational potential energy is converted to kinetic energy. If it started stationary, how fast is it moving after the dive?

c) The falcon misses its prey and soars back up, converting 80.0% of its kinetic energy to gravitational potential energy. How high will it climb before needing to flap its wings?

Figure 4: *Birds of prey are highly streamlined so that only a small amount of energy is transferred to heat through drag.*

Practice Questions — Fact Recall

Q1 What's the principle of conservation of energy?

Q2 What is the efficiency of a mechanical system a measure of?

Section Summary

Make sure you know...

- That whenever work is done, energy is transferred.
- Some examples of work done and the transfers involved.
- That work is measured in joules.
- That one joule is the work done when a force of 1 newton moves an object through a distance of 1 metre.
- How to use $W = \boldsymbol{Fx}\cos\theta$ to calculate the work done by a force moving an object, and recall that $W = \boldsymbol{Fx}$ when the force is in the direction of motion ($\theta = 0°$).
- That power is the rate of doing work, and how to calculate it using $P = \frac{W}{t}$.
- That power is measured in watts.
- That one watt is defined as a rate of energy transfer equal to 1 joule per second.
- How to derive and use $P = \boldsymbol{Fv}$ for calculations involving the force and velocity of moving objects.
- The equation $E_k = \frac{1}{2}mv^2$, how to derive it and how to use it to calculate the kinetic energy of an object.
- The equation $E_p = m\boldsymbol{g}h$, how to derive it and how to use it to calculate the gravitational potential energy of an object in a uniform gravitational field.
- That the principle of conservation of energy says that energy cannot be created or destroyed. Energy can be transferred from one form to another but the total amount of energy in a closed system will not change.
- What is meant by the efficiency of a mechanical system.
- How to calculate efficiency using: $\text{efficiency} = \frac{\text{useful output energy}}{\text{total input energy}} \times 100$.
- How energy is commonly wasted.
- That for a falling object with no air resistance, the gain in kinetic energy is equal to the loss in potential energy.
- How to apply energy conservation to transfer and conservation problems.

Exam-style Questions

1 A mobile phone is connected to a power supply to charge.
Of the 565 J of energy supplied to the phone, 45.2 J is wasted in the form of heat.
What is the efficiency of this process?

A 8.00%

B 12.5%

C 92.0%

D 98.1%

(1 mark)

2 A farmer wants to move some farming equipment down the road.

(a) He lifts the equipment into a cart.
State what the farmer is doing work against as he lifts the equipment.

(1 mark)

The farmer uses a horse to pull the cart along a straight road.
Fig 2.1 shows the horse pulling the cart with a constant force.

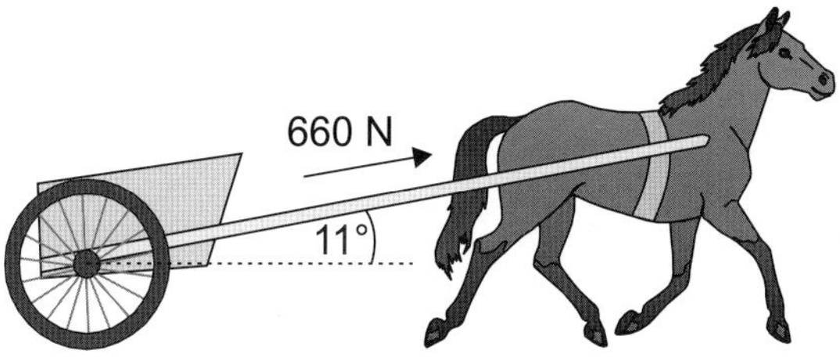

Fig 2.1

(b) Calculate the amount of work done by the horse if it pulls the cart 95 m.

(2 marks)

3 A cyclist pedals along a road.

(a) When the cyclist is travelling at 6.5 ms^{-1}, the brakes are applied and the bike comes to a stop after 3.0 s. If the cyclist and bike together have a mass of 74.8 kg, calculate their combined kinetic energy just before the brakes are applied.

(2 marks)

(b) Calculate the power of the brakes.

(2 marks)

(c) Later on, the cyclist allows himself to roll down a hill from rest without pedalling.
The top of the hill is 22.5 m higher than the bottom of the hill.
Calculate how fast he will be going when he reaches the bottom of the hill.
Assume air resistance and other resistive forces are negligible.

(2 marks)

Learning Objectives:

- Know the terms extension and compression.
- Know what is meant by tensile and compressive deformation.
- Know Hooke's law, and be able to use the formula $F = kx$.
- Know the meaning of a force constant, k, of a spring or wire.
- Be able to interpret force-extension (or compression) graphs.
- Know techniques and procedures used to investigate force–extension characteristics for arrangements which may include springs, rubber bands or polythene strips (PAG2).

    Specification Reference 3.4.1

1. Hooke's Law

Applying a force to a material can stretch it. When some materials are stretched, they follow Hooke's law — but only up to a certain point.

Forces and deformation

When more than one force is applied to an object, **deformation** (a change in the object's shape or size) will occur. More than one force is needed to cause deformation — without a secondary supportive force, the work done by a force on an object will simply move the object.

There are two general types of deformation. **Tensile deformation** is caused by applying balanced outward forces, which leads to extension (stretching). **Compressive deformation** is caused by applying balanced inward forces, which leads to compression (squashing) of the object.

If a light metal wire of original length L is supported at the top and then has a weight attached to the bottom, it stretches. The weight pulls down with force F. Once the wire has stopped stretching, the forces will be in equilibrium and there will be an equal and opposite reaction force at the support.

Tip: The metal wire is light — this means you can ignore the force acting downwards due to the weight of the wire.

Support force, F

Natural length, L

Extension, x

Force, F

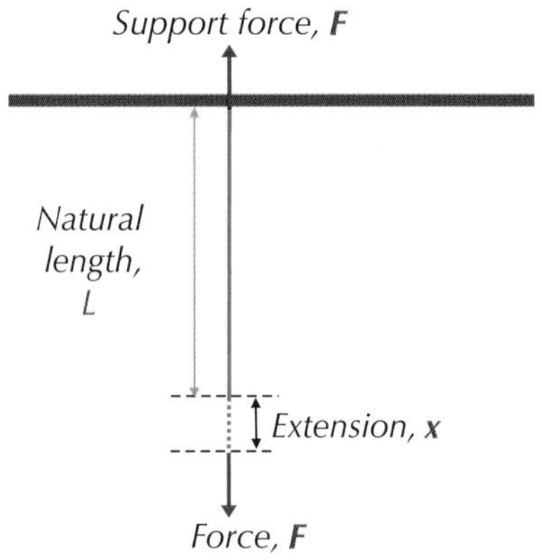

Figure 1: *A supported metal wire extending by x when a weight is attached.*

What is Hooke's law?

Robert Hooke discovered that the extension, x, of some objects (e.g. most wires and springs) is proportional to the load or force applied, F. He wrote this as:

$$F = \text{force in N} \longrightarrow F = kx \begin{cases} k = \text{force constant in Nm}^{-1} \\ x = \text{extension in m} \end{cases}$$

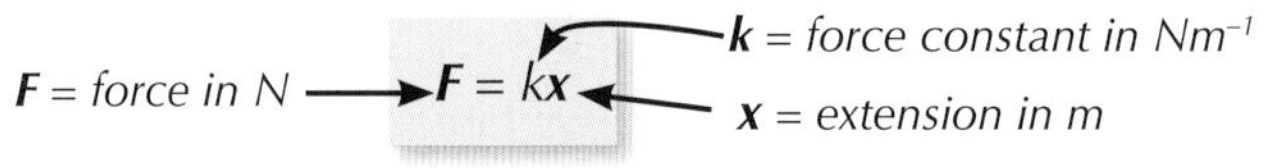

k is the **force constant** (or **stiffness constant**). It is the force needed to extend an object that obeys Hooke's law by 1 m. It depends on the material that the object is made from, as well as its length and shape.

Example — Maths Skills

A force of 6.0 N is applied to a metal wire, which extends by 0.040 m. Calculate the force constant of the wire.

Rearrange the formula $\boldsymbol{F} = k\boldsymbol{x}$ to get $k = \frac{\boldsymbol{F}}{\boldsymbol{x}}$.

Then substitute $\boldsymbol{F} = 6.0$ N and $\boldsymbol{x} = 0.040$ m into the rearranged equation to find the force constant of the wire.

$$k = \frac{6.0}{0.040} = 150\,\text{Nm}^{-1}$$

Exam Tip
If you're given a question like this in the exam, make sure the extension is in m before putting it into the equation.

Hooke's law and springs

A metal spring also changes length when you apply a pair of opposite forces. The extension or compression of a spring is proportional to the force applied — so Hooke's law applies.

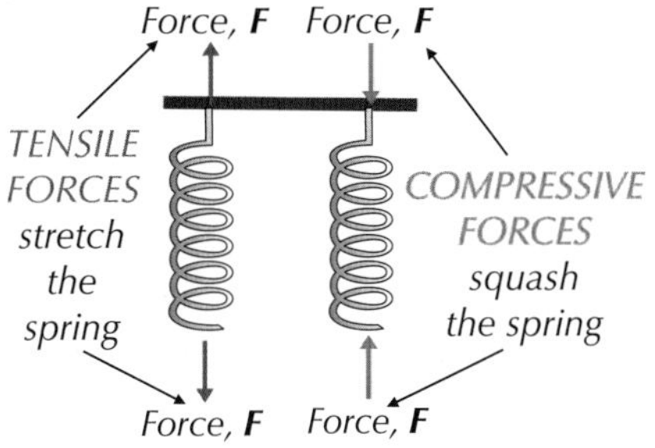

Figure 2: *Metal springs with tensile and compressive forces acting on them.*

Tip: If two things are proportional, it means that if one increases, the other increases by the same proportion.

For springs, k in the formula $\boldsymbol{F} = k\boldsymbol{x}$ is usually called the spring stiffness or spring constant.

Hooke's law works just as well for **compressive forces** as **tensile forces**. For a spring, k has the same value whether the forces are tensile or compressive (though this isn't true for all materials).

Springs in series and parallel

If a force is applied to more than one spring (or wire), you can combine the force constants of the individual objects to find the overall force constant of the system. You can then treat the system as one spring with force constant k. How you combine the force constants depends on how the springs are arranged.

In series, the reciprocal of the combined force constant is equal to the sum of the reciprocals of the individual force constants:

$$\frac{1}{k} = \frac{1}{k_1} + \frac{1}{k_2}$$

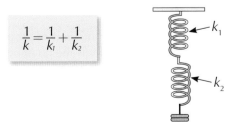

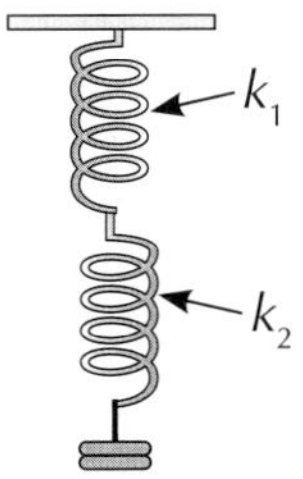

Tip: Don't get these equations confused with the series and parallel resistance equations on page 169.

In parallel, the combined force constant is just the sum of the force constants of the individual springs:

$$k = k_1 + k_2$$

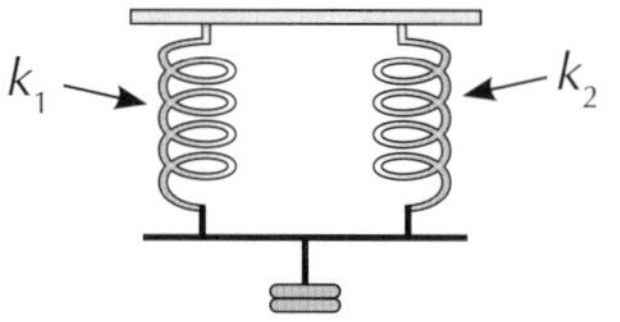

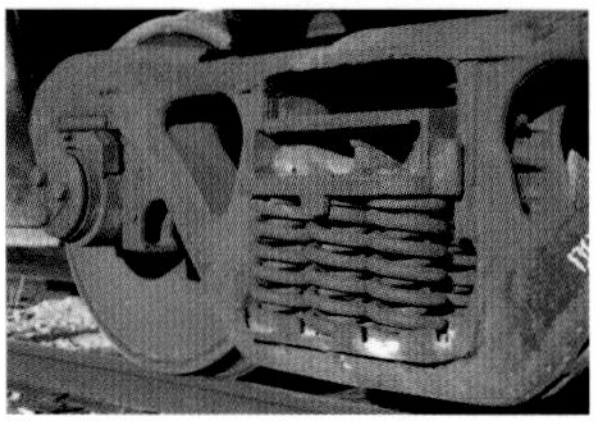

Figure 3: *Springs were used in parallel in old train suspension systems, providing a large combined spring constant.*

Example — Maths Skills

Calculate the combined force constant for the springs shown below.

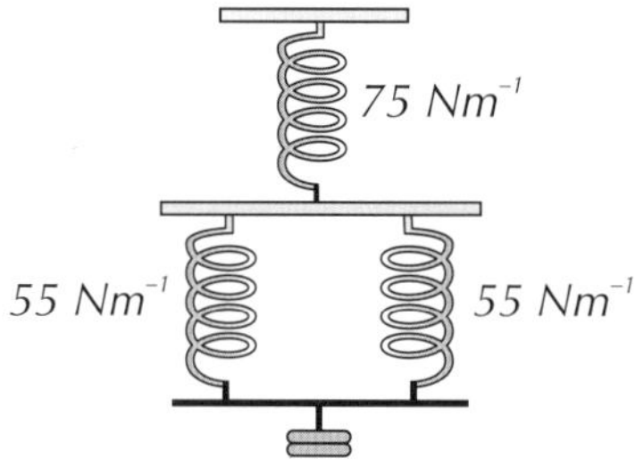

The two springs in parallel at the bottom of the spring have a combined force constant of:

$k_{bottom} = k_1 + k_2 = 55 + 55 = 110\ Nm^{-1}$

Rearrange $\frac{1}{k} = \frac{1}{k_{top}} + \frac{1}{k_{bottom}}$ to get:

$$k = 1 \div \left(\frac{1}{k_{top}} + \frac{1}{k_{bottom}}\right) = 1 \div \left(\frac{1}{75} + \frac{1}{110}\right)$$

$= 44.5945... = 45\ Nm^{-1}$ (to 2 s.f.)

The limit of proportionality

There's a limit to the force you can apply for Hooke's law to stay true. Figure 4 shows force against extension for a typical metal wire or spring.

The first part of the graph shows Hooke's law being obeyed — there's a linear relationship between force and extension and it goes straight through the origin. The gradient of the straight line is the force constant, *k*.

Exam Tip
You may be asked to give two features of a graph which show that the material under test obeys Hooke's law. Just remember, the graph of a material which obeys Hooke's law will start with a straight line through the origin.

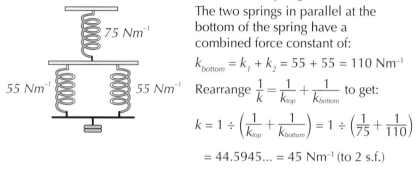

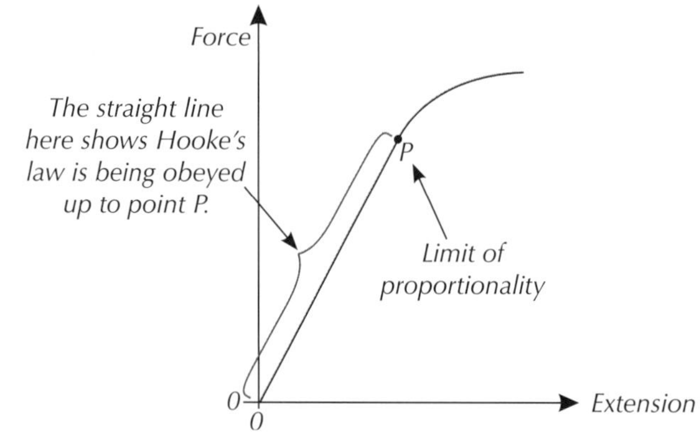

Figure 4: *The graph of force against extension for a typical metal wire.*

Tip: You get a similar graph for compression too.

Tip: There's more on force-extension graphs on pages 111-113.

Tip: The limit of proportionality can also be described as the point beyond which the force-extension graph is no longer linear (straight).

Metals generally obey Hooke's law up to the **limit of proportionality**, marked *P* on the graph. The limit of proportionality is the point beyond which the force is no longer proportional to extension. Beyond *P*, the graph starts to curve. The limit of proportionality is also known as **Hooke's law limit**. Hooke's law doesn't just apply to metal springs and wires — most other materials obey it up to a point. But be careful — there are some materials, like rubber, only obey Hooke's law for really small extensions.

Example — **Maths Skills**

Below is a force-extension graph for a spring.
Calculate the stiffness constant, *k*, in Nm^{-1} for the spring.

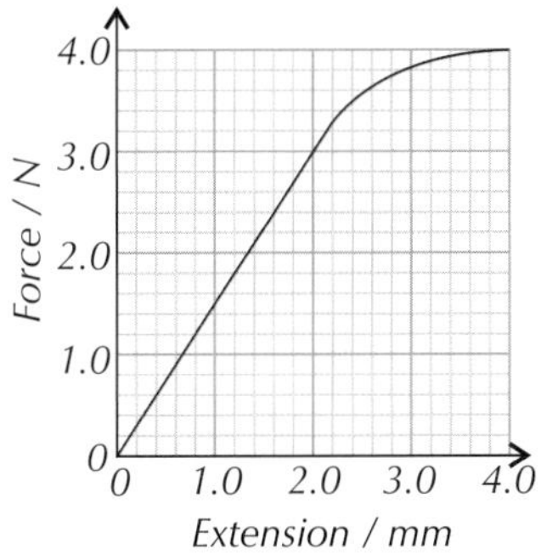

k is the gradient of the graph up to the limit of proportionality.

For this graph, this is shortly after the point where the load is 3.0 N and the extension is 2.0 mm.

Convert 2.0 mm into m, to get 0.0020 m.

Then $k = \frac{F}{x} = \frac{3.0}{0.0020} = 1500\,Nm^{-1}$.

Tip: Force-extension graphs are specific for the tested object and depend on its dimensions — different wire lengths and diameters of the same metal will produce different force-extension graphs.

Investigating extension

PRACTICAL ACTIVITY GROUP 2

Figure 5 shows the experimental set-up you could use in the lab to investigate how the extension of an object varies with the force applied to it.

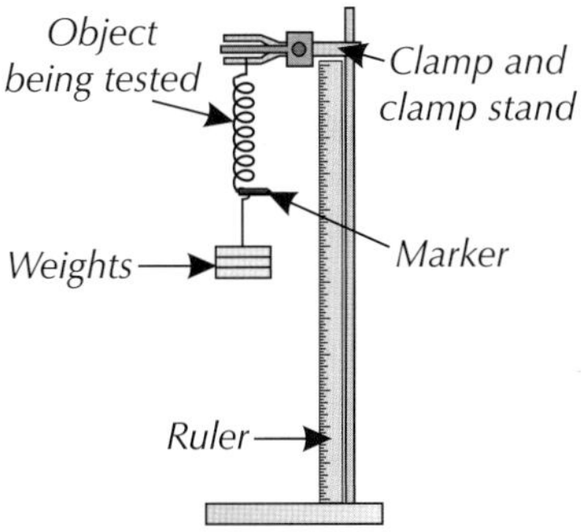

Figure 5: *An experimental set-up used to investigate how extension varies with force.*

Tip: Do a risk assessment before you start. When carrying out this experiment, make sure you're stood up so you can move out of the way quickly if the weights fall, and use goggles in case the spring snaps.

- Measure the natural length of the spring (when no load is applied) with a millimetre ruler clamped to the stand. Make sure you take the reading at eye level and add a marker (e.g. a thin strip of tape) to the bottom of the spring to make the reading more accurate.
- Add a weight to the spring and allow it to come to rest. Record the weight and measure the new length of the spring. The extension is the change in length.
- Repeat this process until you have enough measurements (no fewer than 6).
- Plot a force-extension graph of your results. Where you can draw a straight line of best fit, the object obey's Hooke's law, and the gradient is equal to *k* (from $F = kx$). If you've loaded the object beyond its limit of proportionality, the graph will start to curve.
- You could try measuring and comparing the spring constants and force-extension characteristics of different materials, such as springs, rubber bands and polythene strips.

Tip: You may want to conduct a pilot experiment beforehand to help you work out the sizes of masses to use.

Tip: If you have unknown masses, rather than known weights, the object can be suspended by a newton meter — this will let you calculate the additional force being applied each time a mass is added.

Practice Questions — Application

Q1 A metal spring has a spring constant of 1250 Nm^{-1}. When a force is applied, the spring extends proportionally by 1.60 cm. Calculate the force applied.

Q2 A spring is compressed proportionally 0.80 mm by a force of 20 N (correct to 2 s.f.). Calculate the spring constant of the spring in Nm^{-1}.

Q3 The original length of a metal wire is 20.0 cm. A force of 55.0 N is applied and the wire extends to a new length of 22.0 cm. Assume that the limit of proportionality has not been reached.

a) Calculate the extension of the wire in metres.

b) Calculate the spring constant of the length of wire.

Q4 Calculate the combined force constant for the springs shown in the system below.

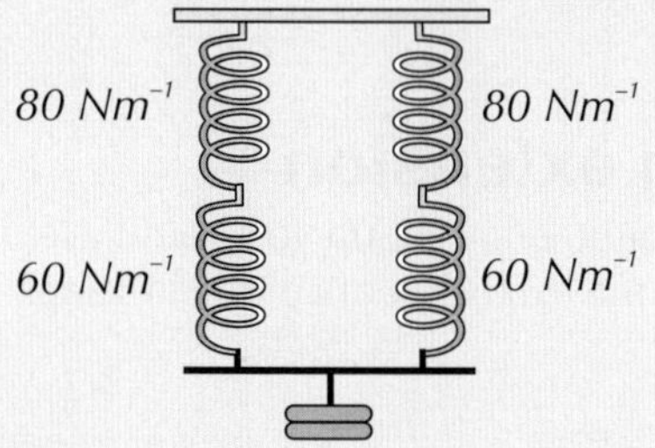

Tip: Remember, Hooke's law applies for compression as well as tension. Huzzah.

Practice Questions — Fact Recall

Q1 Write down the formula for Hooke's law, defining all the symbols you use.

Q2 What is meant by the limit of proportionality for a material?

Q3 A spring suspended from a clamp stretches when a weight is attached to the bottom. Describe the measurements you would need to take and the calculations you would have to perform to find the extension of the spring.

Exam Tip
You'll be given the formula for Hooke's law in your data and formulae booklet, so you don't need to know it by heart.

2. Elastic and Plastic Deformation

It won't surprise you to hear that different objects behave in different ways when a force is applied to them. Force-extension graphs are a useful way of showing these behaviours.

Learning Objectives:

- Apply knowledge and understanding of force–extension (or compression) graphs.
- Know what is meant by elastic and plastic deformations of materials.
- Know that for a force-extension (or compression) graph, work done is the area under the graph.
- Be able to calculate elastic potential energy using $E = \frac{1}{2}Fx$ and $E = \frac{1}{2}kx^2$.

Specification Reference 3.4.2

The elastic limit

Figure 1 shows a graph of force against extension for a typical metal wire or spring. At the limit of proportionality, the graph starts to curve. The point marked *E* on the graph is called the **elastic limit**. If you increase the force past the elastic limit, the material will be permanently stretched. This means when all the force is removed, the material will be longer than at the start.

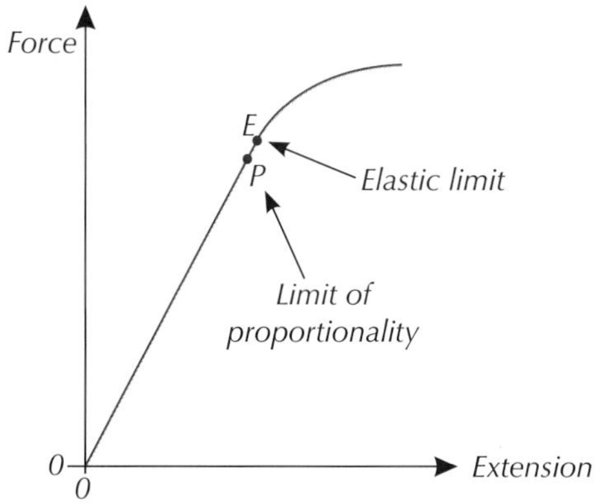

Figure 1: *The graph of force against extension for a typical metal wire.*

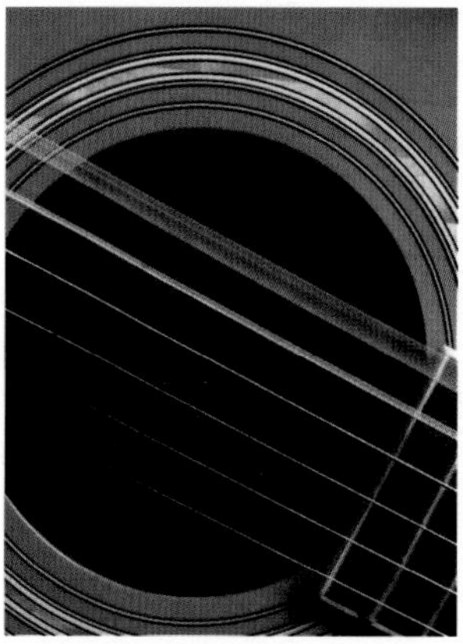

Figure 2: *Guitar strings deform elastically after being plucked.*

Types of deformation

Elastic deformation

Up to their elastic limit, materials behave elastically. This means the material returns to its original shape once the forces are removed. Elastic materials are able to be stretched or compressed without permanently deforming.

Plastic deformation

A material stretched past its elastic limit shows **plastic deformation**. The material does not return to its original shape when the forces on it are removed. Plastic materials are permanently deformed by forces. When we say plastic here, we just mean a material that undergoes plastic deformation. It has nothing to do with the materials called 'plastic', that things like water bottles are made of.

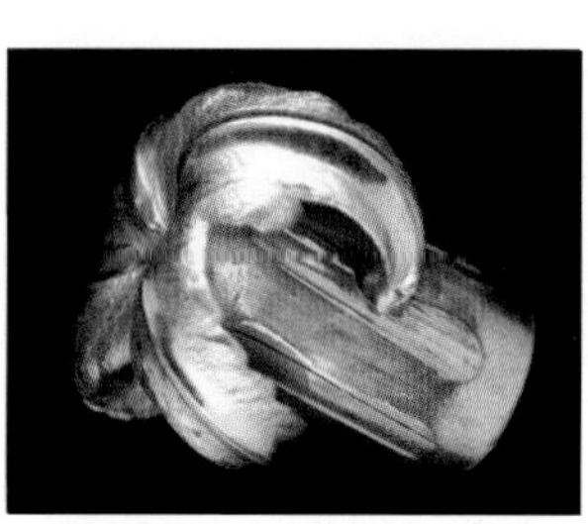

Figure 3: *Bullets made from metals often behave plastically and permanently deform on impact.*

Work done in deformations

When a material is stretched or compressed, work has to be done to deform the material. Force-extension graphs are a useful way of showing how much energy has been stored by the deformed material.

Force-extension graphs

On a force-extension graph, the work done is given by the area under the graph. Before the elastic limit, all the work done in deforming a material is stored as potential energy in the material. This stored energy is called **elastic potential energy**.

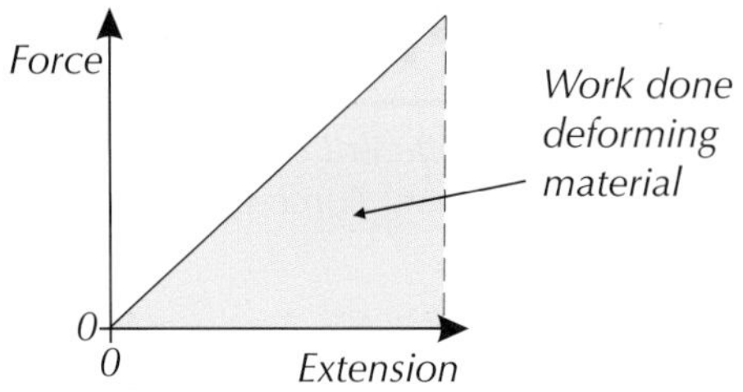

***Figure 4:** The area under a force-extension graph for a stretched material is equal to the work done stretching it.*

Tip: Remember, work done = energy transferred (page 94).

Example — Maths Skills

Shown to the right is a force-extension graph for a metal spring. Find the work done stretching the spring to an extension of 0.3 m.

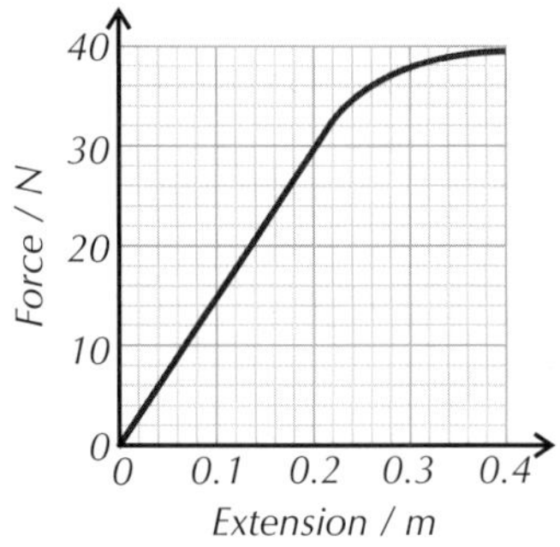

To find the work done, you need to find the area under the graph shown highlighted below:

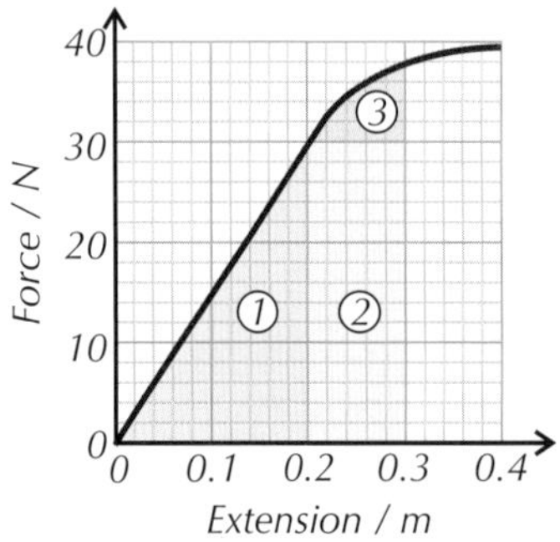

You can approximate the area using triangles and rectangles:

Area 1: ½ × 30 N × 0.2 m = 3 J

Area 2: 30 N × 0.1 m = 3 J

Area 3: ½ × 8 N × 0.1 m = 0.4 J

Total work done ≈ 3 J + 3 J + 0.4 J
= 6.4 J

You can also approximate the area using the squares on the grid:

There are (approximately) 6.5 big squares, each worth: 10 N × 0.1 m = 1 J

So the total work done is ≈ 6.5 × 1 J = 6.5 J.

Exam Tip
The examiners will accept a range of answers for questions like this, as it's tricky to get the area under a curve exactly right. But that doesn't mean you can be slapdash when working areas out — still do it carefully.

Tip: You could also count the number of small squares. Oh joy.

Calculating energy stored

Provided a material obeys Hooke's law, the potential energy stored inside it can be calculated quite easily using a formula. This formula can be derived using a force-extension graph and work done.

The energy stored by the stretched material is equal to the work done on the material in stretching it.

Work done is equal to force × displacement (see page 94). But on a force-extension graph, the force acting on the material is not constant. Therefore you need to work out the average force acting on the material, from zero to F, which is $\frac{1}{2}F$:

$$\text{work done} = \tfrac{1}{2}Fx$$

On the graph, this is just the area underneath the straight line from the origin to the extension (x). So the area under the graph represents the work done or the energy stored. And so the elastic potential energy, E, is:

$$E = \tfrac{1}{2}Fx$$

Tip: This is just the same as working out the area of a triangle: (½ × base × height).

Because Hooke's law is being obeyed, $\boldsymbol{F} = k\boldsymbol{x}$, which means $\boldsymbol{F}$ can be replaced in the equation to give:

$$E = \tfrac{1}{2}k\boldsymbol{x}^2$$

Exam tip
In the exam, they might ask you to explain how the formula $E = \tfrac{1}{2}\boldsymbol{Fx}$ can be derived using a force-extension graph.

Work done to permanently deform an object

If the material is stretched beyond the elastic limit, some work is done permanently deforming the material. This will not be stored as elastic potential energy.

Force-extension graphs can show when work has been done to permanently deform an object. For example, you can plot a force-extension graph of what happens when force has been added and then removed from an object. If the unloading line and the loading line don't start and end at the same points, the material has deformed plastically and work has been done extending the object permanently.

Figure 5 is a force-extension graph for a metal wire that has been stretched beyond its elastic limit (E).

Tip: Remember that up to point P, the gradient of the graph gives the stiffness constant of the wire.

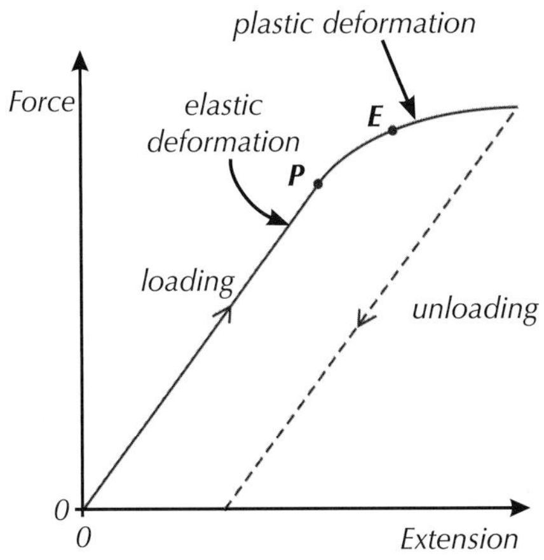

Figure 5: *A force-extension graph for a metal wire.*

Tip: If you apply a big enough force to fracture the object you are investigating, you can't draw the unloading line. The loading line should just stop at the point the fracture occurred (see pages 121 and 123).

When the load is removed, the extension decreases. The unloading line is parallel to the loading line because the force constant k is still the same. Because the wire was stretched beyond its elastic limit (E) and deformed plastically, it has been permanently stretched. This means the unloading line doesn't go through the origin. The area between the two lines is the work done to permanently deform the wire.

Practice Questions — Application

Q1 Calculate the elastic potential energy stored in a spring when a force of 30 N has produced an elastic extension of 1.2 cm. You may assume that the limit of proportionality has not been reached.

Q2 A student hangs weights from the end of a spring and records its extension. Her results are shown in the graph below. Calculate the total work done in stretching the spring during this experiment.

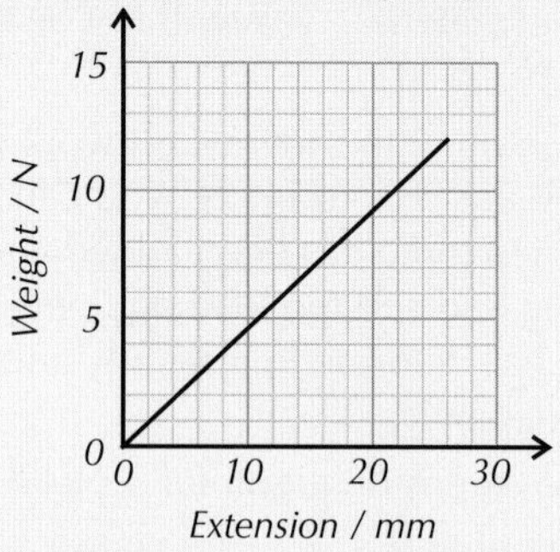

Q3 Sketch and label a typical force-extension graph for a metal wire as a force is applied to stretch the wire up to and beyond its elastic limit, then gradually removed.

Q4 Below is a force-extension graph for an investigation into how extension varies with force for a rubber band. The band was loaded with weights, shown by curve A. The band was then unloaded, shown by curve B.

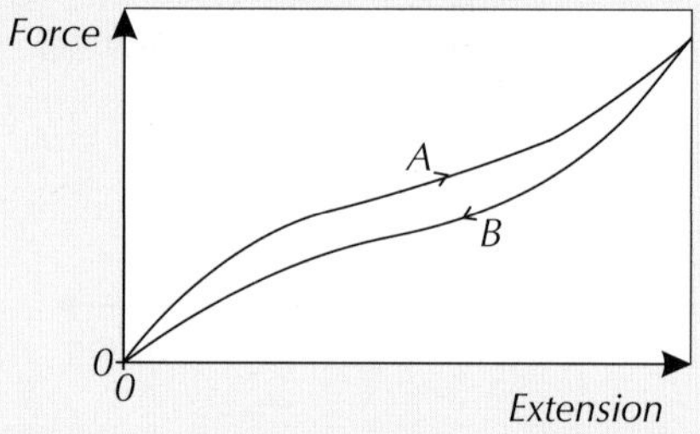

Is the rubber band elastic or plastic? Explain your answer.

Tip: Watch out for the units in Q1 — to calculate the elastic potential energy, the force has to be in newtons and the extension has to be in metres.

Practice Questions — Fact Recall

Q1 What is meant by the elastic limit of a material?

Q2 What does it mean if a material is deforming elastically?

Q3 What does it mean if a material is deforming plastically?

Q4 What is shown by the area between the loading and unloading lines on a force-extension graph of a material undergoing plastic deformation?

3. Stress and Strain

Two samples of the same material with different dimensions will stretch different amounts under the same force. Stress and strain are measurements that take into account the size of the sample, so a stress-strain graph is the same for any sample of a particular material.

Learning Objective:

- Be able to define stress, strain and ultimate tensile strength.

Specification Reference 3.4.2

Tensile stress and tensile strain

A material subjected to a pair of opposite forces may deform, i.e. change shape.

Tensile stress, σ, is defined as the force applied, $\boldsymbol{F}$, divided by the cross-sectional area, A:

$$\sigma = \frac{F}{A}$$

The units of stress are Nm^{-2} or pascals, Pa.

A stress causes a strain. **Tensile strain**, ε, is defined as the change in length, i.e. the extension, divided by the original length of the material:

$$\varepsilon = \frac{x}{L}$$

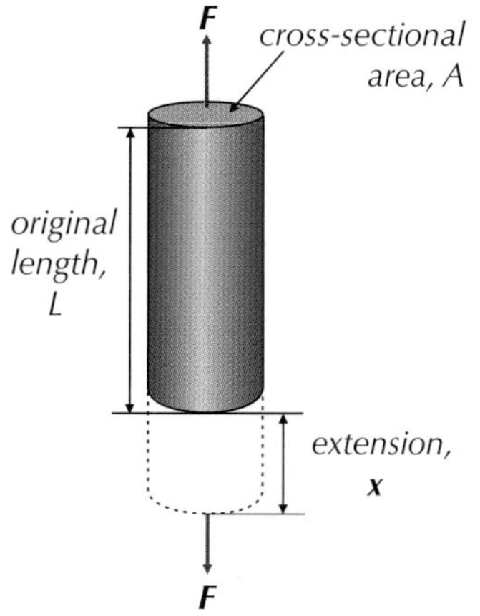

***Figure 1:** A pair of opposite tensile forces acting on an object.*

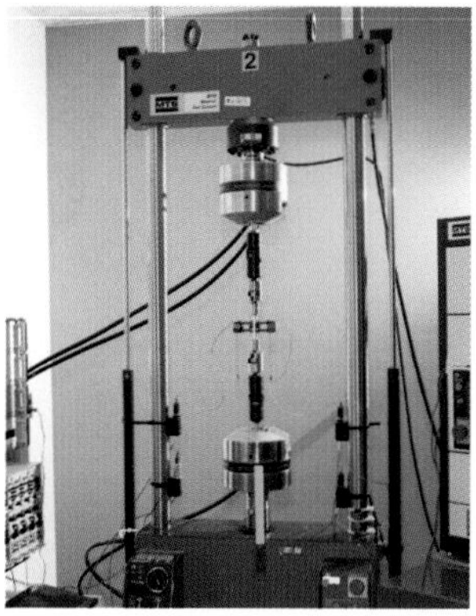
***Figure 2:** A material having its tensile stress tested by a machine.*

Strain has no units because it's a ratio — it's usually just written as a number.

It doesn't matter whether the forces producing the stress and strain are tensile or compressive — the same equations apply. The only difference is that you tend to think of tensile forces as positive, and compressive forces as negative.

Ultimate tensile strength

As a greater and greater tensile force is applied to a material, the stress on it increases.

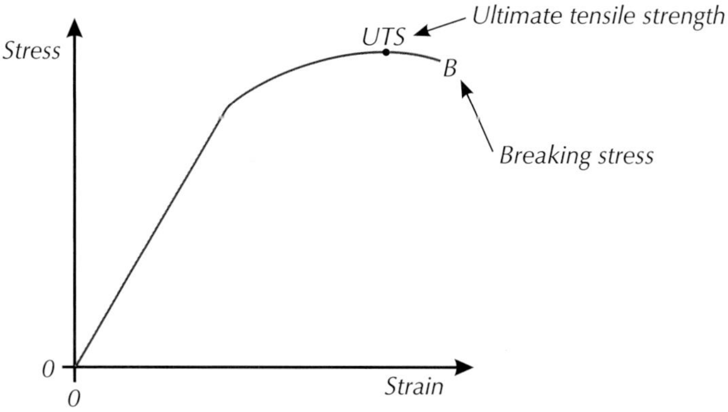

***Figure 3:** A stress-strain graph showing the ultimate tensile strength and breaking stress of a material.*

Tip: The stress-strain graphs for brittle materials don't look like this — see page 121. Page 123 has more on how to interpret stress-strain graphs like this one.

Tip: If an object has an uneven cross-section, the stress and strain will be different in different parts of the object — but it will always be somewhere on the stress-strain graph.

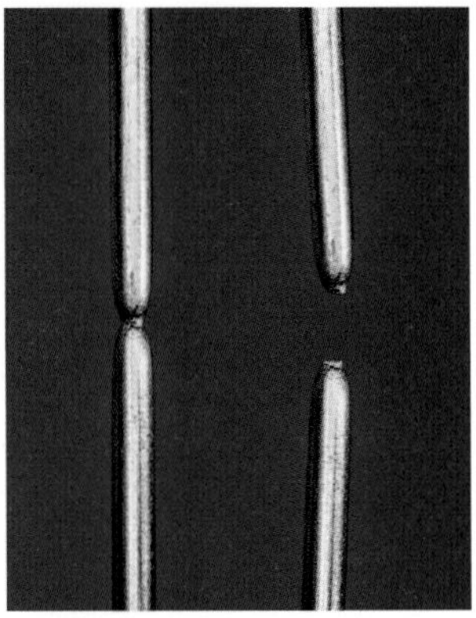

Figure 4: *Copper deforms plastically before breaking under sufficient stress.*

The effect of the stress is to start to pull atoms in the material apart from one another. Eventually the stress becomes so great that atoms separate completely, and the material breaks. This is shown by point B on the graph in Figure 3. The stress an object experiences when this occurs is called the **breaking stress**.

The point marked UTS on the graph in Figure 3 is called the **ultimate tensile strength**. This is the maximum stress that the material can withstand before it will break. Once you go past the UTS, the material will break no matter what you do. Engineers have to consider the UTS and breaking stress of materials when designing a structure.

Tip: 1 MPa is the same as 1×10^6 Pa.

Example — Maths Skills

A rope has a cross-sectional area of 8.0×10^{-3} m². A tensile force is applied to the rope and slowly increased. The rope breaks after a force of 1.8×10^5 N is applied. Calculate the UTS of the material.

$$\sigma = \frac{F}{A} = \frac{1.8 \times 10^5}{8.0 \times 10^{-3}} = 2.25 \times 10^7$$

$$= 2.3 \times 10^7 \text{ Pa (or Nm}^{-2}\text{) (to 2 s.f.)}$$

You could also write 2.3×10^7 Pa as 23 MPa.

Practice Questions — Application

Q1 A force of 50.0 N is applied to wire with a cross-sectional area of 3.1×10^{-6} m². Calculate the stress on the wire.

Q2 A rope has an original length of 12.0 cm. After a force is applied, its length becomes 12.3 cm. Calculate the strain on the rope.

Q3 A wire with a cross-sectional area of 1.2×10^{-7} m² has an ultimate tensile stress of 3.8×10^8 Pa. Calculate the maximum force you could apply to the wire before it breaks.

Practice Questions — Fact Recall

Q1 What is meant by:

a) tensile stress,

b) tensile strain,

c) breaking stress,

d) ultimate tensile strength?

4. The Young Modulus

The Young modulus is a measure of how stiff a material is. It is really useful for comparing the stiffness of different materials, for example if you're trying to find out the best material for making a particular product.

Learning Objectives:

- Know that Young modulus = $\frac{\text{tensile stress}}{\text{tensile strain}}$, and be able to use the equation $E = \frac{\sigma}{\varepsilon}$.
- Be able to describe techniques and procedures used to determine the Young modulus for a metal (PAG2).

Specification Reference 3.4.2

Calculating the Young modulus

When you apply a load to stretch a material, it experiences a tensile stress and a tensile strain (see page 115). Up to a point called the limit of proportionality, the stress and strain of a material are proportional to each other. So below this limit, for a particular material, stress divided by strain is a constant. This constant is called the **Young modulus**, *E*.

$$\text{Young modulus} = \frac{\text{tensile stress}}{\text{tensile strain}}$$

$$E = \frac{\sigma}{\varepsilon} = \frac{\boldsymbol{F} \div A}{\boldsymbol{x} \div L} = \frac{\boldsymbol{F}L}{A\boldsymbol{x}}$$

Where $\boldsymbol{F}$ = force in N, A = cross-sectional area in m^2, L = initial length in m and $\boldsymbol{x}$ = extension in m. The units of the Young modulus are the same as stress (Nm^{-2} or Pa), since strain has no units.

Tip: The Young modulus is used by engineers to make sure their materials can withstand sufficient forces.

The Young modulus experiment

PRACTICAL ACTIVITY GROUP 2

Figure 1 shows an experiment you could use to find out the Young modulus of a metal:

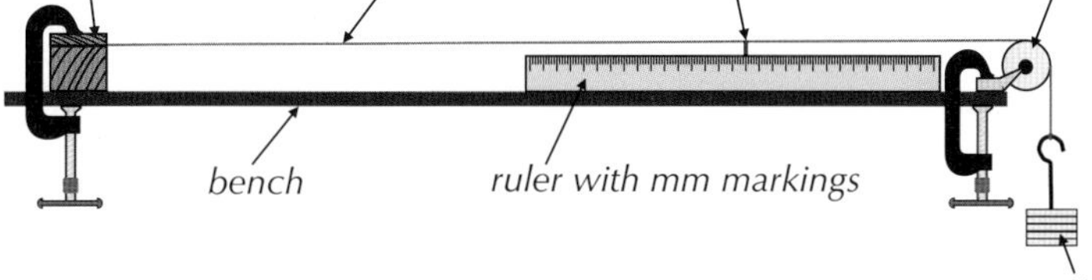

***Figure 1:** Experimental set-up for determining the Young modulus of a test metal.*

- The test wire should be thin, and as long as possible. The longer and thinner the wire, the more it extends for the same force — this reduces the uncertainty in your measurements.
- First you need to find the cross-sectional area of the wire. Use a micrometer to measure the diameter of the wire in several places and take an average of your measurements. By assuming that the cross-section is circular, you can use the formula for the area of a circle: Area = $\pi \times \text{radius}^2$.
- Clamp the wire to the bench (see Figure 1 above) so you can hang weights off one end of it. Start with the smallest weight necessary to straighten the wire. (Don't include this weight in your final calculations.)
- Record the starting position of the marker. Measure the distance between the fixed end of the wire and the marker — this is your unstretched length. Make sure you position yourself so that the marker and ruler are at eye level when measuring the position of the marker.

Tip: Do this experiment standing up so you can get out of the way quickly if the weights fall. And wear safety goggles in case the wire snaps. You should also do a full risk assessment before starting work.

Tip: You should do a pilot experiment in which you plot a force-extension graph for an identical piece of test wire to find its limit of proportionality. That way you can make sure you get nowhere near it in this experiment.

Tip: To reduce random errors you should use a thin marker on the wire.

Tip: Extensions can be very small, so you could use a travelling microscope to measure them more precisely than with a ruler.

- Then if you increase the weight, the wire stretches and the marker moves.
- Increase the weight in steps (e.g. 1 N intervals), recording the marker reading each time — the extension is the difference between this reading and the starting position of the marker. Use a mass meter or a set of digital scales to accurately find the weight you add at each step.
- You can use your results from this experiment to calculate the stress and strain of the wire and plot a stress-strain curve.

Tip: If you unload the wire, you can re-measure the extension for each weight to make sure you haven't gone past the wire's elastic limit.

Finding the Young modulus using a graph

You can plot a graph of stress against strain from your results — see Figure 3. The gradient of the graph gives the Young modulus, E.

$$E = \frac{\text{stress}}{\text{strain}} = \text{gradient}$$

Tip: You can also measure the Young modulus in the lab using Searle's apparatus. This is a bit more accurate, but it's harder to do and the equipment's more complicated.

Example — Maths Skills

The stress-strain graph below is for a thin metal wire. Find the Young modulus of the wire from the graph.

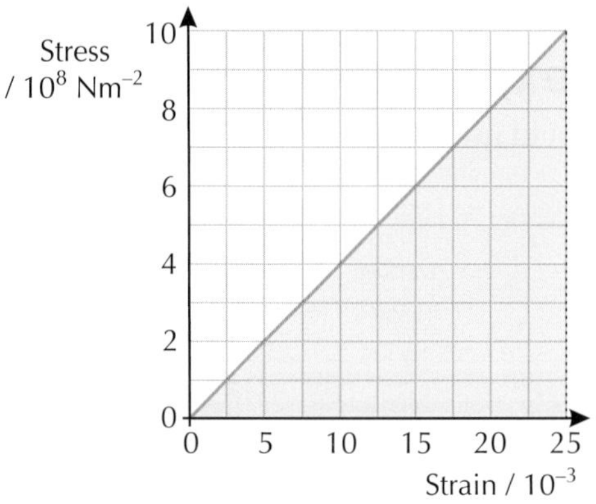

E = stress ÷ strain = gradient

$$\text{Gradient} = \frac{\Delta\text{stress}}{\Delta\text{strain}} = \frac{10 \times 10^8}{25 \times 10^{-3}} = \mathbf{4 \times 10^{10}\ Nm^{-2}}$$

Tip: Remember, when using the gradient to work out the Young modulus, you can only use it up to the limit of proportionality (p.108). After then, the stress and strain are no longer proportional.

Up to the elastic limit, the area under the graph gives the elastic potential energy stored per unit volume, i.e. the energy stored per 1 m^3 of wire.

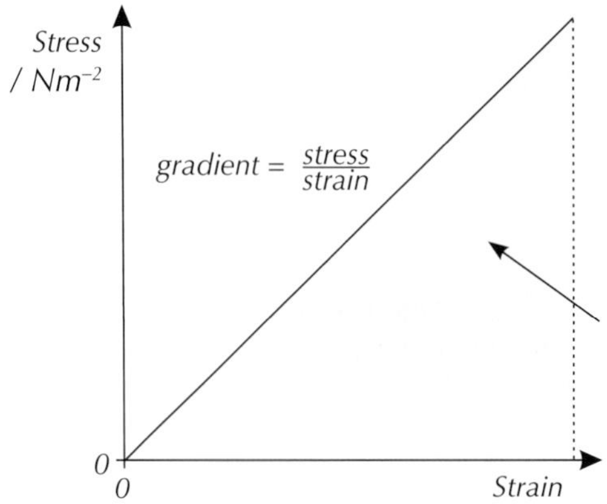

Figure 3: A stress-strain graph showing how to calculate the gradient and energy stored per unit volume.

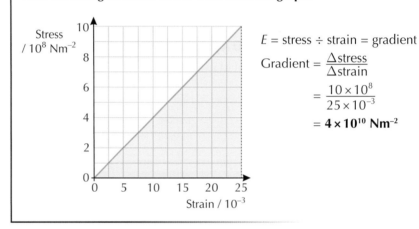

Figure 2: Steel has a high Young modulus, which means under huge stress there's only a small strain. This makes it a useful building material for things like bridges.

The stress-strain graph is a straight line provided that Hooke's law is obeyed, so up to the limit of proportionality you can also calculate the elastic potential energy per unit volume as:

$$\text{energy per unit volume} = \tfrac{1}{2}\sigma\varepsilon$$

Example — Maths Skills

A 1.2 metre long wire with a diameter of 2.0 cm stores 5.2 J when it is stretched. If the stress on the wire is 5.9 × 10^7 Nm^{-2}, calculate the strain on the wire. Assume the wire has not been stretched past its limit of proportionality.

First calculate the energy per unit volume:

$$\text{energy per unit volume} = \frac{5.2}{1.2 \times \pi \times (0.020 \div 2)^2} = 1.3793... \times 10^4 \text{ J m}^{-3}$$

Rearranging the formula above:

$$\varepsilon = \frac{2 \times \text{energy per unit volume}}{\sigma} = \frac{2 \times 1.3793... \times 10^4}{5.9 \times 10^7}$$

$$= 0.0004675... = \mathbf{4.7 \times 10^{-4}} \textbf{ (to 2 s.f.)}$$

Practice Questions — Application

Q1 a) A copper wire has an original length of 1.0 m and a diameter of 1.1 mm. What is the cross-sectional area of the wire?

b) A force of 23 N is applied to the wire and it extends by 0.20 mm. Find the Young modulus of copper.

Q2 A nylon wire with a cross-sectional area of 8.0 × 10^{-7} m^2 has a Young modulus of 3.5 × 10^8 Pa. A force of 100 N is applied to the wire.

a) Calculate the stress on the wire.

b) Calculate the strain on the wire.

Q3 A block with an initial length of 254 cm is compressed by 0.11 cm. The stress on the block is 4 200 000 m^{-2}. Assuming the block has not been deformed past its limit of proportionality, calculate the energy stored per unit volume by the block.

Tip: Don't forget to convert any lengths to m and areas to m^2 when working out the Young modulus.

Practice Questions — Fact Recall

Q1 What are the units of the Young modulus?

Q2 Name four things you would need to measure when carrying out an experiment to find the Young modulus of a wire.

Q3 Give one safety precaution you should take when carrying out an experiment to find the Young modulus of a wire.

Q4 What is the gradient of the linear part of a stress-strain graph equal to?

5. Stress-Strain Graphs

Learning Objective:

- Be able to interpret stress-strain graphs for typical ductile, brittle and polymeric materials.

Specification Reference 3.4.2

Because materials have different properties, their stress-strain graphs look different too — you need to know the graphs for ductile, brittle and polymeric materials.

Ductile materials

The diagram shows a stress-strain graph for a typical **ductile** material, such as copper. You can change the shape of ductile materials by drawing them into wires or other shapes. The important thing is that they keep their strength when they're deformed like this.

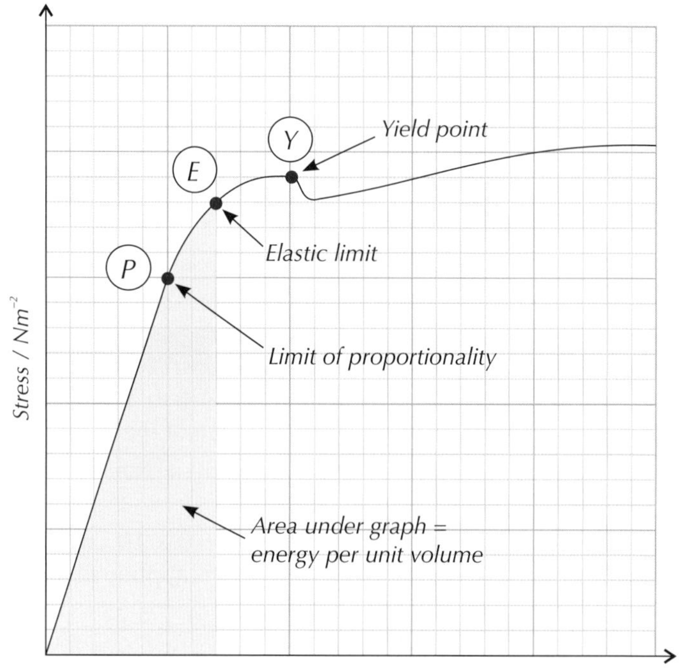

Figure 1: *A stress-strain graph for a typical ductile material.*

Before point P, the graph is a straight line through the origin. This shows that the material is obeying Hooke's law (page 106). The gradient of the line is constant — it's the Young modulus (see pages 117-118).

Point P is the limit of proportionality — after this, the graph starts to bend. At this point, the material stops obeying Hooke's law, but would still return to its original size and shape if the stress was removed.

Point E is the elastic limit — at this point the material starts to behave plastically. From point E onwards, the material would no longer return to its original size and shape once the stress was removed.

Point Y is the **yield point** — here the material suddenly starts to stretch without any extra load. The yield point (or yield stress) is the stress at which a large amount of plastic deformation takes place with a constant or reduced load.

The shaded area under the graph gives the energy stored in the material per unit volume (see page 118) up to the elastic limit.

Tip: Remember, these are different to force-extension graphs. Force-extension graphs are specific to the tested object and are affected by its dimensions. Stress-strain graphs describe the general behaviour of a material, because stress and strain are independent of the dimensions.

Tip: You can plot graphs like this from experiments like the one on p.117. From these graphs you can see if a material is behaving elastically or plastically.

Tip: Plastic deformation is useful if you don't want a material to return to its original shape, e.g. drawing copper into wires or gold into foil (see Figure 2).

Figure 2: *Rolls of gold foil being made at a factory.*

Brittle materials

Brittle materials don't deform plastically, but break when the stress on them reaches a certain point. Glass, ceramics and polystyrene are all brittle materials.

Below is a stress-strain graph typical of a brittle material. The stress-strain graph for a brittle material doesn't curve.

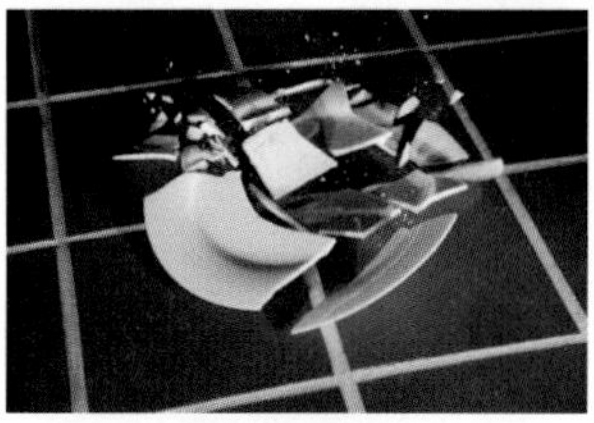
Figure 3: Ceramics are brittle materials.

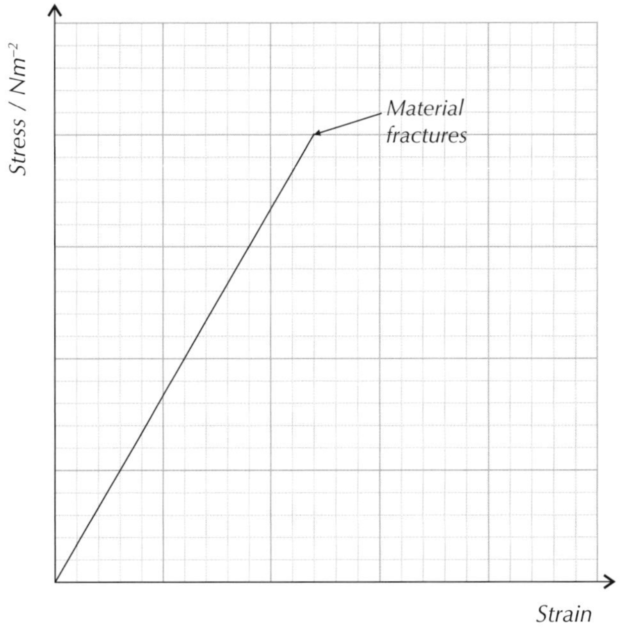

Figure 4: *A typical stress-strain graph for a brittle material.*

Tip: Notice how the straight line just stops. Very dramatic.

The graph starts with a straight line through the origin. So brittle materials also obey Hooke's law. However, when the stress reaches a certain point, the material snaps — it doesn't deform plastically.

Brittle materials can be quite weak if they have cracks. When stress is applied to a brittle material any tiny cracks at the material's surface get bigger and bigger until the material breaks completely. This is called brittle fracture.

Tip: It's not only brittle materials that fracture. Some materials will deform plastically up to a point, then fracture if the force is too great (see page 123).

Polymeric materials

The molecules that make up **polymeric** (or polymer) materials are arranged in long chains. They have a range of properties, so different polymers have different stress-strain graphs.

Polythene

Polythene is a common plastic, and is generally used in packaging. It is a ductile material that behaves plastically — applying a stress to it stretches it into a new shape.

Tip: You might also see polythene referred to as polyethylene.

Figure 5: Polythene is often used to make bottles and containers as it's more resistant to breakage than brittle alternatives like glass.

Figure 6 shows the stress-strain graph for polythene.

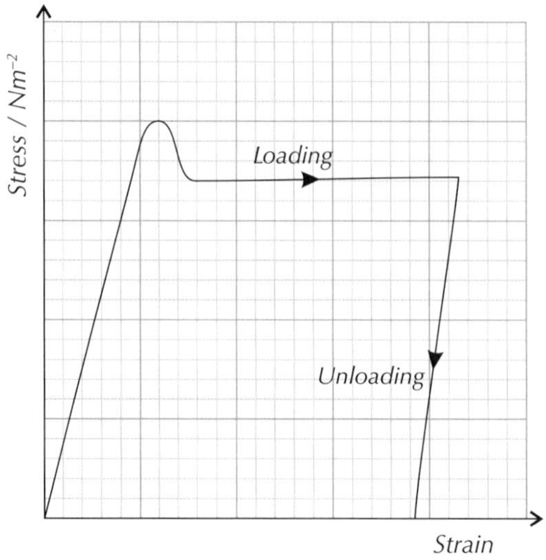

Figure 6: A typical stress-strain graph for polythene.

The graphs starts with a straight line through the origin, as polythene initially obeys Hooke's Law. When the load is increased past its elastic limit, the polythene begins to deform plastically. The graph doesn't return to the origin so the polythene is permanently deformed into a new shape.

Rubber

Rubber is another polymeric material but it behaves differently to polythene. Figure 8 shows a typical stress-strain graph for rubber.

Figure 7: Rubber is used in the manufacture of tyres. Some of the energy transferred to the tyres by bumps in the road is transferred to thermal energy, making the ride less bouncy.

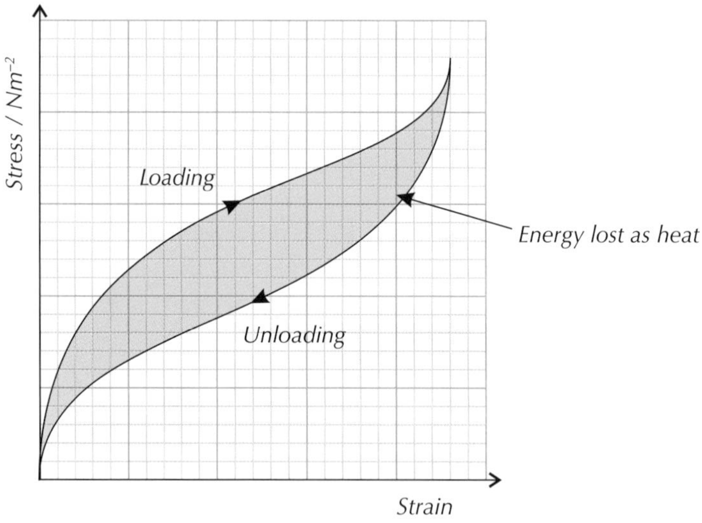

Figure 8: A typical stress-strain graph for rubber.

Rubber returns to its original length when the load is removed — it behaves elastically.

The loading and unloading curves for rubber are different. The energy released when the rubber is unloaded is less than the work done to stretch the rubber. This is because some of the elastic potential energy stored in the stretched rubber is converted to heat.

The amount of energy converted to heat per unit volume is given by the area between the loading and unloading curves.

Tip: Try repeatedly stretching and releasing a rubber band. You should feel it get hotter.

Material properties

It's useful to be able to describe how materials behave under stress so that materials with different properties can be easily compared in areas such as construction and manufacturing. For example, a material that can withstand high stress before deforming may be desirable when building the foundations for a house, but you wouldn't use it for stuffing soft furnishings.

You've already seen that if the stress on a material becomes to great, the material can break (p.115). The **strength** of a material is a measure of its ability to withstand stress without breaking. The stronger the material, the higher its ultimate tensile strength. Materials with a very low ultimate tensile strength are described as being weak.

Stiffness is a measure of how much a material can resist deformation in response to stress. Stiff materials are difficult to stretch or compress, so they have a large Young's modulus. For a given stress, a stiff material will have a lower strain (i.e. a smaller extension) than a less stiff material.

A stiff material doesn't have to be strong (and vice versa). Some stiff materials, such as polystyrene, break under a low stress, and some strong materials aren't very stiff.

Figure 9 shows the stress-strain curves for materials of different strengths and stiffnesses.

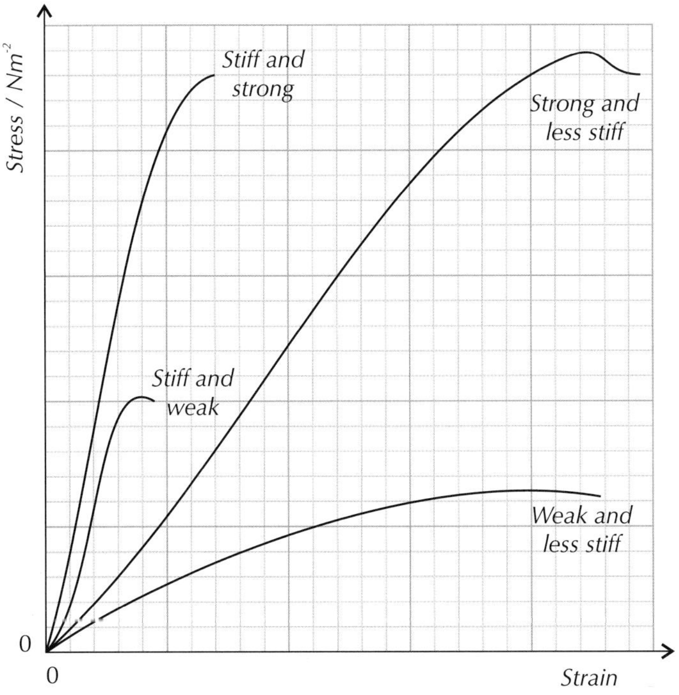

Figure 9: *Stress-strain curves for different materials.*

Stiff materials have a steep gradient on a stress-strain graph, as they show very little strain under stress, while less stiff materials have a shallower gradient. Stress-strain curves for strong materials end at a higher stress than weak materials.

Exam Tip
You might be asked about why a given material is appropriate, or inappropriate, for a specific purpose. Think carefully about the properties of the material and how it might behave under the forces required.

Exam Tip
When a line on a stress-strain graph just stops, you can assume the material has reached its breaking stress and fractured (unless the question says otherwise).

Practice Questions — Application

Q1 The diagram below shows a stress-strain graph for a material with three important points marked on it.

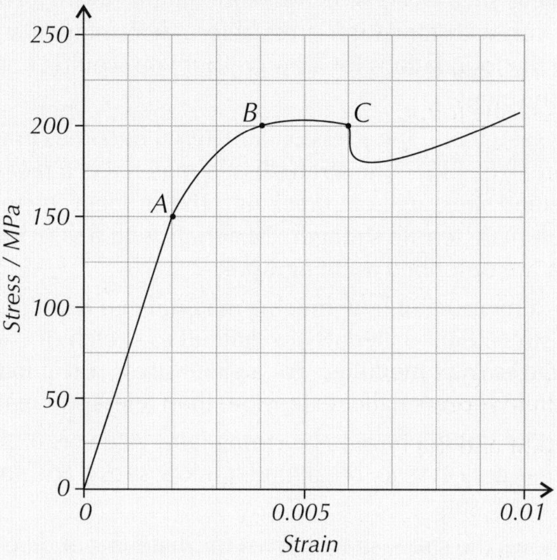

a) After point B the material starts to deform plastically. Give the name of point B.

b) What law does the material obey between the origin and point A?

c) Which point on the graph marks the yield point of the material?

d) Find the Young modulus of the material.

e) Calculate the elastic potential energy stored per unit volume in the material up to the limit of proportionality.

Tip: Think about the features of both lines.

Q2 The graph to the right is a stress-strain graph for two different materials.

Which line, A or B, shows a brittle material? Explain your answer.

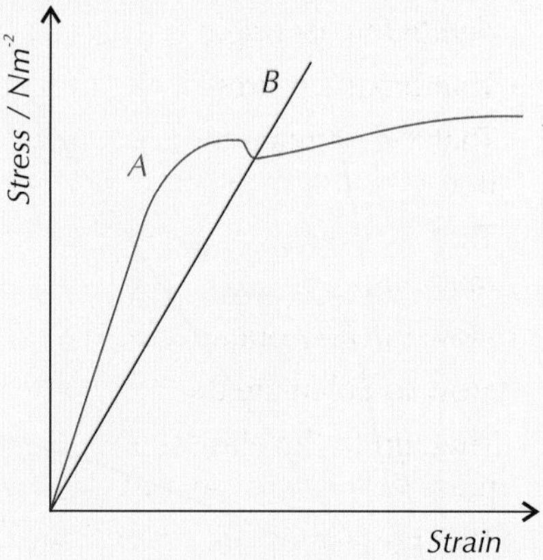

Practice Questions — Fact Recall

Q1 What is the yield point of a material?

Q2 Give one example of a polymeric material.

Q3 Do brittle materials obey Hooke's law? Explain your answer.

Section Summary

Make sure you know...

- What is meant by the terms extension and compression.
- What is meant by the terms tensile deformation and compressive deformation.
- That Hooke's law states that the extension of an object is proportional to the load or force applied to it.
- How to use the formula for Hooke's law, $\boldsymbol{F} = k\boldsymbol{x}$, where k is the force constant of an object.
- That the force constant, k, is the force needed to extend an object that obeys Hooke's Law by 1 m, and it has units of Nm^{-1}.
- How to combine the force constants of individual objects in series or parallel to find the overall force constant of the system.
- That the limit of proportionality of an object is the maximum force that can be applied to an object before it no longer obeys Hooke's Law.
- How to investigate the force-extension characteristics for objects (or arrangements of objects), which may include springs, rubber bands and polythene strips.
- How to plot and interpret force-extension (or compression) graphs for springs and wires.
- That the elastic limit of an object is the maximum force that can be applied to an object before it permanently changes shape.
- That if a material deforms elastically, it will return to its original shape when the force applied to it is removed, but if it deforms plastically, it will permanently change shape.
- That the area under a force-extension (or compression) graph is equal to the work done.
- That all the work done stretching a material elastically is stored as elastic potential energy.
- How to calculate elastic potential energy using $E = \frac{1}{2}\boldsymbol{F}\boldsymbol{x}$ and $E = \frac{1}{2}k\boldsymbol{x}^2$.
- That the tensile stress of a material, σ, is measured in Nm^{-2} or Pa and is defined as the force applied to the material, $\boldsymbol{F}$, divided by its cross-sectional area, A.
- That the tensile strain of a material, ε, has no units and is defined as the extension of the material, $\boldsymbol{x}$, divided by its original length, L.
- That breaking stress is the stress experienced by a material at the point it breaks.
- That the ultimate tensile strength of a material is the maximum stress a material can experience before it will break.
- That the Young modulus of a material is the ratio of stress to strain, and is characteristic of that material.
- How to carry out an investigation to find the Young modulus of a material.
- How to calculate the Young modulus for materials from their stress-strain graphs.
- That, up to the elastic limit, the area under a stress-strain graph is equal to the material's elastic potential energy per unit volume.
- That the energy per unit volume for a deformed object can be calculated up to its limit of proportionality using the formula: energy per unit volume = $\frac{1}{2}\sigma\varepsilon$
- That a ductile material is a material which maintains its strength when it is deformed, and how to interpret the stress-strain graph of a typical ductile material.
- That a brittle material is a material which breaks before it can undergo plastic deformation, and how to interpret the stress-strain graph of a typical brittle material.
- How to interpret typical stress-strain graphs of polymeric materials such as polythene and rubber.
- That the strength of a material is a measure of how large a stress it can withstand before breaking.
- That the stiffness of a material is a measure of how resistant it is to deformation while under stress.

Exam-style Questions

1 The diagram below shows a force-extension graph for a rubber cord. Curve *A* shows loading and curve *B* shows unloading of the cord.

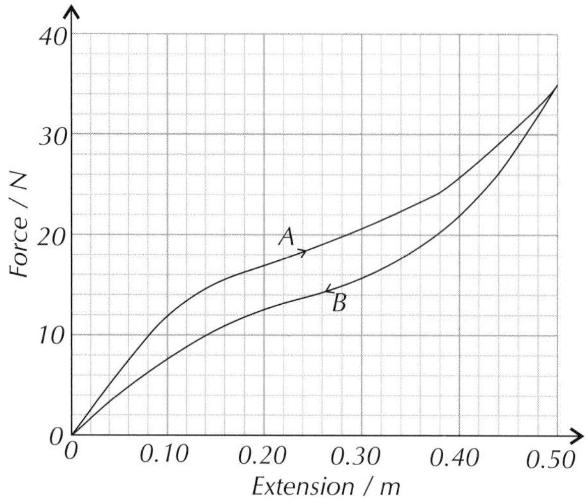

The rubber cord has a cross-sectional area of 5.0×10^{-6} m^2 and had an initial length of 0.80 m.

What is the Young modulus for the material at an extension of 0.080 m? Assume that curve *A* is linear for small loads.

A 1.2×10^5 Pa

B 2.0×10^5 Pa

C 1.2×10^7 Pa

D 2.0×10^7 Pa

(1 mark)

2 A spring is used in a pen as part of the mechanism which opens and closes it. The spring is compressed elastically by 5.0 mm when a user pushes it down with a force of 1.1 N. Calculate the elastic potential energy stored by the spring when it is compressed by 18 mm.

A 0.036 J

B 7.1 J

C 36 J

D 0.071 J

(1 mark)

3 A piano manufacturer wants to find the Young modulus of a sample of piano wire.

(a)* Describe an experimental method that the piano manufacturer could use to find the Young modulus of the piano wire.
Your answer should include:

- a labelled diagram
- a discussion of ways to reduce the effect of errors on the results

(6 marks)

(b) **Fig. 3.1** shows the stress and strain on the piano wire as it was stretched.

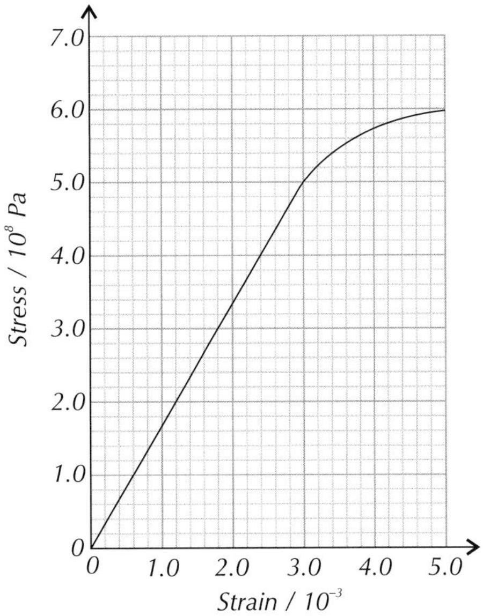

Fig. 3.1

Use the graph to calculate the Young modulus of the wire.
Give your answer in an appropriate unit.

(2 marks)

(c) If the wire has an initial length of 1.6 m and a cross-sectional area of 1.0×10^{-7} m^2, calculate how much elastic potential energy is stored by the wire at a stress of 3.0×10^8 Pa.

(3 marks)

4 A chandelier is used as part of the scenery for a stage show.

(a) The chandelier is suspended from the ceiling above the stage by a 2.0 m steel cable. The tension in the cable will be 2.0 kN and it must not extend more than 0.20 mm. The Young modulus for steel is 2.10×10^{11} Pa.

Calculate the minimum cross-sectional area the cable should have, in m^2.

(2 marks)

(b) As part of the show, the chandelier falls to the floor and shatters.
The chandelier is made from a brittle material that will break under a low stress.

The Young modulus for the material is 6.0×10^{10} Nm^{-2}, and it has a breaking stress of 3.0×10^7 Nm^{-2}. Draw the stress-strain graph for this material.

(3 marks)

* The quality of your response will be assessed in this question.

Learning Objectives:
- Know Newton's three laws of motion.
- Know that net force is equal to the rate of change of momentum, $F = \frac{\Delta p}{\Delta t}$.

Specification Reference 3.5.1

1. Newton's Laws of Motion

Newton's laws of motion describe the relationship between the forces acting on an object and its motion. You might have already met these ideas at GCSE — they're really important in mechanics, so they crop up a lot in physics.

Newton's 1st law of motion

Newton's 1st law of motion states that:

"The velocity of an object will not change unless a resultant force acts on it."

This means a body will stay still or move in a straight line at a constant speed, unless there's a resultant force acting on it. If the forces acting on a body aren't balanced, the overall resultant force will make the body accelerate. This could be a change in direction, speed, or both (see Newton's 2nd law below).

Figure 1: Sir Isaac Newton, the British physicist who devised the three laws of motion still used in modern mechanics.

Example

An apple sitting on a table won't go anywhere because the forces on it are balanced.

reaction (R) (force of table pushing apple up) = **weight** (mg) (force of gravity pulling apple down)

Newton's 2nd law of motion

Newton's 2nd law of motion says that the rate of change of momentum of an object is equal to the net force which acts on the object.
This can be written as the equation:

$$F = \frac{\Delta p}{\Delta t}$$

F = net force (in N)

$\frac{\Delta p}{\Delta t}$ = rate of change of momentum (in kg ms^{-1})

Tip: There's more on this equation on p.135.

Exam Tip
This equation crops up all over the place in physics, so make sure you know how to use it.

Try to remember:
- The net force is the vector sum of all the forces (page 72).
- The net force is always measured in newtons.
- The mass is always measured in kilograms.
- The change in momentum is always in the same direction as the net force and is measured in kg ms^{-1}.

Tip: Momentum (p) is covered on page 131.

In the special case where mass is constant, Newton's 2nd Law can be written as the well-known equation:

$$F = m \times a$$

F = *net force (in N)*

m = *mass (in kg)*

a = *acceleration (in ms^{-2})*

This equation says that the more force you have acting on a certain mass, the more acceleration you get. It also says that for a given force, the more mass you have, the less acceleration you get.

But, if the mass of the object is changing, such as if it is accelerating at close to the speed of light, then you can't use $F = ma$. (You don't need to know why the mass changes in this case.) Newton's 2nd law still applies, it's just that the 'rate of change of momentum' bit refers to a change in mass and velocity.

Tip: Momentum depends on mass and velocity (p.131). As long as v isn't close to the speed of light, an object's mass is constant so momentum only depends on velocity.

Example — Maths Skills

Sarah is playing hockey. The ball is coming towards her at a speed of 4.6 ms^{-1}. She hits it so that it travels in the opposite direction at a speed of 10.2 ms^{-1}. Her stick is in contact with the ball for 0.84 seconds. The ball has a mass of 161 g.
Calculate the average force exerted on the ball during this time.

You'll need to use $F = ma$, so first calculate a:

$$a = \frac{\Delta v}{\Delta t} = \frac{10.2 - (-4.6)}{0.84} = \frac{14.8}{0.84} = 17.619...\ \text{ms}^{-2}$$

$m = 161\ \text{g} = 0.161\ \text{kg}$, so:

$F = 0.161 \times 17.619... = 2.836... = 2.84\ \text{N}$ (to 3 s.f.)

Tip: The ball reverses direction, so you need to give one of the velocities a negative value. Choose whichever makes the maths easier.

Newton's 3rd law of motion

There are a few different ways of stating **Newton's 3rd law**, but the clearest way is:

"If object A exerts a force on object B, then object B exerts an equal but opposite force on object A."

You'll also hear the law as "every action has an equal and opposite reaction". But this can wrongly sound like the forces are both applied to the same object. (If that were the case, you'd get a resultant force of zero and nothing would ever move anywhere.)

The two forces actually represent the same interaction, just seen from two different perspectives:

- If you push against a wall, the wall will push back against you, just as hard. As soon as you stop pushing, so does the wall.
- If you pull a cart, whatever force you exert on the rope, the rope exerts the exact opposite pull on you.
- When you go swimming, you push back against the water with your arms and legs, and the water pushes you forwards with an equal-sized force.

Newton's 3rd law applies in all situations and to all types of force. But the pairs of forces are always the same type, e.g. both gravitational or both electrical. Sometimes it looks like Newton's 3rd law is being applied, but it's not.

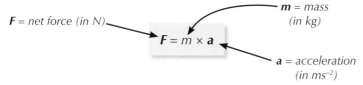

Figure 2: *A swimmer moves forwards because the water pushes back against them, as they push against the water.*

Tip: In this example, the resultant force is zero and the acceleration is zero, which is an example of Newton's Second Law.

Example

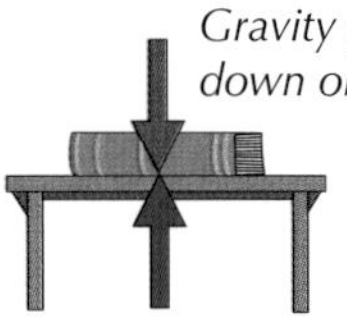
Gravity pulls down on book
Table pushes upwards on book

Both forces are acting on the book, and they're not of the same type. These are two separate interactions. The forces are equal and opposite, resulting in zero acceleration, so this is an example of Newton's First Law.

Practice Questions — Application

Q1 Draw a diagram showing what forces are acting on a ball when it's at rest on the ground.

Q2 A rocket burns through its fuel stores to accelerate upwards. Explain why you cannot use $F = ma$ to calculate the net force on the rocket in this case.

Q3 Why does a bird lift into the air when it flaps its wings?

Q4 A car is pulling a caravan behind it at a constant speed. The additional resistive force acting on the system due to the caravan at this speed is 780 N. The link between the car and the caravan breaks and they separate. The car immediately begins to accelerate at 0.41 ms^{-2}. Calculate the mass of the car.

Q5 Two ice skaters of mass 55.0 kg and 60.0 kg push against each other. The heavier ice skater accelerates away at 2.3 ms^{-2}. What will the magnitude of the lighter ice skater's acceleration be?

Exam Tip
Using ice skaters is a common way of saying there's no friction involved — the only force is from where they push against each other.

Practice Question — Fact Recall

Q1 State Newton's three laws of motion, and briefly explain what they mean.

2. Momentum

Momentum is how much 'oomph' an object has, and the direction in which the 'oomph' acts. When objects collide, their overall momentum is conserved.

What is momentum?

The **linear momentum** of an object depends on two things — its mass and velocity. The product of these two values is the momentum of the object.

$$\mathbf{p} = m \times \mathbf{v}$$

p *= linear momentum in kgms^{-1}*

v *= velocity in ms^{-1}*

m *= mass in kg*

The word 'linear' means that the momentum acts in a straight line. You'll often see it just called momentum. Momentum and velocity are vectors (see page 34), so you need to remember to think about direction when doing calculations.

Example — Maths Skills

A water balloon of volume 4.2×10^{-3} m^3 is thrown at a speed of 8.5 ms^{-1}. If water has density 1.0×10^3 kgm^{-3} and the rubber balloon itself has mass 12 g, calculate the balloon's total momentum.

Before you can calculate the balloon's total momentum, you need to work out the mass of the water.

Rearranging $\rho = \frac{m}{V}$:

$m = \rho V = 1.0 \times 10^3 \times 4.2 \times 10^{-3} = 4.2$ kg

Linear momentum = mass × velocity

= (mass of water + mass of balloon) × velocity

= $(4.2 + 0.012) \times 8.5 = 35.802 = 36$ kgms^{-1} (to 2 s.f.)

The principle of conservation of momentum

Assuming no external forces act, linear momentum is always conserved. This means the total linear momentum of two objects before they collide equals the total linear momentum after the collision. This can be used to work out the velocity of objects after a collision.

Example — Maths Skills

A skater of mass 75 kg and velocity 4.0 ms^{-1} collides with a stationary skater of mass 55 kg. The two skaters join together and move off in the same direction. Calculate their velocity *v* after impact.

***Figure 2:** The skaters, before and after the collision.*

Momentum before = Momentum after

$(75 \times 4.0) + (55 \times 0) = 130\mathbf{v}$

$300 = 130\mathbf{v}$

So $\mathbf{v} = 2.307...$

$= 2.3$ ms^{-1} (to 2 s.f.)

Learning Objectives:

- Be able to calculate linear momentum; $\mathbf{p} = m\mathbf{v}$.
- Understand the vector nature of momentum.
- Know the principle of conservation of momentum.
- Be able to solve collision problems in one dimension and in two dimensions.
- Understand the meaning of a perfectly elastic collision and an inelastic collision.

Specification References 3.5.1 and 3.5.2

Tip: The other kind of momentum is 'angular momentum', but you don't need to know about that for now.

Tip: See page 87 for more on density.

Tip: In the example the positive direction was taken to be the direction in which the balloon was thrown. If you took the opposite direction as the positive, the balloon would have a negative momentum.

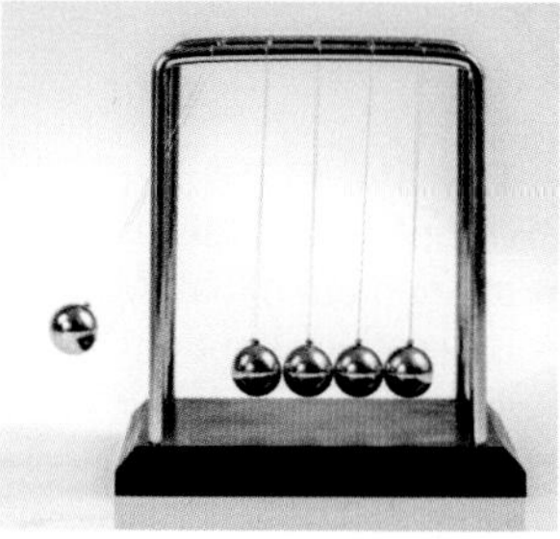

***Figure 1:** Linear momentum is conserved in a Newton's cradle. When the first ball strikes and stops, the last ball moves off with an equal momentum.*

The same principle can be applied in situations that don't involve a collision, like explosions. For example, if you fire an air rifle, the forward momentum gained by the pellet is equal in magnitude to the backward momentum of the rifle, and you feel the rifle recoiling into your shoulder.

Example — Maths Skills

A bullet of mass 0.0050 kg is shot from a rifle at a speed of 220 ms^{-1}. The rifle has a mass of 4.0 kg. Calculate the velocity at which the rifle recoils.

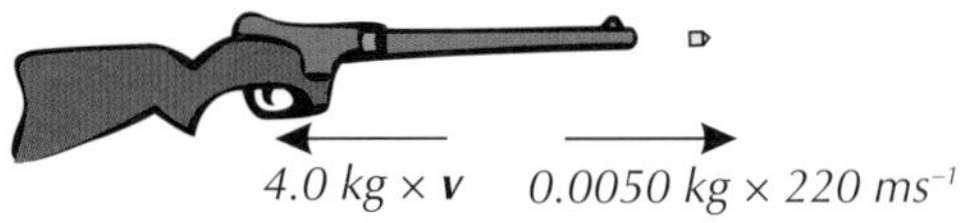

Figure 3: *The rifle and bullet after the explosion.*

Momentum before explosion = Momentum after explosion

$$0 = (0.0050 \times 220) + (4.0 \times \boldsymbol{v})$$
$$0 = 1.1 + 4.0\boldsymbol{v}$$
$$\boldsymbol{v} = -0.275 = -0.28 \text{ ms}^{-1} \text{ (to 2 s.f.)}$$

Tip: There was no momentum before the explosion, so after the explosion both the rifle and the bullet must have the same magnitude of momentum, but in opposite directions. The rifle has a much smaller final velocity than the bullet because it's got a much greater mass.

In reality, collisions and explosions usually happen in more than one dimension. In two-dimensional collisions, momentum is conserved in both dimensions. You can solve two-dimensional collision problems by resolving vectors (see page 36).

Exam Tip
Two-dimensional problems like this will only be in your exam if you're taking the full A-level course.

Example — Maths Skills

Ball A collides with stationary ball B, as shown in Figure 4.
After the collision, the two balls move off in different directions.
Ball A has a mass of 40 g. Calculate the mass, *m*, of ball B.

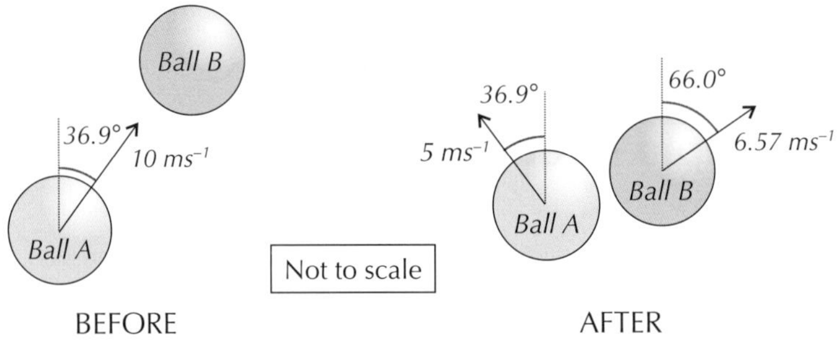

Figure 4: *Balls A and B before and after the collision.*

You can work this out using conservation of momentum in just the horizontal direction (or just the vertical). Start by picking the positive direction — let's say right is positive.

horizontal momentum before the collision
= horizontal momentum after the collision

$$(0.04 \times 10\sin 36.9°) + (m \times 0)$$
$$= -(0.04 \times 5\sin 36.9°) + (m \times 6.57\sin 66.0°)$$

$$\text{so, } m = \frac{0.04 \times (10\sin 36.9° + 5\sin 36.9°)}{6.57\sin 66.0°} = 0.0600... \text{ kg}$$
$$= 60 \text{ g (to 2 s.f.)}$$

Tip: The horizontal component of the momentum of ball A is negative after the collision — it's to the left.

Tip: You could check your answer by doing the same calculation for the vertical direction.

Elastic and inelastic collisions

An **elastic collision** is one where momentum is conserved and **kinetic energy** is conserved — i.e. no energy is dissipated as heat, sound, etc. Kinetic energy is the energy that an object has due to its motion. You saw on page 98 that the equation for kinetic energy is:

$$E_K = \frac{1}{2}mv^2$$

E_K = kinetic energy in J

v = velocity in ms^{-1}

m = mass in kg

Tip: Elastic collisions are sometimes called 'perfectly elastic'.

Tip: Collisions between gas particles are elastic, otherwise air would get colder and colder until there was no motion left.

Example — Maths Skills

A bowling ball of mass 5.00 kg is travelling at a velocity of 5.00 ms^{-1} when it collides with a stationary bowling ball of mass 3.00 kg. The velocity of the lighter ball after the collision is 6.25 ms^{-1} in the same direction as the heavier ball before the collision. Show that the collision is elastic.

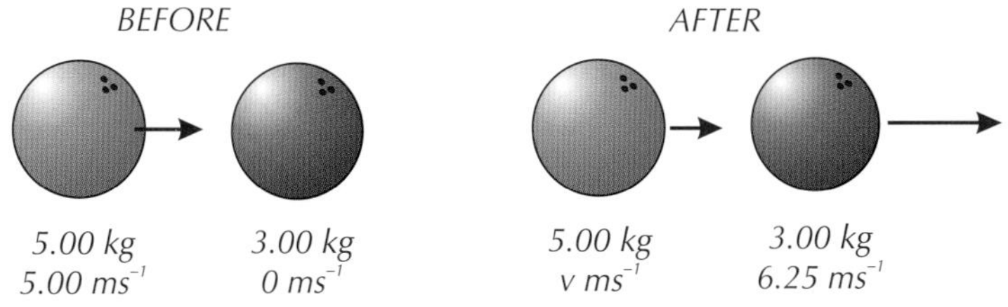

Figure 5: *The balls, before and after the collision.*

Momentum is conserved, so momentum before = momentum after.

$$(5.00 \times 5.00) + (3.00 \times 0) = (5.00 \times \boldsymbol{v}) + (3.00 \times 6.25)$$
$$25 = 5\boldsymbol{v} + 18.75$$
$$\boldsymbol{v} = 1.25\ ms^{-1}$$

Check to see if kinetic energy is conserved:

Kinetic energy before = $(\frac{1}{2} \times 5.00 \times 5.00^2) + (\frac{1}{2} \times 3.00 \times 0^2) = 62.5$ J

Kinetic energy after = $(\frac{1}{2} \times 5.00 \times 1.25^2) + (\frac{1}{2} \times 3.00 \times 6.25^2) = 62.5$ J

So total kinetic energy is conserved in the collision — therefore this is an elastic collision.

Exam Tip
Before you start a momentum calculation, always draw a quick sketch of the relevant objects, before and after the collision — then it's much easier to figure out what's going on.

If a collision is **inelastic**, it means that some of the kinetic energy is converted into other forms during the collision. Linear momentum is always conserved in inelastic collisions though.

Figure 6: *A dropped ball loses energy to heat and sound when it collides inelastically with the floor, and rebounds to a lower height.*

Figure 7: *In the real world, most collisions are at least slightly inelastic. These billiard balls will lose energy as sound when they collide.*

Example — Maths Skills

A toy lorry (mass 2.00 kg) travelling at 3.00 ms^{-1} crashes into a toy car (mass 0.800 kg), travelling in the same direction at 2.00 ms^{-1}. The velocity of the lorry after the collision is 2.60 ms^{-1} in the same direction. Calculate the new velocity of the car and the total kinetic energy before and after the collision.

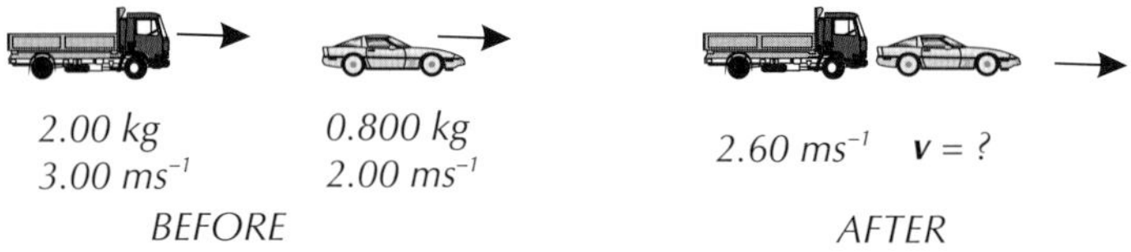

Figure 8: *The toy lorry and car, before and after the collision.*

Momentum is conserved, so:
Momentum before collision = Momentum after collision

$$(2.00 \times 3.00) + (0.800 \times 2.00) = (2.00 \times 2.60) + (0.800 \times \boldsymbol{v})$$

$$7.60 = 5.20 + 0.800\boldsymbol{v}$$

$$2.40 = 0.800\boldsymbol{v}$$

$$\boldsymbol{v} = 2.40 \div 0.800 = 3.00 \text{ ms}^{-1}$$

Kinetic energy before = E_k of lorry + E_k of car
= $\frac{1}{2}m\boldsymbol{v}^2$ (lorry) + $\frac{1}{2}m\boldsymbol{v}^2$ (car)
= $\frac{1}{2}(2.00 \times 3.00^2) + \frac{1}{2}(0.800 \times 2.00^2)$
= 10.6 J

Kinetic energy after = $\frac{1}{2}(2.00 \times 2.60^2) + \frac{1}{2}(0.800 \times 3.00^2)$
= 10.36 = 10.4 J (to 3 s.f.)

The difference in the two values is the amount of kinetic energy dissipated as heat, sound, or in damaging the vehicles — so this is an inelastic collision.

Practice Questions — Application

Q1 A man sitting in a stationary boat throws a 1.0 kg rock horizontally out of the boat at 10 ms^{-1}. If the total mass of the man and boat is 125 kg, how fast will the boat move in the opposite direction to the rock?

Q2 An ice hockey puck of mass 165 g has a velocity 2.25 ms^{-1} (in the positive direction) when it collides with an identical puck moving at 4.75 ms^{-1} in the opposite (negative) direction. If the first puck has a final velocity of –4.25 ms^{-1}, calculate the final velocity of the second puck. Is this an elastic or inelastic collision?

Q3 The nozzle of a fire hose has cross-sectional area 5.6 × 10^{-4} m^2 and shoots water at a rate of 8.4 ×10^{-3} m^{3}s^{-1}. Find the momentum of the water leaving the hose, if water has a density of 1000 kgm^{-3} (to 2 s.f.).

Tip: If you're struggling with Q3, first find the mass of water that leaves the hose every second, then find how fast the water leaves the nozzle.

Practice Questions — Fact Recall

Q1 What is the equation used to calculate linear momentum?

Q2 What is the principle of conservation of momentum?

Q3 What is the difference between a perfectly elastic and an inelastic collision?

3. Impulse and Vehicle Safety

Impulse is just a word for the change in momentum of a body. You can work it out if you know the average force acting on a body and the time it acts over.

Learning Objectives:

- Know what is meant by the impulse of a force and be able to calculate it using: impulse = $F\Delta t$.
- Know that impulse is equal to the area under a force-time graph.

Specification Reference 3.5.1

Calculating impulse

Newton's Second Law can be rearranged to give:

$$F\Delta t = \Delta p$$

The **impulse** of a force is defined as the product of average force and time:

$$\text{impulse} = F\Delta t$$

So, the impulse on a body is equal to the change in momentum of that body.

$F\Delta t$ = *impulse in Ns* → $F\Delta t = \Delta p$ ← Δp = *change in momentum in kg ms⁻¹*

Tip: Impulse is only talking about the change of momentum of one of the objects, whilst conservation of momentum applies to the whole system. So the impulse of an object can change although momentum is conserved.

Example — Maths Skills

A stationary golf ball of mass 45 g is hit with a club. The club provides an average force of 1200 N on the ball, causing the ball to travel at a speed of 25 ms^{-1}. Calculate the time the club was in contact with the ball for.

First calculate the change in momentum of the ball:

$\Delta p = \Delta(mv) = m\Delta v = 0.045 \times (25 - 0) = 1.125 \text{ kg ms}^{-1}$

Rearranging $F\Delta t = \Delta p$:

$\Delta t = \frac{\Delta p}{F} = \frac{1.125}{1200} = 0.0009375 = 0.94 \text{ ms (to 2 s.f.)}$

Impulse is the area under a force-time graph — this is really handy for solving problems where the force changes.

Tip: For improved accuracy, you could use a spreadsheet to plot your *F*–*t* graph and calculate the area underneath it.

Example — Maths Skills

The graph shows the resultant force acting on a toy car.
If the car is initially at rest, calculate the impulse given to the car over the first 3 seconds.

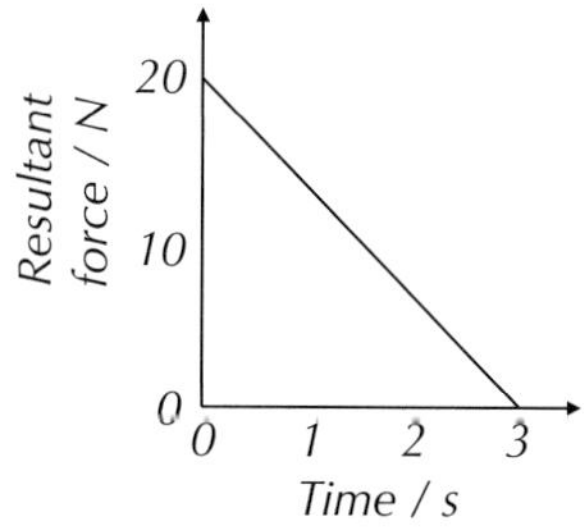

Figure 1: *Graph of resultant force against time.*

Impulse is the area under the graph, so you need to find the area under the graph between 0 and 3 s.

Area under graph = $\frac{1}{2} \times 3 \times 20 = 30$ Ns

For more complicated force-time graphs, you might need to estimate the area under the graph by counting squares or approximating curves as straight lines (see page 246).

Impact forces

Since force is equal to rate of change of momentum — remember $\boldsymbol{F} = \frac{\Delta \boldsymbol{p}}{\Delta t}$, the force of an impact can be reduced by increasing the time of the impact. Similarly, the force can be increased by reducing the impact time.

Tip: The same is true in many other sports — for example, the shorter the impact time between a bat and ball, the greater the force.

Examples

- The less time your foot is in contact with a football when kicking it, the more force you will kick it with (assuming the change in momentum is the same).
- Packaging for fragile objects is designed to reduce the magnitude of any impact forces during transport or storage. The packaging takes longer to deform on impact, and so absorbs the shock and protects the packaged object.

Figure 2: Egg boxes are designed to reduce the impact on the eggs if they're dropped. The packaging crumples, increasing the impact time.

Vehicle design

HOW SCIENCE WORKS

When a car crashes, there is a big change in speed — possibly from 70 mph (about 110 km h^{-1}) to zero. This means there is a big change in momentum, and potentially large forces, which can injure passengers. Modern vehicle safety features are designed using the fact that the force of an impact can be reduced by increasing the time of the impact.

Tip: Understanding the forces involved in road collisions has saved many lives — it's estimated that the three-point seat belt alone has saved over a million lives worldwide in the last 50 years.

Examples

- **Crumple zones**
  These are areas at the front and rear of a car that are designed to crumple on impact. They absorb some of the car's kinetic energy when they deform, which would otherwise be transferred to the passengers and whatever the car had collided with. They also increase the time taken for the car to slow down, which reduces the forces acting on passengers and whatever the car has hit.
- **Seat belts**
  Seat belts are designed to stretch slightly. They protect wearers in a crash in a number of ways. They hold the wearer in place in the car, stopping them from being thrown from their seats. They also absorb some of the wearer's kinetic energy by stretching and increase the time that the wearer comes to a stop over, Δt (again, by stretching).
- **Air bags**
  Air bags are 'cushions' in the dashboard and elsewhere that inflate very quickly on collision. They protect the passengers by making passengers slow down more gradually (increasing Δt) and by stopping passengers from hitting the dashboard, steering wheel, etc. during a crash.

Figure 3: Cars have specially designed 'crumple zones' that extend the time of a collision. This reduces the force experienced by the car and occupants.

Tip: There's more about material deformation over on page 111.

Example — Maths Skills

Giles's car bumps into the back of a stationary bus. The car was travelling at 2 ms^{-1} and comes to a stop in 0.20 s. Giles was wearing his seatbelt and takes 0.80 s to stop. Giles's mass is 75 kg.

a) **Calculate the average force acting on Giles during the accident.**

$F = \frac{\Delta p}{\Delta t}$ So, for Giles: $F = \frac{(75 \times 2) - (75 \times 0)}{0.80} = 187.5$

$= 190$ N (to 2 s.f.)

b) **Calculate the average force that would have acted on Giles if he had stopped as quickly as the car.**

Again, $F = \frac{\Delta p}{\Delta t}$ but $\Delta t = 0.20$ s. So: $F = \frac{(75 \times 2) - (75 \times 0)}{0.20}$

$= 750$ N

Early cars didn't have many safety features in the event of a crash. But as cars became faster and the number of cars on the roads increased, car manufacturers started to think about how to make cars safer. This led to the development of the three-point seat belt, crumple zones and air bags back in the 1950s.

At the same time, engineers were developing better ways of understanding the forces acting on passengers in a collision. They developed increasingly sophisticated crash test dummies that could measure all the forces that different passengers experience in different kinds of collisions. Crash tests also allowed car manufacturers to test the effectiveness of certain safety features, so they could see how much they reduced the likelihood of injury.

Wearing a seat belt is now mandatory (everyone has to do it), and features such as crumple zones and air bags have become standard features of modern cars (along with many more sophisticated safety features).

Figure 4: *Crash test dummies are used in simulations to model the effects of a collision on a human body.*

The risks of car safety features

Seat belts can cause bruising during a crash. They can also be dangerous for small children — if the top part of the belt lies across the child's neck this can cause injury in a crash, and if the child is too small for a seat belt it may not secure them properly. In the UK, children must use booster seats or cushions to reduce these risks.

Air bags are designed for use with seat belts and can be dangerous if you're not wearing one. Air bags inflate very rapidly, with a lot of force. If a passenger seat belt isn't secured properly then the passenger can keep moving forwards quickly as the car slows down. They could hit the air bag as it is inflating with a force big enough to cause injury.

Air bags are also dangerous when using rear-facing child seats — the air bag inflates behind the child and can throw the child seat towards the car seat with some force. It is now illegal to use a rear-facing child seat in the UK in a seat fitted with an air bag.

Most of these risks are caused by not using a car's safety features properly. If you use a seat belt and air bags as you are meant to, you are far safer in a car than you would be without them.

Figure 5: *A young girl using a booster seat to reduce the risks posed by her seatbelt.*

Practice Questions — Application

Q1 The figure on the right shows a graph of force against time for a tennis ball during contact with a racket. Calculate the magnitude of the impulse acting on the ball.

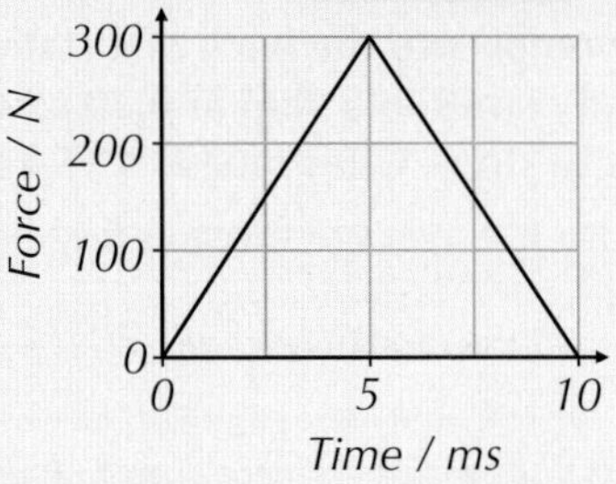

Q2 Until the 1950s, cars were manufactured to be uniformly rigid as it was generally thought that this was safer. Explain why this is incorrect.

Tip: Rigid materials are stiff and difficult to deform.

Q3 A crash test is conducted on a new car model to test the effectiveness of its safety features. A crash test dummy is placed in the driver's seat and the car is driven into a concrete wall.

a) A seat belt was fastened over the dummy before the test. Explain how the seat belt reduces the forces acting on the dummy during the crash.

b) Explain why airbags can be dangerous for passengers when used without a seat belt.

Q4 A landing aeroplane of mass 18 000 kg touches down on a runway at a velocity of 125 km h^{-1}. The brakes are applied and a resultant horizontal force of 62 000 N acts on the aeroplane. Find the time it takes for the aeroplane to come to a stop.

Tip: The mass before and after is the same, so the velocity is the only thing that changes.

Practice Questions — Fact Recall

Q1 What is impulse?

Q2 Describe how airbags protect passengers in the event of a crash.

Q3 Describe the risks associated with seat belts.

Q4 Explain how crumple zones work.

Section Summary

Make sure you know...

- That the velocity of an object will not change unless a resultant force acts on it (Newton's First Law).
- That net force is equal to the rate of change of momentum (Newton's Second Law).
- How to calculate net force, $\boldsymbol{F}$, from change in momentum, $\Delta \boldsymbol{p}$, and change in time, Δt, using $\boldsymbol{F} = \frac{\Delta \boldsymbol{p}}{\Delta t}$.
- That $\boldsymbol{F} = m\boldsymbol{a}$ is a special case of Newton's Second Law, and can only be applied when the body's mass is constant.
- That if object A exerts a force on object B, then object B exerts an equal but opposite force on object A (Newton's Third Law).
- That the forces exerted by objects A and B in Newton's Third Law are always of the same type.
- That linear momentum is the product of mass and velocity.
- That momentum is a vector quantity and so has a magnitude and direction.
- That momentum is always conserved.
- How to use the principle of conservation of momentum to solve one-dimensional and two-dimensional collision problems.
- That kinetic energy is conserved in elastic collisions but not inelastic collisions.
- That the impulse of a force is defined as the product of average force and time.
- That impulse is equal to the area under a force-time graph.
- How to estimate the area under non-linear force-time graphs.
- What crumple zones are, and how they reduce the forces acting on passengers in a collision.
- How seat belts protect wearers and the risks associated with them.
- How airbags protect passengers and the risks associated with them.
- That the introduction of mandatory safety features in cars resulted from research into reducing the forces involved in collisions, and therefore reducing the risk of injury.

Exam-style Questions

1 A ball is shot from a cannon. The ball has a much smaller mass than the cannon. Which combination of the following statements is true?

1. Kinetic energy is conserved when the ball is launched.
2. The momentum of the cannon is equal in magnitude to that of the ball.
3. The cannon moves backwards at the same speed that the ball moves forwards.

A All three statements are true.

B Only 1 and 2 are true.

C Only 2 is true.

D Only 1 and 3 are true.

(1 mark)

2 Which pair of forces below are an example of Newton's Third Law?

A When the end of a spring is pulled downwards, the spring extends downwards.

B When a car is being towed by a lorry, the lorry pulls forwards on the car and friction pulls backwards on the car.

C When a cat jumps, the earth pulls down on the cat and the cat pulls up on the earth.

D When a child moves down a slide, the earth's gravity pulls the child down and the slide pushes up on the child.

(1 mark)

3 A ball of mass 0.25 kg is travelling with velocity 1.2 ms^{-1}. It collides with a second ball that is travelling towards it at 0.3 ms^{-1}. The mass of the second ball is half that of the first ball. After the collision, the two balls move together with the same velocity. How fast are they moving?

A 0.45 ms^{-1}

B 0.70 ms^{-1}

C 0.75 ms^{-1}

D 0.90 ms^{-1}

(1 mark)

4 A 1.00×10^3 kg car is participating in a race. During a long stretch of straight track, it applies a force of 1.70×10^3 N to accelerate from 26.5 ms^{-1} to 31.0 ms^{-1} in 2.50 s.

a) State Newton's Second Law.

(1 mark)

b) During the race, the back bumper, with mass 50.0 kg, falls off the car. When it reaches the straight stretch of track again, the same force again applied again over 2.50 s to increase its speed from 26.5 ms^{-1}. Calculate the speed the car reaches.

(2 marks)

5 At a fairground, a dodgem car of total mass 325 kg travelling at 2.40 ms^{-1} collides loudly with the wall of the dodgem arena, and comes to a complete stop. The wall is fixed and does not move.

(a) Is this an elastic or inelastic collision? Explain your answer.

(2 marks)

(b) Calculate the magnitude of the impulse that acts on the dodgem.

(2 marks)

(c) Calculate what the impulse would have been if the dodgem had been travelling at double the speed.

(1 mark)

(d) Two dodgems of equal mass collide in the arena. **Fig. 5.1a** and **Fig. 5.1b** show the dodgems before and after the collision respectively.

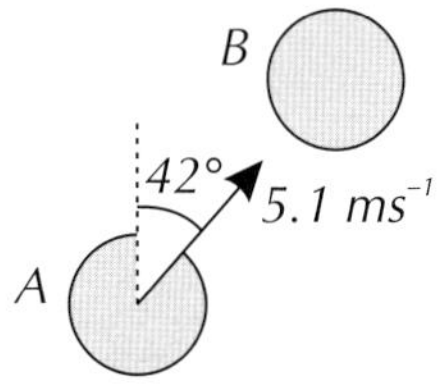

Fig 5.1a

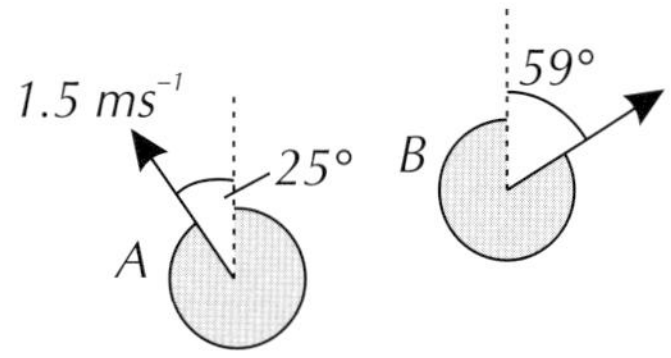

Fig 5.1b

Calculate the velocity of dodgem B after the collision.

(2 marks)

6 A force is applied to a stationary trolley to push it across a horizontal floor. **Fig. 6.1** shows the force applied to the trolley against time.

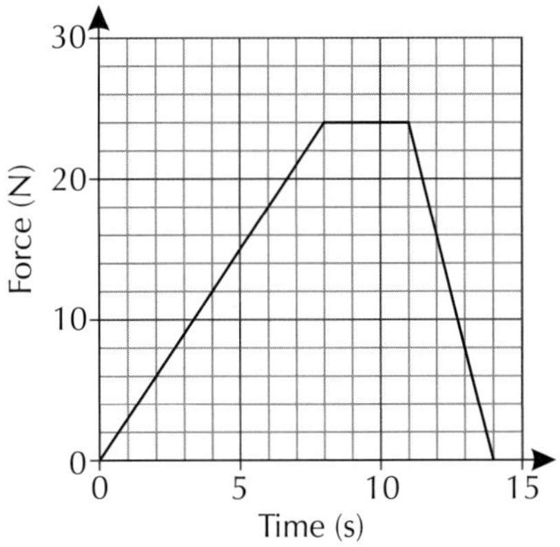

Fig 6.1

(a) Calculate the magnitude of the impulse that acts on the trolley.

(2 marks)

(b) The trolley reaches a velocity of 2.2 ms^{-1} after the force is applied. Assuming friction is negligible, calculate the mass of the trolley.

(2 marks)

(c) Explain why the trolley continues to move at a constant velocity after the force has been removed.

(1 mark)

Learning Objectives:
- Understand circuit symbols.
- Be able to draw circuit diagrams using circuit symbols.

Specification Reference 4.2.1

1. Circuit Diagrams

Module 4: Section 1 is all about electricity. Before we start going into all the detail, it's important that you can understand circuit diagrams.

Circuit symbols

In physics, we use circuit symbols to represent different electrical components. Here are some of the basic ones you should recognise...

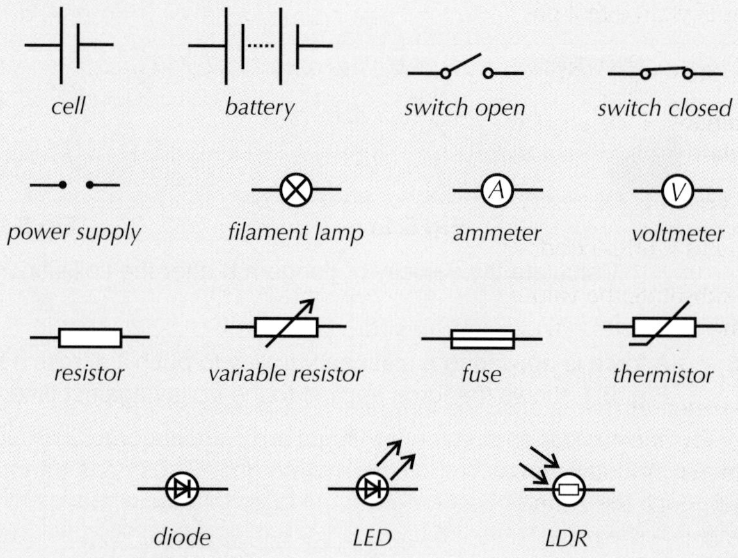

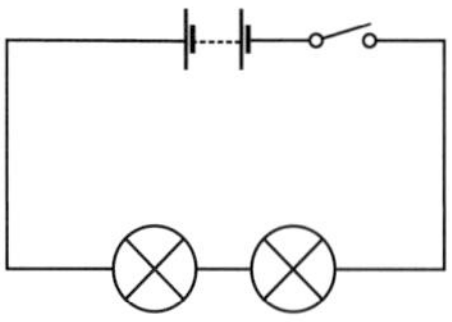

Figure 1: *A simple circuit diagram.*

Figure 2: *An electronic circuit. The red dome-shaped components to the right of the picture are LEDs.*

Drawing circuits

The lines between components in a circuit diagram represent wires and show how the components are connected together. You can connect components in series (see Figure 3) or in parallel (Figure 4).

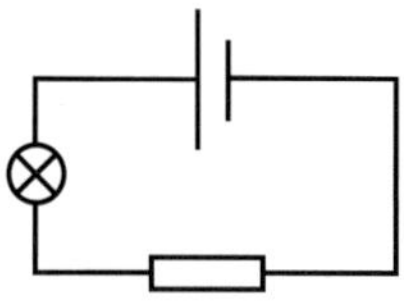

Figure 3: *A simple series circuit.*

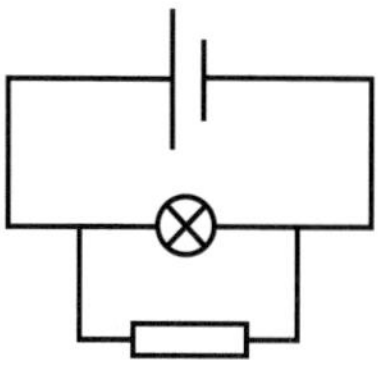

Figure 4: *A simple parallel circuit.*

Exam Tip
You could be asked to draw a circuit diagram in the exam — so make sure you get loads of practice at it before then.

Tip: A circuit needs to be complete for a current to flow through it.

Tip: Series and parallel circuits will be covered in more detail on p.165 and p.169.

Practice Questions — Application

Q1 Draw the circuit symbols for a diode, a fuse and an ammeter.

Q2 Draw a circuit diagram showing a battery, resistor and LDR in series.

2. Current

After all that stuff at GCSE about electricity, you wouldn't think there was much left to learn. Well, unfortunately you'd be wrong...

What is current?

The current in a wire is like water flowing in a pipe. The amount of water that flows depends on the flow rate and the time. It's the same with electricity — **current** is the rate of flow of charge.

$$I = \frac{\Delta Q}{\Delta t}$$

I = *current in amperes (A)*

Q = *charge in coulombs (C)*

t = *time in seconds (s)*

The **coulomb** is the unit of charge. One coulomb (C) is defined as the amount of charge that passes in 1 second when the current is 1 ampere.

Example — Maths Skills

A component has a current of 0.430 A passing through it. Calculate the charge passing through the component in exactly 3 minutes.

First convert the time taken from minutes to seconds:

3 minutes × 60 seconds per minute = 180 seconds.

Then substitute the values for current and time taken into the charge formula given above:

$\Delta Q = I \times \Delta t = 0.430 \times 180 = 77.4$ C

You can measure the current flowing through a part of a circuit using an **ammeter**. You always need to attach an ammeter in series (so that the current through the ammeter is the same as the current through the component — see page 168).

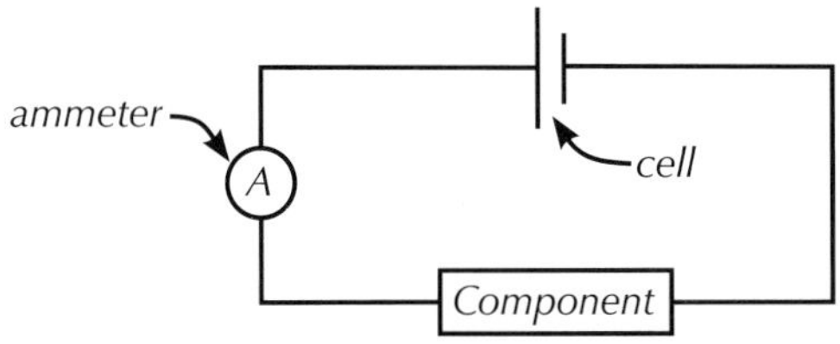

Figure 1: *An ammeter connected in series with a component.*

In Figure 1, you would label the current as flowing from the positive terminal of the cell (the longer line in the cell symbol), through the ammeter and then through the component to the negative terminal (the shorter line in the cell symbol). This is **conventional current** — it is said to flow from positive to negative. However, in most cases the actual movement of particles is in the opposite direction. Electrons, the usual charge carrier in circuits (see next page), are attracted towards the positive terminal, so the flow of electrons is from negative to positive.

This difference occurred because ideas about electricity and current were around long before the electron was actually discovered. Since the direction of flow makes no difference to the effect the current has in a circuit, and current can flow in either direction depending on the charge carriers involved, the idea of conventional current stuck around as the default.

Learning Objectives:

- Know the definition of electric current as rate of flow of charge.
- Be able to calculate current using $I = \frac{\Delta Q}{\Delta t}$.
- Know the coulomb as the unit of charge.
- Understand conventional current and electron flow.
- Know that the elementary charge e equals 1.60×10^{-19} C.
- Know that the net charge on a particle or an object is quantised and a multiple of e.
- Understand current as the movement of electrons in metals and movement of ions in electrolytes.
- Understand the distinction between conductors, semiconductors and insulators in terms of *n*.
- Know what is meant by the mean drift velocity of charge carriers.
- Be able to use $I = Anev$, where *n* is the number density of charge carriers.

Specification References 4.1.1 and 4.1.2

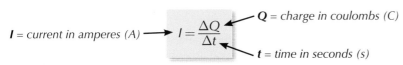

Figure 2: *Ideas about electric charge have been around for hundreds of years. Philosophers in Ancient Greece noticed attraction between pieces of amber and fabric, which we now call static electricity.*

Charge carriers

Charge carriers are electrically charged particles that are free to move in an object. The type of particle and the number of charge carriers in a given volume depend on the material.

Electrons and ions

In most objects (and all metals), the charge carriers are electrons. Each electron carries the same amount of charge, $-e$, where e is the **elementary charge**:

> **Tip:** Protons have an equal but opposite charge to electrons — i.e. each proton has a charge of $+e$.

$$e = 1.60 \times 10^{-19}\,\text{C}$$

The elementary charge is the smallest quantity of charge than can be found on its own — the net charge on any object will always be a multiple of e. This means that we can say that charge is quantised.

> **Tip:** In a metal, the charge carriers are free electrons — the ones from the outer shell of each atom.

In other materials, mainly liquids and gases, **ions** are the charge carriers. Ionic crystals like sodium chloride are insulators. Once molten though, the liquid conducts. Positive and negative ions are the charge carriers. The same is true in an ionic solution like copper sulfate solution. A substance containing ions that conducts electricity like this is called an **electrolyte**.

Conductors and insulators

> **Tip:** Gases are insulators, but if you apply a high enough p.d. across them, electrons get ripped out of atoms, giving you a spark (ions along a path).

In metals and other good conductors, there are lots of charge carriers per unit volume (n). This means that a current can easily flow through them. **Semiconductors** have fewer charge carriers (p.152) and perfect **insulators** have no charge carriers, so they don't allow a current to flow. In real life, insulators just have a very small n.

Mean drift velocity

> **Tip:** The mean drift velocity is much less than the electrons' actual speed (which is about 10^6 ms^{-1}).

When current flows through a wire, you might imagine the electrons all moving uniformly in the same direction. In fact, they move randomly in all directions, but tend to drift towards the positive terminal of the circuit.

The current is proportional to the average speed of this drifting — known as the **mean drift velocity**. You can use the continuity equation below to determine the size of a current if you know the mean drift velocity.

> **Tip:** If you're using different charge carriers, just replace e with the charge on each carrier, and let n be the number density of charge carriers.

$$I = Anev$$

I = *current (in A)*
A = *cross-sectional area (in m^2)*
e = *charge on one electron (in C)*
v = *mean drift velocity (in ms^{-1})*
n = *number density (i.e. number per unit volume) of electrons (in m^{-3})*

> **Tip:** Semiconductors can change their number density of electrons (page 152).

So the current through a wire can be increased by:

- Increasing the number of electrons — more charge is carried past a point in a given time. You can do this by either increasing the number density of electrons or increasing the cross-sectional area of the wire.
- Increasing the mean drift velocity of the electrons — it takes less time for a given amount of charge to be transferred. (You can achieve this by increasing the potential difference across the wire — see page 146.)

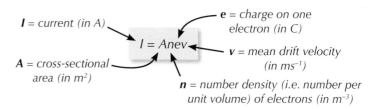

Deriving the continuity equation

First, imagine a section of wire that has a length of L and a cross-sectional area of A (see Figure 3).

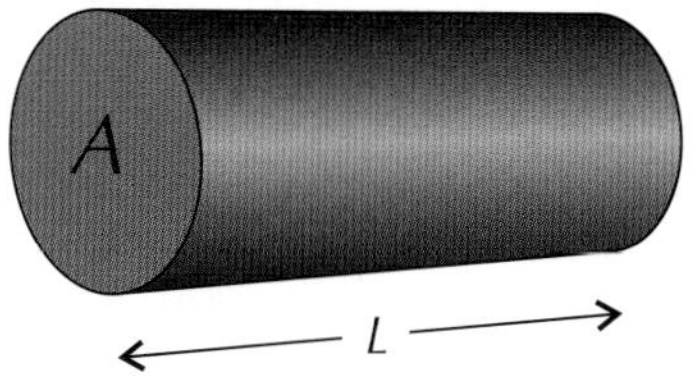

Figure 3: *A section of wire.*

The number of charge carriers in this section is equal to the number of charge carriers per unit volume × the volume of the section, or:

$$\text{no. charge carriers} = ALn$$

The total charge carried by these charge carriers is equal to the number of charge carriers × the charge on each charge carrier, or:

$$Q = ALne$$

To find the time taken for this amount of charge to pass through the section of the conductor, you have to use speed = distance ÷ time.

$$\text{time} = \text{length of section} \div \text{mean drift velocity, or } t = \frac{L}{v}$$

Then substitute both of these into the equation for current from page 143.

$$I = \frac{\Delta Q}{\Delta t} = \frac{ALne}{\left(\frac{L}{v}\right)} = Anev$$

Practice Questions — Application

Q1 A particle has a charge of 4e.
What is the charge of the particle in coulombs?

Q2 A cell has a charge of 91 C passing through it every 32 seconds.
Calculate the current passing through the cell.

Q3 A copper wire has a cross-sectional area of 0.50×10^{-6} m^2.
The number density of electrons for copper is 8.5×10^{28} m^{-3}.
A current of 12 A flows through the wire. Calculate the mean drift velocity of the free electrons in the wire.

Practice Questions — Fact Recall

Q1 Define the term current.

Q2 Describe the direction of the flow of conventional current.

Q3 What is a charge carrier?

Q4 State the value of the elementary charge, e.

Q5 What is the number density of charge carriers for a perfect insulator?

Q6 Give one way of increasing the current through a wire.

Learning Objectives:

- Understand potential difference (p.d.).
- Know that the unit of potential difference is the volt.
- Be able to calculate energy transferred using $W = VQ$.
- Understand the energy transfer $eV = \frac{1}{2}mv^2$ for electrons and other charged particles.

Specification Reference 4.2.2

Tip: When a charge flows through a component, it transfers energy to the component (it does work).

Tip: Back to the 'water analogy' again... the p.d. is like the pressure that's forcing water along the pipe.

3. Potential Difference

So you've learnt all about current, but you can't get a current to flow without a source of potential difference. Potential difference is all about the work done and energy transferred to get a charge carrier around a circuit.

What is potential difference?

To make electric charge flow through a circuit, you need to transfer energy to the charge — this energy is supplied by the power source, e.g. a battery. When a charge flows through the power source it is 'raised' through a potential and energy is transferred to the charge.

When energy is transferred, we say that work is done — so the power source does work to move the charge around the circuit. The **potential difference** (p.d.), or voltage, between two points is defined as the work done to move a unit charge between those points.

$$W = VQ$$

W = *work done in joules (J)*

V = *potential difference in volts (V)*

Q = *charge in coulombs (C)*

The potential difference across a component is 1 volt when 1 coulomb of charge does 1 joule of work to pass through the component.

$$1\,\mathbf{V} = 1\,\mathbf{J}\mathbf{C}^{-1}$$

Example — Maths Skills

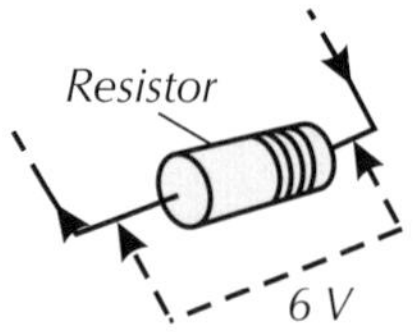

Here you do 6 J of work moving each coulomb of charge through the resistor, so the p.d. across it is 6 V.

$$V = \frac{W}{Q} = \frac{6}{1} = 6\,\text{V}$$

The energy gets converted to heat.

You can measure the potential difference across an electrical component by using a **voltmeter**. You always need to attach a voltmeter in parallel (see Figure 2).

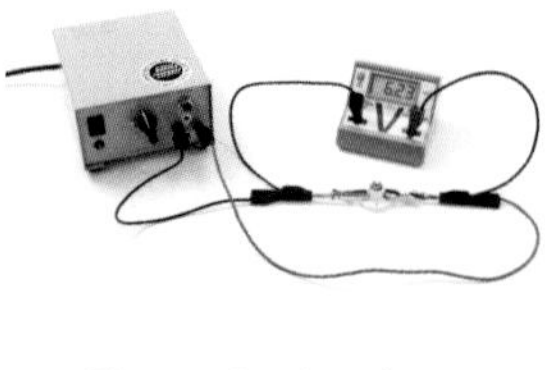

Figure 1: *A voltmeter connected across a filament bulb.*

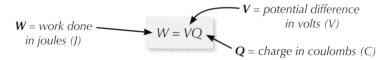

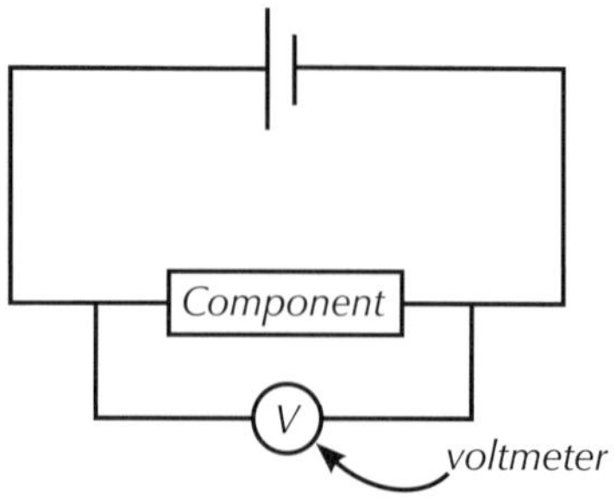

Figure 2: *A voltmeter connected in parallel with a component.*

Tip: The maximum value that a voltmeter or an ammeter can measure is called the full scale deflection.

Kinetic energy of charges

When a charged particle is accelerated by a potential difference, it gains kinetic energy equal to the amount of work done on the particle. The larger the potential difference, the more energy the particle gains and so the faster it travels. You can work out the speed of the particle by using the equation from the last page and $E_k = \frac{1}{2}mv^2$ from page 98.

$$\text{Work done} = \text{Kinetic energy gained}$$
$$VQ = \frac{1}{2}mv^2$$

For electrons, you can write this using the elemental charge, e — see p.144:

$$eV = \frac{1}{2}mv^2$$

- ***e*** = *charge of an electron (in C)*
- ***V*** = *potential difference (in V)*
- ***m*** = *mass of an electron (in kg)*
- ***v*** = *speed (in ms^{-1})*

Tip: You'll come across this equation again in quantum physics on page 226.

Tip: This equation gives you the speed of a single electron. Don't get it confused with the mean drift velocity from p.144.

Example — Maths Skills

An electron is accelerated from rest by a potential difference of 12 V. Calculate the final speed of the electron.

$eV = \frac{1}{2}mv^2$

$v^2 = 2eV \div m$

$v = \sqrt{2eV \div m} = \sqrt{(2 \times 1.60 \times 10^{-19} \times 12) \div (9.11 \times 10^{-31})}$

$= 2.053... \times 10^6 = 2.1 \times 10^6$ ms^{-1} (to 2 s.f.)

Tip: An electron's mass is 9.11×10^{-31} kg (see page 294).

Practice Questions — Application

Q1 In a circuit, it takes 114 J to move 56.0 C of charge through a filament lamp. Calculate the potential difference across the lamp.

Q2 An alpha particle has a mass of 6.64×10^{-27} kg and a charge of $+2e$. It is accelerated from rest to a speed of 2.20×10^4 ms^{-1}. Calculate the size of the potential difference that accelerated the alpha particle.

Practice Questions — Fact Recall

Q1 Define the potential difference between two points.

Q2 How should a voltmeter be connected in a circuit to measure the potential difference across a component?

Q3 State the equation that gives the kinetic energy of an electron after it is accelerated from rest through a potential difference. Define all symbols used.

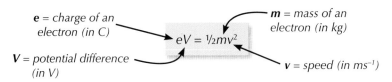

4. Resistance and Resistivity

This topic covers everything you need to know about resistance. It's Georg Simon Ohm you've got to blame for these pages — this German physicist developed Ohm's law and got the unit for resistance named after him.

Learning Objectives:

- Know that resistance is defined by $R = \frac{V}{I}$.
- Know that resistance is measured in ohms.
- Know Ohm's law.
- Know what is meant by the resistivity of a material.
- Be able to use the equation $R = \frac{\rho L}{A}$.
- Understand the variation of resistivity of metals and semiconductors with temperature.
- Know techniques and procedures used to determine the resistivity of a metal (PAG3).

Specification References 4.2.3 and 4.2.4

What is resistance?

If you put a potential difference (p.d.) across an electrical component, a current will flow. How much current you get for a particular potential difference depends on the **resistance** of the component.

You can think of a component's resistance as a measure of how difficult it is to get a current to flow through it. Resistance is measured in **ohms** (Ω). A component has a resistance of 1 Ω if a potential difference of 1 V makes a current of 1 A flow through it. This equation defines resistance:

$$R = \frac{V}{I}$$

R = *resistance in ohms (Ω)*
V = *potential difference in volts (V)*
I = *current in amperes (A)*

This equation is commonly known as **Ohm's law**.

Example — Maths Skills

A fixed resistor has a resistance of 4.43 Ω and the potential difference across it is 12.0 V. Calculate the current flowing through the fixed resistor.

You just need to rearrange the resistance equation and plug the numbers in.

$I = V \div R$
$= 12.0 \div 4.43$
$= 2.7088... = 2.71$ A (to 3 s.f.)

Figure 1: *Georg Simon Ohm — the physicist who developed Ohm's law.*

Resistivity

If you think about a nice, simple electrical component, like a length of wire, its resistance depends on:

- **Length (*L*)**. The longer the wire, the more difficult it is to make a current flow through it. The resistance is proportional to the length of the wire.
- **Area (*A*)**. The thicker the wire, the easier it will be for the electrons to pass along it.
- **Resistivity (*ρ*)**. This is a property of the material the component is made from. It is a measure of how much a particular material resists current flow. It's defined as the resistance of a 1 m length with a 1 m^2 cross-sectional area. It is measured in ohm-metres (Ωm).

Resistivity depends on the structure of the material as well as on environmental factors such as temperature and light intensity.

For metals, the resistivity increases as the temperature increases. This is because charge is carried through metals by free electrons in a lattice of positive ions. Heating the metal causes the ions to vibrate more, which makes the electrons collide with the lattice more often. This causes energy to be lost, usually as heat, and increases the overall resistance of the component.

For semiconductors, increasing the temperature causes more charge carriers to be released (p.152), so the resistivity decreases.

You can calculate the resistance of a component using the equation:

$$R = \frac{\rho L}{A}$$

R = *resistance (in Ω)*
A = *area (in m²)*
ρ = *resistivity (in Ωm)*
L = *length (in m)*

Exam Tip
You'll be given this equation in the exam, but not Ohm's law, so make sure you learn it.

Examples — Maths Skills

A piece of metal has a length of 0.50 cm, a square cross-sectional area with a width of 11 cm, and a resistance of 1.22 × 10⁻⁸ Ω. Find the resistivity of the metal.

Convert all lengths into metres.

The cross-sectional area (A) of the metal = 0.11 m × 0.11 m = 0.0121 m^2

Length = L = 0.0050 m

Rearrange the resistance equation for the resistivity of the metal:

$$\rho = \frac{RA}{L} = \frac{1.22 \times 10^{-8} \times 0.0121}{0.0050} = 2.9524 \times 10^{-8} = 3.0 \times 10^{-8}\ \Omega\text{m (to 2 s.f.)}$$

The heating element in a toaster is a bare nichrome wire with a radius of 0.2 mm and a length of 0.8 m. Find the resistance of the wire. (Resistivity of nichrome = 1.10×10^{-6} Ωm.)

First of all, you need to find the cross-sectional area of the wire (A) in m^2. Assuming the wire to be cylindrical, its cross-sectional area will be the area of the circle, πr^2.

Wire radius = 0.2 mm = 2×10^{-4} m, so $A = \pi(2 \times 10^{-4})^2 = 1.256... \times 10^{-7}$ m^2

Plug the numbers into the equation $R = \frac{\rho L}{A}$ to get:

$R = (1.10 \times 10^{-6} \times 0.8) \div 1.256... \times 10^{-7} = 7.0028...\ \Omega = 7.0\ \Omega$ (to 2 s.f.)

Tip: Don't confuse resistance and resistivity. Resistance is a property of an object and it depends on the material and dimensions of the object. Resistivity is a property of a material.

Exam Tip
For resistivity calculations, don't forget that you need to have the length in m and the cross-sectional area in m^2 — you'll lose marks if you don't use the correct units.

Finding the resistivity of a metal

PRACTICAL ACTIVITY GROUP 3

In this experiment, you'll be finding the resistance of a test wire made from the metal you want to know the resistivity of. You can then use this resistance and the dimensions of the wire to calculate the resistivity of the metal using the resistance equation above.

Before you start, you need to do a risk assessment to make sure you are aware of all the safety issues and risks.

Calculating cross-sectional area

The first thing you want to calculate is the cross-sectional area of the test wire. Measure the diameter of the wire in at least three different places along the wire using a micrometer.

Find the mean diameter and halve it to find the mean radius of the wire. You can assume that the cross-section of the wire is a circle, so you can calculate the cross-sectional area using this formula:

$$A = \pi r^2$$

A = *cross-sectional area in m²*
r = *radius of wire in m*

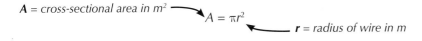

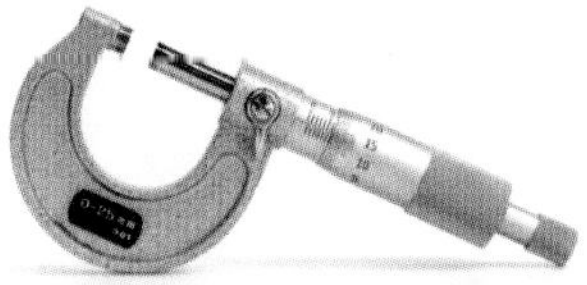

Figure 2: *A micrometer, used to measure very small distances. Micrometers are covered in more detail on page 17.*

Exam Tip
You can assume ammeters and voltmeters are ideal unless you're told otherwise — see page 155.

Tip: A flying lead is just a wire with a crocodile clip at the end to allow connection to any point along the test wire.

Tip: If the wire heats up, its resistance (and resistivity) will increase. You can minimise how much it heats up by keeping the current low and using a switch to make sure current only flows through the wire for short amounts of time while you're taking your measurements.

Tip: Don't forget — if you get an anomalous result when you calculate a resistance, you should discount it from calculations for the average resistance. You should also discount any anomalous values when drawing a line of best fit.

Tip: The main sources of random errors in this experiment are likely to be the temperature of the wire changing and measuring the length of the wire. How to deal with errors and uncertainties in practicals is covered in Module 1 (on pages 16 and 17) and Module 2 (p.29-33).

Measuring resistivity

Set up the experiment as shown in Figure 3, clamping the wire to the ruler so it is aligned with the zero reading on the ruler's scale.

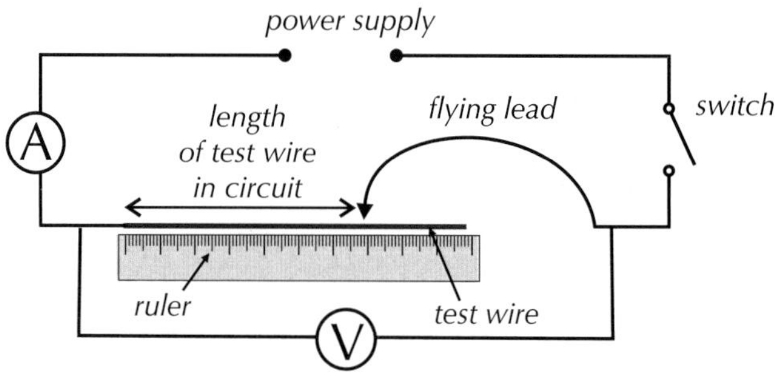

Figure 3: *The experimental set-up for determining resistivity of a metal.*

1. Attach the flying lead to the test wire and measure the length of the test wire connected in the circuit.
2. Close the switch and measure the current through the circuit and the potential difference across the test wire. Open the switch again once you've taken your measurements and use these values to calculate the resistance of the wire.
3. Repeat step 2 at least one more time for this length of wire and calculate the mean resistance.
4. Reposition the flying lead and repeat steps 1 to 3 to get an average resistance for each of several different lengths of test wire.
5. Plot a graph of average resistance (in Ω) against length (in m) using your results. Your graph and line of best fit should look similar to Figure 4.

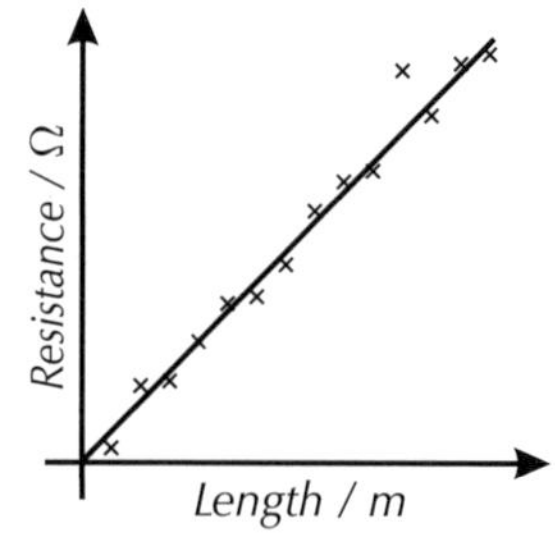

Figure 4: *A typical graph and line of best fit of resistance against length for a uniform wire.*

Since this graph is a straight line through the origin, the gradient of the graph is equal to $\frac{R}{L}$. By rearranging the equation for resistivity (see page 149), you will find that $\frac{R}{L} = \frac{\rho}{A}$.

This means that to find the resistivity of the wire metal in Ωm, you just need to multiply the gradient of the graph by the cross-sectional area of the wire (in m^2).

Practice Questions — Application

Q1 A thermistor has a resistance of 8.62 Ω. Calculate the potential difference across the thermistor when there is a current of 2.10 A flowing through it.

Q2 A fuse has a current of 1.21 A flowing through it. Calculate the resistance of the fuse when the potential difference across it is 13.4 V.

Q3 Copper has a resistivity of 1.72×10^{-8} Ωm. Calculate the resistance of a 40 cm long piece of copper wire that has a cross-sectional area of 2.8×10^{-5} m^2.

Q4 The graph below shows the resistance against length for a test wire of an unknown material. The radius of the test wire was 4.0 mm. Calculate the resistivity of the material the wire was made from.

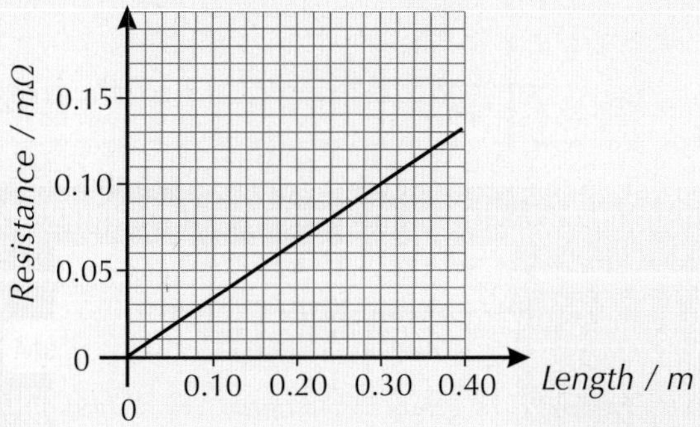

Exam Tip
Remember to look out for prefixes on units. If your results seem too large or too small, check that you haven't missed one. There's more about prefixes on page 25.

Practice Questions — Fact Recall

Q1 What is meant by resistance?

Q2 State the equation used to calculate the cross-sectional area of a wire, stating any assumptions you make.

Q3 Describe an experiment you could do to find the resistivity of a metal.

Q4 Explain why it is important to keep the temperature constant when doing an experiment to find the resistivity of a metal. Suggest how you could keep the temperature of the material constant.

5. Types of Conductor

Learning Objectives:

- Understand the variation of the resistivity of semiconductors with temperature.
- Know what is meant by a negative temperature coefficient (NTC) thermistor and understand the variation of its resistance with temperature.
- Know the term light-dependent resistor (LDR).
- Understand the variation of resistance of an LDR with light intensity.
- Know the techniques and procedures used to investigate the electrical characteristics for a range of ohmic and non-ohmic components (PAG3).

Specification References 4.2.3 and 4.2.4

Tip: The gradient of an *I-V* graph for an ohmic conductor (like the one shown in Figure 1) is $\frac{1}{R}$.

Figure 2: *Semiconductors are used in loads of electrical appliances, like microwaves.*

So you've come across Ohm's law, but not every electrical component follows it. Unfortunately, you have to know the difference between ohmic and non-ohmic components, including some fancy ones like LDRs and thermistors.

Ohmic conductors

Conductors that obey Ohm's law (mostly metals) are called **ohmic conductors**. Ohm's law states that, provided the physical conditions (such as temperature) remain constant, the current through an ohmic conductor is directly proportional to the potential difference across it.

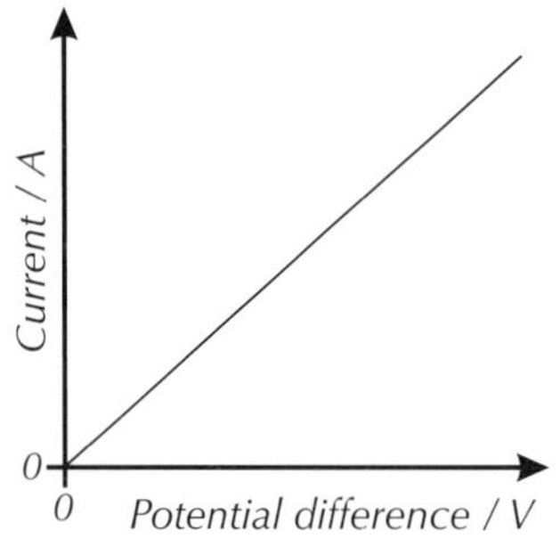

Figure 1: *I-V graph for an ohmic conductor.*

If you plot a graph of current against potential difference (page 155), you get a straight-line graph — doubling the p.d. doubles the current. What this means is that the resistance is constant — the gradient is always a fixed value.

Often factors such as light level or temperature will have a significant effect on resistance, so you need to remember that Ohm's law is only true for ohmic conductors under constant physical conditions.

Conductors that don't follow Ohm's law are called **non-ohmic conductors**. If you plot a graph of current against potential difference for these conductors, you don't get a straight line. There's more on this on pages 156-157.

Semiconductors

Semiconductors are a group of materials that aren't as good at conducting electricity as metals, because they have far fewer charge carriers (i.e. electrons) available.

However, if energy is supplied to a semiconductor, e.g. by an increase in temperature or light intensity, more charge carriers can be released and the resistivity of the material decreases. This means that some can make excellent sensors for detecting changes in their environment (p.173).

Three common semiconductor components are thermistors, diodes and light-dependent resistors (LDRs).

Diodes

You've probably come across **diodes** before, in the form of LED lights. Diodes are designed to only let current flow in one direction, and only when a potential difference above a particular threshold voltage is applied across the diode. There's more about diodes over on page 157.

Thermistors

A **thermistor** is a component with a resistance that depends on its temperature. You only need to know about NTC thermistors — NTC stands for 'Negative Temperature Coefficient'. This means that the resistance decreases as the temperature goes up, see Figure 4.

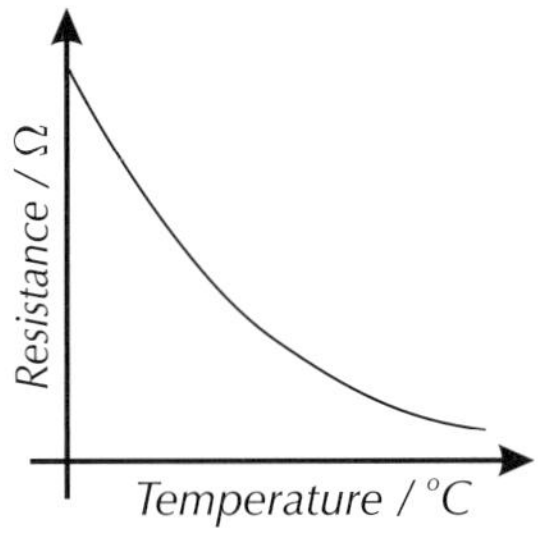

Figure 4: *A resistance vs temperature graph for an NTC thermistor.*

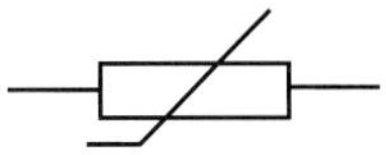

Figure 3: *Thermistor circuit symbol.*

Figure 5: *A thermistor.*

Warming the thermistor gives more electrons enough energy to escape from their atoms. This means that there are more charge carriers available, so the resistance is lower. This sensitivity to temperature makes them really good temperature sensors.

Investigating the resistance of a thermistor

PRACTICAL ACTIVITY GROUP 3

You can use the circuit shown in Figure 6 to investigate how a thermistor's resistance varies with temperature.

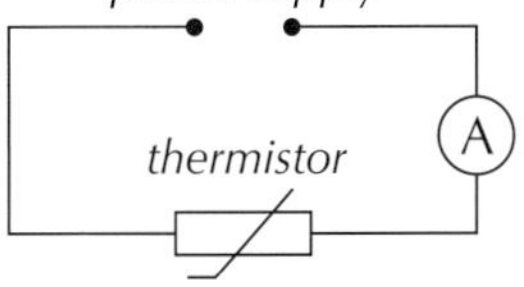

Figure 6: *Circuit used to investigate the resistance of a thermistor.*

You can measure the temperature of a thermistor more easily by putting it in water (provided the thermistor is waterproof). Place the thermistor in a beaker and pour enough boiling water into the beaker to cover the thermistor. Turn on the power supply, and record its potential difference — this should be kept constant throughout the experiment. Measure and record the temperature of the water using a digital thermometer and the current through the circuit using the ammeter.

Continue to record the current and temperature for every 5 °C drop in temperature. Use your recorded values for potential difference and current to calculate the resistance of the thermistor at each temperature. Then plot a resistance-temperature graph. For an NTC thermistor, you should find as the temperature decreases, the resistance increases (and so the current will decrease) — your graph should look like the one in Figure 4.

Tip: Make sure you do a risk assessment before you start any practical. In this practical it's particularly important to make sure that the thermistor and any other components that will be in contact with the water bath are waterproof.

Tip: Having the thermistor in hot water, rather than trying to heat it directly, helps prevent the temperature from fluctuating while you're taking measurements, and affecting your results.

Light-dependent resistors

A **light-dependent resistor** (LDR) is a component with a resistance that depends on the intensity of the light that is incident on it. The greater the intensity, the lower the resistance of the LDR.

The explanation for why this occurs is similar to the thermistor. Light provides the energy to release charge carriers and decrease the resistivity of the material. A higher intensity means that more photons are hitting the LDR each second, so more charge carriers are released each second.

The graph of resistance against light intensity for an LDR is shown in Figure 8.

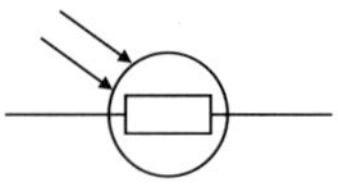

Figure 7: *The circuit symbol for an LDR.*

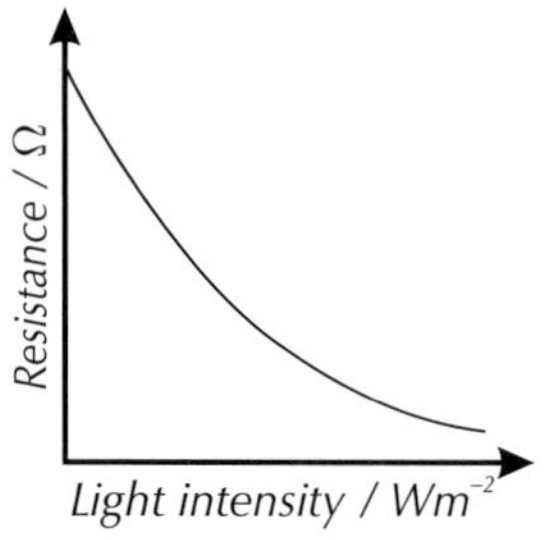

Figure 8: *A resistance vs light intensity graph for an LDR.*

Investigating the resistance of an LDR

PRACTICAL ACTIVITY GROUP 3

You can use the circuit in Figure 6 to investigate the resistance of an LDR — just replace the thermistor with an LDR.

Switch on the power supply, and record its potential difference — this should stay constant. Measure the current through the LDR, and then cover up part of the LDR's surface with a piece of thick paper. This will decrease the light intensity on the LDR. Gradually cover more of the surface with the paper, taking new current readings each time you do. Record the area of the uncovered surface for each current measurement. You can use the current and p.d. data to calculate the resistance of the LDR for different uncovered areas (i.e. light intensities). Then plot a graph of uncovered area against resistance. Your results should match the relationship shown in Figure 8.

Tip: The intensity of light is a measure of the energy transferred to a surface by light per second, per unit area. So the more area light hits, the greater the intensity of light on the surface. See page 185 for more on this.

Practice Questions — Fact Recall

Q1 What happens to the resistance of an ohmic conductor if you double the potential difference across it? Give a reason for your answer.

Q2 What does the resistance of a thermistor depend on?

Q3 Sketch a graph of resistance against light intensity for an LDR.

6. *I-V* Characteristics

You've had a glimpse of the I-V characteristic for an ohmic conductor — now it's time to meet a few more...

Learning Objectives:

- Know the techniques and procedures used to investigate the electrical characteristics for a range of ohmic and non-ohmic components (PAG3).
- Know and understand *I–V* characteristics of a resistor, filament lamp, thermistor, diode and light-emitting diode (LED).

Specification Reference 4.2.3

What are *I-V* characteristics?

The term '***I-V* characteristic**' is just a fancy way of saying a graph which shows how the current (*I*) flowing through a component changes as the potential difference (*V*) across it is increased. The shallower the gradient of a *I-V* characteristic, the greater the resistance of the component.

Example

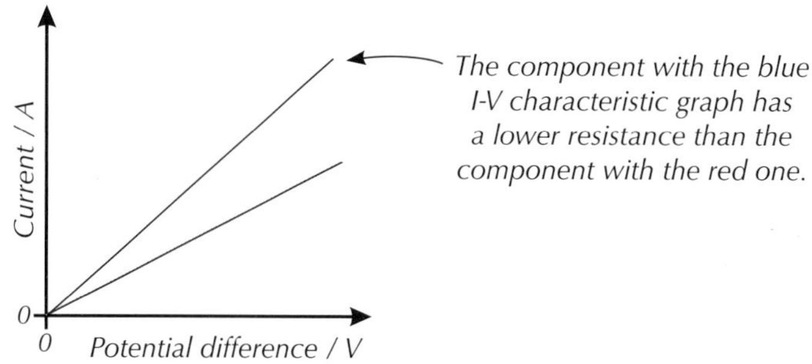

Current / A
0
0
Potential difference / V
The component with the blue I-V characteristic graph has a lower resistance than the component with the red one.

A curve shows that the resistance is changing (see next page).

Finding the *I-V* characteristic of a component

You can use the circuit in Figure 1 to find the *I-V* characteristic for a component.

PRACTICAL ACTIVITY GROUP 3

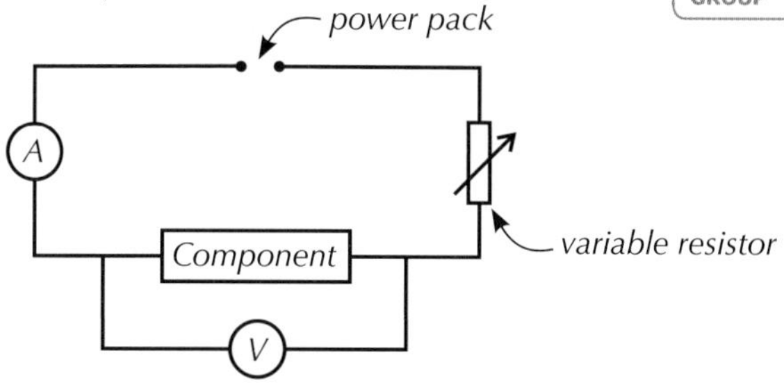

power pack
A
variable resistor
Component
V

Figure 1: *A circuit that could be used to find the I-V characteristic for a component.*

By changing the resistance of the variable resistor, you can change the voltage across the component you're investigating and the current through it. You can plot an *I-V* characteristic for the component by recording a range of current and voltage values and plotting an *I-V* graph using them.

Tip: As always, do a risk assessment before you start any experiment.

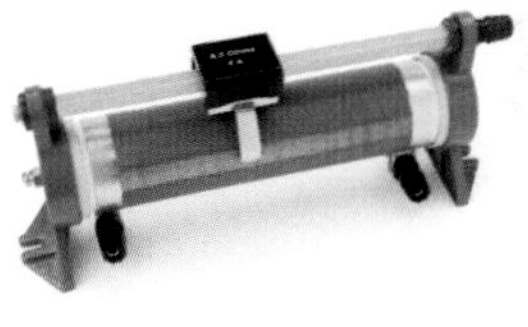

Figure 2: *A variable resistor.*

Tip: You could record your results in a spreadsheet and use computer software to plot your *I-V* characteristics instead of drawing them by hand.

Ideal voltmeters and ammeters

You can normally assume that any voltmeters and ammeters used in an experiment are ideal. Voltmeters are assumed to have an infinite resistance (so no current flows through them) and ammeters are assumed to have no resistance (and so will have no potential difference across them).

Exam Tip
In the exams, you can assume all voltmeters and ammeters are ideal unless the question tells you otherwise.

Ohmic conductors

Tip: Most metallic conductors are ohmic.

As you saw on page 152, the current through an ohmic conductor under constant physical conditions is directly proportional to the voltage. So their *I-V* characteristic is a straight line as their resistance doesn't change (see Figure 3). Fixed resistors and LDRs in constant conditions are both ohmic conductors.

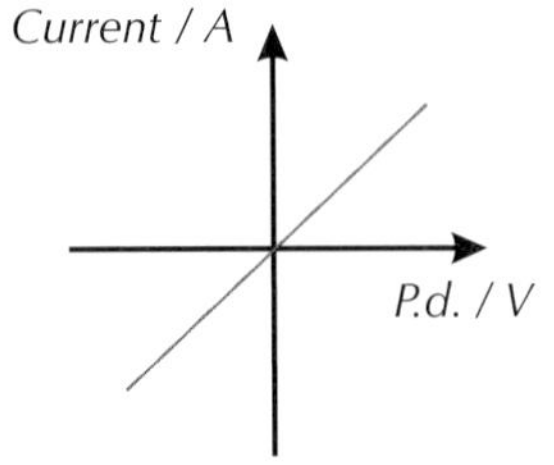

Figure 3: *The characteristic I-V graph for an ohmic conductor.*

Filament lamps

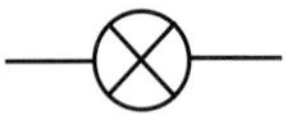

Figure 4: *Filament lamp circuit symbol.*

The *I-V* characteristic for a filament lamp is a curve that is steep for small voltages but gets shallower as the voltage rises (see Figure 5).

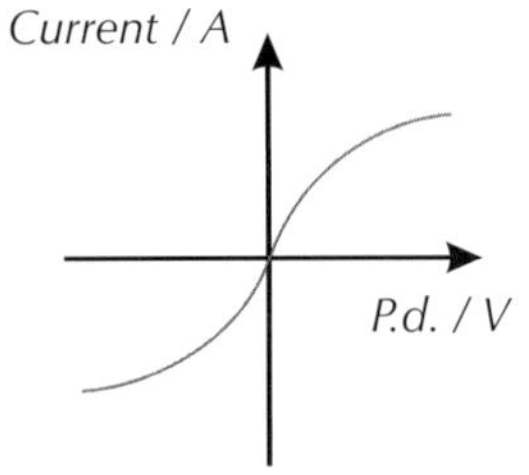

Figure 5: *The characteristic I-V graph for a filament lamp.*

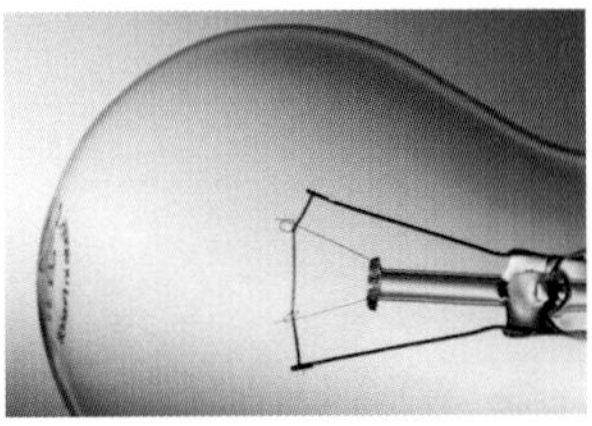

Figure 6: *A filament lamp contains a thin coil of metal wire inside it.*

The filament is a thin coil of metal wire, so you might think it should have the same characteristic graph as a metallic conductor. But, a filament is designed to heat up and glow. An increase in current means an increase in temperature, and an increase in resistance, which causes the current to decrease again. This is why the *I-V* graph for the filament lamp levels off at high currents.

Most components with resistance heat up as the current increases, but at much higher currents than a filament lamp. This means there is usually a limit to the amount of current that can flow through a component.

Thermistors

The *I-V* characteristic for a thermistor gets steeper as the potential difference across it increases.

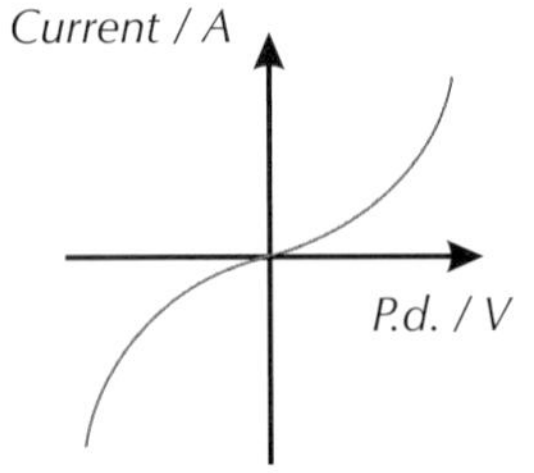

Figure 7: *The characteristic I-V graph for a thermistor.*

The explanation for this is similar to that for the filament lamp. As a current flows through the thermistor, the thermistor heats up. This causes more charge-carriers to be released (p.144), so the resistance of the thermistor decreases and the *I-V* characteristic becomes steeper.

Diodes

Diodes (including light-emitting diodes (LEDs)) are made from semiconductors (see page 152) and are designed to let current flow in one direction only. Forward bias is the direction in which the current is allowed to flow. Most diodes require a voltage of about 0.6 V in the forward direction before they will conduct — this is called the threshold voltage. In reverse bias, the resistance of the diode is very high and the current that flows is very tiny.

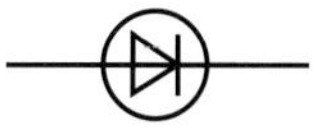

Figure 8: *Diode circuit symbol. Current flows through the diode in the direction of the arrow.*

Tip: You can use the threshold voltages of LEDs to determine Planck's constant — there's more on this on page 227.

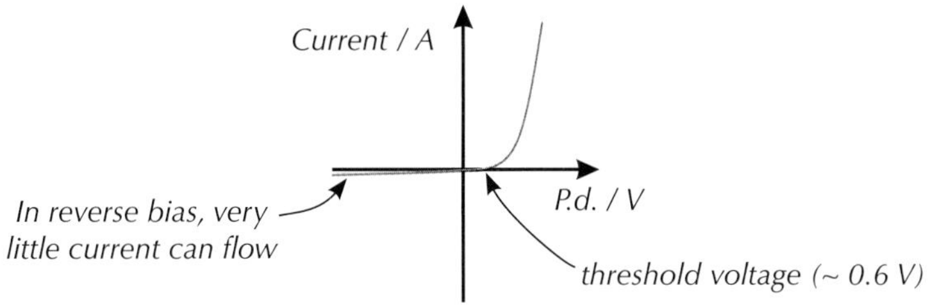

Figure 9: *The characteristic I-V graph for a diode.*

Practice Question — Application

Q1 The graph below shows the *I-V* characteristic for a component.

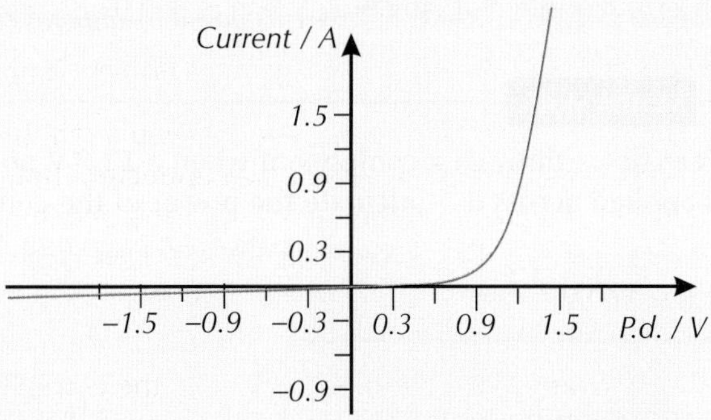

a) What type of component has this *I-V* characteristic?

b) Describe how the current and voltage vary in the forward bias.

c) Describe the resistance of the component in the reverse direction.

Practice Questions — Fact Recall

Q1 What resistances do you normally assume a voltmeter and an ammeter to have?

Q2 Sketch the *I-V* characteristic of:

a) an ohmic conductor under constant physical conditions,

b) a filament lamp.

Q3 Is a filament lamp an ohmic conductor? How can you tell from its *I-V* characteristic?

7. Power and Electrical Energy

Learning Objectives:
- Be able to use the equations $P = VI$, $P = I^2R$ and $P = \frac{V^2}{R}$.
- Be able to calculate energy transferred using $W = VIt$.

Specification Reference 4.2.5

You should remember all about work and power from GCSE. Well, here they are again because you still need to know about them. Remember — the faster a device does work (transfers energy), the more powerful it is.

Power

Power (P) is defined as the rate of doing work. It's measured in watts (W), where 1 watt is equivalent to 1 joule of work done per second.

$$P = \frac{W}{t}$$

P = *power in watts (W)*
W = *work done in joules (J)*
t = *time in seconds (s)*

From this definition, you can derive an equation to find the power of electrical devices.

- From the definition of potential difference, you know that $W = VQ$.
- From the definition of current, you know that $Q = It$.
- Substitute these into the equation for power:

$$P = \frac{VQ}{t} = \frac{VIt}{t}$$

- And you end up with:

$$P = VI$$

P = *power in watts (W)*
V = *potential difference in volts (V)*
I = *current in amperes (A)*

Tip: If your mind needs refreshing about current and potential difference, flick back to pages 143-147.

Example — Maths Skills

A 3.0 A current flows through a component when a 12.0 V potential difference is applied across it. Calculate the power of the component.

$P = VI$
$= 12.0 \times 3.0 = 36$ W

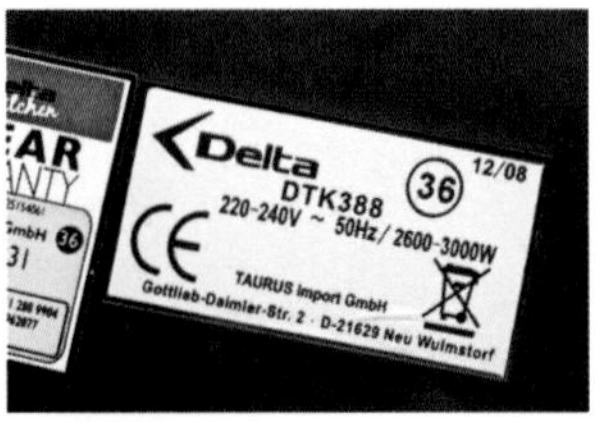

Figure 1: The label on an electrical appliance tells you its power rating — the rate at which it transfers energy.

Equations for calculating power

As well as the two equations above, you can derive two more equations for calculating power in electrical circuits...

You know from rearranging Ohm's Law that:

$$V = IR$$

V = *potential difference in volts (V)*
I = *current in amperes (A)*
R = *resistance in ohms (Ω)*

By substituting this rearranged Ohm's Law into the above equation for power, you get:

$$P = I^2R$$

Exam Tip
The good news is you'll be given most of the boxed equations in the exam, so you don't have to memorise them all — hurrah.

You can also rearrange Ohm's Law to make I the subject:

$$I = \frac{V}{R}$$

And then substitute this into the equation for power to give:

$$P = \frac{V^2}{R}$$

Obviously, which equation you should use depends on what quantities you know.

Examples — Maths Skills

A 24 W car headlamp is connected to a 12 V car battery. Assume the wires connecting the lamp to the battery have negligible resistance.

a) How much work is done by the lamp in 2.0 hours?

b) Find the total resistance of the lamp.

a) Number of seconds in 2.0 hours = 2 × 60 × 60 = 7200 s
Rearrange the equation $P = W \div t$:
$W = P \times t = 24 \times 7200 = 172\ 800$ J = 170 kJ (to 2 s.f.)

b) Rearrange the equation $P = \frac{V^2}{R}$, $R = \frac{V^2}{P} = \frac{12^2}{24} = \frac{144}{24} = 6.0\ \Omega$

A machine does 750 J of work every second.

a) What is the power rating of the machine?

b) All of the machine's components are connected in series, with a total resistance of 30 Ω. What current flows through the machine's wires?

a) Power = $W \div t = 750 \div 1 = 750$ W

b) Rearrange the equation $P = I^2R$, $I = \sqrt{\frac{P}{R}} = \sqrt{\frac{750}{30}} = \sqrt{25} = 5$ A

Exam Tip
Always double-check that you've rearranged equations correctly in the exam — it'd be sad to lose marks for making such an easy mistake.

Energy

Sometimes it's the electrical energy transferred by the device that you're interested in — this is equal to the work done. Just substitute $P = W \div t$ into the power equations, rearrange, and tah dah — you get these equations for the electrical energy transferred by a device:

W = *energy transferred (or work done) in joules (J)*

I = *current in amperes (A)*

V = *potential difference in volts (V)*

$$W = VIt$$

R = *resistance in ohms (Ω)*

$$W = \frac{V^2}{R}t$$

t = *time in seconds (s)*

$$W = I^2Rt$$

Tip: Electrical energy can also be given in kWh (kilowatt hours, see the next page). 1 kWh equals 3.6 MJ, so to convert kWh to J, multiply by 3.6×10^6.

Exam Tip
When you're doing these questions, make sure the time you use is always in seconds, or you'll get the wrong answer.

Example — Maths Skills

It takes 4.5 minutes for a kettle to boil the water inside it. A current of 4.0 A flows through the kettle's heating element once it is connected to the mains (230 V). How much energy does the kettle's heating element transfer to the water in the time it takes to boil?

Time the kettle takes to boil in seconds = $4.5 \times 60 = 270$ s.
Use $W = VIt$

$= 230 \times 4.0 \times 270$
$= 248\ 400$ J
$= 250$ kJ (to 2 s.f.)

Practice Questions — Application

Q1 A battery provides 3400 J of energy per second.
What is the power of the battery?

Q2 A car starter motor requires 12.5 kJ of energy to flow through it in 2.00 seconds to start the engine.
a) Calculate the power necessary to start the engine.
b) The car battery supplies 8.00 V to the starter motor.
Calculate the current required to start the engine.

Q3 A motor has a power rating of 5.2 kW. The potential difference across the motor is 230 V. Calculate the total resistance of the motor.

Q4 A lamp has a potential difference of 230 V across it and a current of 1.2 A flowing through it. Calculate the energy transferred to the lamp in 45 seconds.

Q5 A circuit in an electric car converts 1250 J of electrical energy into heat every second. The resistance in that circuit of the car is 54.2 Ω. Calculate the current through that circuit.

Practice Questions — Fact Recall

Q1 Define the term power.

Q2 Write down three equations you could use to calculate electrical power.

Q3 Give an equation for the energy transferred by a device in terms of current, potential difference and time.

8. Domestic Electricity

Whilst you probably don't have to worry about real electricity bills just yet, you unfortunately need to know about them for your exam...

Learning Objectives:
- Know the kilowatt-hour (kWh) as a unit of energy.
- Be able to calculate the cost of energy.

Specification Reference 4.2.5

Electricity companies

Unless you live somewhere incredibly remote, your house will be connected to the national grid — a network of cables that transfers electricity from power stations to consumers. Of course, this isn't free — you have to pay your electricity supplier. Electricity suppliers charge customers based on the number of 'units' of electricity that have been used.

Another name for a unit is a kilowatt-hour (kWh), where 1 kWh = 3.6 million joules. Kilowatt-hours are used because a typical household uses loads of electricity each month, so it'd be impractical to try to measure this in joules. If you know the power of an appliance and the length of time it's used for, you can calculate the work it does in kWh.

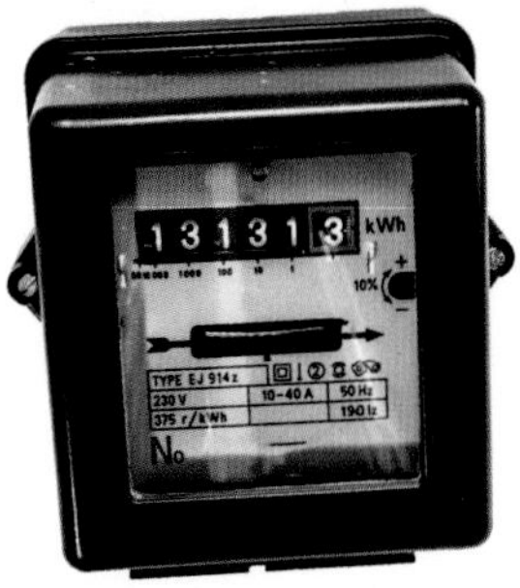

Figure 1: Electricity meters record the units of electricity used by a household.

Example — Maths Skills

A 1500 W hairdryer is on for 10 minutes. How much energy does it use in J and kWh?

In joules: $W = Pt = 1500 \times 10 \times 60 = 900\ 000$ J

In kWh: 10 minutes = $10 \div 60 = 0.166...$ hours

1500 watts = $1500 \div 1000 = 1.5$ kW

$W = Pt = 1.5 \times 0.166... = 0.25$ kWh

Tip: Remember, 1 kWh equals 3.6×10^6 J.

Cost of electricity

To work out the cost of electricity you need to know how much you've used (in units) and the price of each unit. Then it's a simple matter of multiplying these two numbers together:

$$\text{Cost} = \text{Number of units} \times \text{Price per unit}$$

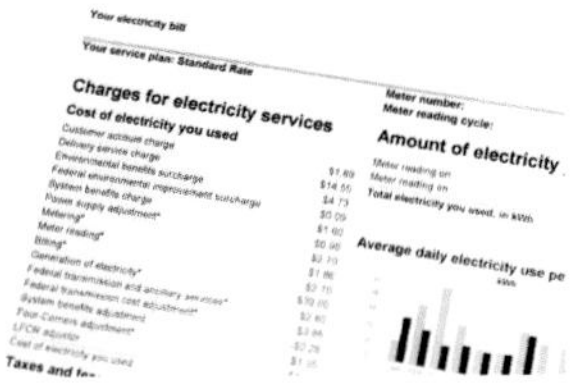

Figure 2: Real electricity bills can have multiple charges and discounts applied to them, but in your exams, you'll only be expected to know the basic equation on the left.

Example — Maths Skills

How much does it cost to use an 800 W microwave oven for 6 minutes? Electricity costs 16.1p per unit.

6 minutes = $6 \div 60 = 0.1$ hours

800 watts = $800 \div 1000 = 0.8$ kW

$W = Pt = 0.8 \times 0.1 = 0.08$ kWh

Cost = $0.08 \times 16.1 = 1.288 = 1$p (to 1 s.f.)

Of course, most people don't make a separate payment for their electricity each time they use a microwave — electricity providers bill them at regular intervals instead.

Electricity bills can look like they're written in a strange code — but luckily for you, the examples you'll see are easy to understand. Real ones aren't really that bad either — you just need to know where to look to find the important information. Take a look at the example on the next page.

Example

Charges for this period

	Previous	Latest	Total
Electricity used	29 125	29 605	480
Unit charge			10.25p
Total for this period			**£49.20**

- The electricity used is given in units (kWh) on an electricity bill.
- The 'previous' value is the reading from the electricity meter in the customer's house from the last time they were billed.
  The 'latest' value is what the electricity meter currently says.
- The total is the difference between the previous and latest values — i.e. the total electricity used in this time.
- The unit charge is the price of one unit of electricity.
- The total cost is found by multiplying the number of units used by the price per unit — 480 × 10.25 = 4920 p or £49.20.

Reducing electricity use

Reducing the amount of electrical energy you use can save you money and it can help the environment too.

HOW SCIENCE WORKS

Environmental impacts of generating electricity

Burning fossil fuels (coal, oil and gas) releases carbon dioxide into the atmosphere, which adds to the greenhouse effect and contributes to global warming. Burning coal and oil also releases sulfur dioxide. This can cause acid rain, which damages plants and buildings.

Nuclear power stations produce radioactive waste, which can be dangerous to the environment and human health if it isn't disposed of safely. Even renewable energy sources like biofuels have an impact because lots of land is needed to produce them.

Energy saving devices

Energy saving (fluorescent) light bulbs are more expensive than traditional filament bulbs, but are about four times more efficient. They also last for about ten years (as opposed to a year for filament bulbs) so reduce the number of bulbs needing to be disposed of and replaced. LED light bulbs are even more efficient than energy saving bulbs, and last even longer, but they cost more.

Domestic appliances (e.g. washing machines and ovens) sold in the UK all have an energy rating. This helps customers choose the appliance that's most efficient to run, which can reduce their environmental impact.

Figure 3: Energy efficiency labelling, used for domestic appliances within the EU.

Tip: Remember, efficiency is the useful output energy ÷ the total input energy (page 100).

Practice Questions — Application

Q1 A device transfers 72 000 J of energy.
Calculate the energy transferred in kWh.

Q2 A household's electricity bill for one month is £28.24.
Electricity is supplied to the house at 12.2p per unit. Calculate how many units of electricity the household used during the month.

9. E.m.f. and Internal Resistance

There's resistance in almost all wires and components — including inside batteries and cells. This makes some resistance calculations a little more tricky. But don't worry — the next few pages will help you with those questions.

What is internal resistance?

Resistance comes from electrons colliding with atoms and losing energy. In a battery, chemical energy is used to make electrons move. As they move, they collide with atoms inside the battery — so batteries must have resistance. This is called **internal resistance**. Internal resistance is what makes batteries and cells warm up when they're used.

Load resistance is the total resistance of all the components in the external circuit. You might see it called 'external resistance'.

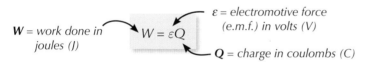

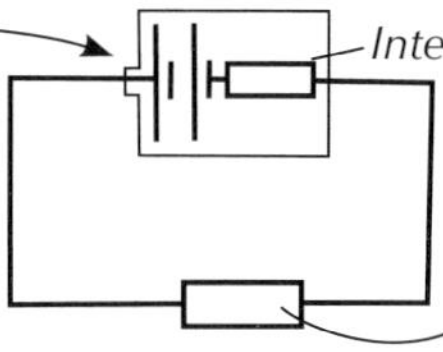

Figure 1: *A circuit diagram showing the internal and external resistances in a circuit.*

What is e.m.f.?

The total amount of work the battery does on each coulomb of charge is called its **electromotive force** or **e.m.f.** (ε). Be careful — e.m.f. isn't actually a force. It's measured in volts.

$$W = \varepsilon Q$$

W = work done in joules (J)

ε = electromotive force (e.m.f.) in volts (V)

Q = charge in coulombs (C)

Example — Maths Skills

A battery has an e.m.f. of 10.2 V. Calculate the work done by the battery when 0.650 C of charge passes through it.

$W = \varepsilon Q$

$= 10.2 \times 0.650 = 6.63$ J

The potential difference (p.d.) across the load resistance (R) is the work done when one coulomb of charge flows through the load resistance. This potential difference is called the **terminal p.d.** (V). If there was no internal resistance, the terminal p.d. would be the same as the e.m.f. However, in real power supplies, there's always some energy lost overcoming the internal resistance. The energy wasted per coulomb overcoming the internal resistance is called the **lost volts** (v).

Conservation of energy tells us for any electrical circuit:

energy per coulomb supplied by the source = energy per coulomb transferred in load resistance + energy per coulomb wasted in internal resistance

Learning Objectives:

- Know what is meant by internal resistance.
- Know what is meant by the electromotive force (e.m.f.) of a source such as a cell or a power supply.
- Be able to calculate energy transferred using $W = \varepsilon Q$.
- Understand the distinction between e.m.f. and p.d. in terms of energy transfer.
- Know the meanings of the terms terminal p.d. and 'lost volts'.
- Be able to use the equations $\varepsilon = I(R + r)$ and $\varepsilon = V + Ir$.
- Be able to analyse circuits with more than one source of e.m.f.
- Understand techniques and procedures used to determine the internal resistance of a chemical cell or other source of e.m.f. (PAG4).

Specification References 4.2.2, 4.3.1 and 4.3.2

Tip: In general, you can assume the connecting wires in a circuit have no resistance — and it's no different for internal resistance problems. But in practice, they do have a small resistance.

Tip: There's more on the conservation of energy on page 100.

Calculations using e.m.f.

Examiners can ask you to do calculations with e.m.f. and internal resistance in lots of different ways. You've got to be ready for whatever they throw at you. Here are some of the equations you might need and how to derive them...

You'll get this equation for e.m.f. in the data and formulae booklet in the exam:

$$\varepsilon = I(R + r)$$

- *ε = electromotive force (e.m.f.) in volts (V)*
- ***R** = load resistance in ohms (Ω)*
- ***I** = current in amperes (A)*
- ***r** = internal resistance in ohms (Ω)*

Expanding the brackets of this equation gives: $\varepsilon = IR + Ir$

Then using the equation $V = IR$, you can substitute V and v for IR and Ir...

$$\varepsilon = V + v$$

- ***V** = terminal p.d. in volts (V)*
- ***v** = lost volts in volts (V)*

Tip: $V = IR$ is just the definition of resistance rearranged (see p.148).

Rearranging the equation gives the equation for terminal p.d...

$$V = \varepsilon - v$$

And re-substituting v for Ir gives...

$$\varepsilon = V + Ir$$

Exam Tip
You'll only be given $\varepsilon = I(R + r)$ and $\varepsilon = V + Ir$ in the exam, so make sure you can work out the other versions of these equations.

These are all basically the same equation, just written differently. Which equation you should use depends on what information you've got, and what you need to calculate.

Example — Maths Skills

A battery has an e.m.f. of 0.15 V and an internal resistance of 0.50 Ω. Calculate the terminal p.d. when the current flowing through the battery is 6.0 mA.

The values for the e.m.f., the internal resistance and the current have been given in the question — so rearrange the equation $\varepsilon = V + Ir$ into $V = \varepsilon - Ir$ to calculate the terminal p.d. 6.0 mA = 0.0060 A.

$V = \varepsilon - Ir = 0.15 - (0.0060 \times 0.50) = 0.147 = 0.15$ V (to 2 s.f.)

As mentioned on the previous page, some power (or energy) is lost as heat when overcoming the internal resistance in a power supply. You can calculate the energy dissipated (lost) per second due to the internal resistance of a power supply using $P = I^2R$ (see page 158).

Example — Maths Skills

A cell has an internal resistance of 0.35 Ω and current flowing through it of 0.60 A. Calculate the energy dissipated due to the internal resistance of the cell every second.

$P = I^2r = (0.60)^2 \times 0.35 = 0.126 = 0.13$ W (to 2 s.f.)

So the energy dissipated every second is 0.13 J (to 2 s.f.)

Exam Tip
You'll be given $P = I^2R$ in your exam data and formulae booklet.

E.m.f. in series and parallel

For cells in series in a circuit, you can calculate the total e.m.f. of their combination by adding their individual e.m.f.s. This makes sense if you think about it, because each charge goes through each of the cells and so gains e.m.f. (electrical energy) from each one.

$$\varepsilon_{total} = \varepsilon_1 + \varepsilon_2 + \varepsilon_3 + ...$$

Example — Maths Skills

Three cells of negligible internal resistance are connected in series, as shown below. Cells *A*, *B* and *C* have an e.m.f. of 1.5 V, 1.0 V and 3.0 V respectively. Find the total e.m.f. of the combination of cells.

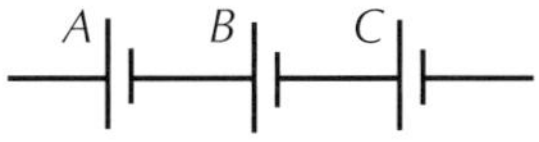

Total e.m.f. = $\varepsilon_A + \varepsilon_B + \varepsilon_C$ = 1.5 + 1.0 + 3.0 = 5.5 V

For identical cells in parallel in a circuit, the total e.m.f. of the combination of cells is the same size as the e.m.f. of each of the individual cells. This is because the amount of charge flowing in the circuit doesn't increase by adding cells in parallel, but the number of paths the charges can take does. The current will split equally between identical cells. The charge only gains e.m.f. from the cells it travels through — so the overall e.m.f. in the circuit doesn't increase.

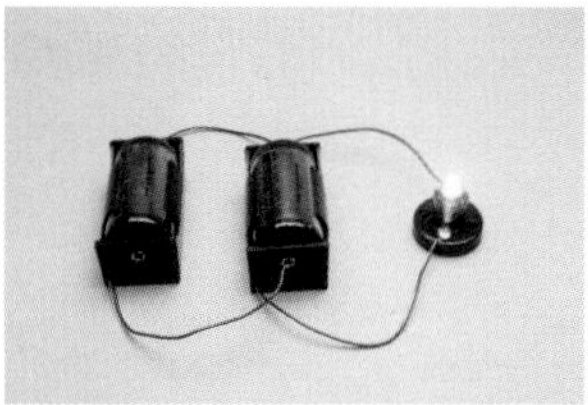

Figure 2: *The total e.m.f. of two identical batteries in parallel will follow the same rule as for cells — see left.*

$$\varepsilon_{total} = \varepsilon_1 = \varepsilon_2 = \varepsilon_3 = ...$$

Example — Maths Skills

Three identical cells, each with an e.m.f. of 2.0 V and an internal resistance of 0.20 Ω, are connected in parallel in the circuit shown to the right. A current of 0.90 A is flowing through resistor *R*. Calculate the total p.d. across the cells.

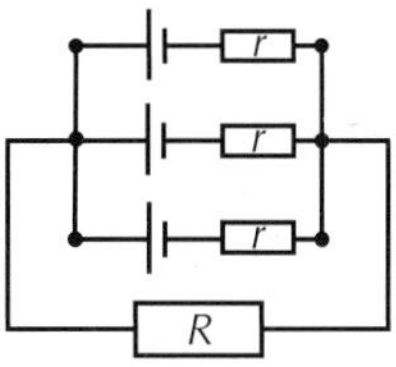

In a parallel circuit, the total p.d. supplied by any number of identical e.m.f. sources connected in parallel is equal to the p.d. supplied by one.

$V_{total} = V_1 = V_2 = V_3$

So we can find the total potential difference from the potential difference of one cell.

Rearranging $\varepsilon = V + Ir$, we get $V = \varepsilon - Ir$

Since the current flowing through the circuit is split equally between each of the three cells, the current through one cell is $I \div 3$.

$I \div 3 = 0.90 \div 3 = 0.30$ A

So, V_{total} = 2.0 – (0.30 × 0.20)
= 2.0 – 0.06
= 1.94 V
= 1.9 V (to 2 s.f.)

Tip: Make sure you have carried out a risk assessment before you start the experiment.

Measuring internal resistance and e.m.f.

PRACTICAL ACTIVITY GROUP 4

You can measure the internal resistance and e.m.f. of a cell or battery using the circuit in Figure 3.

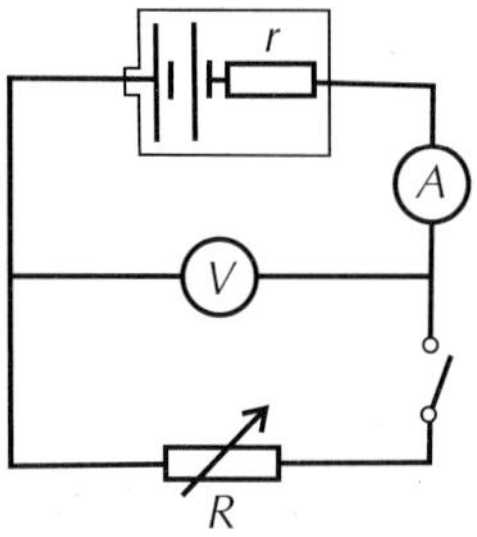

Figure 3: *The circuit needed to work out the internal resistance of a power source.*

1. Set the variable resistor (the load resistance) to its highest resistance.
2. Close the switch and record the current (I) through and potential difference (V) across the circuit.
3. Open the switch and close it again to get another set of current and potential difference readings for this load resistance. Then repeat to get a third set of values. Calculate the mean current and potential difference for this resistance from your results.
4. Decrease the resistance of the variable resistor by a small amount.
5. Repeat steps 2, 3 and 4 until you have a set of mean currents and potential differences for 10 different load resistances (over the widest possible range).
6. Plot a V-I graph for your mean data and draw a line of best fit — you get a straight-line graph (see Figure 4).
7. Make sure all other variables are kept constant when carrying out the experiment, including external factors like temperature (which affects the resistivity of materials, see page 148).

Tip: Remember that ammeters are always connected in series and voltmeters are always connected in parallel (see pages 143 and 146).

Tip: Remember not to include any anomalous measurements when calculating mean values.

Analysing the results

You can rearrange the equation $\varepsilon = V + Ir$ (from page 164) to get $V = -rI + \varepsilon$. The equation of a straight line is $y = mx + c$, where m = gradient and c = y-intercept. Since ε and r are constants, $V = -rI + \varepsilon$ is just the equation of a straight line.

You can just read ε and r from the graph — the intercept on the vertical axis is ε and the gradient is $-r$. As the graph is a straight line, you can find the gradient of the graph by dividing the change in y (p.d.) by the change in x (current).

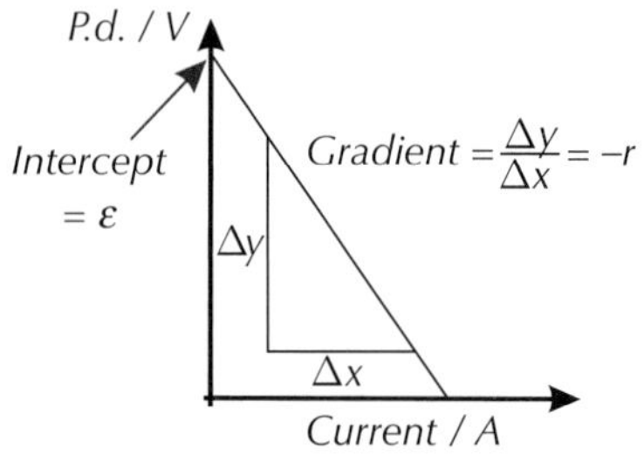

Figure 4: *Using a V-I graph to calculate e.m.f. and internal resistance.*

Tip: You can measure the approximate e.m.f. of a power source by connecting a high-resistance voltmeter across its terminals. Since the resistance of the voltmeter is so high, a very small current will flow, so the lost volts due to the internal resistance will be negligible. But the value you measure will still be very slightly less than the true e.m.f.

Practice Questions — Application

Q1 A power source has an e.m.f. of 2.50 V. The terminal potential difference is 2.24 V. Calculate the lost volts (v) for this power source.

Q2 A battery has a terminal potential difference of 4.68 V and an internal resistance of 0.89 Ω when 0.63 A of current is flowing through it. Calculate the e.m.f. of the battery.

Q3 The power source in a circuit has an e.m.f. of 15.0 V. The internal resistance of the power source is 8.28×10^{-3} Ω. Calculate the load resistance of the circuit when the current flowing through the power source is 26.1 A.

Q4 A power source has a current of 1.2 A flowing through it and an internal resistance of 0.50 Ω. Calculate the energy dissipated in the internal resistance of the power source each second.

Q5 A student varies the load resistance in a circuit to produce the *V-I* graph shown below.

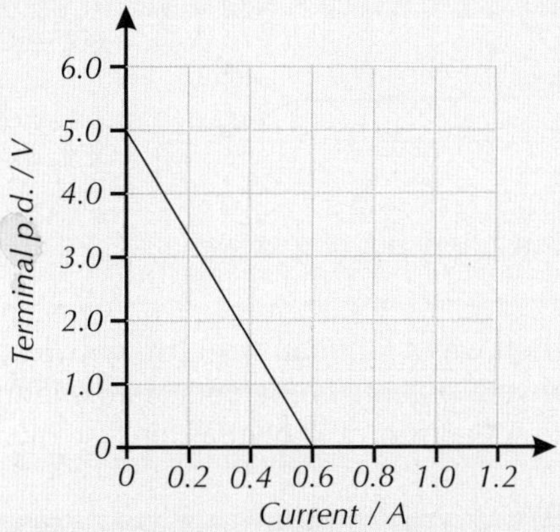

a) Use the graph to find the e.m.f. (ε) of the power supply.

b) Use the graph to find the internal resistance of the power supply.

c) Describe how the graph would be different if the student swapped the power supply for one with the same e.m.f. but half the internal resistance.

Practice Questions — Fact Recall

Q1 What is the load resistance in a circuit?

Q2 What units is electromotive force measured in?

Q3 Explain what lost volts are.

Q4 What do the gradient and vertical intercept on a *V-I* graph for a power supply show?

Tip: For all these questions assume that the resistance due to the wires in the circuit is negligible.

Exam Tip
In the exam, the examiners could write 'find the terminal p.d. of a battery' or 'find the p.d. across the terminals of a battery'. They mean exactly the same thing.

Tip: Remember, voltage and potential difference (p.d.) are the same thing.

10. Conservation of Energy and Charge in Circuits

Learning Objectives:

- Understand Kirchhoff's first and second laws as applied to electrical circuits.
- Understand Kirchhoff's second law in terms of the conservation of energy.
- Be able to calculate the resistance of two or more resistors in series, using $R = R_1 + R_2 + R_3 + ...$
- Be able to calculate the resistance of two or more resistors in parallel, using $\frac{1}{R} = \frac{1}{R_1} + \frac{1}{R_2} + \frac{1}{R_3} + ...$
- Be able to analyse circuits with components in both series and parallel.

Specification Reference 4.3.1

Conservation of energy is another topic you'll probably have met at GCSE. Questions on this stuff are almost guaranteed to be in the exam so I've put in a lot of time and effort to make sure this topic's as easy to grasp as possible...

Conservation of charge

As charge flows through a circuit, it doesn't get used up or lost. This means that whatever charge flows into a junction will flow out again. Since current is rate of flow of charge, it follows that whatever current flows into a junction is the same as the current flowing out of it.

Example

If a charge of 6 C flows into a junction...

$Q_1 = 6\text{ C} \Rightarrow I_1 = 6\text{ A}$

$Q_2 = 2\text{ C} \Rightarrow I_2 = 2\text{ A}$

$Q_3 = 4\text{ C} \Rightarrow I_3 = 4\text{ A}$

$I_1 = I_2 + I_3$

... a charge of 6 C must flow out of it as well.

Gustav Kirchhoff was a German scientist who developed a set of laws for the current through and potential difference across different components in a circuit. Conservation of current is known as his first law.

Figure 1: *Gustav Kirchhoff, the German scientist that formulated Kirchhoff's laws.*

Kirchhoff's first law

The total current entering a junction = the total current leaving it.

Conservation of energy

Energy is conserved. You already know that. In electrical circuits, energy is transferred round the circuit. Energy transferred to a charge is e.m.f. (see page 163), and energy transferred from a charge is potential difference (p.d.). In a closed loop, these two quantities must be equal if energy is conserved (which it is).

Kirchhoff's second law:

The total e.m.f. around a series circuit = the sum of the p.d.s across each component.

This is Kirchhoff's second law in symbols:

$$\varepsilon = \Sigma IR$$

This symbol means 'sum of'.

Applying Kirchhoff's laws

A typical exam question will give you a circuit with bits of information missing, leaving you to fill in the gaps. Not the most fun... but on the plus side you get to ignore any internal resistance stuff (unless the question tells you otherwise)... hurrah. You need to remember the following rules:

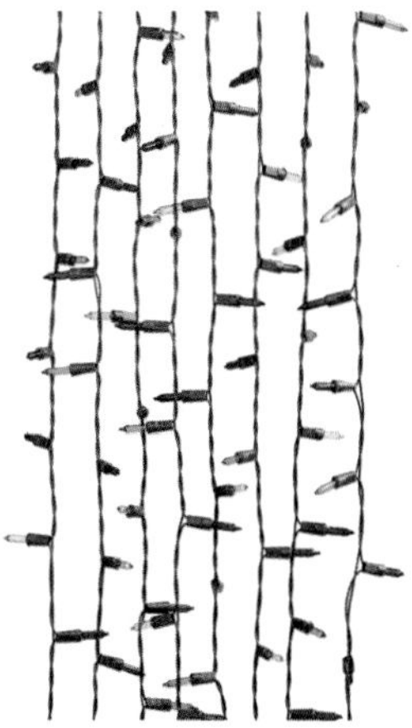

Figure 2: Fairy lights are the classic example of a series circuit.

Series circuits

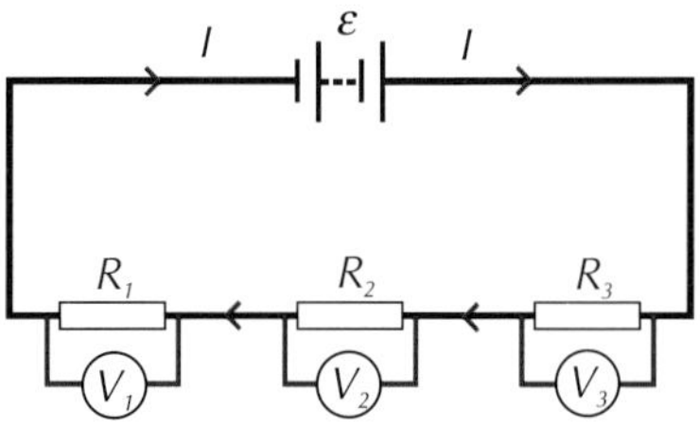

- There will be the same current at all points of the circuit (since there are no junctions).
- The e.m.f. is split between the components (by Kirchhoff's 2nd law), so:

$$\varepsilon = V_1 + V_2 + V_3$$

- The voltage splits proportionally to the resistance, as $V = IR$.

Example

If you had a 1 Ω resistor and a 3 Ω resistor, you'd get 1/4 of the p.d. across the 1 Ω resistor and 3/4 across the 3 Ω.

Tip: Remember that even in series circuits, voltmeters are placed in parallel with components.

- $V = IR$, so if I is constant:

$$IR = IR_1 + IR_2 + IR_3 \text{ where } R \text{ is the total resistance}$$

- Cancelling the Is gives:

$$R = R_1 + R_2 + R_3$$

Parallel circuits

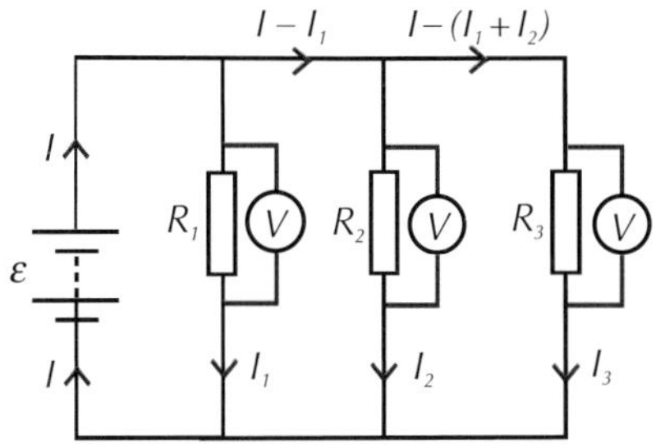

- The current is split at each junction, so:

$$I = I_1 + I_2 + I_3$$

- There is the same p.d. across all components as the p.d. across each branch of the circuit is equal to the e.m.f. So by substituting Ohm's Law rearranged for current, $I = \frac{V}{R}$, into the above equation we get:

$$\frac{V}{R} = \frac{V}{R_1} + \frac{V}{R_2} + \frac{V}{R_3}$$

- Cancelling the Vs gives:

$$\frac{1}{R} = \frac{1}{R_1} + \frac{1}{R_2} + \frac{1}{R_3}$$

Tip: Don't worry if you don't quite understand what's going on here... it'll all become clear when you have a look at the example on the next page.

Tip: Remember, R in both series and parallel circuits represents the total (or effective) resistance of the circuit.

Exam Tip
If an exam question tells you that something's got a negligible internal resistance, you can completely ignore it in your calculations.

Example — Maths Skills

A battery of e.m.f. 16 V and negligible internal resistance is connected in a circuit as shown. All values are given to two significant figures.

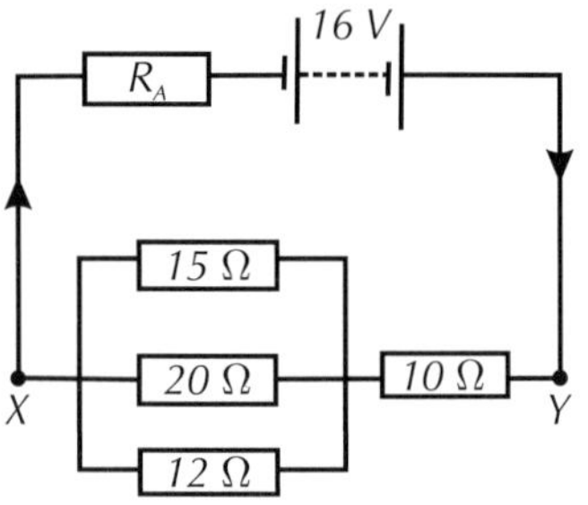

a) Show that the group of resistors between X and Y could be replaced by a single resistor of resistance 15 Ω.

You can find the combined resistance of the 15 Ω, 20 Ω and 12 Ω resistors using:

$1/R = 1/R_1 + 1/R_2 + 1/R_3 = 1/15 + 1/20 + 1/12 = 1/5 \Rightarrow R = 5\ \Omega$

So overall resistance between X and Y can be found by:

$R = R_1 + R_2 = 5 + 10 = 15\ \Omega$

b) If R_A = 20 Ω:

i) calculate the potential difference (p.d.) across R_A.

Careful — there are a few steps here. You need the p.d. across R_A, but you don't know the current through it. So start there:
Total resistance in circuit = 20 + 15 = 35 Ω, so the current through R_A can be found using $I = V_{total} \div R = \frac{16}{35}$ A
Then you can use $V = IR_A$ to find the p.d. across R_A:

$V = \frac{16}{35} \times 20 = 9.1428... = 9.1$ V (to 2 s.f.)

Exam Tip
If you get a question like this in the exam and you don't know where to start, write down all the information you do know and work out anything you can work out. You might spot how to do the question whilst you're playing around with the numbers.

ii) calculate the current in the 15 Ω resistor.

You know the current flowing into the group of three resistors and out of it, but not through the individual branches. But you know that their combined resistance is 5 Ω (from part a)) so you can work out the p.d. across the group:

$V = IR = \frac{16}{35} \times 5 = \frac{16}{7}$ V

The p.d. across the whole group is the same as the p.d. across each individual resistor, so you can use this to find the current through the 15 Ω resistor:

$I = V \div R = \frac{16}{7} \div 15 = 0.15238... = 0.15$ A (to 2 s.f.)

Tip: Keeping numbers as fractions in your working can help avoid rounding errors creeping into your answers.

Practice Questions — Application

Q1 A battery of negligible resistance is connected in a circuit as shown to the right.

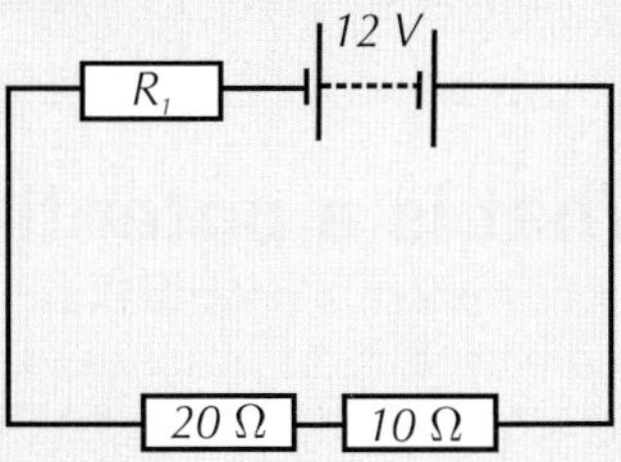

a) The total resistance of the circuit is 40 Ω. What is the resistance of the resistor marked R_1?

b) The current flowing through the battery is 0.4 A. What is the current flowing through the 10 Ω resistor?

Q2 The battery in the circuit below has a negligible internal resistance. The total resistance in the circuit is 10 Ω.

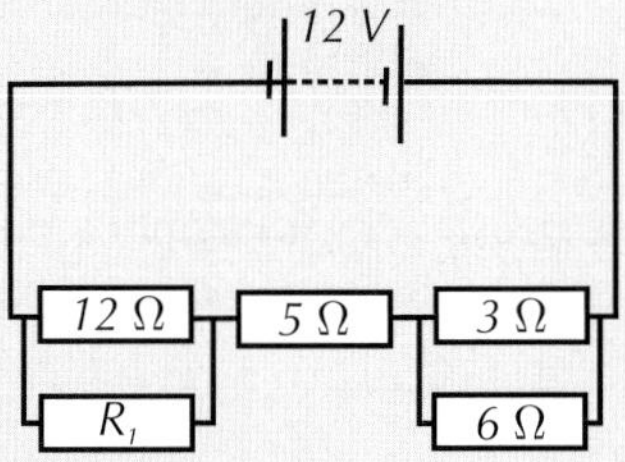

a) Calculate the resistance of R_1.

b) Calculate the potential difference across the 5 Ω resistor.

c) Calculate the current through the 6 Ω resistor.

Tip: Remember to calculate the resistance of resistors in parallel differently to the way you calculate resistors in series.

Practice Questions — Fact Recall

Q1 State Kirchhoff's first law.

Q2 State Kirchhoff's second law.

Q3 How are the resistors R_1 and R_2 connected if their total resistance is equal to $R_1 + R_2$?

Q4 Which type of circuit is $\frac{1}{R} = \frac{1}{R_1} + \frac{1}{R_2} + \frac{1}{R_3}$ true for?

11. The Potential Divider

Learning Objectives:

- Understand a potential divider circuit.
- Be able to use potential divider equations, such as $\frac{V_1}{V_2} = \frac{R_1}{R_2}$ and $V_{out} = \frac{R_2}{R_1 + R_2} V_{in}$.
- Understand potential divider circuits with variable components, e.g. LDRs and thermistors.
- Know techniques and procedures used to investigate potential divider circuits which may include a sensor such as a thermistor or an LDR (PAG4).

Specification Reference 4.3.3

Potential dividers can be used to supply a varying potential difference. If only that was all you needed to know about them, but I'm afraid there's a bit more...

What is a potential divider?

At its simplest, a **potential divider** is a circuit with a voltage source and a couple of resistors in series. The potential difference across the voltage source (e.g. a battery) is split across the resistors in the ratio of the resistances. You can write this as:

$$\frac{V_1}{V_2} = \frac{R_1}{R_2}$$

V_1 = *p.d. across resistor 1 (in V)*
V_2 = *p.d. across resistor 2 (in V)*
R_1 = *resistance of resistor 1 (in Ω)*
R_2 = *resistance of resistor 2 (in Ω)*

So you can choose resistances to supply a potential difference, V_{out}, between zero and the potential difference across the power supply.

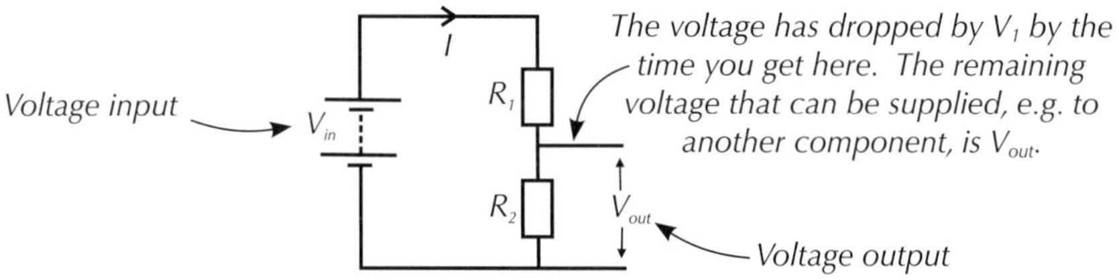

Voltage input
V_{in}
I
R_1
R_2
V_{out}
The voltage has dropped by V_1 by the time you get here. The remaining voltage that can be supplied, e.g. to another component, is V_{out}.
Voltage output

Figure 1: *A simple potential divider made up of two fixed resistors.*

You can find an equation relating V_{in} and V_{out} using $V = IR$ (see p.148). The total resistance in the circuit is $R = R_1 + R_2$, as the resistors are in series (see page 169). The total voltage across the resistors is V_{in} and the current through them is I, so $V_{in} = I(R_1 + R_2)$. Which when rearranged gives:

$$I = \frac{V_{in}}{R_1 + R_2}$$

You can also write I in terms of V_{out}, as $V_{out} = V_2$, and the resistance across R_2.

$$V_{out} = IR_2 \Rightarrow I = \frac{V_{out}}{R_2}$$

Substituting I into the previous equation and rearranging gives:

$$V_{out} = \frac{R_2}{R_1 + R_2} V_{in}$$

Tip: Make sure when you're using this equation that you plug in R_2 as the resistor that you're measuring the voltage over — otherwise you'll get completely the wrong answer.

Example — **Maths Skills**

For the circuit in Figure 1, $V_{in} = 9$ V and $V_{out} = 6$ V. Suggest one set of possible values for R_1 and R_2.

First find what fraction V_{out} is of V_{in}:

$$\frac{V_{out}}{V_{in}} = \frac{6}{9} = \frac{2}{3} \Rightarrow V_{out} = \frac{2}{3} V_{in}$$

$$V_{out} = \frac{R_2}{R_1 + R_2} V_{in}, \text{ so } \frac{R_2}{R_1 + R_2} = \frac{2}{3}$$

This multiplies out to give $3R_2 = 2R_1 + 2R_2 \Rightarrow R_2 = 2R_1$

So you could have, say, $R_2 = 200\ \Omega$ and $R_1 = 100\ \Omega$.

This equation will work as long as something with relatively high resistance is connected across R_2. But if you connect something with a relatively small resistance, then you start to run into problems. The equivalent resistance of the component and R_2 will be notably less than R_2, and so will cause a significant change in the current in the circuit. This will mean the equation no longer works properly, and will not give you an accurate answer for V_{out}.

Tip: Voltmeters have a very high resistance. You can calibrate a voltmeter by connecting it across R_2 and setting it so that its reading matches the value of V_{out} given by the equation.

Light and temperature sensors

PRACTICAL ACTIVITY GROUP 4

A light-dependent resistor (see p.153) has a very high resistance in the dark, but a lower resistance in the light. An NTC thermistor (page 153) has a high resistance at low temperatures, but a much lower resistance at high temperatures (it varies in the opposite way to a normal resistor and to a much greater extent). By using one of these components in a potential divider, your V_{out} can vary with light or heat, so it works as a light or heat sensor.

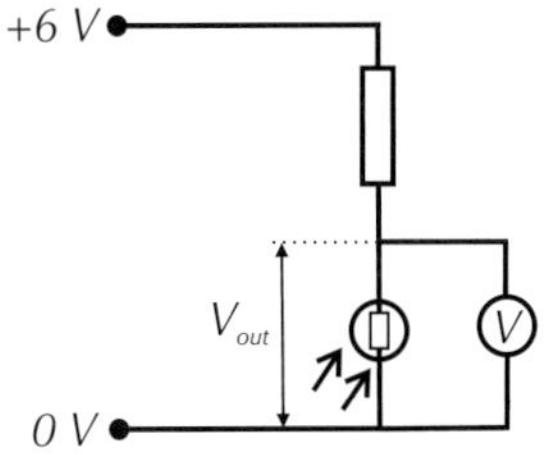
+6 V
V_out
V
0 V

Figure 2: A sensor used to detect changes in light levels — as it gets darker, V_{out} increases.

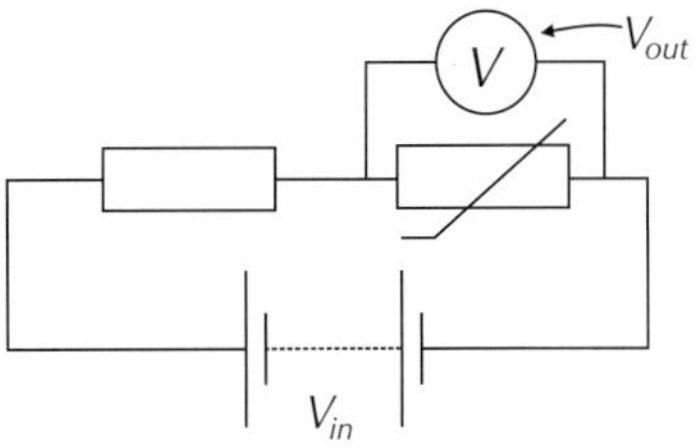
V
V_out
V_in

Figure 3: A heat sensor circuit.

Figure 3 shows the circuit you could use to create a heat sensor. Place the thermistor in a beaker of ice water. Measure the initial temperature of the water and record the voltage across the thermistor.

Heat the beaker gently using a Bunsen burner (make sure the water is well-stirred), and record the temperature and V_{out} at regular intervals over a suitable range (e.g. at 5 °C intervals over a range of 0-100 °C).

Plot a graph of voltage against temperature from your results. You should see that as the temperature of the water increased, V_{out} decreased. This is because as the NTC thermistor got hotter, its resistance decreased so it got a smaller 'share' of the total potential difference.

This kind of circuit could form the basis of a digital thermometer (the graph of voltage against temperature would be the thermometer's calibration curve), or could form part of the circuit for a thermostat in a central heating system.

Tip: Do a risk assessment before you start this experiment. Keep the rest of the circuit as far away from the Bunsen burner and the beaker of water as possible and make sure you waterproof the thermistor, e.g. by wrapping it in polythene.

Potentiometers

A potentiometer has a variable resistor replacing R_1 and R_2 of the potential divider (see Figure 5), but it uses the same idea. You move a slider or turn a knob to adjust the relative sizes of R_1 and R_2, which is useful when you want to change a voltage continuously, like in the volume control of a stereo.

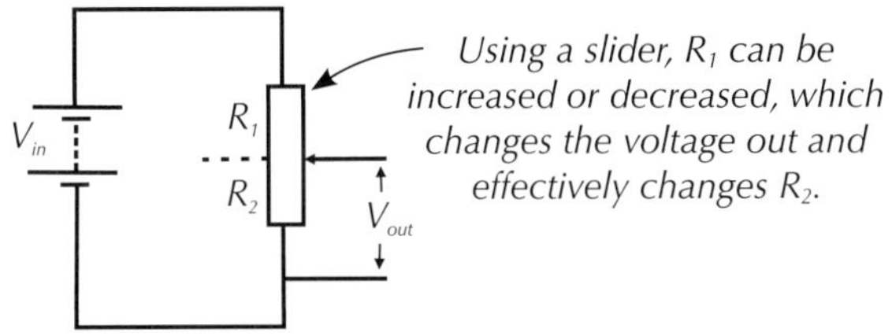
V_in
R_1
R_2
V_out
Using a slider, R_1 can be increased or decreased, which changes the voltage out and effectively changes R_2.

Figure 5: A potentiometer.

Figure 4: A rotary potentiometer. The relative sizes of R_1 and R_2 are controlled by the position of the dial.

Practice Questions — Application

Q1 The circuit below shows a simple potential divider.

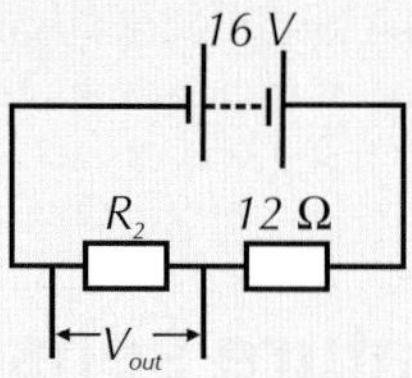

a) What would the output voltage be if $R_2 = 3.0\ \Omega$?

b) What would the resistance of R_2 have to be for V_{out} to be 5.0 V?

Q2 The potential divider below has the values of the resistors missed off.

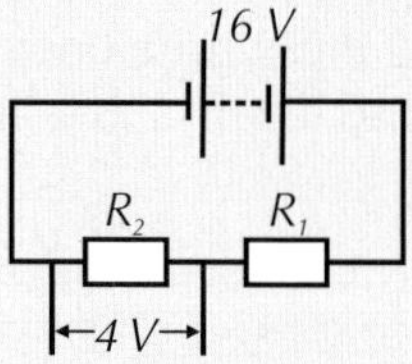

Give one set of possible values for resistors R_1 and R_2.

Q3 The circuit diagram below shows part of a temperature sensor for a greenhouse.

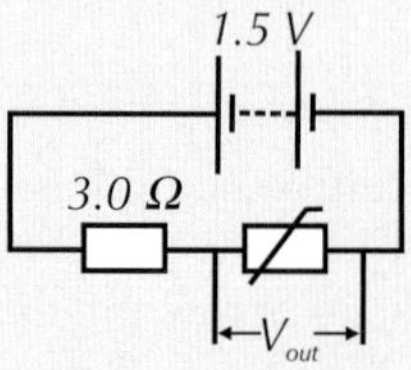

When the greenhouse gets too hot this temperature sensor sets off an alarm.

a) The resistance of the thermistor when the alarm first starts to go off is 1.5 Ω. Calculate the voltage output of the circuit at this point.

b) The gardener starts to grow tropical plants in his greenhouse. He wants the alarm to go off when the voltage output drops to 0.30 V. Calculate the new resistance of the thermistor when the alarm first starts to go off.

Practice Questions — Fact Recall

Q1 What is a potential divider?

Q2 Write down the equation you would use to work out the voltage output of a potential divider. Define all the symbols you use.

Q3 How can you make a light sensor using a potential divider?

Q4 What is a potentiometer? Give an example of when it could be used.

Section Summary

Make sure you know...

- The circuit symbols for various components and how to draw circuit diagrams using these symbols.
- The definition of electric current as rate of flow of charge, and how to calculate its size using $I = \frac{\Delta Q}{\Delta t}$.
- That the coulomb is the unit of charge.

cont...

- The direction of flow of conventional current is opposite to the direction of actual electron flow.
- That the net charge on an object is quantised and a multiple of e, where e equals 1.6×10^{-19} C.
- That current is the movement of electrons in metals and movement of ions in electrolytes.
- How number density of charge carriers, n, differs between conductors, semiconductors and insulators.
- That the mean drift velocity of charge carriers is a measure of the average speed of the charge carriers.
- Know how to use the equation $I = Anev$ to calculate the current through a conductor with cross-sectional area, A, charge carrier number density, n, and mean drift velocity, v.
- That the potential difference (p.d.) between two points is the work done to move a unit charge between those two points, and is measured in volts.
- How to calculate the work done, or energy transferred, using $W = VQ$.
- That, for electrons and other charged particles being accelerated from rest by a potential difference V, $eV = \frac{1}{2}mv^2$, where e is the charge of the particle, m is the particle's mass , and v is its velocity.
- That resistance is defined by Ohm's law, $R = \frac{V}{I}$, and it is measured in ohms.
- That the resistivity of a material is a measure of how much that particular material resists current flow.
- How to use the equation $R = \frac{\rho L}{A}$ to calculate the resistance of a conductor.
- How the resistivity of metals and semiconductors varies with temperature.
- The techniques and procedures used to determine the resistivity of a metal.
- That a diode is a semiconductor device which will only let current flow through it in one direction, and that current will only flow if the p.d. across the diode is greater than the threshold voltage.
- That a negative temperature coefficient (NTC) thermistor is a semiconductor device whose resistance decreases with increasing temperature.
- That an LDR is a semiconductor device whose resistance decreases with increasing light intensity.
- How to carry out an experiment to investigate the electrical characteristics for a range of ohmic and non-ohmic components.
- The I-V characteristics of a resistor, filament lamp, thermistor, diode and a light-emitting diode (LED).
- How to use the power equations, $P = VI$, $P = I^2R$ and $P = \frac{V^2}{R}$.
- How to calculate energy transferred by an electrical component using $W = VIt$.
- That the kilowatt-hour (kWh) is a unit of energy and it can be used to calculate the cost of energy.
- What is meant by the internal resistance and electromotive force (e.m.f.) of a power supply.
- How to calculate the energy transferred by a source of e.m.f. using $W = \varepsilon Q$.
- What is meant by 'terminal potential difference' and the distinction between e.m.f. and p.d. in terms of energy transfer.
- That the 'lost volts' of an e.m.f. source is the energy wasted per coulomb due to internal resistance.
- How to use the equations $\varepsilon = I(R + r)$ and $\varepsilon = V + Ir$ and how to deal with sources of e.m.f. in series and parallel.
- The method used to determine the internal resistance of a chemical cell or other source of e.m.f.
- Kirchhoff's first and second laws as applied to electrical circuits, including understanding Kirchhoff's second law in terms of the conservation of energy.
- How to analyse circuits with components in both series and parallel.
- How to calculate the equivalent resistance of two or more resistors in series and in parallel.
- What is meant by a potential divider circuit and how to use the equations $\frac{V_1}{V_2} = \frac{R_1}{R_2}$ and $V_{out} = \frac{R_2}{R_1 + R_2} V_{in}$
- How to investigate potential divider circuits, which may include a sensor such as a thermistor or an LDR.

Exam-style Questions

1 Calculate the resistance of a component that has a power rating of 11 W if the potential difference being supplied is 230 V.

A $2.5 \times 10^3\ \Omega$

B $4.8 \times 10^3\ \Omega$

C $21\ \Omega$

D $5.8 \times 10^5\ \Omega$

(1 mark)

2 A wire made from a material with a constant resistivity ρ is placed in a complete circuit. An experiment is carried out in which X is the independent variable, and Y is the dependent variable. Assume all other variables remain constant.
Which of the following X and Y quantities would produce the graph shown below?
Wire length = L, radius of the wire = r and resistance of a wire = R.

	X	Y
A	L	R
B	R	L
C	r	R
D	L	r

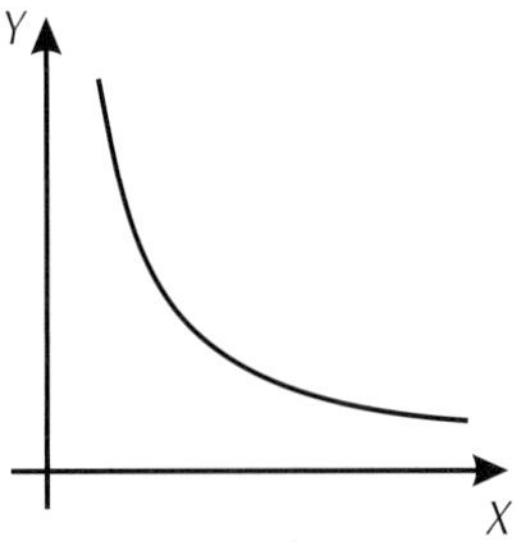

(1 mark)

3 In one minute, an electric heater connected to a 160 V power supply transfers 120 kJ of heat energy. What is the current flowing through the electric heater?

A 8.00×10^{-2} A

B 1.25×10^{-2} A

C 750 A

D 12.5 A

(1 mark)

4 Which of the following statements is true?

A A diode is an example of an ohmic conductor.

B The resistance of a diode is dependent on the light intensity of its surroundings.

C Diodes are designed to let current flow in one direction only.

D A diode is an example of an insulator.

(1 mark)

5 The circuit on the right has a cell connected in series to an ammeter, two resistors and a filament bulb.

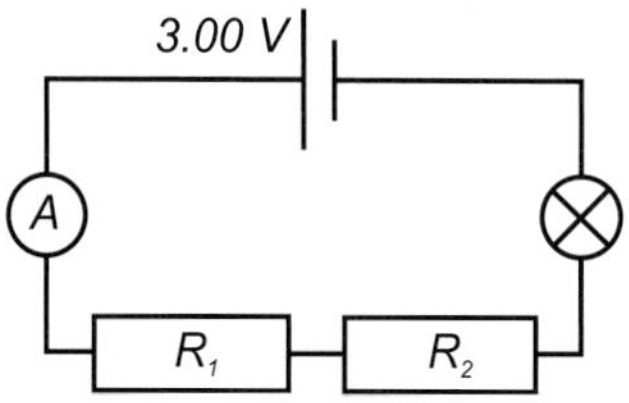

The current flowing through the cell is 0.724 A.

(a) Calculate the power of the cell.

(2 marks)

(b) Calculate the charge passing through the cell in exactly 5 minutes.

(2 marks)

(c) It takes 56.5 J of energy to move the charge through resistor R_1 in exactly 5 minutes. Calculate the potential difference across R_1.

(2 marks)

(d) The ammeter and the cell have negligible resistances. The filament lamp has a resistance of 2.00 Ω. Calculate the potential difference across resistor R_2.

(2 marks)

(e) The *I-V* graph for the filament lamp is shown on the right. State whether the filament lamp is an ohmic conductor. Explain your answer.

(1 mark)

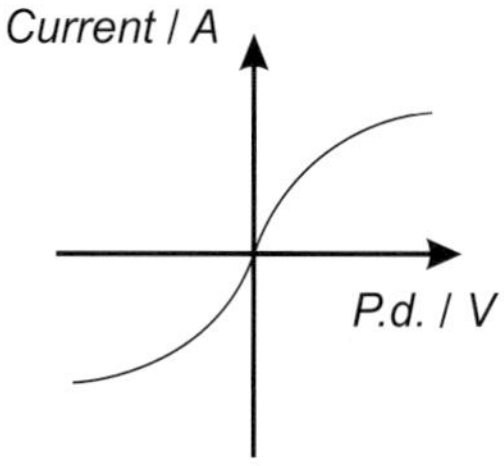

6 All batteries and power supplies have an internal resistance.

(a) Explain why a battery has an internal resistance.

(1 mark)

(b) Describe an experiment that could be carried out to accurately determine the internal resistance of a battery. Include a labelled circuit diagram in your answer.

(5 marks)

In an experiment to find the internal resistance of a battery, a student gathered the following data:

Terminal voltage (V)	Current (A)
1.00	2.79
3.00	2.36
4.00	1.18
6.00	1.71
8.00	1.29
9.00	1.07

(c) Draw a *V-I* graph of the data shown in the table.

(2 marks)

(d) Use the graph to find the e.m.f. of the battery.

(1 mark)

(e) Use the graph to determine the internal resistance of the battery.

(2 marks)

7 The circuit shown in **Fig 7.1** contains a battery with an e.m.f. of 12 V with a negligible internal resistance.
Component *A* has a resistance that varies with temperature.

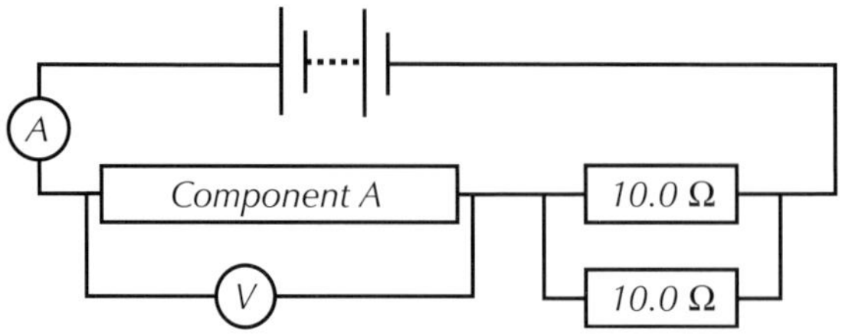

Fig 7.1

At 298 K the resistance of component *A* is 10.0 Ω.

(a) Calculate the total resistance in the circuit at 298 K.

(2 marks)

(b) Calculate the potential difference across component *A* at 298 K.

(2 marks)

Component *A* is cooled to 96 K. The resistance of the component drops to 3.21 mΩ.

(c) Calculate the current flowing through component *A* at 96 K.

(2 marks)

(d) Component *A* is a wire with a cross-sectional area of 3.05×10^{-6} m^2 and a length of 3.00 cm. Calculate the resistivity of the wire's material at 96 K.

(2 marks)

8 This question is about potential dividers.

(a) Draw a circuit to show the set-up of a potential divider using the following components: two cells (connected in series), a thermistor, a resistor and wires. The circuit must be set up so that the output voltage is the same as the potential difference across the resistor.

(2 marks)

Use the circuit drawn in part (a) to answer the following questions.

(b) The two cells connected in series provide an e.m.f. of 22 V. The resistor has a resistance of 6.0 Ω. At a temperature of 12°C the resistance of the thermistor is 9.2 Ω. Calculate the output voltage. Assume the cells have negligible internal resistance.

(1 mark)

(c) Calculate the energy dissipated by the resistor when the potential divider is used for 12 minutes.

(2 marks)

(d) The temperature of the circuit increases to 21°C. The output voltage is now 13 V. Calculate the resistance of the thermistor at 21°C.

(2 marks)

1. Progressive Waves

Waves are just vibrations. They transfer energy, but once they've passed through a region, everything goes back to normal... like they were never there.

What is a progressive wave?

A **progressive wave** (moving wave) carries energy from one place to another without transferring any material. Imagine a buoy bobbing up and down on a water wave — the buoy doesn't move from its location except to move up and down as the wave passes.

A wave is caused by something making particles or fields (e.g. electric or magnetic fields) oscillate (or vibrate) at a source. These oscillations pass through the medium (or field) as the wave travels, carrying energy with them in the direction of travel. A wave transfers this energy away from its source — so the source of the wave loses energy. You can tell waves carry energy from looking at the effects different waves can have. For example:

- Electromagnetic waves cause things to heat up.
- X-rays and gamma rays transfer so much energy that they knock electrons out of their orbits, causing ionisation.
- Loud sounds cause large oscillations of air particles which can make things vibrate.
- Sea waves can be used to generate electricity.

Wave basics

There are lots of quantities that you can use to describe a wave.

- **Displacement**, x, measured in metres
  — how far a point on the wave has moved from its undisturbed position. Going back to the buoy example above, the displacement would be how high the buoy is above sea level, or how low it is below sea level.
- **Amplitude**, A, measured in metres
  — the maximum magnitude of the displacement, i.e. the distance from the undisturbed position to the crest, or trough (see Figure 1). The amplitude of a bobbing buoy would be the distance from the undisturbed position (sea level) to the highest point it reaches above sea level, or the lowest point it reaches below sea level.

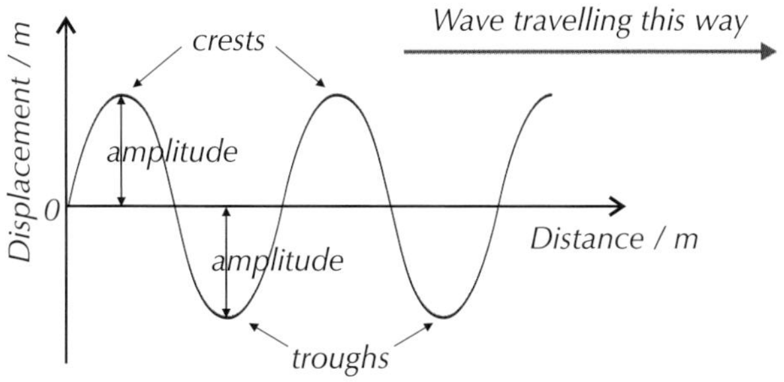

Figure 1: *Diagram showing the displacement and amplitude of a wave.*

Learning Objectives:

- Understand the meaning of the term 'progressive waves'.
- Know the meaning of the terms displacement, amplitude, wavelength, period, frequency and phase difference in relation to waves.
- Understand what transverse waves and longitudinal waves are.
- Understand and be able to draw graphical representations of transverse and longitudinal waves.

Specification Reference 4.4.1

Tip: Make sure you learn all these wave properties, their symbols and the units they're given in. You could be asked to find them from a graph or a diagram of a wave.

Tip: Amplitude can either be measured at a crest or a trough. It doesn't have direction, only magnitude.

Tip: One oscillation or wave cycle is a 'section' of a wave from crest to crest, or trough to trough.

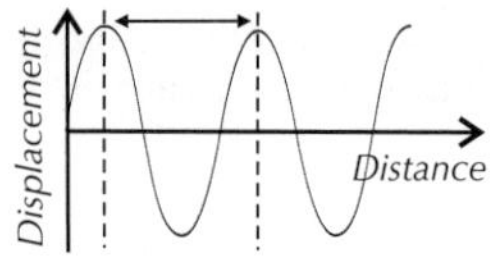

- **Wavelength**, λ, measured in metres
  — the length of one whole wave oscillation or wave cycle, e.g. the distance between two crests (or troughs) of a wave.

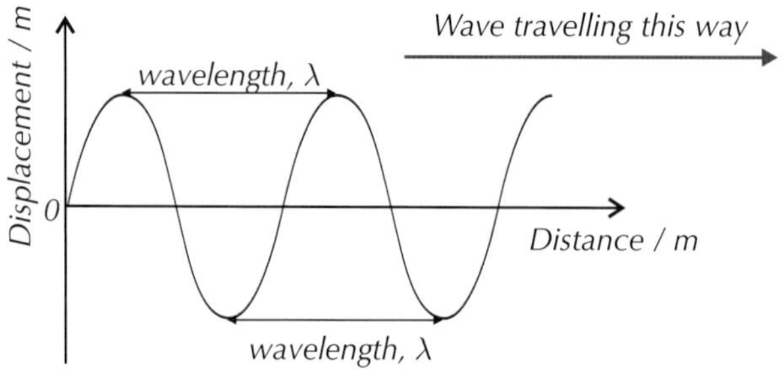

Figure 2: *Diagram to show the wavelength of a wave.*

Tip: Waves with different frequencies and wavelengths can have very different properties (see page 188).

- **Period**, T, measured in seconds
  — the time taken for one whole wave cycle, e.g. the time it takes a buoy to go from its highest point, back to its highest point again.
- **Frequency**, f, measured in hertz
  — the number of whole wave cycles (oscillations) per second passing a given point. Or the number of whole wave cycles (oscillations) given out from a source per second. For a buoy, it's the number of times it reaches its highest point per second.
- **Phase**
  — a measurement of the position of a certain point along the wave cycle.
- **Phase difference**
  — the amount by which one wave lags behind another wave, or the difference in phase between two points on a single wave.

Tip: The phase difference between two waves is the difference between a point on one wave, and the next identical point on the second wave.

Phase and phase difference can be measured in angles (in degrees or radians) or in fractions of a cycle (see page 201).

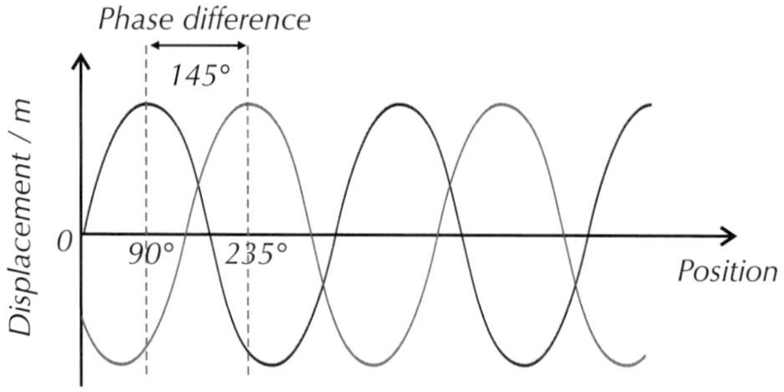

Figure 3: *Diagram to show the phase difference between waves.*

Types of wave

Waves can be either **transverse waves** or **longitudinal waves**.

Transverse waves

In transverse waves, the oscillation of the particles or field (i.e. the displacement) is at right angles to the direction of energy propagation (the direction the wave is travelling in). All electromagnetic waves (see page 187) are transverse. They travel as oscillating magnetic and electric fields — with oscillations perpendicular to the direction of energy transfer. Other examples of transverse waves are ripples on water, waves on strings, and some types of earthquake shock wave (S-waves).

Figures 4 and 5 show how a transverse wave can be demonstrated using a long spring.

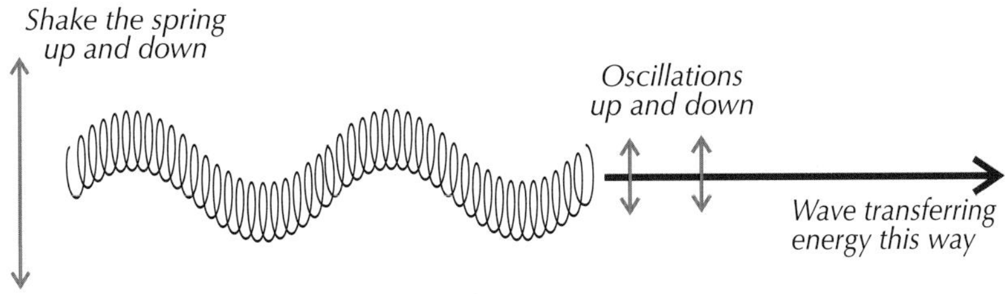

Figure 4: *A transverse wave on a spring.*

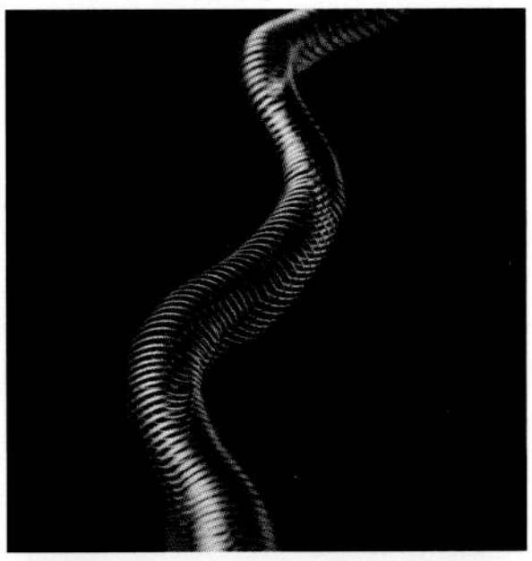

Figure 5: *A photograph of a transverse wave produced on a spring.*

You can work out what direction a point on a transverse wave is moving in when given a snapshot of the wave.

Example

Look at the snapshot of the wave below. Which direction is point A on the wave moving in?

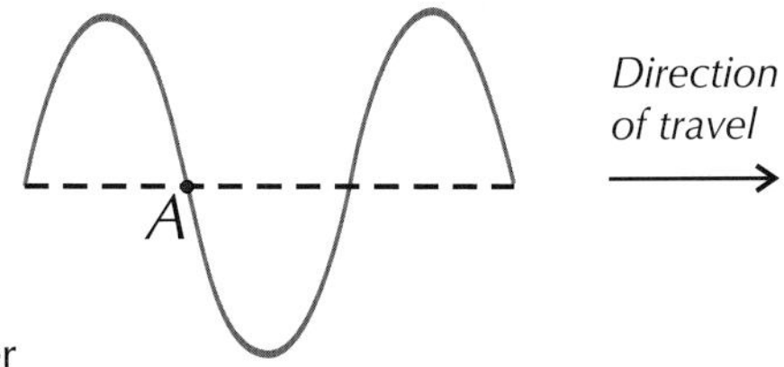

1. Look at which direction the wave is travelling in — here the wave is moving from left to right.
2. The displacement of the wave just to the left of point A is greater than point A's. So as the wave travels along, point A will need to move upwards to have that displacement. (If the displacement to the left was less than point A's, point A would need to move down.)

Tip: This can be pretty confusing at first. If you're struggling, try drawing the wave moved slightly further along in the direction of travel. Look at how it lines up with the point you're given. If the wave is now above the point, it's moving upwards. If it's below the point, it's moving downwards.

There are two main ways of drawing transverse waves, as shown in Figure 6. They can be shown as graphs of displacement against distance along the path of the wave, or as graphs of displacement against time for a point as the wave passes.

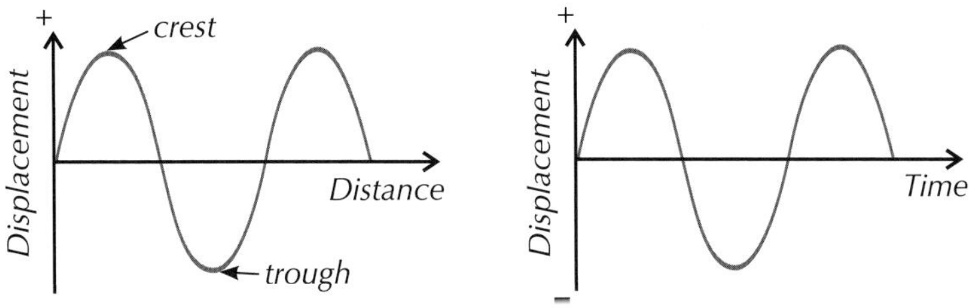

Figure 6: *Two ways of representing transverse waves graphically — as a displacement-distance graph (on the left) or as a displacement-time graph (on the right).*

Tip: When you use an oscilloscope (p.183) to look at a wave, it produces a displacement-time graph.

Both sorts of graph often give the same shape, so make sure you check out the label on the *x*-axis. On a displacement-distance graph, the separation between two crests (a wave cycle) gives the wavelength of the wave. On a displacement-time graph, this gives the period of the wave.

Displacements upwards from the centre line are given a + sign. Displacements downwards are given a – sign.

Tip: Displacement is a vector so it has direction and magnitude (see page 34) — if a point has moved below its undisturbed position, it will have a negative displacement.

Longitudinal waves

In longitudinal waves the oscillations of the particles or field are in the direction of energy propagation. The most common example of a longitudinal wave is sound. A sound wave consists of alternate compressions and rarefactions of the medium it's travelling through. That's why sound can't go through a vacuum. Some earthquake shock waves (P-waves) are longitudinal.

Figures 7 and 8 show how a longitudinal wave can be demonstrated using a long spring.

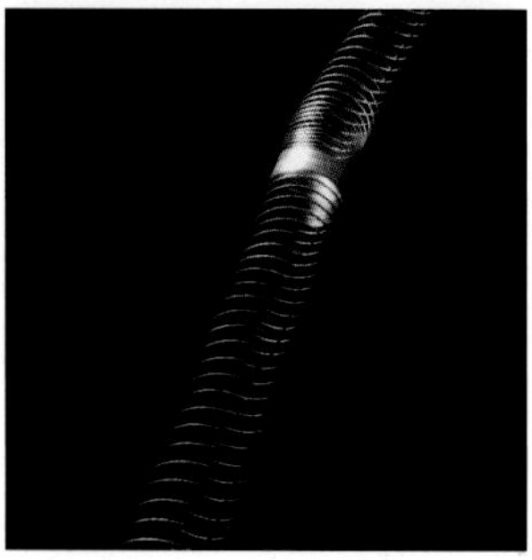

Figure 7: *A photograph of a longitudinal wave produced on a spring.*

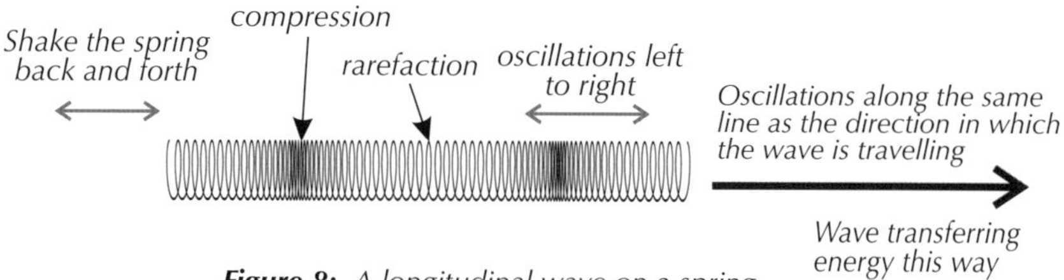

Figure 8: *A longitudinal wave on a spring.*

It's hard to represent longitudinal waves graphically. You can plot them on displacement-distance or displacement-time graphs, just like transverse waves. They'll give you graphs that look exactly like the graphs for transverse waves in Figure 6. This can be confusing, as, unlike transverse waves, these graphs look nothing like the waves themselves. You'll usually see longitudinal waves plotted as displacement-time graphs.

Practice Questions — Application

Q1 The diagram on the right shows a snap shot of a transverse wave. The point marked *X* is moving upwards. What is the direction of travel of the wave?

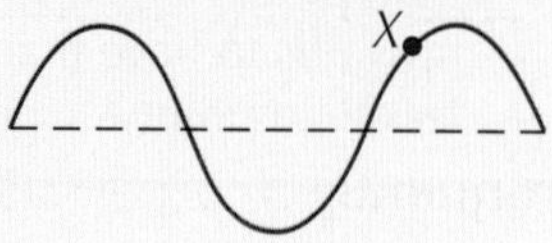

Q2 For the wave shown, find:

a) the displacement at A,

b) the amplitude,

c) the wavelength.

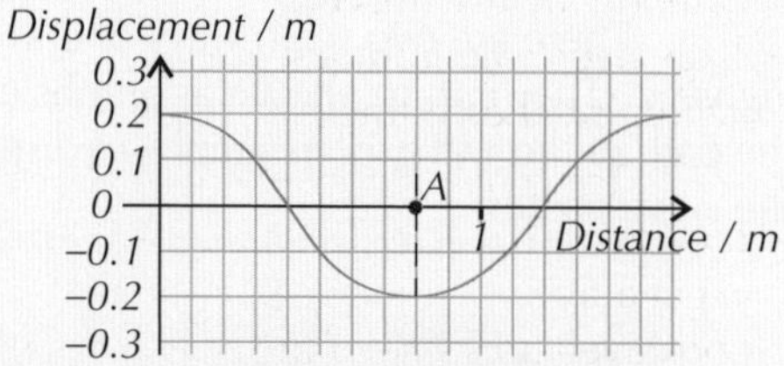

Practice Questions — Fact Recall

Q1 How does a wave transfer energy through a region?

Q2 On the diagram below, what's shown by *A*, *B* and *C*?

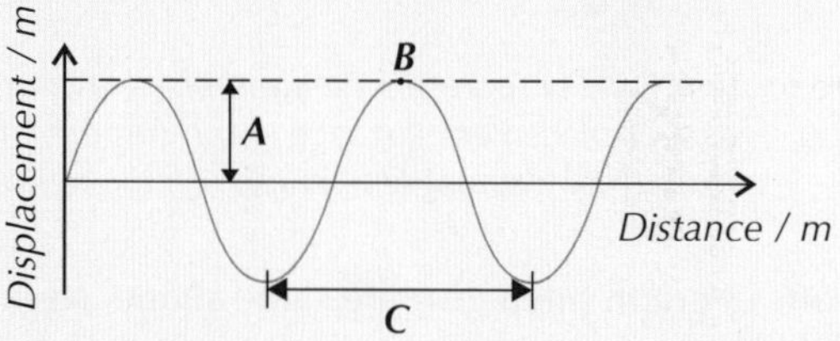

Q3 Describe what is meant by the phase difference of two waves.

Q4 Describe the difference between longitudinal and transverse waves in terms of their oscillations.

Q5 Sketch a displacement-time graph for a longitudinal wave.

2. Frequency, Speed and Intensity

Now it's time for a bit of maths. You'll have probably come across the frequency and wave speed equations before now, but the new and exciting world of intensity is also coming up in this topic...

Frequency and period

Frequency and period are linked to each other. The number of whole wave cycles (oscillations) per second is 1 ÷ (time taken for one oscillation). So, by definition, the frequency is the inverse of the period:

$$f = \frac{1}{T}$$

f *= frequency in Hz (= s^{-1})*

T *= period in s*

Example — Maths Skills

A wave has a period of 0.25 seconds.
How many oscillations will pass a given point each second?

The number of oscillations passing a point per second is the frequency, so

$f = \frac{1}{T} = \frac{1}{0.25} = 4.0$ Hz

So 4.0 oscillations pass each second.

Frequency and period on an oscilloscope

PRACTICAL ACTIVITY GROUP 5

A cathode ray **oscilloscope** (CRO) produces a function of voltage over time from a signal generator. The displayed function is called a trace.

The type of trace you get on an oscilloscope depends on the source it is connected to. If you plug an AC (alternating) supply into an oscilloscope, you get a trace that goes up and down in a regular pattern — some of the time it's positive and some of the time it's negative. A microphone converts sound waves into electrical signals which can be seen on an oscilloscope.

An example of an oscilloscope display is shown in Figure 2.

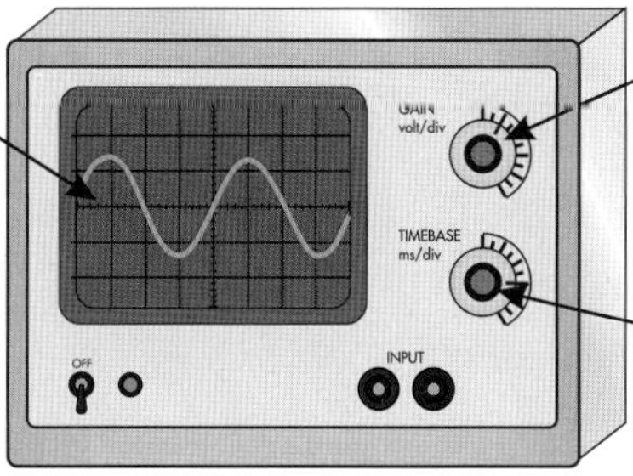

Figure 2: *A diagram of an oscilloscope, showing its display along with its gain and timebase dials.*

Learning Objectives:

- Be able to use the equation $f = \frac{1}{T}$.
- Know techniques and procedures involved in using an oscilloscope to determine frequency (PAG5).
- Be able to use the equation for the speed of a wave, $v = f\lambda$.
- Be able to use the equation for the intensity of a progressive wave, $I = \frac{P}{A}$.
- Know that, for a wave, intensity $\propto$ (amplitude)^2

Specification Reference 4.4.1

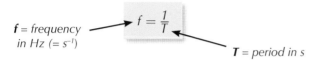

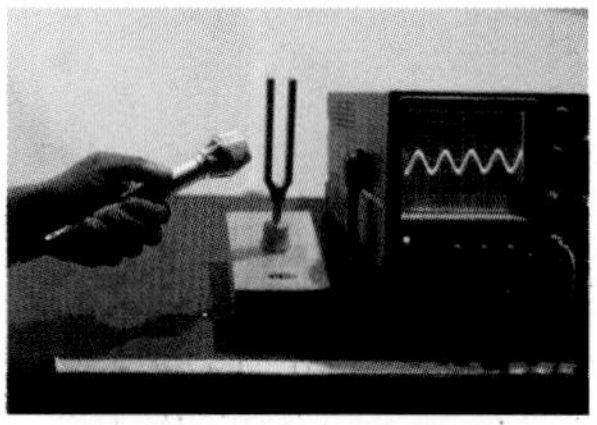

Figure 1: *An oscilloscope displaying the sound wave produced by a tuning fork.*

Tip: As always, remember to do a risk assessment before working in the lab.

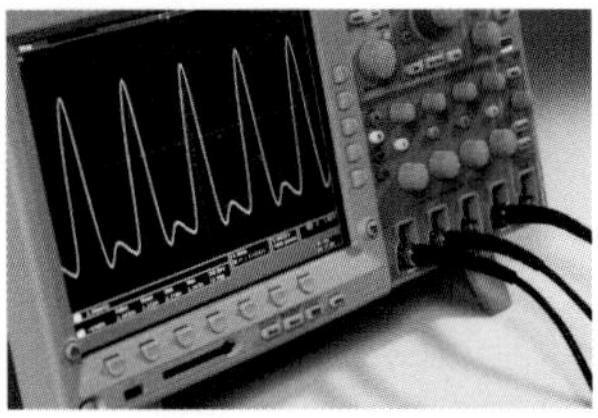

Figure 3: An example of an oscilloscope being used to measure a wave.

The screen is split into squares called divisions. The vertical axis is in volts. The volts per division shown on this axis is controlled by the gain dial. The horizontal axis is in seconds — also called the timebase. The seconds per division shown on this axis is controlled by the timebase dial. You can alter the gain and timebase to make it easy to read off measurements.

You can use oscilloscope traces to calculate wave properties, like frequency.

Tip: Make sure you carefully read the timebase and gain on an oscilloscope before you use it to do any calculations.

Example — Maths Skills

Find the frequency shown by the oscilloscope trace on the right. The timebase is set to 4.0 ms / div.

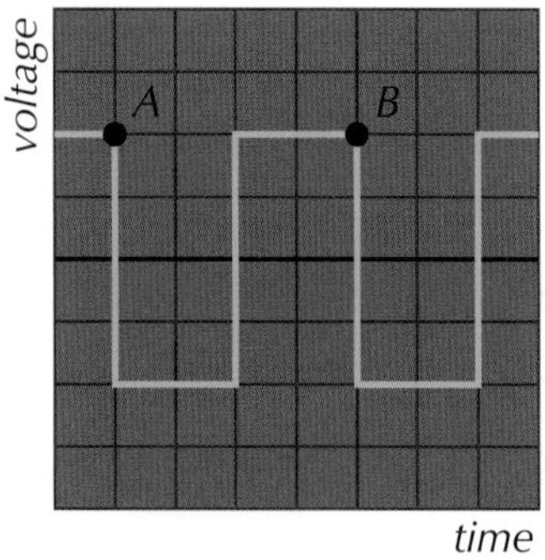

First calculate the period of the trace. Point A to B is one cycle — it is 4 squares wide.

This means for one cycle, it takes

4×4.0 ms = 16 ms.

So, the period T = 16 ms.

Now, use $f = \frac{1}{T}$ to find the frequency:

$$f = \frac{1}{16 \times 10^{-3}} = 62.5\,\text{Hz} = 63\,\text{Hz (to 2 s.f.)}$$

Exam Tip
If you can remember 1 Hz = 1 s^{-1}, it'll help you get your units right. Don't write s^{-1} in an exam though — Hz is the standard unit for frequency (see p.24 for more on units).

Wave speed

You can use speed = distance ÷ time to find wave speed.

$$v = \frac{d}{t}$$

v = wave speed in ms^{-1}

d = distance in m

t = time in s

Exam Tip
You don't need to know this derivation, but this should help you understand where the equation comes from, and why it works.

You can derive the wave speed equation by imagining how long it takes for the crest of a wave to move across a distance of one wavelength.

- The distance travelled is the wavelength, λ.
- The time taken to travel one wavelength is the period of the wave, which is equal to $\frac{1}{f}$.

Now substitute these values into the equation above to get the speed of a wave in terms of wavelength and frequency:

$$\text{wave speed } (v) = \frac{\text{distance } (\lambda)}{\text{time } \left(\frac{1}{f}\right)}$$

Dividing something by $\frac{1}{f}$ is the same as multiplying it by f.

So you get the wave speed equation:

$$v = f\lambda$$

v = wave speed in ms^{-1}

λ = wavelength in m

f = frequency in Hz (= s^{-1})

Tip: Remember, you're not measuring how fast a physical point (like one molecule of rope) moves. You're measuring how fast a point on the wave pattern moves.

Example — Maths Skills

Below is a diagram of a water wave.
Calculate the speed of the wave, if the frequency is 5 Hz.

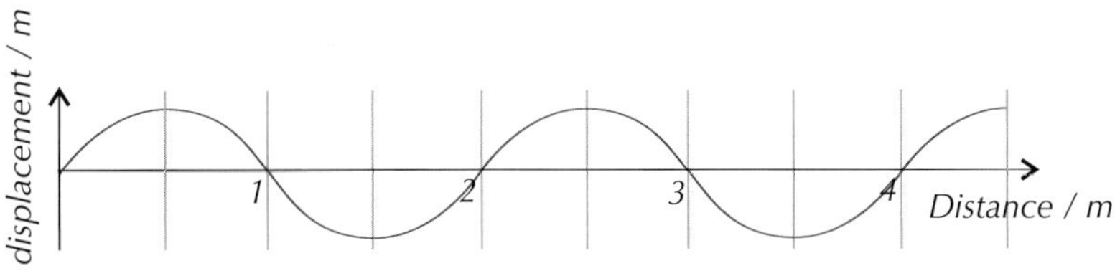

First find λ by calculating the distance, e.g., between the first two peaks:

$\lambda = 2.5 - 0.5 = 2$ m

Then substitute λ and f into $v = f\lambda$ to find the speed of the wave:

$v = f\lambda = 5 \times 2 = 10$ ms^{-1}

Tip: When a wave changes speed, its wavelength changes but its frequency remains constant (see p.192).

Intensity

When you talk about "brightness" for light or "loudness" for sound, what you really mean is how much light or sound energy hits your eyes or your ears per second. The scientific measure of this is **intensity**. Intensity is the rate of flow of energy per unit area at right angles to the direction of travel of the wave. It's measured in Wm^{-2}.

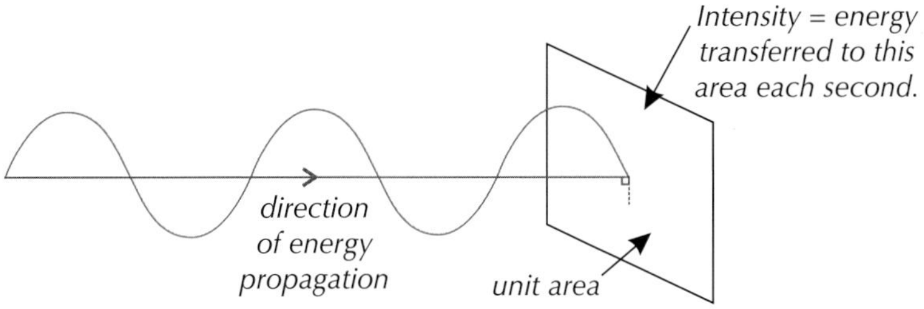

Figure 4: *A diagram demonstrating the intensity of a wave on a unit area.*

You can calculate intensity using the equation:

$$I = \frac{P}{A}$$

- ***I*** = intensity in Wm^{-2}
- ***P*** = power in W
- ***A*** = area (at right angles to the wave's motion) in m^2

Tip: Remember, power is a measure of energy transferred per second.

Example — Maths Skills

A 28.0 W sound wave is incident at right angles to the surface of a square metal plate. The plate has sides of length 1.20 m. Calculate the intensity of the sound wave on the metal plate.

Surface area of the plate, $A = 1.2 \times 1.2$
$= 1.44$ m^2

$$I = \frac{P}{A}$$

$$= \frac{28.0}{1.44} = 19.44... = 19.4 \text{ Wm}^{-2} \text{ (to 3 s.f.)}$$

Tip: If two variables are proportional like this, then you can say that one variable is equal to the other variable multiplied by a constant. E.g. Intensity = constant × (amplitude)². This is helpful for finding missing values.

The intensity of a wave is also proportional to its amplitude squared. You don't need to know why this is the case, but you do need to learn the proportionality relation:

$$\text{Intensity} \propto (\text{Amplitude})^2$$

Example — Maths Skills

A wave has an intensity of 18 Wm^{-2}, and an amplitude of 1.5 m. The wave's intensity is reduced to 2 Wm^{-2}. Calculate the new amplitude of the wave.

We know that intensity $\propto$ (amplitude)^2.

So, $\frac{\text{intensity}}{(\text{amplitude})^2} = \text{constant}$

This means that $\frac{\text{final intensity}}{(\text{final amplitude})^2} = \frac{\text{initial intensity}}{(\text{initial amplitude})^2}$

$$\Rightarrow \text{final amplitude} = \sqrt{\frac{\text{final intensity}}{\text{initial intensity}}} \times \text{initial amplitude}$$

$$= \sqrt{\frac{2}{18}} \times 1.5 = \frac{1}{3} \times 1.5 = 0.5\text{ m}$$

Practice Questions — Application

Q1 A wave hits a 0.2 m^2 panel at a right angle to the panel's surface. The intensity of the wave on the panel is 5 Wm^{-2}.

a) Calculate the power of the wave.

b) The amplitude of the wave is then doubled. Calculate the new intensity of the wave.

Q2 For the wave shown below:

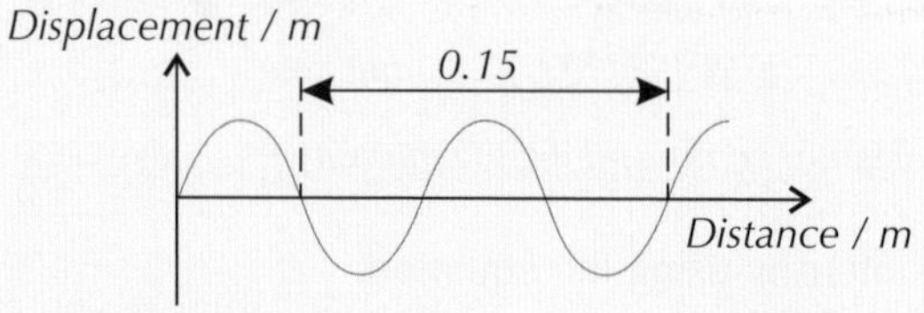

a) Find its wavelength.

b) Find how long it takes the wave to travel 1.0 m, given that the frequency is 30.0 Hz.

Practice Questions — Fact Recall

Q1 How would you calculate the frequency of a wave, given its period?

Q2 What are the two axes of an oscilloscope display?

Q3 Describe how you would find the frequency of a wave shown on an oscilloscope from the oscilloscope display.

Q4 What is the equation that links wave speed, frequency and wavelength?

Q5 Define the intensity of a progressive wave.

Q6 What is the proportionality relation between intensity and amplitude?

3. Electromagnetic Waves

Perhaps the most important family of waves in physics is the electromagnetic spectrum. You need to know all the different types of EM waves, their properties, and how these properties change depending on wavelength.

Learning Objectives:

- Know the properties of electromagnetic waves.
- Know the electromagnetic spectrum.
- Know the orders of magnitude of wavelengths of the principal EM radiations from radio waves to gamma rays.

Specification Reference 4.4.2

What are electromagnetic waves?

Electromagnetic (EM) waves are a group of transverse waves. They consist of vibrating electric and magnetic fields, not matter, which means they are able to travel through a vacuum. These electric and magnetic fields are always at right angles to each other and to the direction of travel.

All electromagnetic waves have some properties in common:

- They all travel at the same speed in a vacuum — 3.00×10^8 ms^{-1} (to 3 s.f.).
- Like all waves, they can be refracted, reflected, diffracted and can undergo interference.
- They can be polarised, because they are transverse.
- They all obey the wave equation, $v = f\lambda$ (like all waves).

Tip: The speed of EM waves in a vacuum is often referred to as *c*. It's an important number in quantum physics (see pages 225-237) and will be given to you in the data and formulae booklet.

EM waves form a continuous series of waves, called the **electromagnetic spectrum**. The electromagnetic spectrum is split into seven categories based on wavelength. From the longest to the shortest wavelength, these are: radio waves, microwaves, infrared (IR), visible light, ultraviolet (UV), X-rays and gamma rays (see Figure 1).

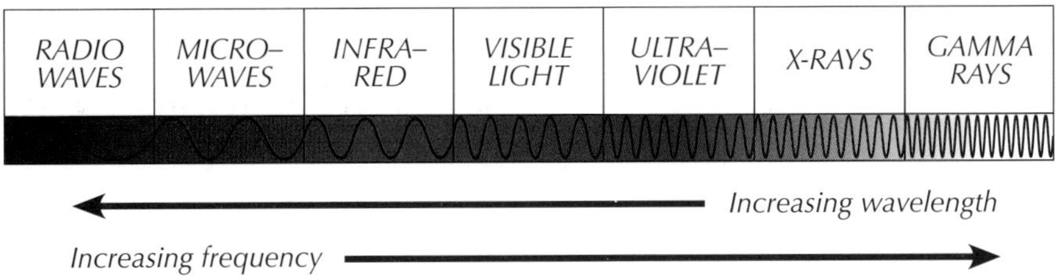

Figure 1: *The electromagnetic spectrum.*

Figure 2: *The visible light portion of the EM spectrum. Just like the colours above, each category of wave in the EM spectrum flows smoothly into the next one.*

Like all progressive waves, progressive EM waves carry energy. As you go along the spectrum, the frequency increases and the waves carry more energy. This is because the energy of an EM wave is proportional to its frequency (from $E = hf$, see p.225). So gamma rays have the highest energy, while radio waves have the lowest.

Towards the high frequency end of the UV range, waves become energetic enough to cause **ionisation**. This is where they transfer so much energy to an atomic electron, that the electron is removed from the atom. If this occurs in the human body it can kill cells or cause cancer. So, in general, the higher the frequency, the more dangerous the EM wave is.

Due to their wavelengths, different electromagnetic waves also behave differently in a given situation (e.g. some EM waves can diffract around hills, whilst others cannot). This means that electromagnetic waves have a range of uses. Figure 3 on the next page describes some of the most common uses.

Tip: Diffraction is where waves spread out, and it depends on the wavelength of the wave compared to the gap or obstacle causing the diffraction (p.204).

Figure 4: An infrared camera being used to monitor the skin temperature of people arriving at an airport. High skin temperature can be a sign of illnesses such as flu.

Figure 5: Banknotes contain a fluorescent ink pattern, making them harder to forge. It only shows up under UV light of the correct frequency.

Type	Approximate Wavelength /m	Penetration	Uses
Radio waves	10^{-1} — 10^{6}	Pass through matter.	Radio transmissions.
Microwaves	10^{-3} — 10^{-1}	Mostly pass through matter, but cause some heating.	Radar. Microwave cooking. TV transmissions.
Infrared (IR)	7×10^{-7} — 10^{-3}	Mostly absorbed by matter, causing it to heat up.	Heat detectors. Night vision cameras. Remote controls. Optical fibres.
Visible light	4×10^{-7} — 7×10^{-7}	Absorbed by matter, causing some heating.	Human sight. Optical fibres.
Ultraviolet (UV)	10^{-8} — 4×10^{-7}	Absorbed by matter. Cause some ionisation.	Sunbeds. Security marks that show up under UV.
X-rays	10^{-13} — 10^{-8}	Mostly pass through matter, but cause ionisation as they pass.	To see damage to bones and teeth. Airport security scanners. To kill cancer cells.
Gamma rays	10^{-16} — 10^{-10}	Mostly pass through matter, but cause ionisation as they pass.	Irradiation of food. Sterilisation of medical instruments. To kill cancer cells.

Figure 3: A table showing the different types of EM wave, their wavelength ranges, penetration properties, and examples of their uses.

Tip: Remember, $v = f\lambda$ (see page 184).

Practice Question — Application

Q1 A radio wave with wavelength of 2.40×10^{5} m is travelling through a vacuum. Calculate the frequency of the radio wave.

Practice Questions — Fact Recall

Q1 Are electromagnetic waves transverse or longitudinal waves?

Q2 Which type of wave in the EM spectrum has the highest energy?

Q3 State the wavelength range of the following parts of the electromagnetic spectrum:

a) microwaves b) ultraviolet light c) X-rays

Q4 State the three parts of the electromagnetic spectrum that are mostly absorbed by matter.

4. Polarisation

When we draw waves, we usually show them vibrating in a single plane. But when real waves are produced, they're usually oscillating in a lot of different directions. This is where polarisation comes in...

Learning Objectives:

- Understand what is meant by the term 'plane polarised waves'.
- Understand the polarisation of electromagnetic waves, e.g. light and microwaves.
- Know techniques and procedures used to observe polarising effects using light (PAG5).
- Know techniques and procedures used to observe polarising effects using microwaves (PAG5).

Specification References 4.4.1 and 4.4.2

Polarised waves

If you shake a rope to make a wave you can move your hand up and down or side to side or in a mixture of directions — it still makes a transverse wave. But if you try to pass waves in a rope through a vertical fence, the wave will only get through if the vibrations are vertical. The fence filters out vibrations in other directions. The result is a **plane polarised wave** (see Figure 1).

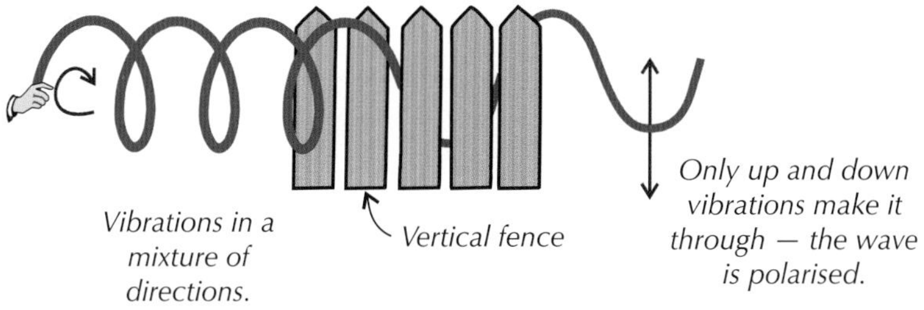

Vibrations in a mixture of directions.
Vertical fence
Only up and down vibrations make it through — the wave is polarised.

Figure 1: *The polarisation of a transverse wave through a fence.*

The plane in which a plane polarised wave vibrates is called the plane of polarisation — e.g. the rope wave was polarised in the vertical plane by the fence. Polarisation can only happen for transverse waves. The fact that you can polarise EM waves is one proof that they're transverse waves.

Tip: A plane is a flat surface in 3D space.

Polarising light

PRACTICAL ACTIVITY GROUP 5

Ordinary light waves are a mixture of different directions of vibration. A **polarising filter** can be used to polarise light (and other waves). It only transmits vibrations in one direction. If you have two polarising filters at right angles to each other, then no light will get through — see Figure 2.

You can observe polarisation by shining unpolarised white light through two polarising filters. Start by aligning the transmission axes of two polarising filters so they are both vertical. Shine unpolarised light on the first filter. Keep the position of the first filter fixed and rotate the second one.

Figure 2: *Two polarising filters at right angles to each other block all light.*

Tip: The transmission axis of a polarising filter shows the only direction of vibrations which can pass through the filter.

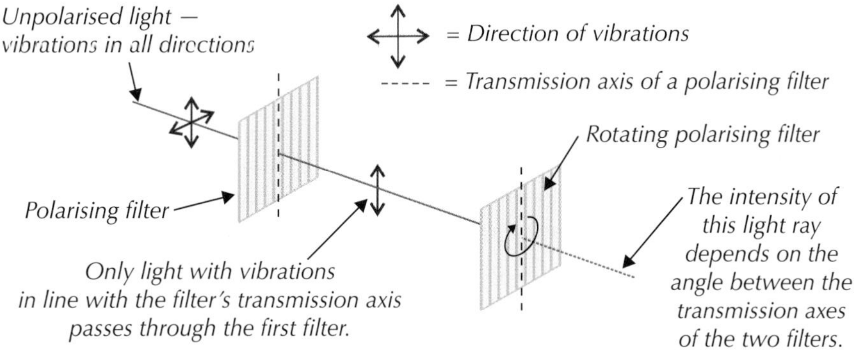

Unpolarised light — vibrations in all directions
= Direction of vibrations
= Transmission axis of a polarising filter
Rotating polarising filter
Polarising filter
The intensity of this light ray depends on the angle between the transmission axes of the two filters.
Only light with vibrations in line with the filter's transmission axis passes through the first filter.

Figure 3: *An unpolarised light wave passing through two polarising filters.*

Tip: Just like vectors, you can think of the transmission axis of the rotating filter as having a vertical and horizontal component. The larger the vertical component, the more vertically polarised light will pass through the filter.

Light that passes through the first filter in Figure 3 will always be vertically polarised. When the transmission axes of the two filters are aligned, all of the light that passes through the first filter also passes through the second. As you rotate the second filter, the amount of light that passes through the second filter varies.

As the second filter is rotated, less light will get through it as the vertical component of the second filter's transmission axis decreases. This means the intensity of the light getting through the second filter will gradually decrease. When the two transmission axes are at 45° to each other, the intensity will be half that getting through the first filter. When they're at right angles to each other no light will pass through — intensity is 0.

As you continue turning, the intensity should then begin to increase once again. When the two axes realign (after a 180° rotation), all the light will be able to pass through the second filter again. This is shown in Figure 4.

Tip: Light intensity is just the brightness of the light. See more about it on page 185.

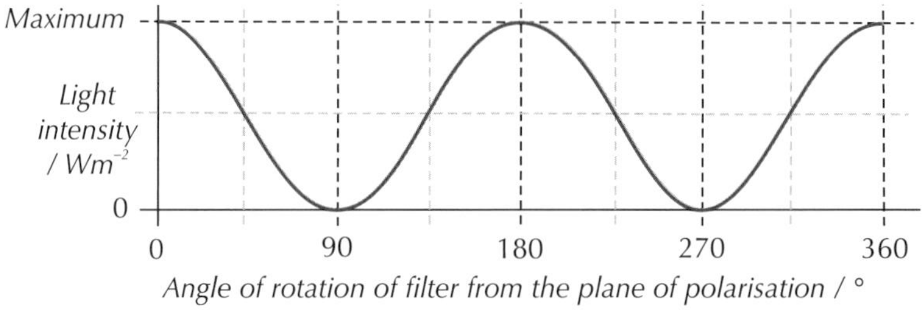

Figure 4: *The effect of rotating a polarising filter on the intensity of polarised light passing through it.*

As shown in Figure 4, at 90° and 270°, the light intensity is zero. This is because the transmission axis of the second filter will be perpendicular to the first filter, so no light will be able to get through. At 180° and 360°, the light intensity is at a maximum. This is because the transmission axes of both filters will be aligned, so all of the light passing through the first filter will be able to pass through the second.

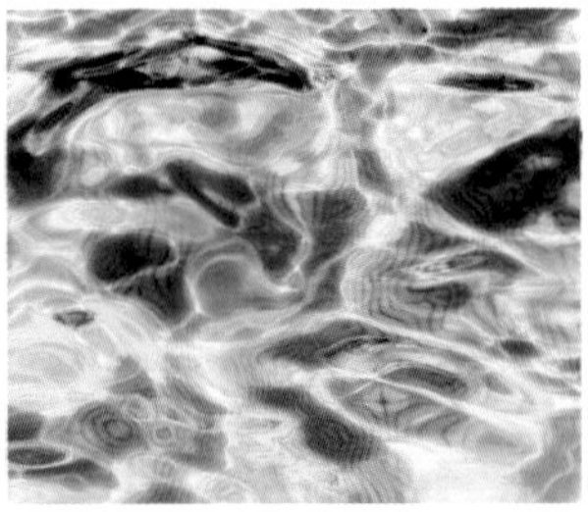

Figure 5: *The light reflecting off water is partially polarised, so a polarising filter can let you see underwater shapes more clearly.*

Uses of polarising filters

You come across polarising filters more often than you might think.

Examples

- 3D films use polarised light to create depth — the filters in each lens are at right angles to each other so each eye gets a slightly different picture.
- Polaroid sunglasses also use polarising filters — light reflected off some surfaces is partially polarised so the sunglasses block this out to help prevent glare.

Polarising microwaves

PRACTICAL ACTIVITY GROUP 5

Polarising filters don't work on microwaves — their wavelength is too long. Instead, metal grilles (squares full of metal wires which are all aligned, see Figure 6) are used to polarise them.

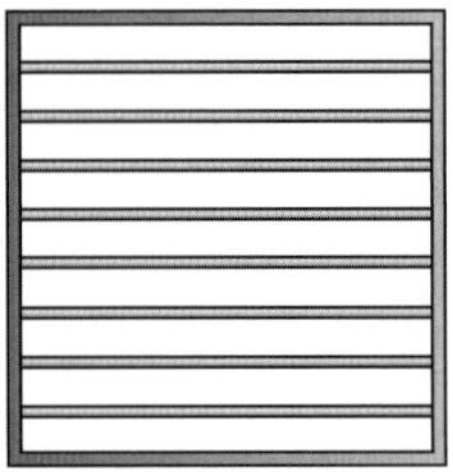

Figure 6: *A diagram of a metal grille, used to polarise microwave radiation.*

You can investigate the polarisation of microwaves using a microwave transmitter and a microwave receiver linked to a voltmeter. Place a metal grille between the microwave transmitter and receiver as shown in Figure 7. (Handily, microwave transmitters transmit vertically polarised microwaves, so you only need one metal grille.)

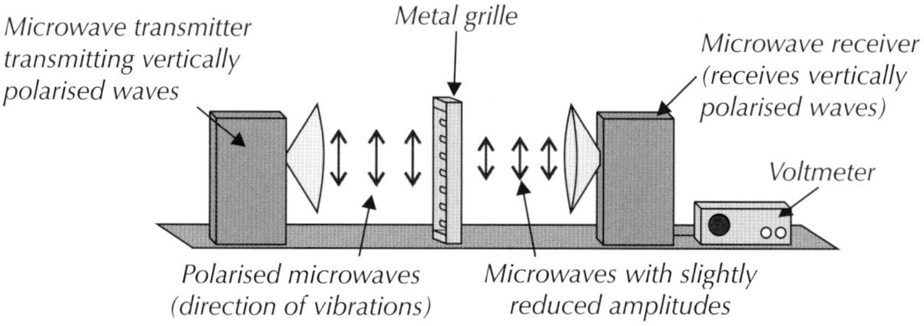

Figure 7: *A diagram of the experimental set-up for investigating the polarisation of microwaves by a metal grille.*

Tip: As always, make sure you carry out a risk assessment before you do either of the polarisation experiments. Make sure all of your electrical equipment is safely connected before you turn it on — microwave transmitters operate at very high voltages.

When microwaves meet a metal grille, some of their energy is absorbed by the grille. This is because the vibrating electric field of the microwave excites electrons in the metal. When the electrons de-excite, they re-emit this energy in all directions as microwaves. Only some of the emitted microwaves have oscillations in the vertical direction.

Microwave receivers only detect vertically polarised microwaves, so even if a re-emitted microwave travels towards the receiver, it might not be picked up. So whenever microwaves are absorbed by a metal grille, only a small fraction of their energy reaches the receiver.

Microwaves are absorbed most when the grille wires are aligned with the vibrations, and least when they're perpendicular to the vibrations. So a metal grille lets through most vibrations when the oscillations of the microwaves and the grille wires are at right angles to each other.

When using the setup in Figure 7, the voltmeter will measure the intensity of the radiation reaching the receiver. The intensity of microwaves passing through the grille is at a maximum when the direction of the vibration of the microwaves and the wires on the grille are at right angles to each other. This is because the minimum amount of energy is being absorbed. As you rotate the grille, the intensity of polarised microwaves able to pass through the grille decreases, so the reading on the voltmeter decreases. When the wires of the metal grille are aligned with the direction of vibration of the polarised waves, little to no signal will be shown on the voltmeter because most of the energy is being absorbed and re-emitted in all directions.

Figure 8: *A microwave transmitter.*

Tip: Don't get confused by metal grilles. The transmission axis for microwaves is perpendicular to the direction of the wires — which is the opposite of what you'd expect.

Practice Question — Application

Q1 The diagram below shows an unpolarised wave passing through two polarising filters.

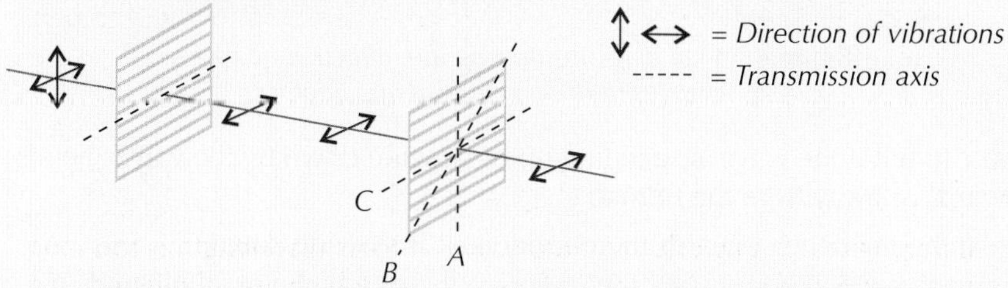

a) Is this wave transverse or longitudinal? Explain your answer.

b) Which line, A, B or C, represents the transmission axis of the second polarising filter? Explain your answer.

c) Explain what would happen if the second polarising filter was rotated by 90°.

5. Reflection and Refraction

Learning Objectives:

- Understand reflection and refraction for all waves.
- Know and understand techniques and procedures used to demonstrate reflection and refraction using a ripple tank.

Specification Reference 4.4.1

Tip: A ray shows the path taken by a wave.

Reflection and refraction are two important wave effects that can change the direction a wave is travelling in. They happen when a wave hits a boundary between two different materials.

What is reflection?

Reflection is when a wave is bounced back when it hits a boundary, as shown in the ray diagram in Figure 1.

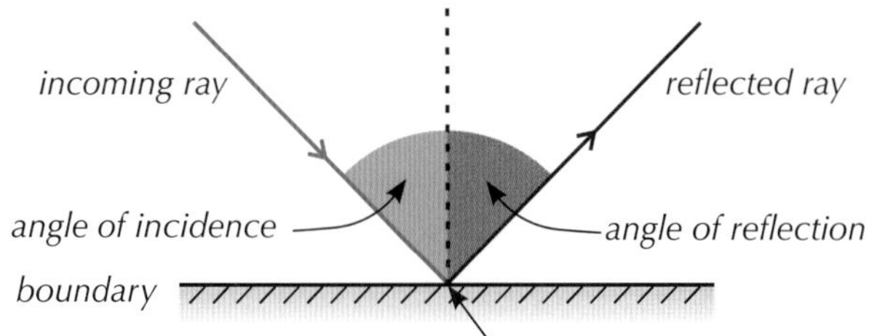

Figure 1: *A ray diagram to show the reflection of a wave at a boundary.*

Figure 2: *A ray of light being reflected by a flat mirror.*

A reflected wave always bounces off a boundary at the same angle to the normal as it hit the boundary. This is the law of reflection:

angle of incidence = angle of reflection

Figure 3: *The pencil in the glass of water looks bent because of the refraction of light as it passes between the water and the air.*

What is refraction?

Refraction is the way a wave changes direction as it enters a different medium at an angle to the boundary, as shown by the ray diagram in Figure 4. The change in direction is a result of the wave slowing down or speeding up.

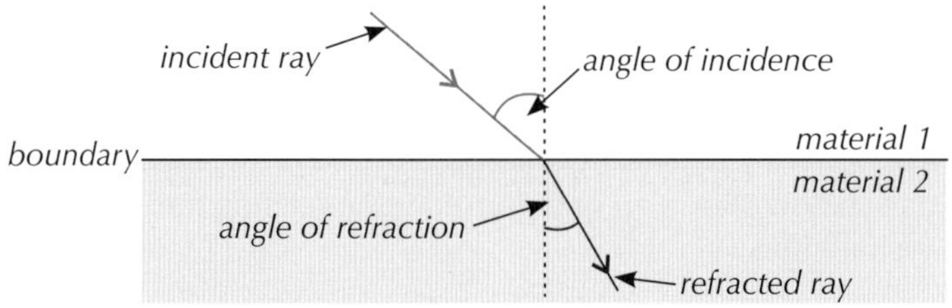

Figure 4: *A ray diagram showing the refraction of a wave as it moves from one material into another.*

Tip: For light, and other EM waves, we can talk about the 'optical density' of materials. Light will slow down when it passes into a more optically dense medium, and speed up when it passes into one that is less optically dense (p.195).

You can tell if the wave is speeding up or slowing down by the way it bends towards or away from the normal.

- If the ray bends towards the normal — it is slowing down.
- If the ray bends away from the normal — the wave is speeding up.

The frequency of a wave remains constant, no matter what the wave is travelling through. As $v = f\lambda$, this means that when a wave has changed speed, its wavelength must also have changed. If a wave speeds up in a medium, its wavelength increases and if it slows down, its wavelength decreases.

Using ripple tanks to show wave effects

You can show the reflection and refraction of water waves using a ripple tank.

Tip: A ripple tank is a large, shallow tank of water which can be used to observe wave effects using water.

Demonstrating reflection

Set up the ripple tank so an oscillating paddle (connected to a signal generator and vibration generator) is creating regular waves with straight, parallel wave fronts, as shown in Figure 6. Place a barrier in the tank at an angle to the wave fronts.

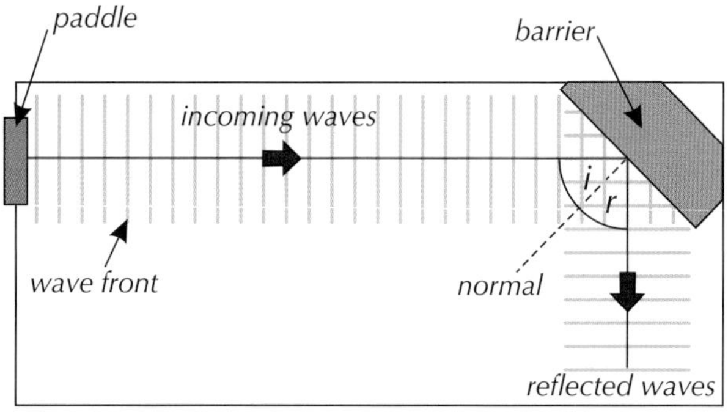

Figure 6: A diagram of a ripple tank being used to demonstrate the reflection of water waves.

Figure 5: A series of straight, parallel wave fronts, produced in a ripple tank.

The angle the incoming waves make with the normal to the barrier is the angle of incidence, *i*. The angle between the direction of the reflected waves and the normal to the barrier is the angle of reflection, *r*.

You should see the waves reflecting off the barrier and travelling in a different direction to the way they arrived. You can change the angle of incidence to see that the angle of reflection changes by the same amount. They are always equal to each other.

Tip: Close to the barrier, it might be difficult to make out the waves. This is because the incoming waves will be interfering with the reflected waves — there's more on this on pages 200-202.

Demonstrating refraction

Put a block of plastic into the ripple tank, so that part of the tank contains a different depth of water than the rest of the tank. The point where the tank suddenly changes depth is the 'boundary'. Water waves travel faster in deeper water, so when they cross the boundary they should refract.

Set up the oscillating paddle so it is creating regular waves with straight, parallel wave fronts at an angle to the boundary, as shown in Figure 7.

Tip: Take care when working with ripple tanks. Make sure that the electrical cables powering the paddle don't come into contact with the water. And make sure you clear up any water spillages quickly, to prevent any damage to equipment, or accidents like people slipping on a wet floor.

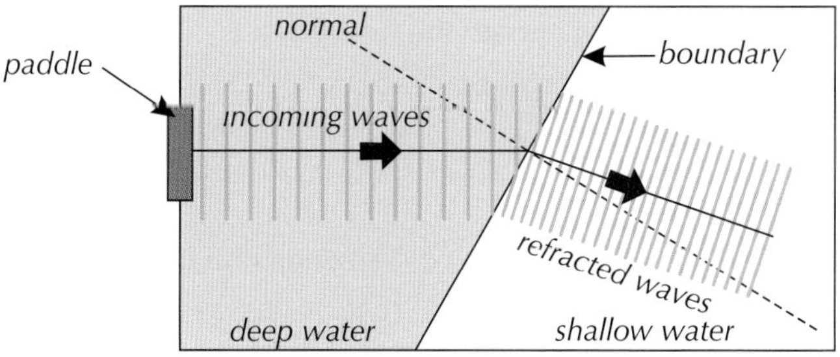

Figure 7: A diagram of a ripple tank being used to demonstrate the refraction of water waves.

Tip: The change in depth of the ripple tank probably won't be enough to have a really strong effect. So you'll have to look closely to see the change in direction and wavelength.

When the wave moves from the deeper water into the shallower water, it will slow down and refract. You should see the wave bend towards the normal to the boundary. You should also see that the wave fronts get closer together, which shows that the wavelength has decreased (due to $v = f\lambda$).

If you set up the experiment with the waves starting in the shallow end, you should see the opposite — the waves will bend away from the normal as they cross the boundary, and the wave fronts get further apart when they pass into the deeper water.

Tip: Remember, in calculations of reflection and refraction, the angles aren't measured from the surface or boundary, but from the normal to the surface/boundary.

Practice Questions — Application

Q1 A light ray is incident on a mirror as shown below. Calculate the angle of reflection for the light ray.

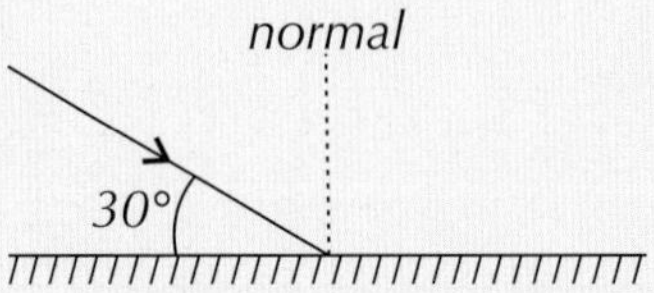

Q2 A student is using a ripple tank to investigate wave effects. The ripple tank has two sections, A and B, which are at different depths. A snapshot of the student's experiment is shown below.

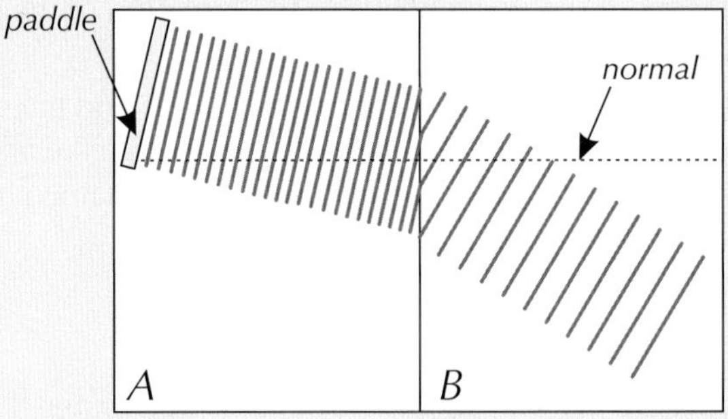

Which side of the tank, A or B, is deeper? Explain your answer.

Practice Questions — Fact Recall

Q1 State the law of reflection.

Q2 A wave hits a boundary between two materials at an angle to the normal. It slows down as it crosses the boundary.

a) State how its direction of motion changes.

b) State what happens to the wave's wavelength and frequency.

6. Refractive Index and Total Internal Reflection

You saw in the previous topic that waves changes speed and direction if they pass into a different medium. For light, you can work out the new direction if you know the refractive index of the materials.

The refractive index of a material

Light goes fastest in a vacuum. It travels slower in other materials, because it interacts with the particles in them. The more optically dense a material is, the more light slows down when it enters it. The **optical density** of a material is measured by its refractive index — the higher a material's optical density is, the higher its refractive index.

The **refractive index** of a material, n, is the ratio between the speed of light in a vacuum, c, and the speed of light in that material, v.

$$n = \frac{c}{v}$$

$c = 3.00 \times 10^8$ ms^{-1}

***n** = refractive index of the material*

***v** = speed of light in material in ms^{-1}*

The refractive index of a material is a property of that material only. The speed of light in air is only a tiny bit smaller than c. So you can assume the refractive index of air, $n_{air} = 1$.

Example — Maths Skills

The refractive index of a plastic block is 1.47. What's the speed of light in the plastic?

First rearrange the refractive index equation to make v the subject:

$$n = \frac{c}{v} \Rightarrow v = \frac{c}{n}$$

$$v = \frac{c}{n} = \frac{3.00 \times 10^8}{1.47} = 2.04... \times 10^8 = 2.04 \times 10^8 \text{ ms}^{-1} \text{ (to 3 s.f.)}$$

Snell's law

If light is passing through a boundary between two materials, you can use Snell's law to calculate unknown angles or refractive indices.

The angle that incoming light makes to the normal, θ_i, is called the **angle of incidence**. The angle the refracted ray makes with the normal, θ_r, is the **angle of refraction**.

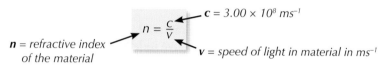

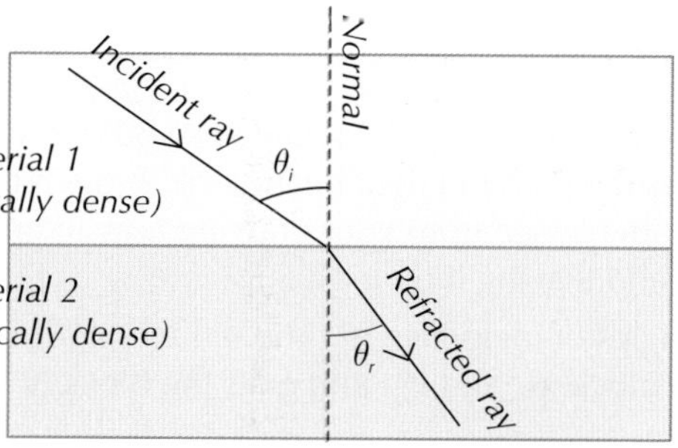

***Figure 1:** Refraction of light passing into a more optically dense material.*

Learning Objectives:

- Know and understand the refraction of light.
- Know what is meant by the 'refractive index' of a material.
- Be able to calculate the refractive index of a material using $n = \frac{c}{v}$.
- Be able to use $n \sin\theta$ = constant to solve problems involving a ray crossing a boundary, where θ is the angle to the normal.
- Know and understand techniques and procedures used to investigate the refraction of light using ray boxes and transparent rectangular blocks (PAG6).
- Know what is meant by the term 'critical angle'.
- Be able to use the equation $\sin C = \frac{1}{n}$.
- Know what is meant by the total internal reflection of light.
- Know and understand techniques and procedures used to investigate total internal reflection of light using ray boxes and semi-circular blocks (PAG6).

Specification Reference 4.4.2

Tip: Remember, light bends towards the normal when it slows down (see page 192).

When a light ray passes across a boundary between two materials:

$$n \sin\theta = \text{constant}$$

n *= refractive index of material*

θ *= angle of ray to the normal*

This means that for a light ray at a boundary between two materials, $n \sin\theta$ must be the same on either side. This can be written nicely as Snell's law:

$$n_1 \sin\theta_1 = n_2 \sin\theta_2$$

θ_1 *= angle of ray to the normal in material 1*

θ_2 *= angle of ray to the normal in material 2*

n_1 *= refractive index of material 1*

n_2 *= refractive index of material 2*

Exam Tip
You'll only get given the '$n \sin\theta$ = constant' equation in the exam, so make sure you remember what that equation actually tells you — that $n_1 \sin\theta_1 = n_2 \sin\theta_2$ at any boundary.

Example — Maths Skills

Calculate the refractive index of material 2 in the diagram, given that the refractive index is 1.1 for material 1.

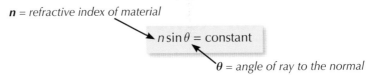

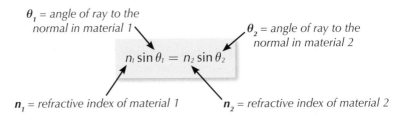

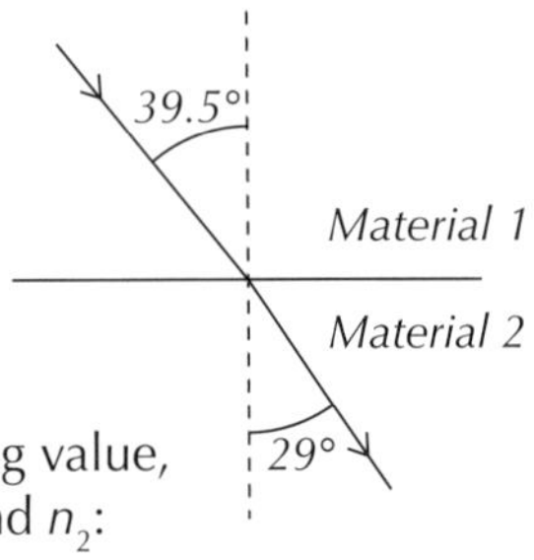

First look at what information you've been given:

$n_1 = 1.1$, $n_2 = ?$, $\theta_1 = 39.5°$, $\theta_2 = 29°$

You can use the law of refraction to find the missing value, but you'll have to rearrange the equation first to find n_2:

$$n_1 \sin\theta_1 = n_2 \sin\theta_2 \Rightarrow n_2 = \frac{n_1 \sin\theta_1}{\sin\theta_2}$$

$$\Rightarrow n_2 = \frac{1.1 \sin 39.5°}{\sin 29°} = 1.44... = 1.4 \text{ (to 2 s.f.)}$$

Tip: You can check your answer seems right by looking at how the direction changes. Here $\theta_1 > \theta_2$ so the ray has bent towards the normal. This shows the light ray has slowed down (p.192) so it has travelled into an optically denser material. This means that $n_1 < n_2$, which your answer shows.

Investigating refractive indices

PRACTICAL ACTIVITY GROUP 6

You can find the refractive index of a (transparent) material using a rectangular block of that material and a ray box.

- Place the rectangular block on a piece of paper and draw around it.
- Use the ray box to shine a beam of light into the glass block. Dim any other lights so you can see the path of the light beam through the block clearly.
- Trace the path of the incoming and outgoing beams of light either side of the block.
- Remove the block and join up the two paths you've drawn with a straight line. This shows the path the light beam took through the glass block. You should be able to see from your drawing how the path of the ray bent when entering and leaving the block.
- Measure the angles of incidence (θ_i) and refraction (θ_r) where the light enters the block (θ_{i1} and θ_{r1}) and exits the block (θ_{i2} and θ_{r2}) — see Figure 2.

Tip: Remember to carry out a risk assessment before starting any experiment.

Tip: You can also use a device called a refractometer to accurately measure the refractive index of a material. The machine shines a beam of light at the sample. You then view the refracted beam through a microscope and measure its angle of refraction.

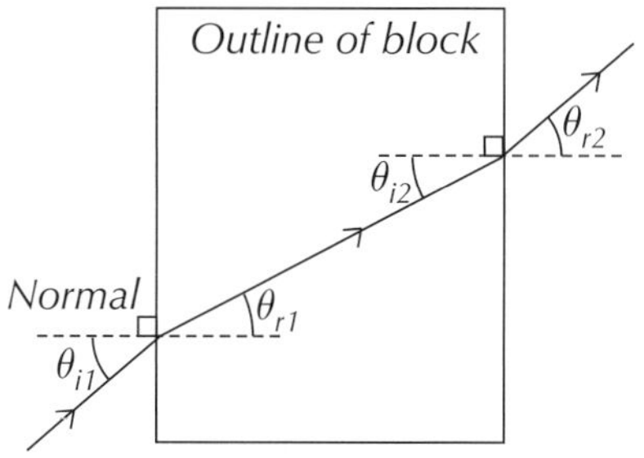

Figure 2: *An example of the type of drawing obtained from carrying out an experiment into the refraction of light through a transparent block.*

You can calculate the refractive index of the block using Snell's Law. Since $n_{air} = 1$, Snell's Law can be simplified to $\sin\theta_{i1} = n\sin\theta_{r1}$ at the entry point and $n\sin\theta_{i2} = \sin\theta_{r2}$ at the exit point. Plug in your measurements to calculate n for both points, and then find the average of the two to get your final value of n.

Tip: Remember to draw a normal at the point where the ray enters and leaves the block.

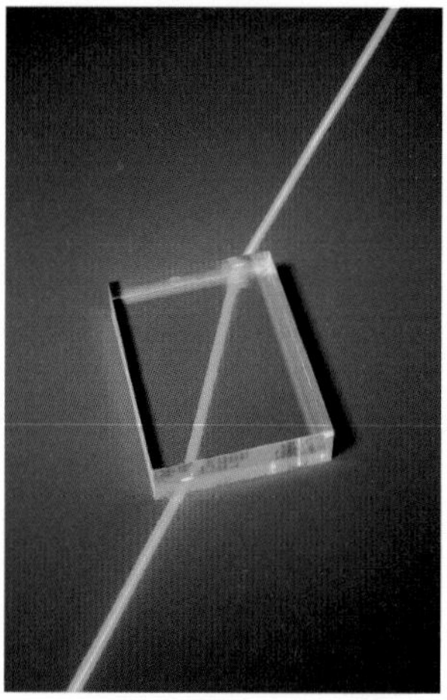

Figure 3: *A green laser beam being refracted as it passes through a transparent rectangular block.*

The critical angle of a boundary

When light goes from a more optically dense material into a less optically dense material (e.g. glass to air), it can get refracted along the boundary.

Shine a ray of light at a boundary going from refractive index n_1 to n_2, where $n_1 > n_2$, then gradually increase the angle of incidence. The light is refracted away from the normal, so as you increase the angle of incidence in material 1 (θ_1), the angle of refraction in material 2 (θ_2) gets closer and closer to 90°. Eventually θ_1 reaches a **critical angle** (C) for which $\theta_2 = 90°$. The light is refracted along the boundary — see Figure 4.

This can happen for any boundary where the light is passing from a more optically dense material (n_1, higher refractive index) into a less optically dense material (n_2, lower refractive index).

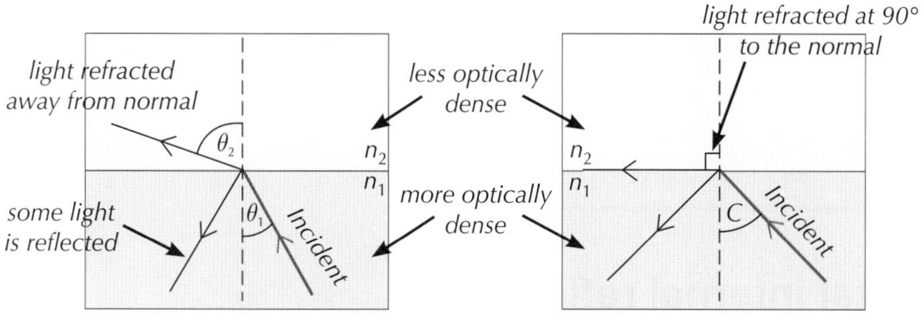

Figure 4: *Refraction of light near to and along a boundary, when incident below and at the critical angle.*

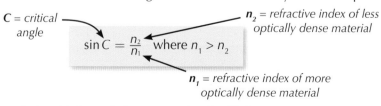

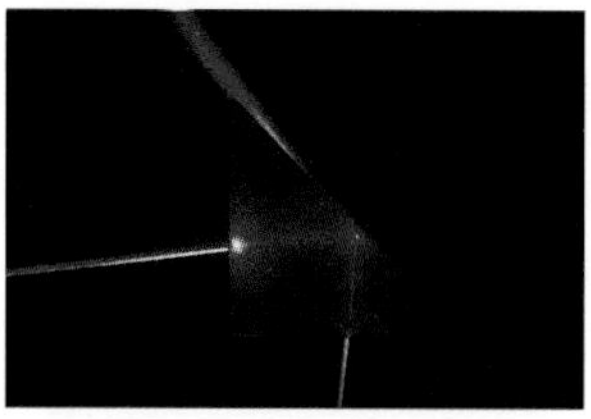

Figure 5: *Light enters the prism from underneath and then strikes the prism-air boundary at around the critical angle. Some light is reflected (left) and some continues parallel to the prism surface (top).*

You can work out the critical angle for a certain boundary with the equation:

$$\sin C = \frac{n_2}{n_1} \text{ where } n_1 > n_2$$

C = critical angle

n_2 = refractive index of less optically dense material

n_1 = refractive index of more optically dense material

You can derive this formula by rearranging Snell's law:

$$n_1 \sin\theta_1 = n_2 \sin\theta_2$$

First, rearrange it to get the angles on the same side:

$$\frac{\sin\theta_1}{\sin\theta_2} = \frac{n_2}{n_1}$$

The angle of incidence is equal to the critical angle when the angle of refraction is 90°, so put these values in:

$$\frac{\sin C}{\sin 90^\circ} = \frac{n_2}{n_1}$$

$\sin 90° = 1$, so the formula becomes:

$$\sin C = \frac{n_2}{n_1}$$

Tip: The assumption here is that air is the less optically dense material — this is usually the case, because its refractive index is 1.0002...

The refractive index of air is 1, so this can be simplified for a material to air boundary by letting $n_2 = 1$:

critical angle for material to air boundary → $$\sin C = \frac{1}{n}$$ ← *refractive index of material*

Examples — Maths Skills

Find the critical angle of a glass to air boundary if the glass has a refractive index of 1.5.

You've been asked to find the critical angle for a boundary with air, and you know the refractive index of the other material. So you can use the formula for the critical angle of a material to air boundary shown above.
But you need to rearrange it for *C* first:

$\sin C = \frac{1}{n}$, which gives:

$C = \sin^{-1}\left(\frac{1}{n}\right) = \sin^{-1}\left(\frac{1}{1.5}\right) = 41.8...° = 42°$ (to 2 s.f.)

Tip: Make sure your calculator is set to degrees mode to work out the inverse sin ($\sin^{-1}$) of this angle.

A plastic block is immersed in a liquid. If the refractive index of the liquid is 1.40 and the critical angle for light travelling from the plastic to the liquid is 79.1°, find the refractive index of the plastic.

Write down what you know: $C = 79.1°$, $n_1 = ?$, $n_2 = 1.40$

Then rearrange $\sin C = \frac{n_2}{n_1}$ to find n_1:

$\sin C = \frac{n_2}{n_1} \Rightarrow n_1 = \frac{n_2}{\sin C} = \frac{1.40}{\sin 79.1°} = 1.425... = 1.43$ (to 3 s.f.)

Total internal reflection

At angles of incidence greater than the critical angle, refraction can't happen. That means all the light is reflected back into the material. This effect is called **total internal reflection** (**TIR**) — see Figures 6 and 7.

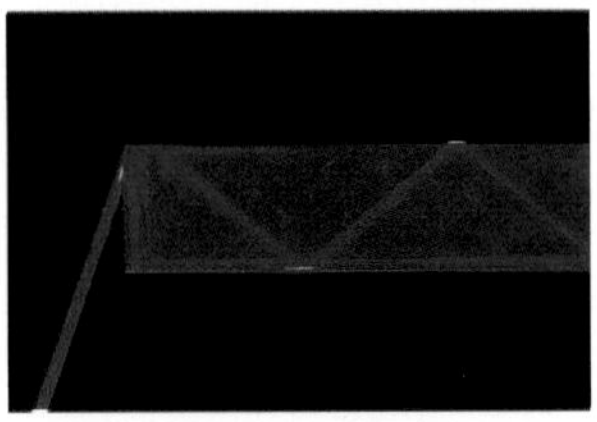

Figure 6: *Total internal reflection of a laser beam inside an optical fibre (light travelling from right to left). An optical fibre is used in communications.*

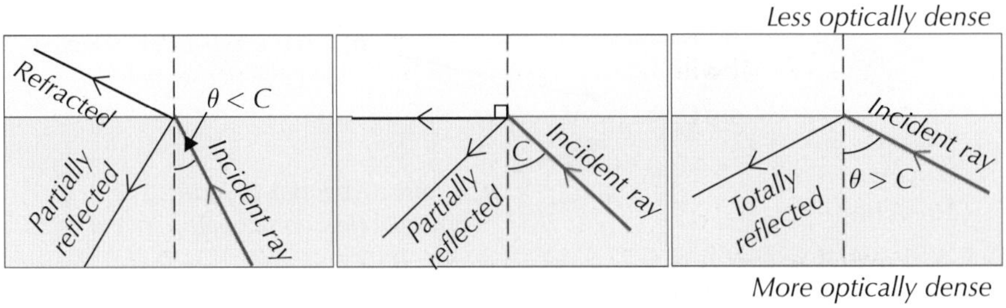

Figure 7: *Light hitting a boundary with a less optically dense material at different angles of incidence.*

Investigating critical angles and TIR

PRACTICAL ACTIVITY GROUP 6

You can measure the critical angle of a glass-to-air boundary by finding the angle at which light refracts along the boundary. Shine a light ray into the curved face of a semi-circular glass block so that it always enters at right angles to the edge — this means the ray won't refract as it enters the block, just when it leaves from the straight edge. Vary the angle of incidence, θ_i, until the light beam refracts so much that it exits the block along the straight edge (see Figure 8). This angle of incidence is now the critical angle, C, for the glass-air boundary.

You can then rearrange the formula for the critical angle at a material-air boundary ($\sin C = \frac{1}{n}$) and put in your value for C to find the refractive index of the block. If you increase the angle of incidence so it's greater than C, you'll find the ray is entirely reflected from the straight edge of the block. This is total internal reflection (TIR).

Tip: Carry out a risk assessment before starting this experiment. If you're using a laser, see page 209 for more about how to use them safely.

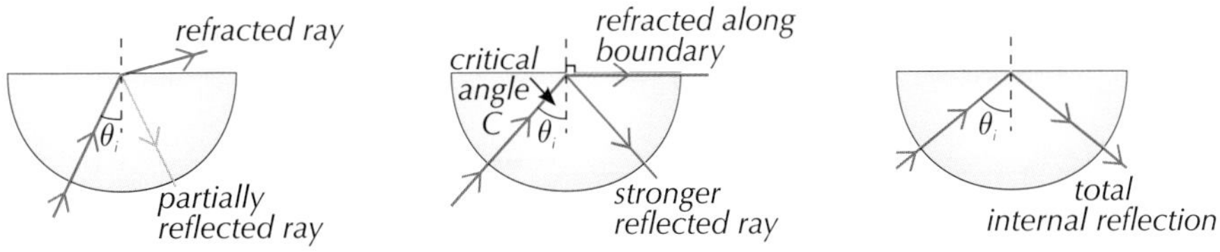

Here the angle of incidence is less than the critical angle.

Here the angle of incidence is equal to the critical angle.

Here the angle of incidence is greater than the critical angle.

Figure 8: *Ray diagrams showing wave behaviour at different angles of incidence.*

Practice Questions — Application

Q1 The speed of light in a material is 1.94×10^8 ms^{-1}.

a) Calculate the refractive index of the material.

b) Light travels from air into the material. Explain whether the light bend towards or away from the normal as it enters the material.

c) Calculate the critical angle for the material to air boundary.

Q2 A student is using a semi-circular glass block to measure the critical angle for the glass-air boundary. Why is it important that light rays enter the block at right angles to the edge?

Q3 A fisherman sees a lobster cage on the sea floor and tries to retrieve it by lowering a winch directly over where the cage appears to be. The winch lands behind the cage.

a) Explain why the cage isn't exactly where he thought it was.

b) The fisherman uses an underwater camera to get a better view. Light travels from the lobster cage and hits the camera lens at an angle of 37.2° to the normal. If the water has a refractive index of 1.38 and the lens has a refractive index of 1.49, at what angle to the normal will the refracted ray in the camera lens be?

Practice Questions — Fact Recall

Q1 What is the refractive index of a material?

Q2 In what way will light bend if it passes at an angle into a medium with a higher refractive index than the material it just left?

Q3 What conditions need to be met for total internal reflection?

7. Superposition and Interference

Learning Objectives:
- Know the principle of superposition of waves.
- Use graphical methods to illustrate the principle of superposition.
- Understand what is meant by interference, phase difference and coherence.
- Be able to describe constructive interference and destructive interference in terms of phase difference.

Specification Reference 4.4.3

When waves pass through each other, they combine their displacements — they can make a bigger wave, a smaller wave, or cancel each other out...

Superposition of waves

Superposition happens when two or more waves pass through each other. At the instant that waves cross, the displacements due to each wave combine. Then each wave continues on its way. You can see this if two pulses are sent simultaneously from each end of a rope, as in Figure 1.

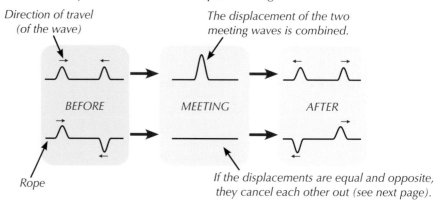

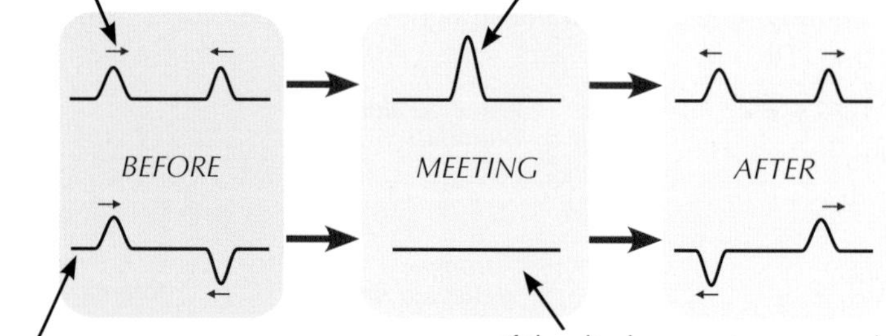

Direction of travel (of the wave)
The displacement of the two meeting waves is combined.
BEFORE
MEETING
AFTER
Rope
If the displacements are equal and opposite, they cancel each other out (see next page).

Figure 1: *Superposition of waves.*

The principle of **superposition** of waves says that when two or more waves cross, the resultant displacement equals the vector sum of the individual displacements.

"Superposition" means "one thing on top of another thing". You can use the same idea in reverse — a complex wave can be separated out mathematically into several simple sine waves of various sizes.

Tip: The vector sum is just the sum of the two displacements taking into account both magnitude and direction (see page 34).

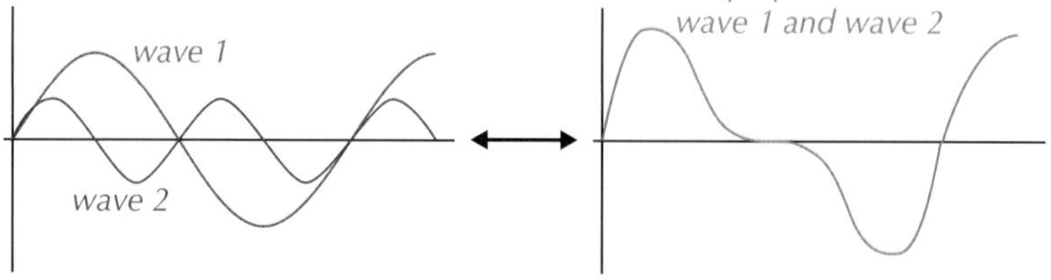

wave 1
wave 2
superposition of wave 1 and wave 2

Figure 2: *Two sine waves shown as separate waves and as a superposition.*

Constructive and destructive interference

The superposition of two or more waves can result in **interference**. Interference can either be constructive or destructive.

- When two waves meet, if their displacements are in the same direction, the displacements combine to give a bigger displacement. A crest plus a crest gives a bigger crest. A trough plus a trough gives a bigger trough. This is known as **constructive interference**.
- If a wave with a positive displacement (crest) meets a wave with a negative displacement (trough), they will undergo **destructive interference** and cancel each other out. The displacement of the combined wave is found by adding the displacements of the two waves (see Figure 3).

Tip: Remember, amplitude only has magnitude, but displacement has direction and magnitude. See page 179 for more.

Tip: A trough and a crest won't cancel each other out completely unless they have the same magnitude.

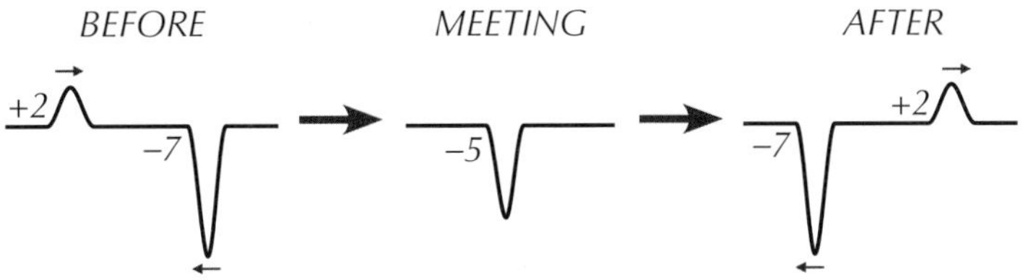

Figure 3: *Destructive interference.*

Tip: Graphically, you can superimpose waves by adding the individual displacements at each point along the x-axis, and then plot them.

- If two waves with equal and opposite displacements meet (e.g. a crest and a trough with equal magnitudes), they cancel each other out completely. This is total destructive interference.

Figure 4: *Constructive and destructive interference can be shown by water waves in a ripple tank.*

Phase difference

Two points on a wave are in phase if they are both at the same point in the wave cycle (the same phase — see p.180). Points in phase have the same displacement and velocity.

In Figure 5, points A and B are in phase; points A and C are out of phase; and points A and D are exactly out of phase.

Tip: If two points are exactly out of phase, they're an odd integer of half-cycles apart (1 half-cycle, 3 half-cycles, etc.).

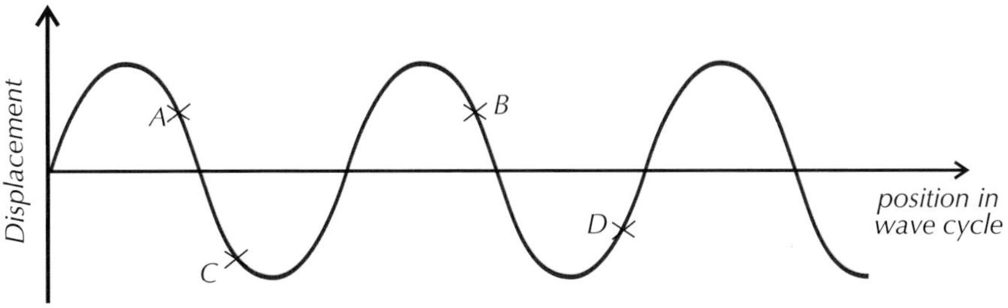

Figure 5: *Points in and out of phase on a wave pattern.*

Tip: The position on the x-axis tells you at what point in the wave cycle you are. It's usually measured as an angle or fraction of a cycle (see below).

It's mathematically handy to show one complete cycle of a wave as an angle of 360° (2π radians) — see Figure 6. The phase difference of two points on a wave is the difference in their positions in a wave's cycle, measured in degrees, radians or fractions of a cycle. Two points with a phase difference of zero or a multiple of 360° (i.e. a full cycle) are in phase. Points with a phase difference of odd-number multiples of 180° (π radians, or half a cycle) are exactly out of phase.

Tip: Radians are just a different unit for angle measurement — see page 251.

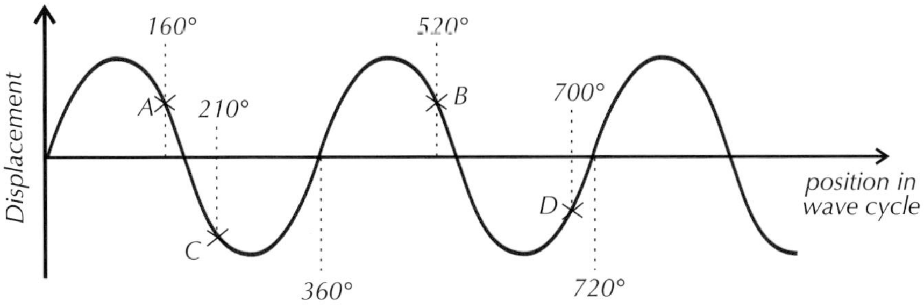

Figure 6: *The points from Figure 5 shown as angles.*

Tip: Points A and B are a full cycle apart (360°), while points A and D are three half-cycles apart (180° × 3 = 540°).

Phase difference between waves

You can also talk about the phase difference between two **coherent** waves (rather than two points on one wave). Two waves are coherent if they have the same wavelength and frequency and a fixed phase difference between them.

The phase difference is the amount by which one wave lags behind the other. So you can also talk about two waves being in or out of phase. Two waves are in phase if their phase difference is 0 or a multiple of 360° — see Figure 7. In practice this is usually because both waves come from the same oscillator. In other situations there will nearly always be a phase difference between two waves.

Tip: Waves don't need to have the same amplitude to be in phase, but they do need to have the same frequency and wavelength.

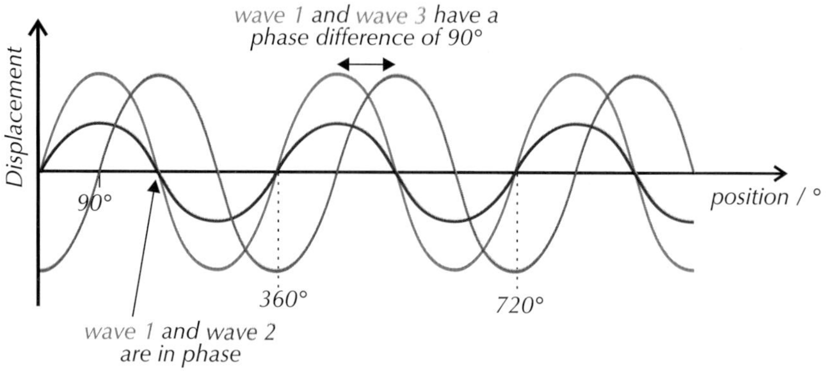

Figure 7: *Three coherent waves. Two waves are in phase and the third wave is out of phase by 90°.*

Tip: Compare the position of two equivalent points on two coherent waves (e.g. the top of two crests) to find the phase difference between them.

When two waves that are in phase with each other are superposed, they will interfere constructively with each other. Destructive interference occurs when two waves that are exactly out of phase with each other are superposed. For any other phase difference, there will be a mixture of constructive and destructive interference.

Tip: Superposing these waves would give total destructive interference:

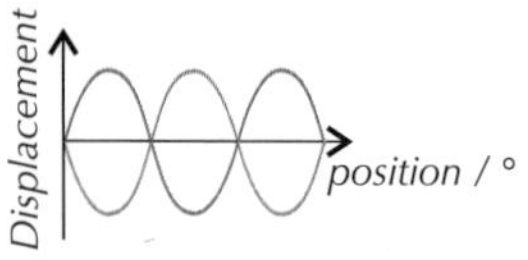

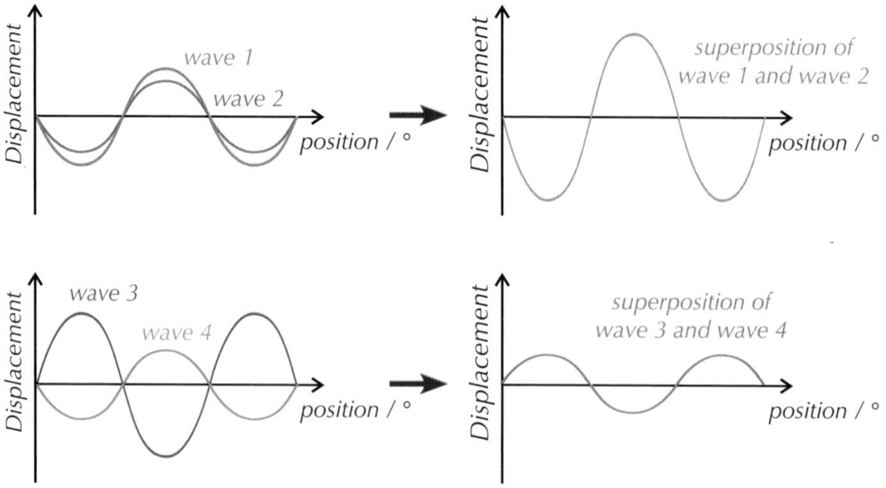

Figure 8: *Waves 1 and 2 are in phase, so interfere constructively. Waves 3 and 4 are exactly out of phase and interfere destructively.*

Practice Questions — Application

Q1 What is the phase difference between the two waves in the diagram below?

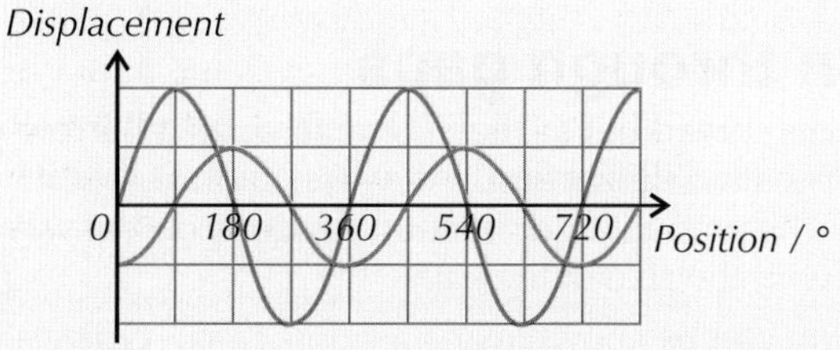

Q2 Sketch two waves that, when superposed, will have total destructive interference.

Q3 a) In the diagram below, which point (if any) is in phase with

i) point A ii) point B iii) point C

b) How many of the points are exactly out of phase with point G?

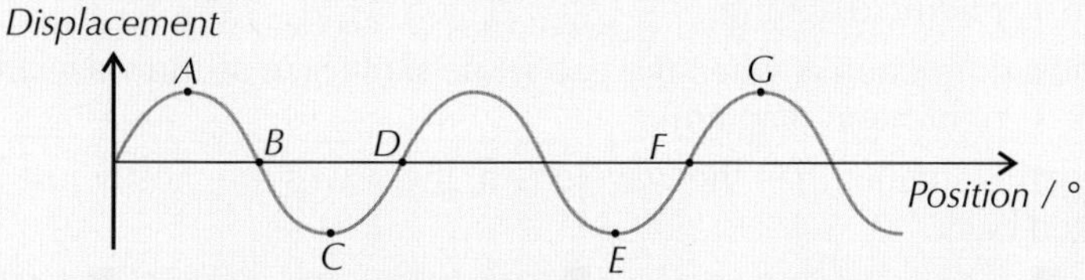

Practice Questions — Fact Recall

Q1 What does the principle of superposition say?

Q2 Describe constructive interference.

Q3 What is meant by the phase difference of two points on a wave?

Q4 Give three possible units for phase difference.

Q5 When are two points on a wave exactly out of phase?

Q6 What does it mean for two wave sources to be coherent?

Q7 What does it mean for two coherent waves to be in phase?

8. Diffraction

Diffraction is the reason you can hear sound when you're round a corner from the source — it's just waves spreading out through gaps or around obstacles.

Learning Objectives:

- Understand what is meant by diffraction for all waves, including light.
- Know and understand techniques and procedures used to demonstrate diffraction using a ripple tank.

Specification Reference 4.4.1

Diffraction through gaps

The way that waves spread out as they come through a narrow gap or go round obstacles is called **diffraction**. All waves diffract, but it's not always easy to observe. The amount of diffraction depends on the wavelength of the wave compared with the size of the gap.

Diffraction can be shown using a ripple tank. Objects can be placed into the ripple tank to create a barrier with a gap in the middle of it. This gap can be varied to see the effects this has on how the waves spread through the tank:

- When the gap is a lot bigger than the wavelength, diffraction is unnoticeable — see Figure 1, left-hand diagram.
- You get noticeable diffraction through a gap several wavelengths wide (Figure 1, middle diagram).
- The most diffraction is when the gap is the same size as the wavelength (Figure 1, right-hand diagram).
- If the gap is smaller than the wavelength, the waves are mostly just reflected back.

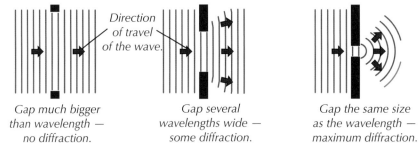

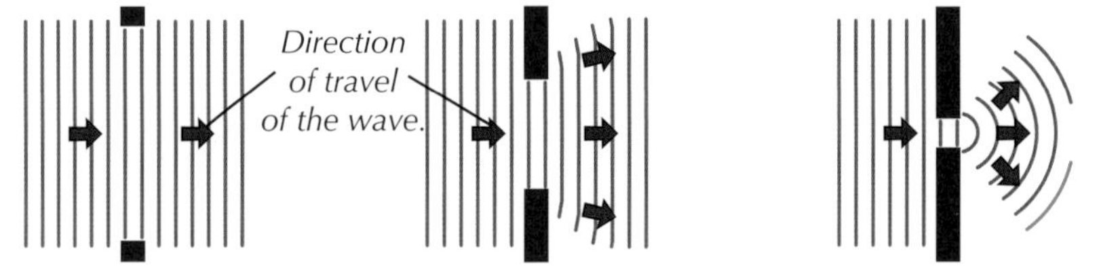
Direction of travel of the wave.
Gap much bigger than wavelength — no diffraction.
Gap several wavelengths wide — some diffraction.
Gap the same size as the wavelength — maximum diffraction.

Figure 1: *The diffraction of water waves in a ripple tank.*

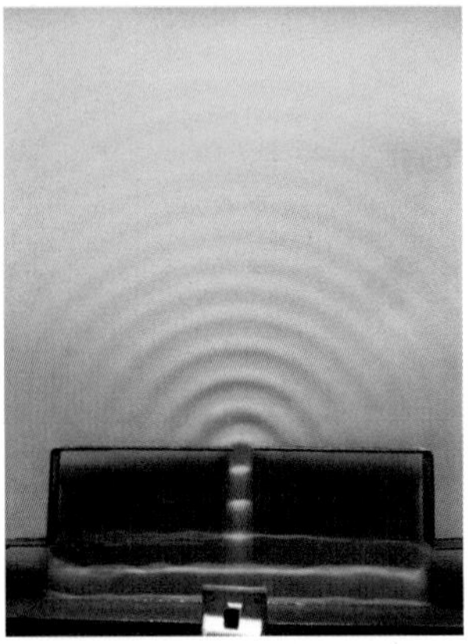

Figure 2: *Diffraction in a ripple tank.*

When sound passes through a doorway, the size of the gap and the wavelength are usually roughly equal, so a lot of diffraction occurs. That's why you have no trouble hearing someone through an open door to the next room, even if the other person is out of your line of sight. The reason that you can't see him or her is that when light passes through the doorway, it is passing through a gap around a few million times bigger than its wavelength — the amount of diffraction is tiny. So to get noticeable diffraction with light, you must shine it through a very narrow slit.

Diffraction around obstacles

When a wave meets an obstacle, you get diffraction around the edges. Behind the obstacle is a 'shadow', where the wave is blocked. The wider the obstacle compared with the wavelength of the wave, the less diffraction you get, and so the longer the shadow.

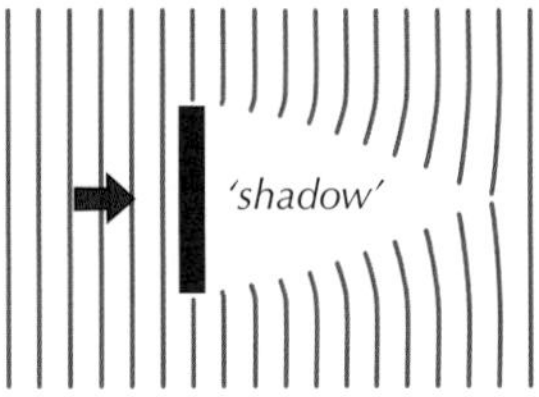
'shadow'

Figure 3: *The diffraction of waves around an obstacle.*

Tip: Radio waves with long wavelengths (or long wave, LW, radio) can reach receivers in valleys and across mountain ranges, because diffraction allows the waves to bend around the hills.

The diffraction of light

Diffraction of light can be demonstrated by shining light through a very narrow slit (or aperture) onto a screen. If the wavelength of a light wave is roughly similar to the size of the aperture, you get a diffraction pattern of light and dark fringes — see Figure 4. You should use monochromatic, coherent light (such as laser light — see page 206).

Monochromatic light is light of a single wavelength, and so a single colour. If you use light that isn't monochromatic, different wavelengths will diffract by different amounts and the pattern produced won't be very clear.

Tip: This is often called the single-slit experiment — you'll come across the double-slit experiment on page 209.

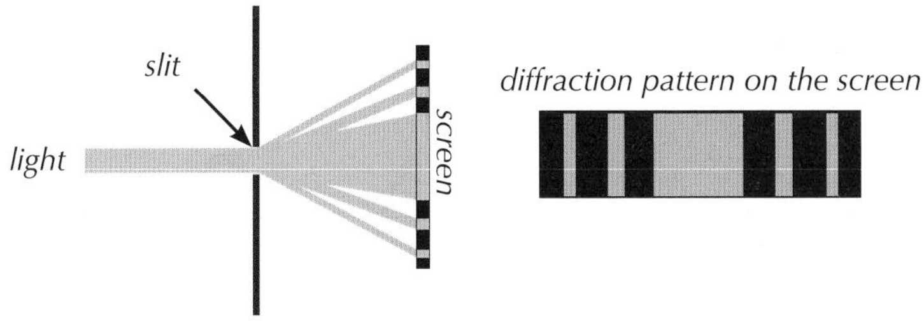

Figure 4: *Diffraction pattern from monochromatic light through a single slit.*

Tip: You need to be careful using lasers. Laser beams are very powerful and could damage your eyesight, so you should take precautions when using them (page 209).

The pattern has a bright central fringe with alternating dark and bright fringes on either side of it. You can alter the amount of diffraction by changing the width of the slit. The narrower the slit, the wider the diffraction pattern. The fringe pattern is due to interference:

- The bright fringes are due to constructive interference, where waves from across the width of the slit arrive at the screen in phase.
- The dark fringes are due to total destructive interference, where waves from across the width of the slit arrive at the screen completely out of phase.

You can do a similar experiment using a white light source and a set of colour filters instead of the laser. The size of the slit can be kept constant while the wavelength is varied by putting different colour filters over the slit.

Figure 5: *Diffraction of a laser beam through a single slit.*

Practice Question — Application

Q1 A water wave with a wavelength of 2 m passes through a gap that is 5 cm wide. Will diffraction effects be noticeable? Explain your answer.

Practice Questions — Fact Recall

Q1 What sort of waves diffract?

Q2 Explain, in terms of diffraction, why someone stood next to an open doorway can be heard from the other side but not seen.

Q3 What is monochromatic light?

Q4 Describe the diffraction pattern produced when monochromatic light is shone through a single narrow slit.

Tip: The wavelength of sound waves is of the order of 1 m.

9. Two-Source Interference

Learning Objectives:

- Know the meaning of the term path difference.
- Be able to describe constructive interference and destructive interference in terms of path difference.
- Understand two-source interference with sound and microwaves.
- Know techniques and procedures used for superposition experiments involving sound and microwaves (PAG5).

Specification Reference 4.4.3

When two wave sources interfere, they can make pretty interference patterns. You need both sources to be pretty much identical...

What is two-source interference?

Two-source interference is when the waves from two sources interfere to produce a pattern. In order to get clear interference patterns, two or more sources must be coherent (page 202). If a light source is coherent and in phase, the troughs and crests line up — this causes constructive interference and a very intense beam.

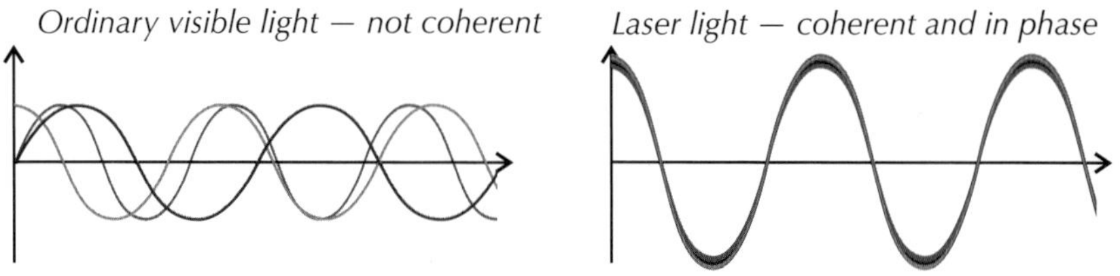

Figure 1: *Coherent and non-coherent light sources.*

Interference still happens when you're observing waves of different wavelength and frequency — but it happens in a jumble. If the sources are coherent, clear patterns of constructive and destructive interference are seen. Whether you get constructive or destructive interference at a point depends on how much further one wave has travelled than the other wave to get to that point. The amount by which the path travelled by one wave is longer than the path travelled by the other wave is called the **path difference**.

At any points an equal distance from two sources in phase you will get constructive interference (see Figure 2). These points are known as **maxima**. You also get constructive interference at any point where the path difference is a whole number of wavelengths. At these points the two waves are in phase and reinforce each other, which is why you get constructive interference.

At points where the path difference is half a wavelength, one and a half wavelengths, two and a half wavelengths, etc., the waves arrive exactly out of phase and you get total destructive interference. These points are known as **minima**.

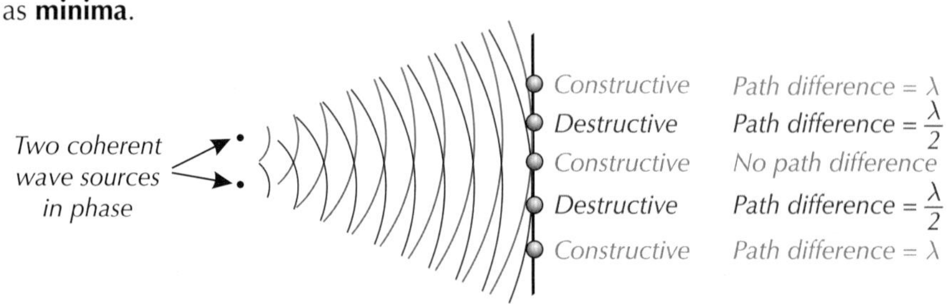

Figure 2: *Two-source interference.*

Constructive interference occurs when:

$$\text{path difference} = n\lambda \text{ (where } n = 0, 1, 2, \ldots)$$

Total destructive interference occurs when:

$$\text{path difference} = \frac{(2n+1)\lambda}{2} = \left(n + \tfrac{1}{2}\right)\lambda$$

Exam Tip
In exam questions at AS, the two sources will almost certainly be in phase. The fixed phase difference will be zero.

Tip: Path difference and phase difference are different things.
The two waves below are in phase — they have 0 phase difference, but their path difference is λ.

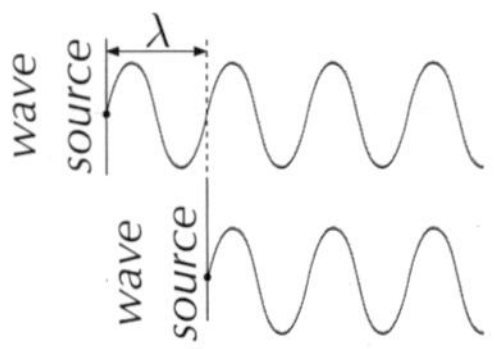

Example — Maths Skills

Two coherent sources of sound waves each with a wavelength of 1.5 m are set up so that they produce interference fringes. When the path difference is 3.75 m, would you expect constructive or destructive interference?

- Find out how many times the wavelength goes into the path difference:

$$\frac{3.75}{1.5} = 2.5.$$

- So the path difference is $2.5 \times \lambda$ so the interference is destructive.

Demonstrating two-source interference

PRACTICAL ACTIVITY GROUP 5

It's easy to demonstrate two-source interference for either sound or water because they've got relatively large wavelengths. This makes it easier to detect interference patterns. The trick for getting them coherent and in phase is to use the same oscillator to drive both sources. For water, one vibrator drives two dippers (see Figure 3). For sound, one amplifier is connected to two loudspeakers (see Figure 4).

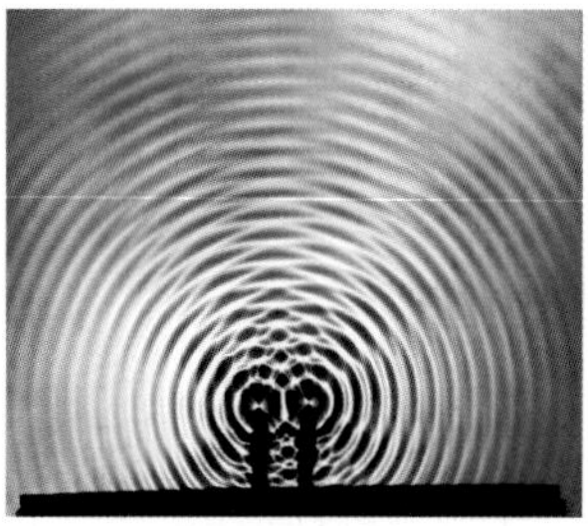

Figure 3: *Two-source interference of water waves demonstrated by two dippers vibrating at the same frequency in a ripple tank.*

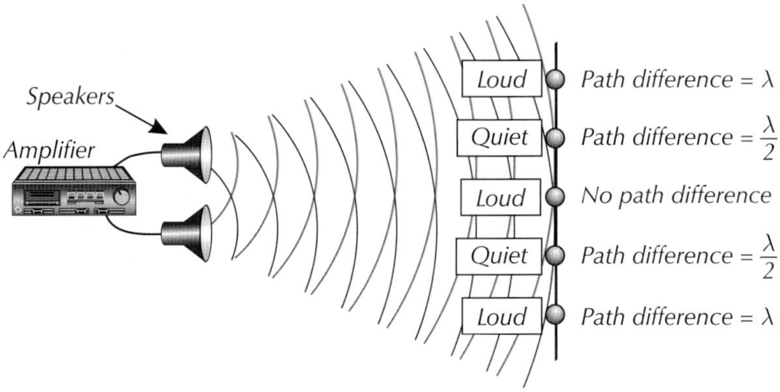

Figure 4: *Demonstrating two-source interference of sound waves.*

Tip: You could use a microphone and an oscilloscope to investigate how interference varies with position along this line.

In Figure 4, an interference pattern is produced at the black line. You can observe this by having someone walk in a straight line, parallel to the line of the speakers. They will observe areas of loud and quiet sound. Constructive interference (at p.d. = $n\lambda$) causes the sound to increase in volume, so you get a loud area. Destructive interference causes the sound to decrease in volume, so you get a quiet area.

To see interference patterns with microwaves, you can use two microwave transmitter cones attached to the same signal generator (see Figure 5 on the next page). You also need a microwave receiver probe (like the one used in the stationary waves experiment on page 218). As you move the probe along the path of the orange arrow in Figure 5, you'll get an alternating pattern of strong and weak signals.

Tip: You may still hear some sound at the quietest points due to sound being reflected off walls and around the room.

Tip: Make sure you take all necessary safety precautions when doing these two experiments and carry out a risk assessment first.

Tip: As usual, strong signals occur where the two sources interfere constructively and weak signals occur where the two sources interfere destructively.

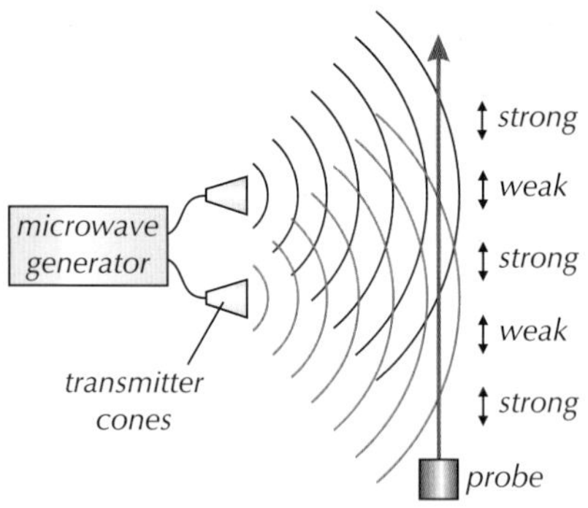

Figure 5: *Two-source interference with microwaves.*

Practice Questions — Application

Q1 A wave, W, is produced and looks as follows:

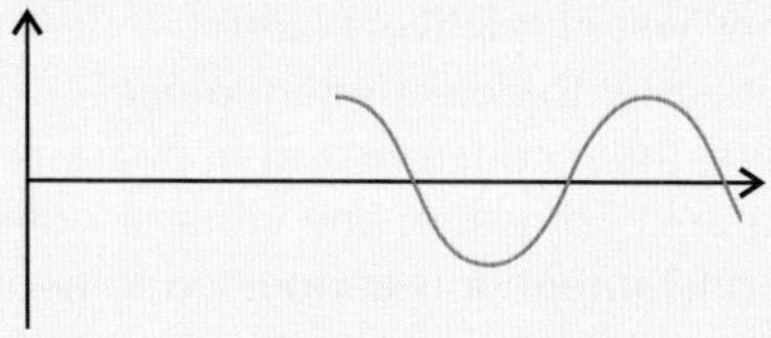

a) Draw a second wave which is in phase with wave W, where the path difference between them is $\frac{\lambda}{2}$.

b) Draw another wave which also has a path difference of $\frac{\lambda}{2}$ but which is completely out of phase with wave W.

Q2 Two coherent sources produce microwaves which have a wavelength of 12 cm. At a point where the path difference is 42 cm, would there be constructive or destructive interference?

Tip: If you're struggling, go back to page 201 to refresh your memory about phase.

Practice Questions — Fact Recall

Q1 What must be true of two wave sources if they produce a clear, standard two-source interference pattern?

Q2 What is meant by the path difference of two waves?

Q3 For two coherent, in phase waves, at what path differences will you see constructive interference?

Q4 How can you create two coherent sources of sound waves?

Q5 Describe an experiment to produce and observe an interference pattern with sound waves.

Q6 Explain what you would observe if you moved a microwave probe in a straight line parallel to the line of two coherent microwave transmitters.

10. Young's Double-Slit Experiment

Just like for sound and microwaves, two sources of light can interfere. It's much harder to produce and observe clear diffraction patterns though.

Double-slit interference of light

PRACTICAL ACTIVITY GROUP 5

To see two-source interference with light, you can either use two coherent light sources or you can shine a laser through two slits. Remember, a laser is a source of monochromatic and coherent light. This means you can effectively create two coherent light sources by shining a single laser through a mounted card containing two slits (known as a single-source double-slit set-up).

The slits have to be about the same size as the wavelength of the laser light so that it is diffracted (see page 204). This makes the light from the slits act like two coherent point sources. You get a pattern of light and dark fringes, depending on whether constructive or destructive interference is taking place — see Figure 1.

You might see this experiment referred to as "Young's double-slit experiment" — Thomas Young was the first person to carry it out, although he used a source of white light instead of a laser. He then came up with an equation to work out the wavelength of the light from the experiment (p.210).

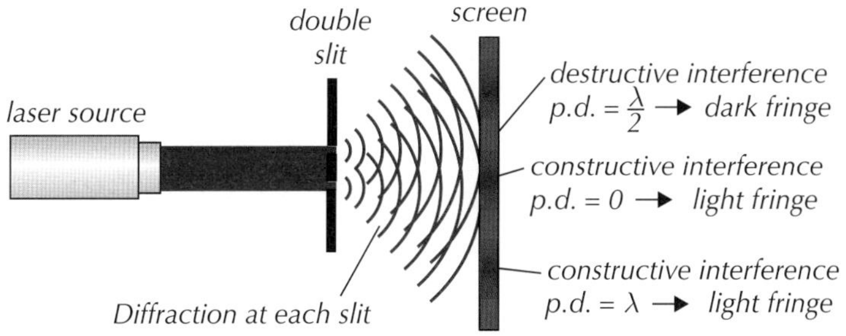

Figure 1: *Two-source interference of laser light.*

If you were to use a white light source instead of a coherent monochromatic laser, the diffraction pattern would be less intense, with wider maxima. The pattern would also contain different colours with a central white fringe, because white light is made up of a mixture of frequencies (see page 215).

Laser safety precautions

Working with lasers is very dangerous because laser light is focused into a very direct, powerful beam of monochromatic light. To make sure you don't cause damage while using lasers, make sure you:

- Never shine the laser towards a person.
- Are wearing laser safety goggles.
- Avoid shining the laser beam at a reflective surface.
- Have a warning sign on display (see Figure 2).
- Turn the laser off when it's not needed.

Learning Objectives:

- Know techniques and procedures used for superposition experiments involving light (PAG5).
- Be able to explain Young's double-slit experiment using visible light.
- Be able to use $\lambda = \frac{ax}{D}$ for all waves where $a << D$.
- Know techniques and procedures used to determine the wavelength of light using a double-slit (PAG5).

Specification Reference 4.4.3

Tip: Create a risk assessment before doing this experiment and follow all of the laser safety precautions given on this page.

Tip: Remember, light that isn't monochromatic is made up of different wavelengths of light, which will diffract by different amounts and makes the fringes much less clear.

Figure 2: *Laser warning signs should be used to alert people of the danger of laser beams.*

The double-slit formula

The fringe spacing (x), wavelength (λ), spacing between slits (a) and the distance between the slits and screen (D) (see Figure 3) are all related by Young's double-slit formula, which works for all waves when $a << D$.

$$\lambda = \frac{ax}{D}$$

***a** = spacing between slits in m*

***λ** = wavelength in m*

***x** = fringe spacing, the distance between two adjacent maxima or two adjacent minima in m*

***D** = distance between slits and screen in m*

Exam Tip
You need to be able to use and rearrange this formula, but you don't need to memorise it or know how to derive it.

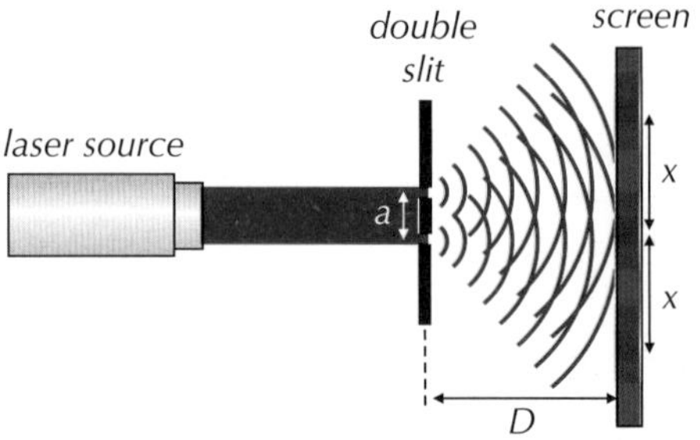

Figure 3: *A diagram to show a, x and D from the double-slit formula.*

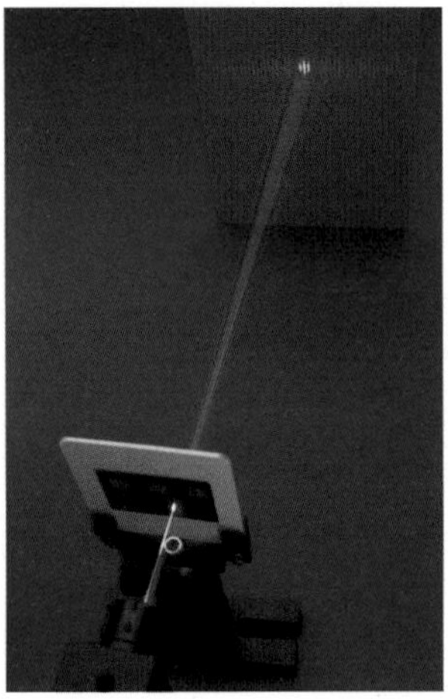

Figure 4: *A laser beam passing through a double slit and forming a diffraction pattern on a screen.*

You can derive this equation by considering the path difference between the waves from each slit when the light interferes constructively to form the first bright fringe — see Figure 5. The path difference between the light waves at the first bright fringe is λ.

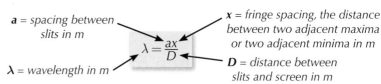

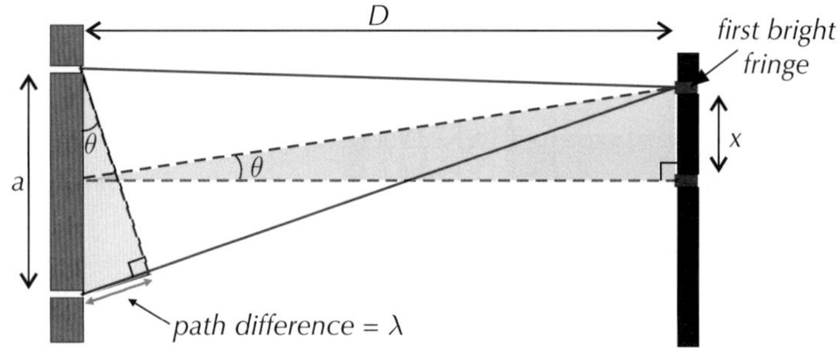

Figure 5: *Light waves from each slit of a double slit, with a path difference of λ, interfering to form the first bright fringe of the diffraction pattern.*

Tip: Figure 5 is not to scale, x would have to be much bigger than a for the pattern to be easily visible.

Look at the green and purple triangles in the diagram — the angle θ is the same in each triangle. Using SOH CAH TOA on the green triangle:

$$\sin\theta = \frac{\text{opposite}}{\text{hypoteneuse}} = \frac{\text{path difference}}{\text{slit separation}} = \frac{\lambda}{a}$$

Using SOH CAH TOA on the purple triangle:

$$\tan\theta = \frac{\text{opposite}}{\text{adjacent}} = \frac{x}{D}$$

Tip: You don't need to know this derivation — it's just to help you understand where the equation comes from.

By small angle approximations: $\tan\theta \approx \theta$ and $\sin\theta \approx \theta$. Remember, this is only true if θ is in radians.

So we can say that $\tan\theta = \sin\theta$ for small angles.

$$\frac{x}{D} = \frac{\lambda}{a} \text{ so } \lambda = \frac{ax}{D}$$

Finding wavelength using the double-slit formula

PRACTICAL ACTIVITY GROUP 5

You can investigate this formula using the double-slit apparatus on page 209. You'll need to measure D and x using a ruler, and a should be printed on the double slit.

Since the wavelength of light is so small, you can see from the formula that a high ratio of D/a is needed to make the fringe spacing big enough to see. You can use $\lambda = \frac{ax}{D}$ to calculate the wavelength of the light.

The fringes are usually so tiny that it's very hard to get an accurate value of x. It's easier to measure across several fringes then divide by the number of fringe widths between them.

Tip: As with all experiments, you should carry out a risk assessment before you start.

Example — Maths Skills

The maxima of an interference pattern produced by shining a laser light through a double slit onto a screen is shown in Figure 6. The slits were 0.20 mm apart and the distance between the slits and the screen was 15 m. Find the wavelength of the laser light.

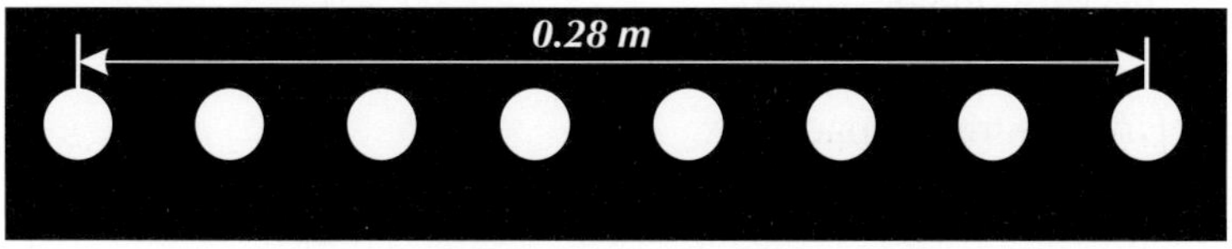

Figure 6: *A double-slit interference pattern.*

You can use Young's double-slit formula to find the wavelength (λ). But first you need to find the fringe spacing of one fringe (x). Seven fringe widths in Figure 6 have a spacing of 0.28 m, so one fringe width has a spacing of $\frac{0.28}{7} = 0.040\,\text{m}$.

Substitute the information you know into the formula: $x = 0.040$ m, $a = 0.00020$ m and $D = 15.0$ m.

$$\lambda = \frac{ax}{D} = \frac{0.040 \times 0.00020}{15} = 5.333... \times 10^{-7} = 5.3 \times 10^{-7}\,\text{m (to 2 s.f.)}$$

Tip: Measuring across several fringes will reduce the uncertainty. E.g. if you measure the width of one fringe as 1.0 ± 0.1 cm, then the percentage uncertainty is 10%. But if you measure the width of 10 fringes as 10.0 ± 0.1 cm, then the average fringe width is 1.0 ± 0.01 cm (you divide the result and the uncertainty by the number of fringes), so the percentage uncertainty is only 1.0%.

Tip: Don't get confused here. There are 8 bright spots (maxima), but only 7 gaps (fringe widths) between them. So you need to divide the total width by 7 and not 8.

You can investigate a range of relationships using Young's double-slit experiment. Try:

- Varying D to see how it affects x.
- Varying a by using different double-slit systems to see how it affects x.
- Varying the wavelength/colour of the light to see how it affects x.

You should find that all of these change x in line with $\lambda = \frac{ax}{D}$.

Figure 7: *Coloured lenses can be used to limit the range of wavelengths from a light source.*

Evidence for the wave nature of light

HOW SCIENCE WORKS

Towards the end of the 17th century, two important theories of light were published — one by Isaac Newton and the other by a chap called Huygens. Newton's theory suggested that light was made up of tiny particles, which he called "corpuscles". And Huygens put forward a theory using waves.

The corpuscular theory could explain reflection and refraction, but diffraction and interference are both uniquely wave properties. If it could be shown that light showed interference patterns, that would help settle the argument once and for all.

Tip: It was later discovered that light has properties of both waves <u>and</u> particles. See pages 234-237 for more on wave-particle duality.

Young's double-slit experiment (over 100 years later) provided the necessary evidence. It showed that light could both diffract (through the two narrow slits) and interfere (to form the interference pattern on the screen).

Tip: A nanometre (nm) is equal to 1×10^{-9} m.

Practice Questions — Application

Q1 A blue-violet laser with a wavelength of 450 nm is shone through a double-slit system to produce an interference pattern on a screen, as shown in Figure 8. The screen is 12.0 m from the slits and the slits are 0.30 mm apart.

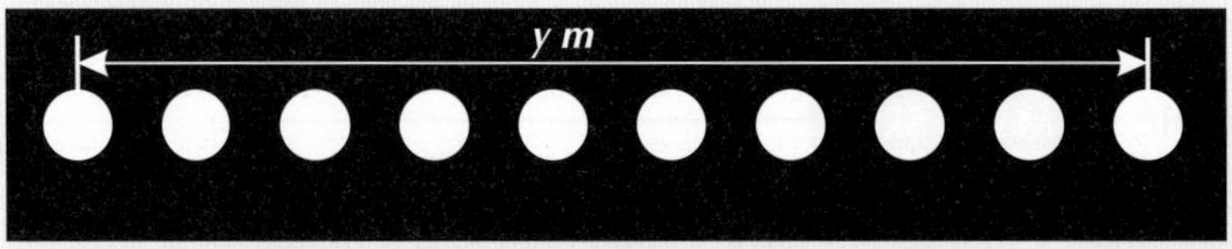

Figure 8: *A double-slit interference pattern.*

a) Give one property of a laser that makes it better than white light in this experiment.

b) Where are light and dark fringes produced?

c) Find the fringe spacing, x.

d) Find the value of y.

Q2 A laser with $\lambda = 615$ nm is shone through a double slit to produce a diffraction pattern on a screen with fringes 1.29 cm apart. If the slits are 0.11 mm apart, find the distance, D, between the slits and the screen.

Practice Questions — Fact Recall

Q1 How can you create two coherent sources of light waves?

Q2 Describe an experiment to measure the wavelength of a laser light source by using a double slit.

Q3 Explain how Young's double-slit experiment suggested that light was a wave.

11. Diffraction Gratings

If you're only doing AS Physics, you don't need to know about diffraction gratings — it's only if you're doing Year 1 of A-level Physics that you'll need this. Diffraction gratings are particularly handy for analysing light from stars.

Learning Objective:

- Know techniques and procedures used to determine the wavelength of light using a diffraction grating (PAG5).

Specification Reference 4.4.3

Interference with a diffraction grating

You can carry out single-source, double-slit type experiments (see p.209) using more than two equally spaced slits. You get basically the same shaped pattern as for two slits — but the bright bands are brighter and narrower and the dark areas between are darker, so the interference pattern produced is sharper.

A **diffraction grating** contains lots of equally spaced slits very close together and so can be used to do this (see Figure 1). When monochromatic light (all of the same wavelength) is passed through a diffraction grating with hundreds of slits per millimetre at normal incidence (right angles to the grating), the interference pattern is really sharp because there are so many beams reinforcing the pattern. Sharper fringes make for more accurate measurements.

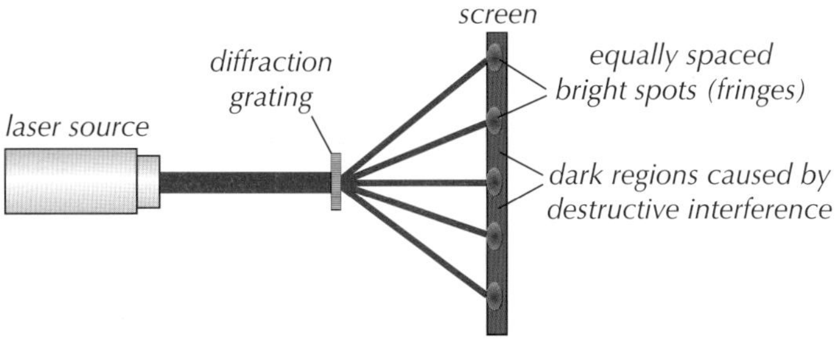

Figure 1: *Laser light passing through a diffraction grating.*

For monochromatic light, all the maxima in the diffraction pattern formed are sharp lines. This means the distance between the maxima can be easily measured (fringe width). There's a line of maximum brightness at the centre called the **zero order line** — which is in the same direction as the beam incident on the grating (see Figure 3). The lines just either side of the central one are called first order lines. The next pair out are called second order lines, and so on.

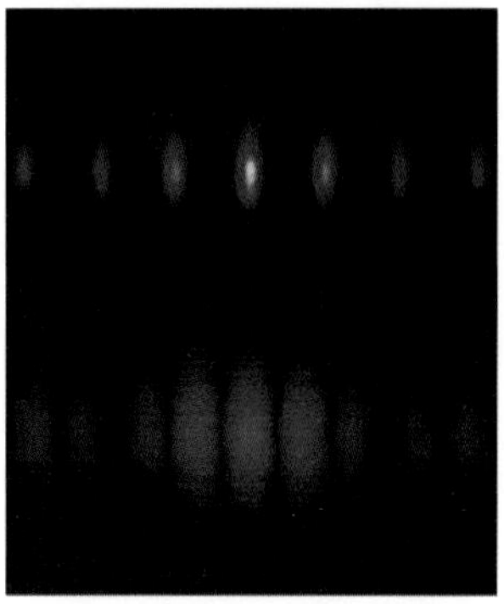

Figure 2: *Interference patterns produced by a laser going through a diffraction grating (top) and a double-slit set-up (bottom).*

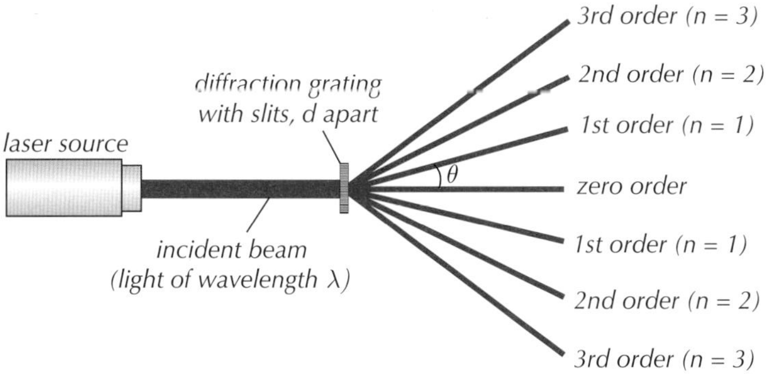

Figure 3: *The order of maxima for light passing through a diffraction grating.*

Tip: Be careful here — the space between slits is d, but for double-slit experiments it was a.

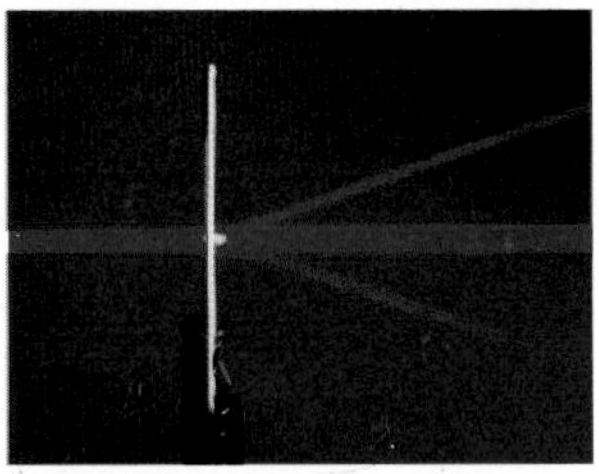

Figure 4: A laser beam is split into zero order and first order maxima by a diffraction grating.

Tip: Make sure you follow the laser safety precautions on page 209.

Tip: The slit separation is often written on the slide frame.

Tip: If multiple orders are visible, you could try repeating your measurements for different orders of n.

Determining the wavelength of light

PRACTICAL ACTIVITY GROUP 5

You can find the wavelength of a light source from the interference pattern produced when it passes through a diffraction grating. It's just like Young's double-slit experiment, p.209-212, but you use a diffraction grating instead of a mounted double-slit card.

Using the fringe width, x, and the distance to the screen, D, the angle the 1st order fringe makes with the zero order line can be calculated using small angle approximations.

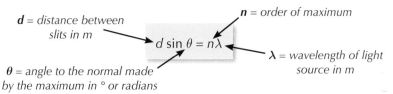

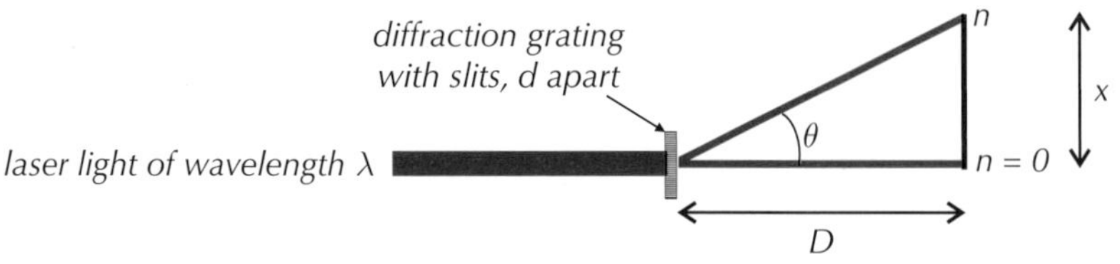

Figure 5: *The 1st order maxima for light passing through a diffraction grating onto a screen.*

For small angles where θ is in radians, $\tan\theta \approx \theta$ and $\tan\theta = \frac{x}{D}$, so:

$$\theta \approx \frac{x}{D}$$

The slit separation, d, for the diffraction grating is usually given. If the grating has N slits per metre, then the slit spacing, d, is just $1/N$ metres. If you know the slit separation, d, what order maximum you're observing, n, and the angle between this maximum and the incident light, θ, you can find the wavelength of the incident light using this equation:

$$d \sin\theta = n\lambda$$

d = *distance between slits in m*

n = *order of maximum*

θ = *angle to the normal made by the maximum in ° or radians*

λ = *wavelength of light source in m*

Example Maths Skills

Green laser light of wavelength 5.00 × 10^{-7} m is transmitted through a perpendicular diffraction grating with 3.00 × 10^{5} slits per metre. At what angle to the normal are the second order maxima seen?

There are 3.00 × 10^5 slits per metre, so the slit spacing is:

$$d = \frac{1}{3.00 \times 10^5} = 3.33... \times 10^{-6}\text{m}$$

Rearrange the diffraction grating equation, $d \sin\theta = n\lambda$, for θ, and remember $n = 2$, as it's the second order we're after. So:

$$\theta = \sin^{-1}\left(\frac{n\lambda}{d}\right) = \sin^{-1}\left(\frac{2 \times (5.00 \times 10^{-7})}{3.33... \times 10^{-6}}\right)$$

$$= 17.457... = 17.5° \text{ (to 3 s.f.)}$$

Tip: Make sure that your calculator is working in the correct mode, depending on whether you want degrees or radians. You'll need the button for $\sin^{-1}$ (inverse sin).

From this equation you can draw a few conclusions:

- If λ is bigger, $\sin\theta$ is bigger, and so θ is bigger. This means that the larger the wavelength, the more the pattern will spread out.
- If d is bigger, $\sin\theta$ is smaller. This means that the coarser the grating, the less the pattern will spread out.
- Values of $\sin\theta$ greater than 1 are impossible. So if for a certain n you get a result of more than 1 for $\sin\theta$, you know that that order doesn't exist.

Tip: Coarser just means fewer slits in a given width.

The diffraction of white light

White light is really a mixture of colours. If you diffract white light through a diffraction grating then the patterns due to different wavelengths within the white light are spread out by different amounts. Each order in the pattern becomes a spectrum, with red on the outside and violet on the inside. The zero order maximum stays white because all the wavelengths just pass straight through.

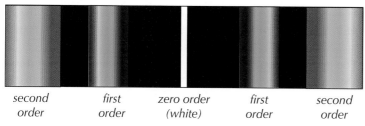

second order
first order
zero order (white)
first order
second order

Figure 6: *The diffraction pattern for white light.*

Astronomers and chemists often need to study spectra to help identify elements. They use diffraction gratings rather than prisms because they're more accurate.

Figure 7: *The surface of a CD contains many tiny grooves that cause it to act in a similar way to a diffraction grating. When white light is shone on it, a spectrum is visible.*

Practice Question — Application

Q1 An orange laser beam with a wavelength of 590 nm is transmitted through a perpendicular diffraction grating with 4.5×10^5 slits per metre.

a) At what angle to the normal is the third order maximum seen? Use the diffraction grating formula $d\sin\theta = n\lambda$, where d is the slit spacing, θ is the angle to the normal made by the maximum, n is the order of maximum and λ is the wavelength of the light source.

b) Use the diffraction grating formula to show whether there will be a fourth order maximum.

c) A red laser beam is used instead with a wavelength of 700 nm. Describe what will happen to the interference pattern, and explain why.

Practice Questions — Fact Recall

Q1 Describe an experiment you could carry out to measure the wavelength of a monochromatic light source using a diffraction grating and an observation screen.

Q2 Why are spectra formed when white light passes through a diffraction grating?

12. Stationary Waves

Learning Objectives:
- Know the similarities and differences between stationary and progressive waves.
- Be able draw graphical representations of a stationary wave.
- Know what nodes and antinodes are.
- Understand the idea that the separation between adjacent nodes (or antinodes) is equal to $\lambda/2$, where λ is the wavelength of the progressive wave.
- Know what is meant by the fundamental mode of vibration (1st harmonic) and the harmonics.
- Know the stationary wave patterns for a stretched string.
- Demonstrate understanding of stationary (standing) waves using stretched strings, air columns and microwaves.
- Know the stationary wave patterns for air columns in closed and open tubes.
- Know techniques and procedures used to determine the speed of sound in air by formation of stationary waves in a resonance tube (PAG5).

Specification Reference 4.4.4

Exam Tip
If you're asked to sketch a standing wave, make sure you make it clear where the nodes and antinodes are. You don't need to draw loads of lines like in Figure 2, just show what shape the string is vibrating in.

So far you've been looking at progressive waves — waves that move. Now it's time for stationary waves — waves that stay where they are.

What is a stationary wave?

A **stationary (standing) wave** is the superposition of two progressive waves with the same wavelength and frequency, moving in opposite directions. So a stationary wave has all the same properties as a progressive wave, however unlike progressive waves, no energy is transmitted by a stationary wave.

You can demonstrate stationary waves by attaching a vibration transducer (an oscillator) at one end of a stretched string with the other end fixed. The transducer is given a wave frequency by a signal generator and creates that wave by vibrating the string.

The wave generated by the transducer is reflected back and forth. For most frequencies the resultant pattern is a jumble. However, if the transducer happens to produce an exact number of waves in the time it takes for a wave to get to the end and back again, then the original and reflected waves reinforce each other.

The frequencies at which this happens are called **resonant frequencies** and it causes a stationary wave where the overall pattern doesn't move along — it just vibrates up and down, so the string forms oscillating 'loops' — see Figure 1.

These stationary waves are transverse, so each particle vibrates at right angles to the string. **Nodes** are where the amplitude of the vibration is zero — they just stay perfectly still. **Antinodes** are points of maximum amplitude. The separation between any two adjacent nodes (or antinodes) is equal to $\lambda/2$, where λ is the wavelength of the progressive wave.

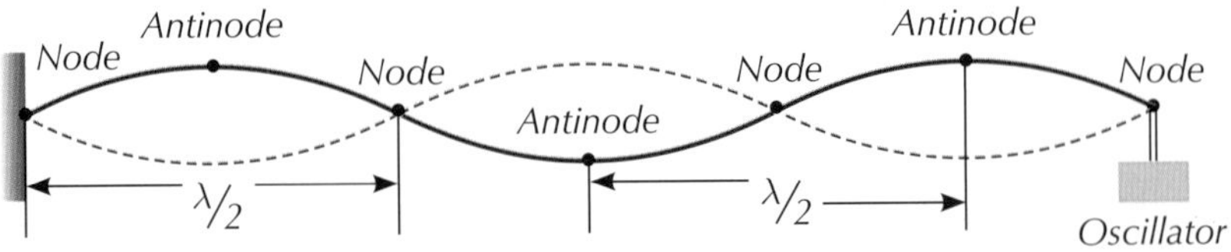

Figure 1: *A stationary wave oscillating on a string.*

Resonant frequencies

A stationary wave is only formed at a resonant frequency (when an exact number of half wavelengths fits on the string). There are some special names for each resonant frequency.

The fundamental mode of vibration

The standing wave in Figure 2 is vibrating at the lowest possible resonant frequency, called the **fundamental mode of vibration** or the first harmonic. It has one "loop" with a node at each end. One half wavelength fits onto the string, and so the wavelength is double the length of the string.

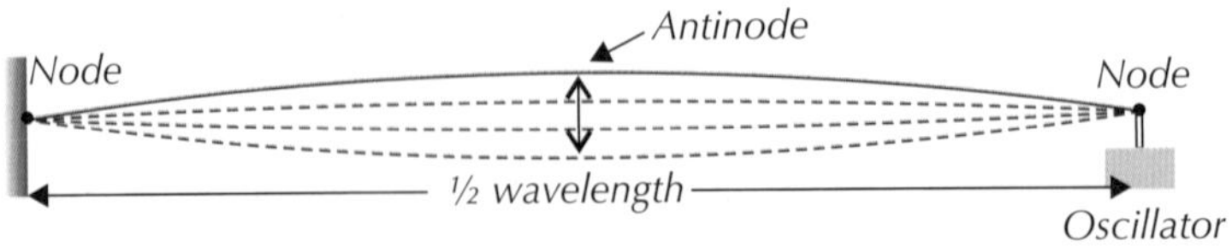

Figure 2: *A stationary wave vibrating at its first harmonic.*

Second harmonic

Figure 3 shows the second harmonic. It has twice the frequency of the fundamental mode of vibration. There are two "loops" with a node in the middle and one at each end. Two half wavelengths fit on the string, so the wavelength is the length of the string.

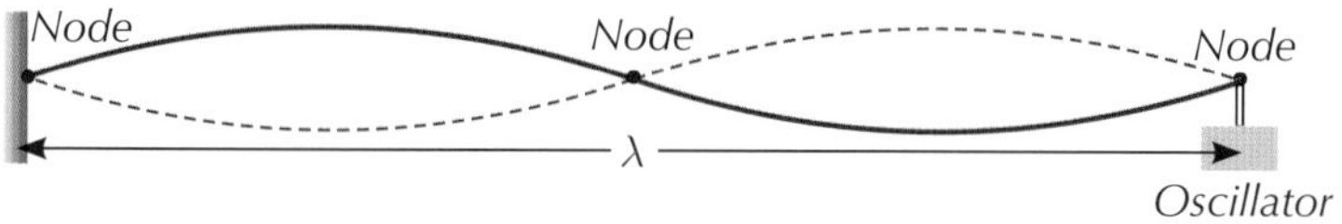

Figure 3: *A stationary wave vibrating at its second harmonic.*

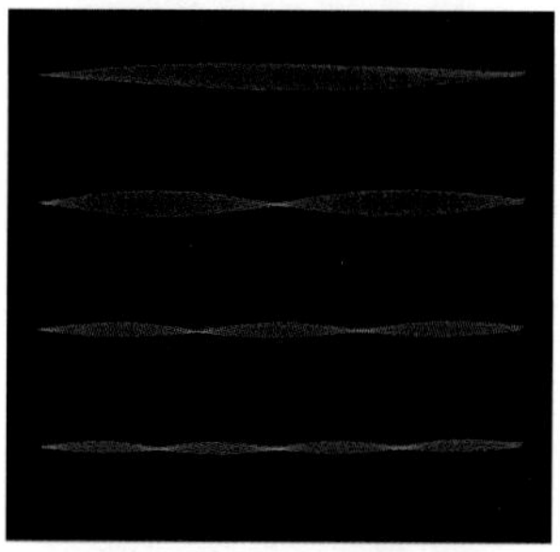

Figure 4: *A stationary wave vibrating at its first, second, third and fourth harmonics (going from top to bottom).*

Third harmonic

The third harmonic is three times the frequency of the first harmonic — see Figure 5. One and a half wavelengths fit on the string.

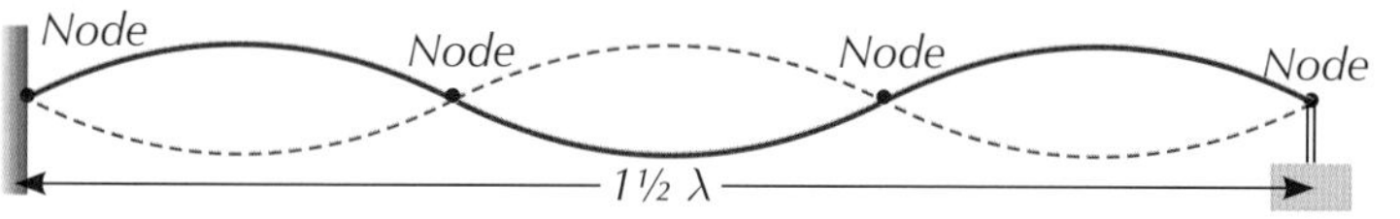

Figure 5: *A stationary wave vibrating at its third harmonic.*

You can have as many harmonics as you like — an extra loop and an extra node are just added with each one, the number of λ that fit goes up by ½, and the frequency increases by the value of the frequency of the first harmonic. For example, Figure 4 shows the fourth harmonic of a stationary wave.

Tip: At the ath harmonic, the number of antinodes is equal to a, and the number of nodes is equal to $a + 1$.

Tip: At the ath harmonic, $\frac{a}{2}$ wavelengths will fit on the string.

Example — Maths Skills

A banjo string vibrates with a first harmonic frequency of 290 Hz. Find the frequency of vibration of the string at the third harmonic.

The third harmonic is three times the frequency of the first harmonic, so:
$f = 290 \times 3 = 870$ Hz

A violin string is vibrating at fives times the frequency of its first harmonic. How many wavelengths fit onto the string?

The fifth harmonic is made up of five 'loops'. Each loop is ½λ long.
5 × ½ = 2.5, so there are two and a half wavelengths on the string.

Tip: If you're given the first harmonic frequency, you can work out the resonant frequency f at the ath harmonic with $f = a \times$ first harmonic frequency.

Other examples of stationary waves

Stretched strings

Just like the strings in the demonstration on the previous page, transverse stationary waves form on the strings of stringed instruments like violins and guitars. Your finger or the bow sets the string vibrating at the point of contact. Waves are sent out in both directions and reflected back at both ends.

Air columns

Longitudinal stationary waves form in a wind instrument or other air column. If a source of sound is placed at the open end of a flute, piccolo, oboe or other column of air, there will be some frequencies for which resonance occurs and a stationary wave is set up.

Figure 6: The individual pipes in a set of panpipes are cut to different lengths to give them different fundamental frequencies.

Tip: Remember, the sound waves in wind instruments are longitudinal — they don't actually look like these diagrams.

If the instrument has a closed end, a node will form there. You get the lowest resonant frequency when the length, l, of the pipe is a quarter wavelength. Antinodes form at the open ends of pipes.

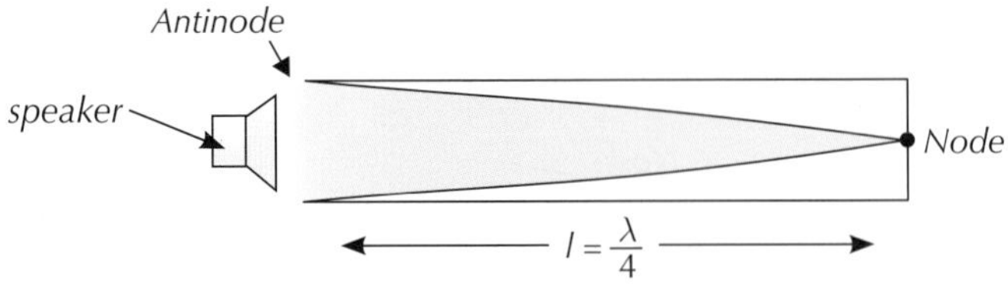

Figure 7: *An air column vibrating at the fundamental mode of vibration in a pipe with one closed end.*

If both ends are open, there are antinodes at both ends. You get the lowest resonant frequency when the length, l, of the pipe is a half wavelength.

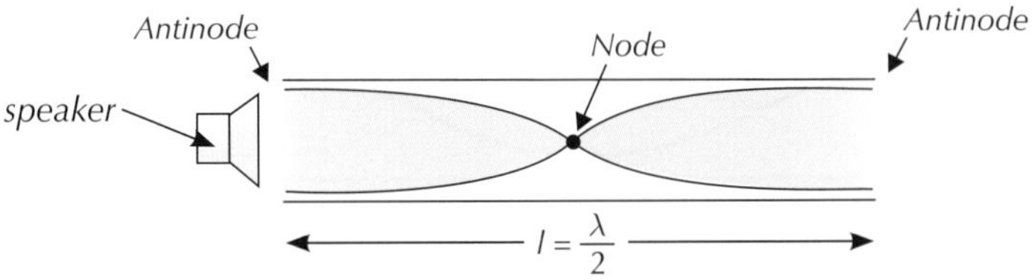

Figure 8: *An air column vibrating at the fundamental mode of vibration in an open-ended pipe.*

All harmonics have nodes at closed ends and antinodes at open ends. For example, the second harmonic for the open-ended pipe is shown in Figure 9.

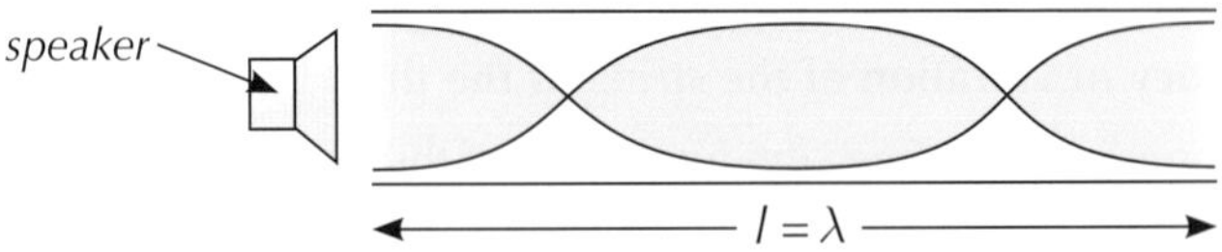

Figure 9: *An air column vibrating at the second harmonic in an open-ended pipe.*

Tip: You could do a similar experiment using a loud speaker by moving around a microphone connected to a meter.

Tip: The string demonstration on page 216 gives you the best idea of what stationary waves actually look like, but this experiment also shows the presence of stationary waves.

Stationary microwaves

You can set up a stationary wave by reflecting a microwave beam at a metal plate (see Figure 10). The superposition of the wave and its reflection produces a stationary wave. You can find the nodes and antinodes by moving the probe between the transmitter and reflecting plate. The meter or loudspeaker receives no signal at the nodes and maximum signal at the antinodes.

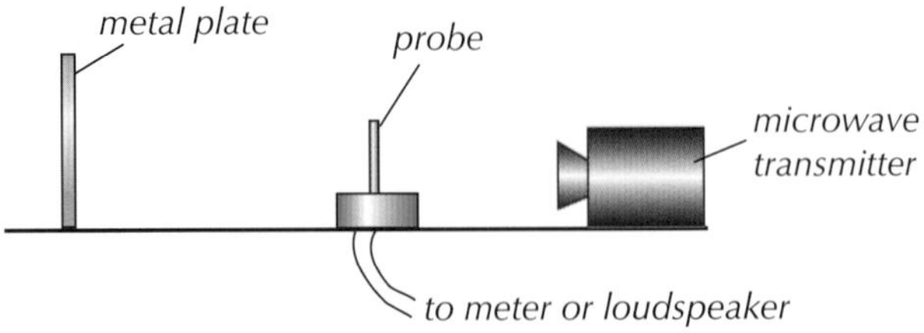

Figure 10: *Apparatus for demonstrating stationary microwaves.*

Measuring the speed of sound

PRACTICAL ACTIVITY GROUP 5

You can use the known wavelength of a stationary wave in an air column to calculate the speed of sound in air.

Create a closed-end pipe by placing a hollow tube into a measuring cylinder of water (see Figure 11). Choose a tuning fork and note down the frequency of sound it produces (it'll be stamped on the side of it).

Gently tap the tuning fork and hold it just above the hollow tube. The sound waves produced by the fork travel down the tube and get reflected (and form a node) at the air/water surface. Move the tube up and down until you find the shortest distance between the top of the tube and the water level that the sound from the fork resonates at (when the sound is at its loudest). At this point the frequency of the sound wave is equal to the lowest resonant frequency of the closed tube.

Just like with any closed pipe, the length of the tube at its lowest resonant frequency is a quarter of the wavelength of the stationary sound wave (see page 218). Once you know the frequency and wavelength of the stationary sound wave, you can work out the speed of sound (in air), v, using the equation $v = f\lambda$.

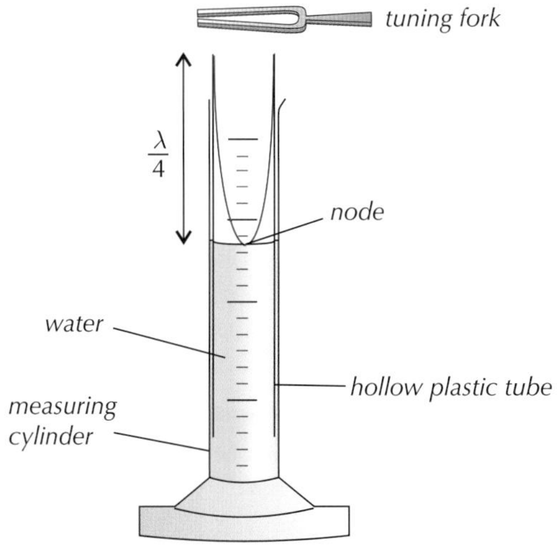

Figure 11: *Apparatus for measuring the speed of sound.*

Repeat the experiment with different tuning forks and calculate an average value of v from your results.

Example — Maths Skills

A student conducts an experiment to measure the speed of sound. He holds one end of a hollow tube in water and uses a tuning fork to send sound waves with a frequency of 424 Hz into the tube. He finds that the shortest distance between the water level and the top of the tube when the sound is loudest is 20.1 cm. What is the speed of sound?

Wavelength = 4 × pipe length = 4 × 0.201 = 0.804 m

$v = f\lambda = 424 \times 0.804 = 340.896 = 341$ ms^{-1} (to 3 s.f.)

Tip: Make sure you carry out this experiment safely — you should clear up any water spillages that occur to prevent anybody slipping on a wet floor.

Tip: The antinode of the wave actually forms slightly above the top of the tube. You'd add an 'end correction value' on to take this into account, but you don't need to worry about it.

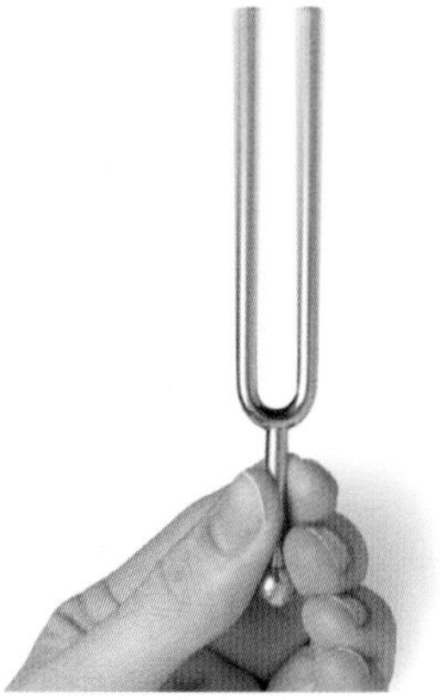

Figure 12: *Tuning forks produce a very pure sound at one frequency.*

Practice Questions — Application

Q1 For the stationary wave in the diagram below, find the wavelength.

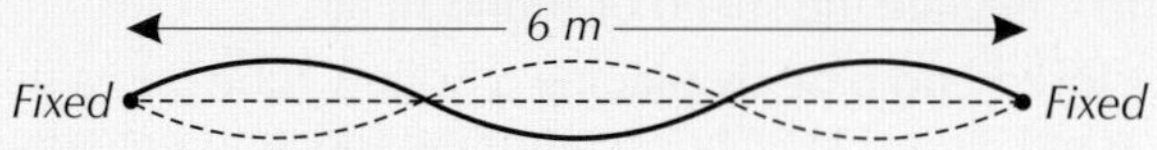

Q2 The diagram below represents a stationary wave on a string which is fixed at A and driven by an oscillator at B.

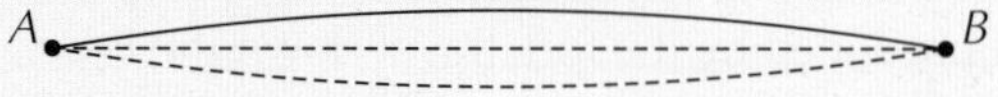

a) The length of the string AB is 2.5 m and the frequency of the wave is 100 Hz.
Calculate the speed of the waves forming the stationary wave.

Tip: Remember $v = f\lambda$.

b) If the wave is now vibrating at a frequency of 200 Hz, how many wavelengths would fit on the string? What is the name for this resonant frequency?

Q3 A student holds one end of hollow tube in water and uses a tuning fork to send sound waves into the tube. She moves the tube up and down in the water until she finds the lowest resonant frequency of the wave. What is the length of the pipe equal to in terms of the wavelength of the sound waves?

Q4 A speaker is used to set up a stationary sound wave in a pipe which is open at both ends. The wave is at the lowest fundamental frequency and has a wavelength of 3.2 m. The last 0.2 m of the pipe is then blocked up as shown in the diagram on the right. Again, the speaker is used to set up a stationary sound wave in the blocked pipe at the lowest fundamental frequency. Calculate the wavelength of the new stationary wave.

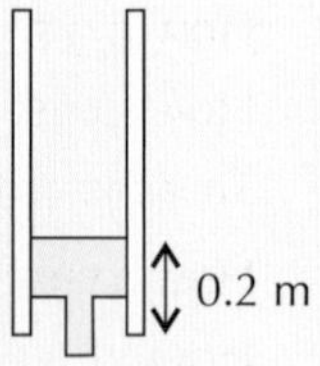

Not to scale

Practice Questions — Fact Recall

Q1 What is a stationary wave?

Q2 What is the difference between stationary and progressive waves in terms of energy transfer?

Q3 Describe what a resonant frequency of a string is.

Q4 What is the distance between two adjacent nodes on a stationary wave?

Q5 What is the fundamental mode of vibration?

Q6 Sketch a string vibrating at its second harmonic and label the positions of all nodes and antinodes.

Q7 Give an example of a way to observe stationary microwaves.

Section Summary

Make sure you know...

- That a wave which carries energy without transferring any material is called a progressive wave.
- What displacement, amplitude, wavelength, period, frequency and phase difference mean for waves.
- The nature of transverse and longitudinal waves, and be able to draw graphical representations of each.
- How to calculate the period of a wave using $f = \frac{1}{T}$.
- How to determine the frequency of a wave using an oscilloscope.
- How to calculate wave speed using $v = f\lambda$.
- That the intensity of a wave is proportional to the square of its amplitude and how to calculate it using $I = \frac{P}{A}$.
- What the electromagnetic spectrum is and the properties of electromagnetic waves.
- The orders of magnitude of the wavelengths of each of the seven categories of electromagnetic wave.
- That plane polarised waves are waves that only oscillate in one direction, and be able to describe how polarising effects can be observed using light and microwaves.
- That waves can be reflected and refracted, and how to demonstrate their effects using a ripple tank.
- That the refractive index of a material is the ratio between the speed of light in a vacuum and the speed of light in that material, and how to calculate it using $n = \frac{c}{v}$.
- How to use $n\sin\theta$ = constant and $n_1\sin\theta_1 = n_2\sin\theta_2$ to solve problems at a boundary between materials.
- How to use ray boxes and transparent rectangular blocks to investigate the refraction of light.
- That the critical angle is the angle of incidence at which the angle of refraction is 90°.
- How to use the equation $\sin C = \frac{1}{n}$ to calculate the critical angle of light at a material-air boundary.
- How to use ray boxes and semi-circular blocks to investigate total internal reflection of light.
- The principle of superposition and how it can be illustrated graphically.
- What the terms interference, phase difference and coherence mean.
- How to describe constructive interference and destructive interference in terms of phase difference.
- That diffraction is the way that waves spread out as they pass through a narrow gap or go round obstacles, and how it can be demonstrated using a ripple tank.
- That all waves can be diffracted and that diffraction effects become significant when the wavelength is comparable to the gap width that a wave is travelling through.
- Know what the term path difference means.
- How to describe constructive interference and destructive interference in terms of path difference.
- How to carry out experiments using sound and microwaves to demonstrate superposition.
- How visible light can be used to carry out Young's double-slit experiment, and how this experiment gave a classical confirmation of the wave-nature of light.
- That Young's double slit formula, $\lambda = \frac{ax}{D}$, can be used for all waves where $a << D$.
- How to determine the wavelength of light using a double-slit or using a diffraction grating.
- The similarities and differences between stationary and progressive waves.
- How a stationary wave can be represented graphically.
- What nodes and antinodes are and that the separation between adjacent nodes (or antinodes) is $\lambda/2$.
- That the resonant frequencies at which stationary waves are formed are called the harmonics, and that the lowest possible resonant frequency is the fundamental mode of vibration (1st harmonic).
- How to demonstrate stationary waves using stretched strings, air columns and microwaves.
- The stationary wave patterns for a stretched string and air columns in closed and open tubes.
- How the speed of sound in air can be found using stationary waves in a resonance tube.

Exam-style Questions

1 Two waves that are in phase and coherent interfere.
Which of the following could be correct?

A The waves have a path difference of λ and interfere destructively.

B The waves have a path difference of $\frac{\lambda}{2}$ and interfere constructively.

C The waves have a path difference of 3λ and interfere destructively.

D The waves have a path difference of 4λ and interfere constructively.

(1 mark)

2 Unpolarised white light is incident on two polarising filters placed one in front of the other. The transmission axes of the two filters are aligned horizontally, then one filter is gradually rotated. At what angle of rotation is all light blocked from passing through the filters?

A 0°

B 45°

C 90°

D 180°

(1 mark)

3 X-rays with a period of 1.7×10^{-16} ms travel through a vacuum.
What is the value of λ?

A 5.1×10^{-11} m

B 1.76×10^{24} m

C 5.1×10^{-8} m

D 1.76×10^{27} m

(1 mark)

4 A wave has an amplitude of 78 cm. The intensity of the wave is reduced from $0.42\ \text{W m}^{-2}$ to $0.11\ \text{W m}^{-2}$. What is the new amplitude of the wave?

A 5.4 cm

B 20 cm

C 152 cm

D 40 cm

(1 mark)

5 **Fig 5.1** shows a graphical representation of a stationary sound wave in an air column.

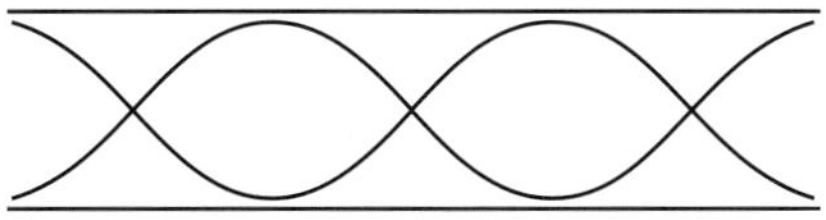

Fig 5.1

(a) What is the name for the resonant frequency displayed?

(1 mark)

(b) The tube is 1.25 m long. Calculate the wavelength of the stationary wave.

(1 mark)

(c) Describe an experimental method that a student could use to measure the speed of sound using the phenomenon of standing sound waves in air columns.
Your answer should include a labelled diagram and one way to improve the accuracy of the experiment.

(6 marks)

6 A scientist is testing a transmitter of electromagnetic (EM) radiation. He connects an oscilloscope to the transmitter to display the EM wave being produced. A sketch of the trace is shown in **Fig 6.1**. The timebase of the oscilloscope is set to 0.500 μs/div.

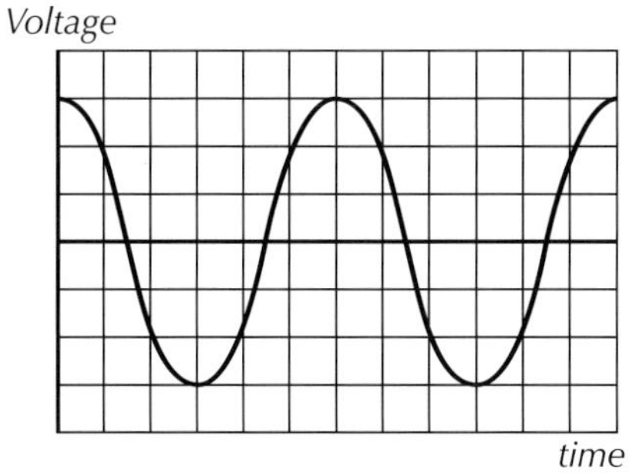

Fig 6.1

(a) Calculate the wavelength of the detected wave. You can assume the wave is travelling at the speed of light in a vacuum.

(3 marks)

(b) Which part of the electromagnetic spectrum does the wave belong to?

(1 mark)

(c) The scientist connects the oscilloscope to a second transmitter, which produces EM waves with the same frequency and wavelength as the first transmitter, but half the amplitude. The waves of both transmitters are displayed on the screen. The scientist notes that the wave from the second transmitter is 90° in front of the wave from the first transmitter. Sketch what the scientist sees on the oscilloscope screen.

(2 marks)

(d) The scientist measures the power of the first wave to be 15.2 W.
Calculate the power of the second wave.

(2 marks)

7 A student is investigating diffraction patterns. He directs a laser beam through a double-slit system, where the slits are 0.15 mm apart and the screen is 7.5 m from the slits. The interference pattern produced is shown in **Fig 7.1**.

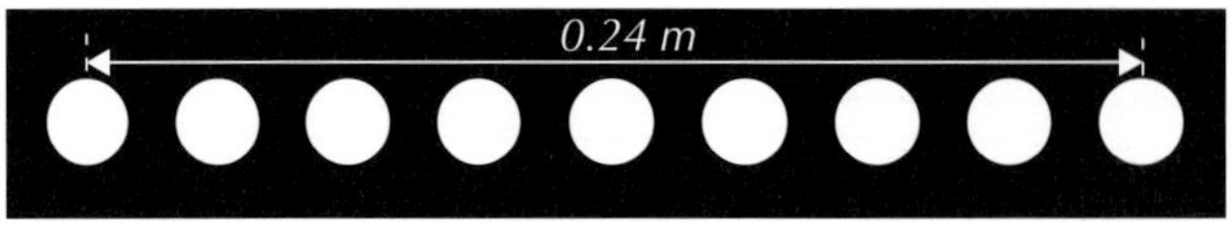

Fig 7.1

(a) Find the wavelength of the laser beam.

(3 marks)

(b) Explain why the student used a laser and not a standard light source.

(2 marks)

(c) Calculate the angle of the first order maxima if the same laser is shone through a diffraction grating with 2.55×10^5 slits per metre.

(4 marks)

(d) Describe the difference you would expect to see in the interference pattern if a diffraction grating was used instead of the double slit in this experiment.

(1 mark)

8 **Fig 8.1** shows two rays of light at a frequency of 5.00×10^{14} Hz entering an optical fibre used for communications.

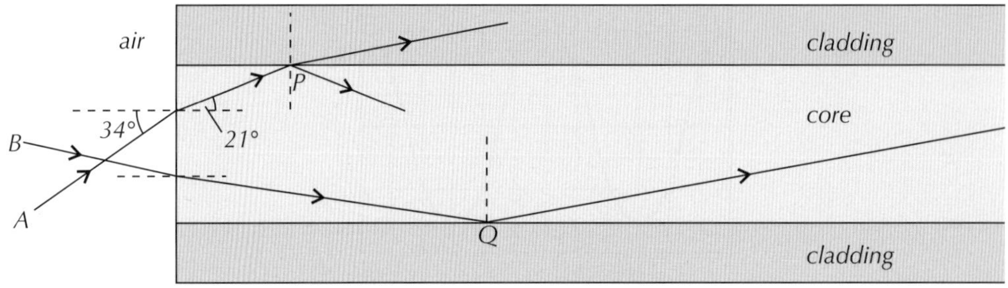

Fig 8.1 ***not drawn to scale***

(a) Light travels at 2.03×10^8 ms^{-1} in the cladding.
Calculate the refractive index of the cladding.

(2 marks)

(b) Find the refractive index of the core of the optical fibre.

(3 marks)

(c) Find the wavelength of the light as it travels through the core.

(3 marks)

(d) Calculate the critical angle of the core-cladding boundary.

(2 marks)

(e) Explain why light ray A enters the cladding of the optical fibre.

(2 marks)

(f) Describe what has happened to ray B, and explain why.

(2 marks)

Module 4 Section 3: Quantum Physics

1. The Photon Model

You might think that light and all other electromagnetic waves are, well, waves. But you can use a particle model called the photon model to describe them...

Learning Objectives:
- Understand the particulate nature (photon model) of electromagnetic radiation.
- Know that a photon is a quantum of energy of electromagnetic radiation.
- Know how to calculate the energy of a photon, using $E = hf$ and $E = \frac{hc}{\lambda}$.
- Know and be able to use the electronvolt (eV) as a unit of energy.

Specification Reference 4.5.1

Photons

HOW SCIENCE WORKS

When Max Planck was investigating black body radiation (don't worry, you don't need to know about this), he suggested that electromagnetic (EM) waves can only be released in discrete packets. This meant that the energy carried by a wave could only be released in fixed 'lumps' of energy, called quanta.

Einstein went further by suggesting that EM waves (and the energy they carry) can only exist in discrete packets. He called these wave-packets **photons**. One photon is one quantum of energy of electromagnetic radiation.

He believed that a photon acted as a neutral particle. He said that it would either transfer all or none of its energy when interacting with one other particle (this is called a **one-to-one interaction**). The energy, *E*, carried by one of these photons had to be:

$$E = hf$$

E = *energy of one photon in J*

f = *frequency of light in Hz*

h = *Planck's constant* $= 6.63 \times 10^{-34}$ *Js*

Tip: The photon model is needed to explain the photoelectric effect, which is on pages 230-233.

So, the higher the frequency of the electromagnetic radiation, the more energy its photons carry. The frequency, wavelength and speed of light are related by the equation:

$$f = \frac{c}{\lambda}$$

f = *frequency in Hz*

c = *speed of light in a vacuum* $= 3.00 \times 10^8$ *ms*$^{-1}$

λ = *wavelength in m*

Tip: This is just the wave speed equation from page 184.

You can substitute this equation into $E = hf$ to give another equation for the energy of one photon:

$$E = hf = \frac{hc}{\lambda}$$

Exam Tip
In the exam you'll be given a data and formulae booklet that has these equations, as well as the values of *c* and *h*. So you don't have to worry about learning them — just make sure you can use them.

Example — Maths Skills

Calculate the energy of a photon with a wavelength of 3.9×10^{-9} m.

Substitute $\lambda = 3.9 \times 10^{-9}$ m, $h = 6.63 \times 10^{-34}$ Js and $c = 3.00 \times 10^8$ ms^{-1} into the equation $E = \frac{hc}{\lambda}$ to find the energy, *E*, of the photon.

$$E = \frac{hc}{\lambda} = \frac{(6.63 \times 10^{-34}) \times (3.00 \times 10^8)}{3.9 \times 10^{-9}} = 5.1 \times 10^{-17} \text{J}$$

Figure 1: Electron tubes are used to produce and accelerate electrons.

Tip: To convert energy from electronvolts to joules, just multiply it by 1.60×10^{-19}.
To convert from joules to electronvolts, divide by 1.60×10^{-19}.

Tip: Prefixes like 'M' are covered on page 25.

The electronvolt

The energies involved when you're talking about photons are usually so tiny that it makes sense to use a more appropriate unit than the joule. So the electronvolt (eV) is used.

When you accelerate an electron in a potential difference (p.147), it transfers some electrical potential energy (= eV) into kinetic energy (= $\frac{1}{2}mv^2$).

$$eV = \frac{1}{2}mv^2$$

e = *charge of one electron in C*

v = *speed of the electron in ms*$^{-1}$

V = *potential difference between electrodes in V*

m = *mass of an electron in kg*

The electronvolt is defined as the kinetic energy gained by an electron when it is accelerated through a potential difference of one volt. So the value of one electronvolt can be found using:

$$1 \text{ electronvolt} = e \times V = 1.60 \times 10^{-19} \text{ C} \times 1 \text{ JC}^{-1}$$

$$1 \text{ eV} = 1.60 \times 10^{-19} \text{ J}$$

Example — Maths Skills

A photon has a frequency of 100 MHz.
Calculate the energy of the photon in eV.

100 MHz = $100 \times 10^6 = 1 \times 10^8$ Hz,

Substitute $f = 1 \times 10^8$ Hz and $h = 6.63 \times 10^{-34}$ Js into $E = hf$:

$E = 6.63 \times 10^{-34} \times 1 \times 10^8 = 6.63 \times 10^{-26}$ J

Divide this by 1.60×10^{-19} to get the energy in eV:

$(6.63 \times 10^{-26}) \div (1.60 \times 10^{-19}) = 4.14... \times 10^{-7}$ eV $= 4.1 \times 10^{-7}$ eV (to 2 s.f.)

Practice Questions — Application

Q1 A photon has an energy of 2.20 eV. Calculate its energy in J.

Q2 A photon has a frequency of 6.0×10^{13} Hz. Calculate its energy in J.

Q3 A photon has an energy of 8.2×10^{-20} J. Calculate its wavelength.

Practice Questions — Fact Recall

Q1 What is a photon?

Q2 What equation would you use to calculate the energy of a photon from its wavelength?

Q3 What is an electronvolt a measure of?

2. The Planck Constant

The Planck constant is used in loads of equations in quantum physics. It's one of the smallest physical constants, and you need to know how to find it...

Threshold voltage of LEDs

You can find the value of Planck's constant by doing a simple experiment with light-emitting diodes (LEDs) — see below.

LEDs, like all electrical components, have a potential difference across them when they're part of a complete circuit. This potential difference accelerates the electrons flowing around the circuit (the current) and causes them to gain kinetic energy, like you saw on the last page. This kinetic energy is transferred into a photon that is emitted by the LED.

However, current will only pass through an LED after a minimum voltage (potential difference) is placed across it — the **threshold voltage** V_0. This is the voltage needed to give the electrons the same energy as a photon emitted by the LED.

Finding the Planck constant

PRACTICAL ACTIVITY GROUP **6**

You can use the threshold voltage of LEDs to find the Planck constant. To do this, you'll need to use monochromatic LEDs — i.e. LEDs that emit a single colour. The colour of light depends on its wavelength, so monochromatic LEDs only emit a single wavelength of light. You should know the wavelength of the LED from the manufacturer.

At the threshold voltage, the kinetic energy of each electron is equal to eV_0 (from the equation on page 226) where V_0 is the threshold voltage. All of this energy is transferred into one photon that is emitted by the LED. The energy of any photon is given by $E = \frac{hc}{\lambda}$ (page 225). So to find the Planck constant, equate the energy of one electron to the energy of a photon emitted:

$$e = \text{charge of one electron in C} \longrightarrow eV_0 = \frac{hc}{\lambda} \longleftarrow \text{energy of one photon}$$

V_0 = *threshold voltage in V*

Then rearrange this for the Planck constant to get:

$$h = \frac{eV_0\lambda}{c}$$

To determine the Planck constant from an LED, you will need to set up the circuit shown in Figure 2.

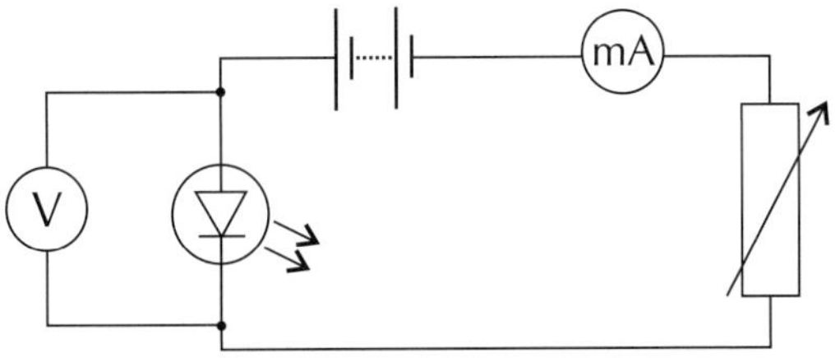

Figure 2: A circuit used to find the Planck constant from an LED.

Learning Objectives:

- Be able to use LEDs and the equation $eV = \frac{hc}{\lambda}$ to estimate the value of the Planck constant, h.
- Determine the Planck constant using different coloured LEDs (PAG6).

Specification Reference 4.5.1

Figure 1: LEDs come in a range of sizes and colours. They're often used because they produce light at a lower potential difference than traditional filament bulbs.

Tip: You may see this written as $eV = \frac{hc}{\lambda}$, but don't panic, V is still the threshold voltage.

Tip: Make sure you do a risk assessment before you start this experiment, to ensure your experiment is carried out as safely as possible.

Tip: A milliammeter is most suitable (p.17) for this experiment, as it will allow you to more accurately tell when a current has just begun to flow.

- Start off with the variable resistor set to its maximum resistance, so no current can flow through the circuit.
- Adjust the variable resistor until a current just begins to flow through the circuit (and the LED lights up).
- Record the voltage across the LED. This is the threshold voltage, V_0.
- Record the wavelength of the light emitted by the LED.
- Disconnect the circuit to allow all of the components to cool.
- Repeat the experiment several times and take an average of your result for V_0.
- Then repeat the experiment for a range of LEDs.

If you look at $eV_0 = \frac{hc}{\lambda}$ from the previous page, you can see that $V_0 \propto 1/\lambda$ (as e, h and c are all constants). So a graph of the threshold voltages against $1/\lambda$ will give you a straight line of best fit. You can use the gradient of this line to find the Planck constant (see below).

You should get a straight line graph similar to the one shown in Figure 3. Your line of best fit must go through the origin.

Tip: Doing this experiment in a dark room, or placing a tube of paper around the LED, makes it easier to see when the LED just begins to light up.

Tip: If your LED doesn't light up, swap over the wires connected to it. LEDs have a positive and a negative end, and they won't work unless they're connected the right way round.

Tip: Make sure you use the same equipment for each repeat, and control variables like temperature to make the experiment a fair test that will give you valid results (p.18).

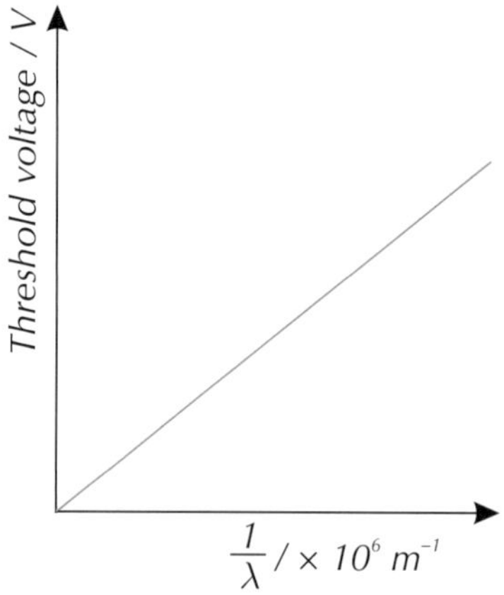

Figure 3: *A graph of threshold voltage against 1/λ for LEDs.*

The gradient of this graph is equal to:

$$\text{gradient} = \frac{\Delta y}{\Delta x} = V_0\lambda$$

Substitute this into the equation from the previous page:

$$h = \frac{eV_0\lambda}{c} = \frac{e \times \text{gradient}}{c}$$

Tip: There's more about graphs and how to calculate a gradient on page 14.

Example — Maths Skills

A student investigates the threshold voltages of some LEDs. They plot a graph of threshold voltage against 1/λ. The gradient of the graph is equal to 1.24×10^{-6} Vm. Use this data to calculate Planck's constant.

Substitute the gradient into $h = \frac{e \times \text{gradient}}{c}$:

$$h = \frac{(1.60 \times 10^{-19}) \times (1.24 \times 10^{-6})}{3.00 \times 10^{8}}$$

$h = 6.613.... \times 10^{-34}$ Js $= 6.61 \times 10^{-34}$ Js (to 3 s.f.)

Tip: All of the data here is to three significant figures. As the question doesn't specify the number of significant figures for the answer, you should match the data given in the question (page 9).

Practice Questions — Application

Q1 An LED emits light at a wavelength of 600 nm.
Calculate the threshold voltage for the LED, to 2 significant figures.

Q2 A student investigates the Planck constant using LEDs. He measures the threshold voltage for a range of monochromatic LEDs of different wavelengths. He then produces a graph of his results, shown below. Use the graph to determine the Planck constant.

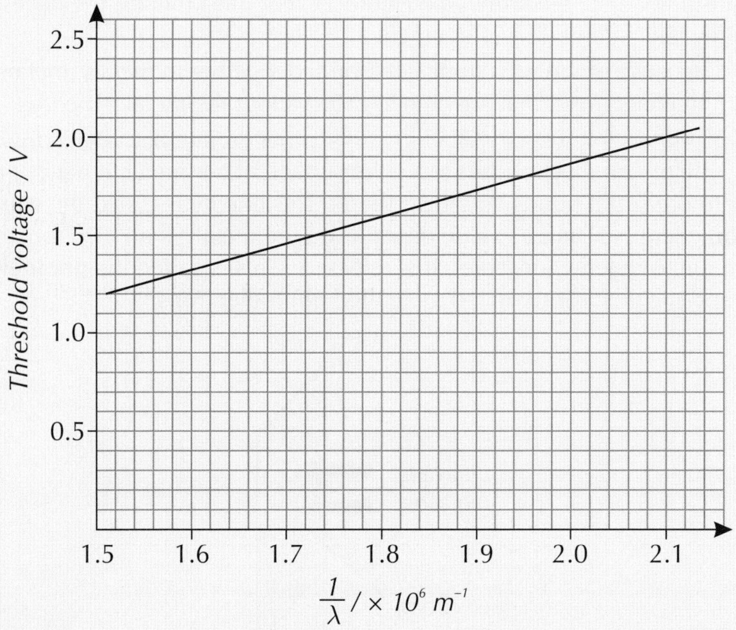

Tip: Remember to watch out for prefixes and scaling factors on axis labels.

Practice Questions — Fact Recall

Q1 What is the threshold voltage of an LED?

Q2 State the equation that links threshold voltage to the Planck constant.

Q3 a) Draw a circuit diagram for the circuit you could use to determine the Planck constant using LEDs.

b) Explain why a milliammeter is more suitable than an ammeter in this circuit.

3. The Photoelectric Effect

Learning Objectives:

- Understand the term work function.
- Understand the photoelectric effect, including a simple experiment to demonstrate this effect, e.g. using a gold-leaf electroscope and a zinc plate.
- Understand the term threshold frequency.
- Know that there is a one-to-one interaction between a photon and a surface electron.
- Know how to use Einstein's photoelectric equation $hf = \phi + KE_{max}$.
- Understand the idea that the maximum kinetic energy of photoelectrons is independent of the intensity of the incident radiation.
- Understand the idea that rate of emission of photoelectrons above the threshold frequency is directly proportional to the intensity of the incident radiation.

Specification Reference 4.5.2

One of the most famous cases of light acting like a particle is the photoelectric effect. Read on to find out more...

What is the photoelectric effect?

If you shine radiation of a high enough frequency onto the surface of a metal, it will instantly eject electrons (see Figure 1). For most metals, the necessary frequency falls in the ultraviolet range.

Because of the way atoms are bonded together in metals, metals contain 'free electrons' that are able to move about the metal. The free electrons on or near the surface of the metal absorb energy from the radiation.

Before an electron can leave the surface of the metal, it needs enough energy to break the bonds holding it there. This energy is called the **work function** energy (ϕ) and its value depends on the metal. If an electron absorbs this amount of energy (or more), it is released. This is called the **photoelectric effect** and the electrons emitted are called **photoelectrons**.

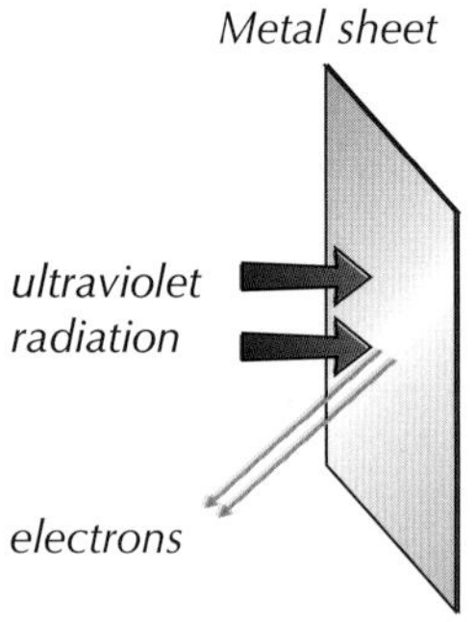

Figure 1: *The photoelectric effect.*

The photoelectric effect can be demonstrated with a simple experiment that uses a gold-leaf electroscope (a box containing a piece of metal with a strip of gold leaf attached).

A zinc plate is attached to the top of the electroscope (see Figure 3). The zinc plate is given a negative charge (which in turn means the metal and the gold leaf in the box are negatively charged). The negatively charged metal repels the negatively charged gold leaf, causing it to rise up. UV light is then shone onto the zinc plate. The energy of the light causes electrons to be lost from the zinc plate via the photoelectric effect. As the zinc plate, the metal and the gold leaf lose their negative charge, the gold leaf is no longer repelled and so falls back down.

Figure 2: *Solar cells use the photoelectric effect to convert light energy into electricity.*

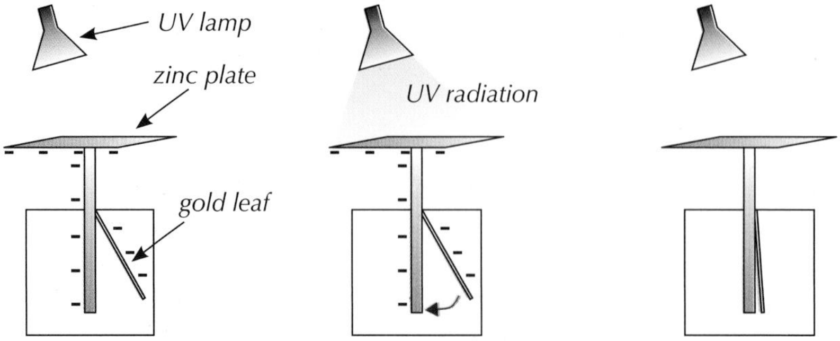

Figure 3: *Demonstration of the photoelectric effect using a UV lamp and a zinc plate attached to the top of an electroscope.*

Conclusions from the photoelectric effect

From photoelectric experiments, scientists came up with these conclusions:

Conclusion 1 For a given metal, no photoelectrons are emitted if the radiation has a frequency below a certain value — called the **threshold frequency**.

HOW SCIENCE WORKS

Conclusion 2 The photoelectrons are emitted with a variety of kinetic energies ranging from zero to some maximum value. This value of maximum kinetic energy increases with the frequency of the radiation, but is independent of the intensity of the incident radiation.

Conclusion 3 The number of photoelectrons emitted per second is directly proportional to the intensity of the radiation.

But they couldn't explain the first two conclusions if EM radiation only acts as a wave...

Threshold frequency

Wave theory says that for a particular frequency of EM wave, the energy carried should be proportional to the intensity of the beam. The energy carried by the EM wave would also be spread evenly over the wavefront.

This means that if an EM wave were shone on to a metal, each free electron on the surface of the metal would gain a bit of energy from each incoming wavefront. Gradually, each electron would gain energy until its energy equalled the work function and it could leave the metal. If the EM wave had a lower frequency (i.e. was carrying less energy) it would take longer for the electrons to gain this energy, but it would happen eventually. However, electrons are never emitted unless the wave is above a threshold frequency — so wave theory can't explain the threshold frequency.

Kinetic energy of photoelectrons

The higher the intensity of the wave, the more energy it should transfer to each electron — the kinetic energy of the electrons should increase with intensity.

Wave theory can't explain the fact that the kinetic energy depends only on the frequency in the photoelectric effect.

Tip: The key thing about the photoelectric effect is that it shows that light can't just act as a wave. Certain observations of the photoelectric effect can't be explained by classical wave theory.

Explaining the photoelectric effect

HOW SCIENCE WORKS

According to the photon model, when EM radiation hits a metal, the metal's surface is bombarded by photons. If one of these photons collides with a free electron, there is a one-to-one interaction between the photon and the surface electron. The electron gains energy equal to hf (as all of the photon's energy is transferred to the electron, p.225). This idea could be used to explain the conclusions from the photoelectric effect, meaning that the photoelectric effect supported the particulate (particle-like) nature of EM radiation.

Threshold frequency

If the energy gained by an electron (on the surface of the metal) from a photon is greater than the work function, the electron is emitted. If the energy is lower, the electron will just shake about a bit, then release the energy as another photon. The metal will heat up, but no electrons will be emitted.

So for electrons to be released $hf \geq \phi$. The value of f is the threshold frequency when $hf = \phi$, as this is the minimum requirement for electrons to be emitted.

Figure 4: Albert Einstein, the physicist who explained the photoelectric effect using photons.

Tip: Remember — Einstein saw photons of light as having particle-like interactions. So they either transfer all of their energy, or none of it (page 225).

Exam Tip
Asking you to explain why there's a threshold frequency and how this shows light acts as a particle is an exam favourite — make sure you know it.

Exam Tip
You won't get this equation in the exam, but you are given $hf = \phi + KE_{max}$. At the threshold frequency, $KE_{max} = 0$. This leaves you with $hf = \phi$, which you can rearrange to get the threshold frequency.

Tip: There are loads of ways electrons leaving the metal can lose energy, e.g. they might have to do work to get to the surface of the metal.

So you can find the threshold frequency, f_0, by rearranging $hf_0 = \phi$ to get:

$$f_0 = \frac{\phi}{h}$$

Example — **Maths Skills**

A metal has a work function of 7.2 × 10^-19 J. Calculate the minimum frequency of EM radiation needed for a photoelectron to be released.

$$f_0 = \frac{\phi}{h} = \frac{7.2 \times 10^{-19}}{6.63 \times 10^{-34}} = 1.1 \times 10^{15}\ \text{Hz (to 2 s.f.)}$$

Maximum kinetic energy

The energy transferred from EM radiation to an electron is the energy it absorbs from one photon, hf. The kinetic energy it will be carrying when it leaves the metal is hf minus any energy losses. These energy losses are the reason the electrons emitted from a metal have a range of kinetic energies.

The minimum amount of energy an electron can lose is the work function energy, so the maximum kinetic energy, KE_{max}, is given by the equation $KE_{max} = hf - \phi$. Rearranging this equation gives you Einstein's photoelectric equation:

$$hf = \phi + KE_{max}$$

Kinetic energy = ½ × mass × speed², so the maximum kinetic energy a photoelectron can have is:

$$KE_{max} = \frac{1}{2}mv_{max}^2$$

KE_{max} = maximum kinetic energy of a photoelectron

v_{max} = maximum speed of an emitted electron

m = mass of an electron = 9.11×10^{-31} kg

You can use this to write the photoelectric equation as:

$$hf = \phi + \frac{1}{2}mv_{max}^2$$

The intensity of radiation is the power transferred by the radiation over a given area. In the photon model, this is the number of photons that hit a given area every second. Increasing the intensity just means more photons per second on an area — each photon has the same energy as before. The kinetic energy of the electrons is independent of the intensity, as they can only absorb one photon at a time and the energy of each photon has not changed.

Example — Maths Skills

The threshold frequency of radiation needed to cause the photoelectric effect in aluminium is 1.03×10^{15} Hz. Radiation with a frequency of 3.45×10^{15} Hz is shone on an aluminium sheet. Calculate the maximum kinetic energy of a photoelectron emitted from the surface of this sheet.

To work out the maximum kinetic energy you need to rearrange and use the photoelectric equation.

First, use the threshold frequency to calculate the work function, ϕ.

$\phi = hf_0 = (6.63 \times 10^{-34}) \times (1.03 \times 10^{15}) = 6.82... \times 10^{-19}$ J

Then substitute this, Planck's constant and the frequency of the radiation being shone on the metal into the photoelectric equation $hf = \phi + KE_{max}$, so

$$KE_{max} = hf - \phi$$
$$= (6.63 \times 10^{-34} \times 3.45 \times 10^{15}) - (6.83 \times 10^{-19})$$
$$= 1.60 \times 10^{-18} \text{ J (to 3 s.f.)}$$

Rate of emission of photoelectrons

Providing the incident radiation is above the threshold frequency of a metal, the number of photoelectrons emitted every second (the rate of emission) is directly proportional to the intensity of the radiation. This is because each collision liberates an electron, so if more collisions occur in a given time, more photoelectrons must be released in that time.

Practice Questions — Application

Q1 Photons each with an energy 6.0×10^{-18} J strike the surface of a sheet of zinc. The work function of zinc is 5.82×10^{-19} J. Will any photoelectrons be emitted from the surface of the zinc sheet? Explain your answer.

Q2 Electrons are emitted from a metal's surface when it is irradiated with radiation with a frequency of 1.20×10^{16} Hz.

a) What effect would increasing the frequency of the incident radiation have on the electrons emitted by the metal? Explain your answer.

b) Calculate the energy of a single photon of incident radiation.

c) The maximum kinetic energy of an electron emitted from the metal's surface is 7.26×10^{-18} J. Calculate the work function of the metal.

Tip: These calculations involve a lot of numbers written in standard form — be careful when you're punching them into your calculator that silly mistakes don't creep into your calculations.

Tip: If you get asked to find the maximum speed of an emitted electron — just rearrange good old $KE_{max} = \frac{1}{2}mv_{max}^2$.

Practice Questions — Fact Recall

Q1 Describe what is meant by the 'photoelectric effect'.

Q2 Explain what happens when UV radiation is incident on a negatively charged zinc plate which is attached to a gold-leaf electroscope.

Q3 Describe what will happen to the electrons emitted by a metal if the intensity of the light shining on it is increased.

Q4 Explain why there is a threshold frequency below which no electrons will be emitted by a metal.

Q5 Explain why electrons emitted due to the photoelectric effect have a maximum possible kinetic energy.

Learning Objectives:

- Be able to use the de Broglie equation, $\lambda = \frac{h}{p}$.
- Know about electron diffraction, including experimental evidence of this effect.
- Know that diffraction of electrons occurs for electrons travelling through a thin slice of polycrystalline graphite, caused by the atoms of the graphite and the spacing between the atoms.

Specification Reference 4.5.3

4. Wave-Particle Duality

The photoelectric effect shows that light can act as a particle, but there's plenty of evidence that it acts as a wave too. It turns out that not only can waves act like particles, but particles can also act like waves.

Is light a particle or a wave?

Diffraction

When a beam of light passes through a narrow gap, it spreads out. This is called diffraction (see page 204). Diffraction can only be explained using waves. If the light was acting as a particle, the light particles in the beam would either not get through the gap (if they were too big), or just pass straight through and the beam would be unchanged.

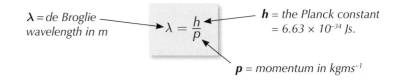

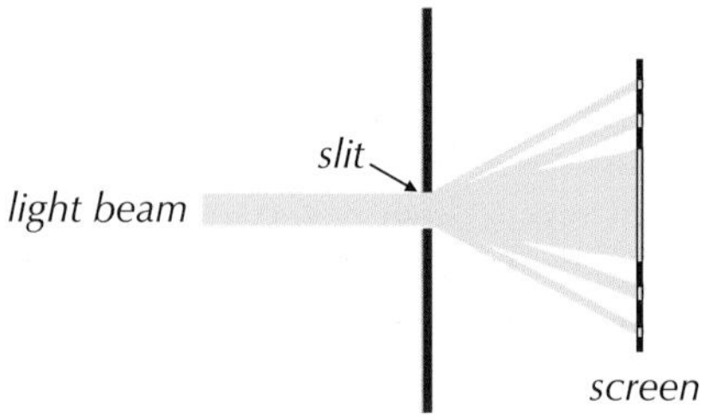

Figure 1: *Diffraction of light waves as they pass through a narrow slit.*

Exam Tip
Make sure you know the two examples that show light acts as both a wave and a particle — they might just come up in the exam.

The photoelectric effect

The results of photoelectric effect experiments (see p.231) can only be explained by thinking of light as a series of particle-like photons. If a photon of light is a discrete bundle of energy, then it can interact with an electron in a one-to-one way. All the energy in the photon is given to one electron.

The photoelectric effect and diffraction show that light behaves as both a particle and a wave — this is an example of a phenomenon known as **wave-particle duality**.

Wave-particle duality theory

Louis de Broglie made a bold suggestion in his PhD thesis. He said if 'wave-like' light showed particle properties (photons), 'particles' like electrons should be expected to show wave-like properties.

The de Broglie equation relates a wave property (wavelength, λ) to a moving particle property (momentum, p).

$$\lambda = \frac{h}{p}$$

λ = de Broglie wavelength in m

h *= the Planck constant = 6.63 × 10^{-34} Js.*

p *= momentum in kgms^{-1}*

Tip: Remember that momentum is the mass multiplied by the velocity of an object (page 131).

Tip: The derivation of the de Broglie equation is beyond the scope of this course, so you don't need to worry about it.

The de Broglie wave of a particle can be interpreted as a 'probability wave'. Many physicists at the time weren't very impressed — his theory wasn't accepted straight away. Other scientists had to evaluate de Broglie's theory (by a process known as peer review, p.1) before he published it, and then it was tested with experiments, such as electron diffraction (see below). Once enough evidence was found to back it up, the theory was accepted as validated by the scientific community.

Scientists' understanding of the nature of matter has changed over time through this process of hypothesis and validation. De Broglie's theory is accepted to be true — at least until any new conflicting evidence comes along.

***Figure 2:** Louis de Broglie, the physicist who first suggested the idea of wave-particle duality.*

Electron diffraction

In 1927, two American physicists, Clinton Davisson and Lester Germer succeeded in diffracting electrons using an electron diffraction tube. In the tube, electrons are accelerated to high velocities in a vacuum and then passed through a thin sheet of polycrystalline graphite. As they pass through the spaces between the carbon atoms of the graphite, they diffract just like waves passing through a narrow slit and produce a pattern of rings. This provides evidence that electrons have wave properties, supporting de Broglie's theory.

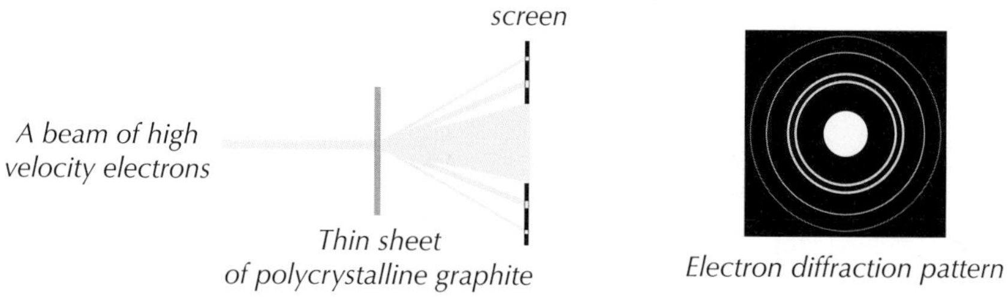

***Figure 3:** An electron diffraction tube experiment shows electrons have wave properties.*

Tip: There's more about diffraction on page 204.

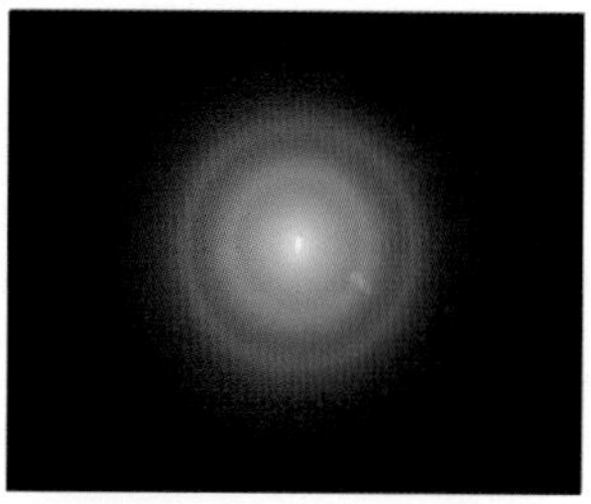

***Figure 4:** An electron diffraction pattern from an electron diffraction tube.*

You only get diffraction if a particle interacts with an object of about the same size as its de Broglie wavelength. Electrons with a wavelength of around 1×10^{-10} m are likely to be diffracted by the atoms in polycrystalline structures, like the ones used by Davisson and Germer.

Example

A 0.058 kg tennis ball travelling at 100 ms^{-1} has a de Broglie wavelength of 10^{-34} m. That's 10^{19} times smaller than an atom's nucleus. There's nothing that small for it to interact with, and so it only acts as a particle.

Tip: Electrons can be used to investigate the spacing between atoms in a crystal — an electron beam will diffract when the de Broglie wavelength of the electrons is roughly the same size as the spaces between the atoms.

According to wave theory, the spread of the lines in the diffraction pattern increases if the wavelength of the wave is greater. In electron diffraction experiments, a smaller accelerating voltage, i.e. slower electrons, gives widely spaced rings. Increase the electron speed and the diffraction pattern circles squash together towards the middle. This fits in with the de Broglie equation — if the velocity is higher, the wavelength is shorter and the spread of lines is smaller.

If particles with a greater mass (e.g. neutrons) were travelling at the same speed as the electrons, they would show a more tightly-packed diffraction pattern. That's because a neutron's mass (and therefore its momentum) is much greater than an electron's, and so a neutron has a shorter de Broglie wavelength.

Example — Maths Skills

An electron of mass 9.11×10^{-31} kg is fired from an electron gun at 7.0×10^6 ms^{-1}. What size object will the electron need to interact with in order to diffract?

An electron will diffract when the size of the object is roughly the same size as its de Broglie wavelength, so you need to find λ.

Momentum of electron, $\mathbf{p} = m\mathbf{v}$

$$= 9.11 \times 10^{-31} \times 7.0 \times 10^6$$
$$= 6.377 \times 10^{-24} \text{ kg ms}^{-1}$$

Substitute this into de Broglie's equation:

$$\lambda = \frac{h}{p} = \frac{6.63 \times 10^{-34}}{6.377 \times 10^{-24}}$$
$$= 1.03... \times 10^{-10} \text{ m} = 1.0 \times 10^{-10} \text{ m (to 2 s.f.)}$$

So, only crystals with atom layer spacing around this size are likely to cause the diffraction of this electron.

Tip: Momentum is a vector quantity, but we're only interested in its magnitude here — which is why p isn't bolded in the de Broglie equation.

Example — Maths Skills

Electrons with a wavelength of 0.170 nm are diffracted as they pass between atoms in a crystal lattice. Calculate the velocity of the electrons.

To convert from nm to m, multiply by 10^{-9}:

$\lambda = 0.170 \times 10^{-9} = 1.70 \times 10^{-10}$ m

Substitute $\lambda = 1.70 \times 10^{-10}$ m, $h = 6.63 \times 10^{-34}$ Js, and $m = 9.11 \times 10^{-31}$ kg into the de Broglie equation.

$$\lambda = \frac{h}{p} = \frac{h}{mv}, \text{ so } v = \frac{h}{m\lambda} = \frac{6.63 \times 10^{-34}}{9.11 \times 10^{-31} \times 1.70 \times 10^{-10}}$$
$$= 4\,281\,009.8... \text{ ms}^{-1}$$
$$= 4.28 \times 10^6 \text{ ms}^{-1} \text{ (to 3 s.f.)}$$

Tip: Remember — nm is nanometres and should be converted to m before using the de Broglie equation.

Tip: You could write the answer to this calculation in standard form as 4.28×10^6 ms^{-1}.

Example — Maths Skills

An electron and a neutron are travelling with velocities such that they have equal wavelengths. The mass of an electron is 9.11×10^{-31} kg and the mass of a neutron is 1.675×10^{-27} kg. If the electron has velocity 5.00×10^6 ms^{-1}, what is the velocity of the neutron?

Substitute $v = 5.00 \times 10^6$ ms^{-1} and $m = 9.11 \times 10^{-31}$ kg into the de Broglie equation to find the wavelength of the electron:

$$\lambda = \frac{h}{p} = \frac{h}{mv}, \text{ so } \lambda = \frac{6.63 \times 10^{-34}}{9.11 \times 10^{-31} \times 5.00 \times 10^6} = 1.455... \times 10^{-10} \text{ m}$$

Use this wavelength in the de Broglie equation to find the velocity of the neutron:

$$\lambda = \frac{h}{p} = \frac{h}{mv}, \text{ so } v = \frac{h}{m\lambda} = \frac{6.63 \times 10^{-34}}{1.675 \times 10^{-27} \times 1.455... \times 10^{-10}}$$
$$= 2719.4... \text{ ms}^{-1} = 2.72 \times 10^3 \text{ ms}^{-1} \text{ (to 3 s.f.)}$$

Exam Tip
The mass of an electron and the mass of a neutron will be given in the data and formulae booklet in the exam.

Electron microscopes

HOW SCIENCE WORKS

A shorter wavelength gives smaller diffraction effects. This fact is used in the electron microscope. Diffraction effects blur detail on an image. If you want to resolve tiny detail in an image, you need a shorter wavelength.

Light blurs out detail more than 'electron-waves' do, so an electron microscope can resolve finer detail than a light microscope. They can let you look at things as tiny as a single strand of DNA.

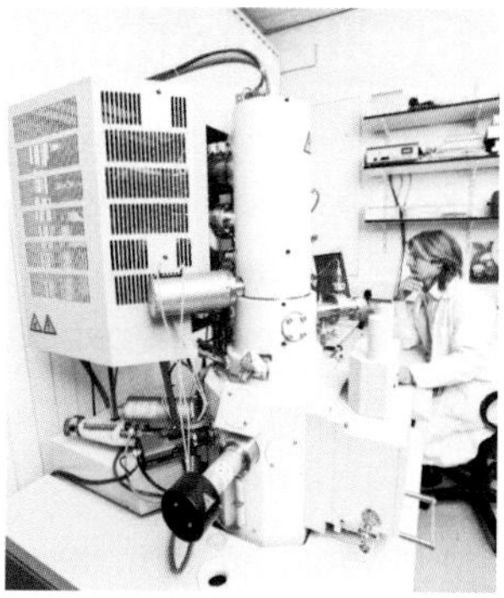

Figure 5: *A laboratory technician using an electron microscope.*

Tip: Remember kinetic energy $E_k = \frac{1}{2}mv^2$.

Practice Questions — Application

Q1 Explain how a particle's velocity affects its de Broglie wavelength.

Q2 An electron has a de Broglie wavelength of 0.162 nm. The mass of an electron is 9.11×10^{-31} kg.

a) Calculate the momentum of the electron.

b) Calculate the kinetic energy of the electron.

Q3 An alpha particle has a mass of 6.646×10^{-27} kg.

a) Calculate the de Broglie wavelength of an alpha particle travelling at a velocity of 60.0 ms^{-1}.

b) Calculate the speed of an electron that has the same de Broglie wavelength as the alpha particle in part a). (The mass of an electron is 9.11×10^{-31} kg.)

Practice Questions — Fact Recall

Q1 Name one effect demonstrating that electromagnetic waves have wave properties and one demonstrating that they have particle properties.

Q2 Describe what is meant by wave-particle duality.

Q3 What phenomenon shows that electrons have wave-like properties?

Section Summary

Make sure you know...

- That electromagnetic radiation exists in discrete packets, called quanta.
- That Einstein called these packets photons.
- That photons behave like particles — they have one-to-one interactions with other particles.
- That the energy of a photon can be found using $E = hf$ or $E = \frac{hc}{\lambda}$.
- That the electronvolt is a unit of energy.
- What the term threshold voltage means and the equation relating it to the Planck constant, $h = \frac{eV_0\lambda}{c}$.
- How to use LEDs to determine the value of the Planck constant.
- That the work function is the minimum energy a surface electron needs to absorb to be released from a metal.
- What the photoelectric effect is and how it can be demonstrated, e.g. using a gold-leaf electroscope and a zinc plate.
- That for a given metal, if the incident radiation is below the threshold frequency, photoelectrons won't be emitted.
- That the kinetic energy of photoelectrons ranges from zero to a maximum value, and that this maximum value increases with the frequency of the radiation.
- That the number of photoelectrons emitted each second is directly proportional to the intensity of the incident radiation.
- That wave theory cannot explain the idea of a threshold frequency, or why the kinetic energy of photoelectrons doesn't depend on the intensity of the incident radiation.
- That ideas about photons can be used to explain the photoelectric effect.
- That photons have a one-to-one interaction with surface electrons, so all of a photon's energy is transferred to a single electron in the photoelectric effect.
- That one-to-one interactions explain why there is a threshold frequency in the photoelectric effect and why the kinetic energy of the electrons is independent of intensity.
- How to calculate the threshold frequency of a metal, using $f_0 = \frac{\phi}{h}$.
- How to use Einstein's photoelectric equation, $hf = \phi + KE_{max}$.
- That diffraction shows that light behaves like a wave, but the photoelectric effect shows that light behaves like a particle.
- The idea of wave-particle duality — that waves display particle-like properties and particles display wave-like properties.
- How to use the de Broglie equation, $\lambda = \frac{h}{p}$, which relates wavelength (a wave property) to momentum (a particle property).
- That electrons are diffracted when they travel through a thin sheet of polycrystalline graphite.
- That electron diffraction supports the theory of wave-particle duality.
- That you only get diffraction if a particle interacts with an object of about the same size as its de Broglie wavelength.

Exam-style Questions

1 Radiation is made of photons that each have an energy of 2.0 GeV. What is the frequency of the radiation?

A 3.0×10^{42} Hz

B 4.8×10^{14} Hz

C 4.8×10^{23} Hz

D 2.1×10^{-24} Hz

(1 mark)

2 The work function of a metal is 4.33 eV. What is the maximum wavelength of radiation that could liberate electrons from the metal?

A 7.35×10^{-45} m

B 2.87×10^{-7} m

C 3.47×10^{6} m

D 4.59×10^{-26} m

(1 mark)

3 A monochromatic LED emits light with a frequency of 5.8×10^{14} Hz. What is the threshold voltage for this LED?

A 0.4 V

B 1.2 V

C 2.2 V

D 2.4 V

(1 mark)

4 A beam of neutrons is fired at a grating. The neutrons travel at 3200 ms^{-1}. The spacing of the grating is 2 μm. Which of the following statements is/are correct?

1 The neutrons diffract when they go through the grating.

2 If the speed of the neutrons was doubled, they would diffract as they went through the grating.

3 If the speed of the neutrons was halved, they would diffract as they went through the grating.

A 1, 2 and 3

B Only 1 and 2

C Only 3

D None of the statements are correct.

(1 mark)

5 An LED emits light at a wavelength of 5.00×10^{-7} m.

(a) Calculate the energy carried by each photon emitted from the LED in electronvolts.

(2 marks)

(b) The LED is connected in a circuit. The potential difference across the LED is 2.0 V. Determine whether or not the LED will light up.

(2 marks)

6 Louis de Broglie was the first scientist to propose wave-particle duality. His ideas were later supported by electron diffraction experiments.

(a) Describe what is meant by the term 'wave-particle duality'.

(1 mark)

(b) An electron gun contains two electrodes. The potential difference across the electrodes causes electrons to be accelerated between them, so that each electron is fired out of the electron gun with a kinetic energy of 1.02×10^{-26} J.

(i) Calculate the velocity of one electron.

(2 marks)

(ii) Calculate the de Broglie wavelength of each electron.

(2 marks)

(iii) By what factor would the de Broglie wavelength of the electrons increase or decrease if the potential difference across the electrodes was halved?

(1 mark)

7 A metal surface emits electrons when a certain frequency of light is shone onto it. This effect is called the photoelectric effect.

(a) State what is meant by the work function of a metal.

(1 mark)

(b) Explain why there is a threshold frequency for the light being shone onto the metal, below which no electrons are emitted.

(2 marks)

(c) Describe an experiment using a gold-leaf electroscope that illustrates the photoelectric effect.

(5 marks)

(d) A beam of light is shone onto a sheet of lead. Each photon has an energy of 3.0×10^{-18} J. The threshold frequency of lead is 1.03×10^{15} Hz. Calculate the maximum kinetic energy of an electron emitted from this surface.

(3 marks)

(e) The intensity of the radiation is increased.

(i) Explain how this affects the maximum speed of the photoelectrons emitted.

(2 mark)

(ii) Explain how this affects the rate at which photoelectrons are emitted.

(1 mark)

Maths Skills

1. Calculations

Sometimes the numbers you use in Physics are just plain awkward — they're either too big, too small or go on forever. The next few pages show how numbers can be written in different ways to make calculations a lot easier.

Standard form

When you are doing a calculation, it's sometimes easier to give your answer in standard form — or you might be given values in standard form. **Standard form** is used for writing very big or very small numbers in a more convenient way. Standard form must always look like this:

$$A \times 10^n$$

This number must always be between 1 and 10. (A)

'n' is the number of places the decimal point moves. (n)

Tip: If you don't write a number in standard form, it's known as decimal form — e.g. 0.00012 or 34 500.

Tip: Standard form is a great way to show significant figures (see next page). For example, the number 230 is ambiguous, it could be to 2 or 3 significant figures. Writing it as 2.30×10^2 makes it clear that it is to 3 significant figures.

Examples — Maths Skills

Here's how to write 3 500 000 in standard form.

- First, move the decimal point until the number you've got is between 1 and 10. In this example, the number is 3.5.
- Then count how many places the decimal point has moved to the left. This number sits to the top right of the 10.

6 5 4 3 2 1

$$3\,500000 = 3.5 \times 10^6$$

- Et voilà... that's 3 500 000 written in standard form.

Here are some more examples.

- You can write 450 000 as 4.5×10^5.
- The number 0.000056 is 5.6×10^{-5} in standard form — the n is negative because the decimal point has moved to the right instead of the left.
- You can write 0.003456 as 3.456×10^{-3}.

There's a special button on your calculator for using standard form in a calculation — it's the 'Exp' button. So if, for example, you wanted to type in 2×10^7, you'd only need to type in: '2' 'Exp' '7'. Some calculators may have a different button that does the same job, for example it could say 'EE' or '$\times 10^x$' instead of 'Exp' — see Figure 1.

Figure 1: *The 'Exp' or '$\times 10^x$' button is used to input standard form on calculators. Don't confuse it with the power buttons x^2 or $x^{\blacksquare}$, which are used for raising numbers to a power.*

Tip: You should never round before you get to your final answer. It will introduce rounding errors and you may end up with the wrong answer.

Exam Tip
In your exam, you might lose a mark on an otherwise correct answer if it's not given to an appropriate number of significant figures. Make sure you always round your answers to the correct number of significant figures.

Significant figures

You've already seen that you should always give your answer to the lowest number of significant figures (s.f.) used in the calculation (p.9). So, in exam questions you can use the number of significant figures given in the question as a guide for how many to give in the answer. It's always good to write down the full unrounded answer, followed by your rounded answer. You should write down the number of significant figures you've rounded to after your answer too — it shows the examiner you really know what you're talking about.

Examples — Maths Skills

In this question the data given to you is a good indication of how many significant figures you should give your answer to:

1 a) Calculate the extension measured by the student in m. (The force constant of the metal is 1.24×10^3 Nm^{-1}.)

The data in the question is given to 3 s.f. so it makes sense to give your answer to 3 s.f. too. But sometimes it isn't as clear as that:

2 b) A force of 48 N is applied to a steel girder with a cross-sectional area of 0.519 m^2. Calculate the tensile stress in the girder.

There are two types of data in this question, force data and cross-sectional area data. The force data is given to 2 s.f. and the cross-sectional area data is given to 3 s.f. You should give your answer to the lowest number of significant figures given — in this case that's to 2 s.f. The answer is 92.48... Nm^{-2} so the answer rounded correctly would be 92 Nm^{-2} (to 2 s.f.).

Tip: Simplifying a ratio can be done in the same way as simplifying a fraction. It's just that instead of the numbers being on top of each other, they're next to each other.

Ratios, fractions and percentages

Ratios, fractions and percentages are all ways of expressing proportions. They're often used to show relationships in Physics, and you'll be expected to convert between them effortlessly. Here's a quick reminder:

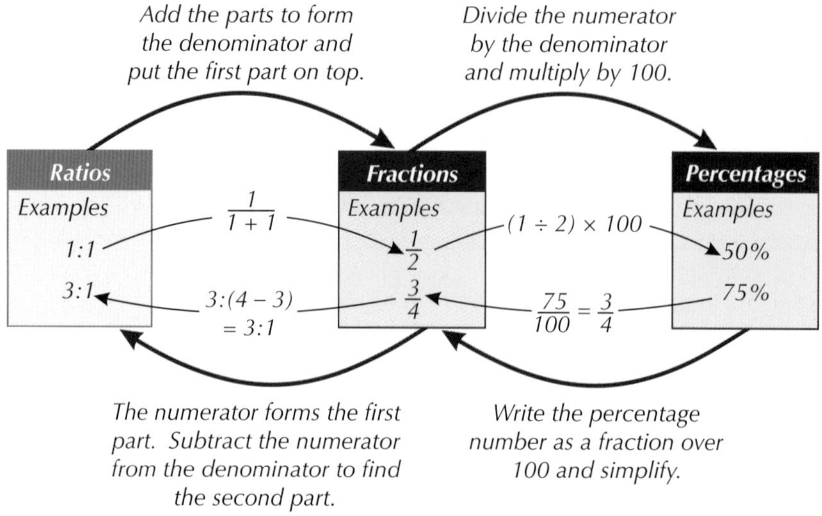

Figure 2: *Converting between ratios, fractions and percentages.*

Example — Maths Skills

The length of a desk is measured as 1.62 m with a ruler that has a scale with 5 mm increments. Calculate the percentage uncertainty for the measurement.

When measuring with a ruler you get an uncertainty from both ends, the 0 end and the end you're reading from.

5 mm = 0.005 m, so the uncertainty on each end is $\frac{0.005}{2} = 0.0025$.

So the absolute uncertainty is 0.0025 + 0.0025 = 0.005.

$$\begin{aligned}\text{Percentage uncertainty} &= (0.005 \div 1.62) \times 100 \\ &= 0.3086...\ \% \\ &= 0.31\%\ \text{(to 2 s.f.)}\end{aligned}$$

Tip: See page 16 for more on uncertainty when measuring lengths.

Probabilities are likelihoods that something will happen. Probabilities are often expressed as fractions, percentages or ratios.

Example — Maths Skills

Alpha particles are being fired at a thin sheet of gold foil. A scientist calculated that the probability of an alpha particle being deflected by the gold foil (i.e. not passing straight through) is 1.2%.

Write the ratio of the number of particles that are likely to be deflected to the number of particles that are likely to pass straight through.

1.2% is equal to $\frac{1.2}{100} = \frac{12}{1000}$ as a fraction.

So the first part of the ratio is 12 — the number of particles (out of 1000) that are likely to be deflected.

The second part is 1000 – 12 = 988 — the number of particles (out of 1000) that are likely to pass straight through.

The ratio is then written as 12 : 988, which simplifies to 3 : 247.

Tip: The probability that an alpha particle will be deflected is 1.2% — i.e. 1.2 out of 100 are likely to be deflected.

Tip: Remember that the numerator and denominator in fractions should be whole numbers.
Some calculators will do this for you — type $\frac{0.005}{1.62}$ into your calculator and press '='. Hey presto, the fraction it returns is $\frac{1}{324}$.

If not, you can always do it the old fashioned way.

You can use your calculator to simplify the ratio too by entering it as a fraction.

Showing your working

In all calculation questions, whether you are converting units (p.25), switching between fractions and decimals or rearranging equations (see next page), you always need to show your working.

This is important because there are sometimes marks available for intermediate steps in a calculation question — so even if you get the answer wrong, you might get some credit if you've shown your working. You are also more likely to spot any accidental mistakes if you can see the steps you took in your working — particularly useful if you have some spare time at the end of the exam.

2. Algebra

Physics involves a lot of rearranging formulas and substituting values into equations. Easy stuff, but it's also easy to make simple mistakes.

Algebra symbols

Here's a reminder of some of the symbols that you will come across:

Symbol	Meaning
$=$	equal to
$<$	less than
$\leq$	less than or equal to
$<<$	much less than
$>$	greater than
$\geq$	greater than or equal to
$>>$	much greater than
$\propto$	directly proportional to
$\approx$	roughly equal to
Δ	change in (a quantity)
Σ	sum of

Tip: An example of using $\propto$ can be found on page 186.

Tip: Δ is the Greek capital letter 'delta'. An example of using Δ can be found on page 49.

Figure 1: *It can be easy to make a mistake rearranging equations when you're stressed in an exam. It's a good idea to double check rearrangements, especially if it's a tricky one where you've had to combine and rearrange equations.*

Rearranging equations

Being able to rearrange equations is a must in Physics — you'll often need to make a different quantity the subject in an equation. Just remember the golden rule — whatever you do to one side of the equation, you must do to the other side of the equation.

Example — Maths Skills

The equation for the volume of a sphere is $V = \frac{4}{3}\pi r^3$. Rearrange the equation to make r the subject.

$V = \frac{4}{3}\pi r^3$

Multiply by 3 and divide by 4π

$\frac{3V}{4\pi} = r^3$

Take the cube root

$\sqrt[3]{\frac{3V}{4\pi}} = r$

Tip: Taking a value outside a bracket is known as factorising. You often need to factorise to solve quadratic equations like this one. Just write the value to the left of the bracket and write each term, divided by the number you've taken outside, inside the brackets. You should have done this at GCSE.

Example — Maths Skills

One of the equations of motion is $s = ut + \frac{1}{2}at^2$. When $t = 0$, $s = 0$. Find an expression for t at another point where $s = 0$.

If $s = 0$, the equation can be written as: $\boldsymbol{u}t + \frac{1}{2}\boldsymbol{a}t^2 = 0$

Take t outside the bracket: $t\left(\boldsymbol{u} + \frac{1}{2}\boldsymbol{a}t\right) = 0$

Two things multiplied together to give 0 means one of them must be 0, so $t = 0$ or $\left(\boldsymbol{u} + \frac{1}{2}\boldsymbol{a}t\right) = 0$

We're interested in the non-zero solution, which can be rearranged to give: $t = -\frac{2\boldsymbol{u}}{\boldsymbol{a}}$

Substituting into equations

Once you've rearranged your equation, you'll probably need to substitute values into the equation to find your answer. Pretty easy stuff — make sure you avoid the common mistakes by putting values in the right units and putting numbers in standard form before you substitute.

Example — Maths Skills

A proton is accelerated to a speed of 3.00 kms^{-1}.
The proton will diffract if it interacts with an object of about the same size as its de Broglie wavelength, λ.
Use the equations $p = mv$ and $\lambda = \frac{h}{p}$ to work out its de Broglie wavelength.

h = the Planck constant = 6.63×10^{-34} Js

$m = 1.673 \times 10^{-27}$ kg

h and m are in the right units but v is not, so you need to convert it to ms^{-1}.

$\mathbf{v}$ = 3.00 kms^{-1} = 3.00×10^3 ms^{-1}

So $\mathbf{p} = m\mathbf{v} = 1.673 \times 10^{-27} \times 3.00 \times 10^3 = 5.019 \times 10^{-24}$ kg ms^{-1}

Substitute this into de Broglie's equation:

$$\lambda = \frac{h}{p} = \frac{6.63\times10^{-34}}{5.019\times10^{-24}}$$
$$= 1.320... \times 10^{-10} \text{ m} = 1.32\times 10^{-10} \text{ m (to 3 s.f.)}$$

Exam Tip
The values of h and m are given in your data and formulae booklet.

Tip: Be careful when using numbers in standard form in your calculator. Double-check you've typed it right and make sure your answer seems a sensible order of magnitude (page 27).

Example — Maths Skills

A train pulls out of a station and is initially travelling at 2.0 cms^{-1}. The train accelerates with a constant acceleration over a distance of 74 km. At this distance, the train reaches a final velocity of 150 kmh^{-1}. Calculate the acceleration of the train.

All given values are in different units, so you need to convert them.

$\mathbf{u}$ = 2.0 cms^{-1} = $2.0 \times (1 \times 10^{-2})$ ms^{-1} = 0.020 ms^{-1}

$\mathbf{s}$ = 74 km = $74 \times 1 \times 10^3$ m = 74 000 m

$\mathbf{v}$ = 150 kmh^{-1} = $150 \times 1 \times 10^3$ mh^{-1} = 150 000 mh^{-1}
= 150 000 ÷ 3600 ms^{-1} = 41.66... ms^{-1}

Rearrange the equation of motion $\mathbf{v}^2 = \mathbf{u}^2 + 2\mathbf{as}$ to make $\mathbf{a}$ the subject:

$$\mathbf{a} = \frac{\mathbf{v}^2 - \mathbf{u}^2}{2\mathbf{s}}$$
$$= \frac{41.66...^2 - 0.020^2}{2\times 74\,000}$$
$$= 0.0117... \text{ ms}^{-2}$$
$$= 0.012 \text{ ms}^{-2} \text{ (to 2 s.f.)}$$

Tip: Converting all the values into the correct units <u>before</u> putting them into the equation helps you avoid making silly mistakes.

Tip: This equation is on page 42.

3. Graphs

You can get a lot of information from a graph — you'll need to know what the area under a graph and the gradient represent, and be able to sketch and recognise simple graphs, given an equation.

Area under a graph

Sometimes a quantity can be found from the area between the curve or line and the horizontal axis of a graph. Here are a few examples:

- Displacement, $\mathbf{s} = \mathbf{v}t$, is the area under a velocity-time graph (see p.54).
- Impulse, $\mathbf{F}\Delta t$, is the area under a force-time graph (see page 135).
- Energy stored per unit volume, $\frac{1}{2}\sigma\varepsilon$, is the area under a stress-strain graph.

To find an area under a graph, you'll either need to work it out exactly or estimate the area — it depends on the graph's shape. You'll need to estimate the area if the graph is not made up of straight lines.

Tip: You'll need to remember all the examples you've seen in this book.

Example — Maths Skills

A car accelerates from rest. The force-time graph for this motion is shown below. Use the graph to find the impulse on the car after 12 s.

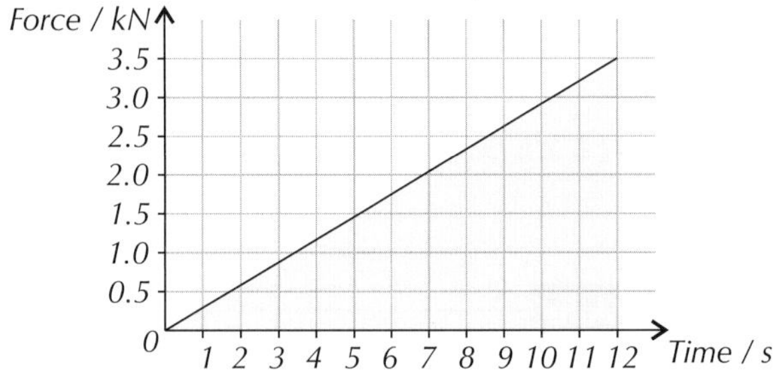

Impulse = $\mathbf{F}\Delta t$ = area under graph. The area is a triangle, so the area under the graph = $\frac{1}{2}$ × base × height = $\frac{1}{2} \times 12 \times (3.5 \times 10^3)$ = 21 000 Ns

Tip: This is a straight-line graph, which you've seen before on page 13. Remember, they have the form $y = mx + c$, where m is the gradient and c is the y-intercept (the value of y when $x = 0$).

Tip: Don't forget — the force is given in kN, so the change in force is 3.5×10^3 N, not just 3.5 N.

Example — Maths Skills

The velocity-time graph for a cyclist's motion is shown below. Use the graph to find the cyclist's displacement during the time shown.

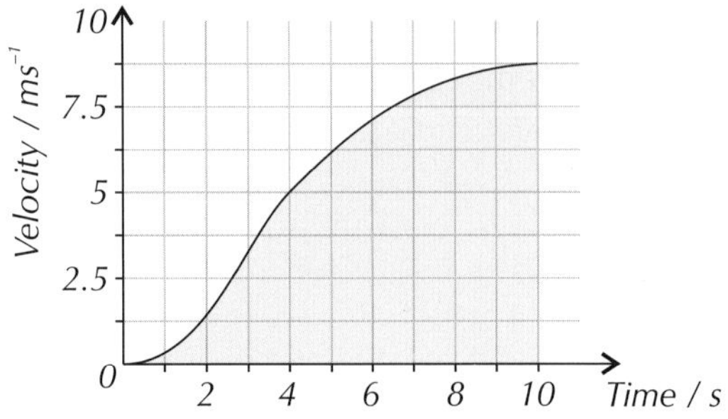

The displacement is the area under the velocity-time graph.
For a curved graph, you can estimate the area by counting the number of squares under the graph, which is approximately 42.
The area of one square = velocity × time = 1.25 ms^{-1} × 1 s = 1.25 m.
So the displacement ≈ 1.25 × 42 = 52.5 m

Tip: Draw a dot or a cross inside every square you count, to help you keep track of them.

Negative areas

You can end up with negative areas when the quantity on the vertical axis is a vector. For example, on a graph of velocity against time, the area between the curve and the horizontal axis is displacement. The velocity can be negative, so the area enclosed by the negative part of the curve and the horizontal axis is the 'negative area'. So displacement is negative (i.e. in the negative direction).

Example — Maths Skills

The velocity-time graph for a model train is shown below. The displacement of the train can be worked out from the area under the graph. The blue area indicates the 'positive area' and the red area indicates the 'negative area'.

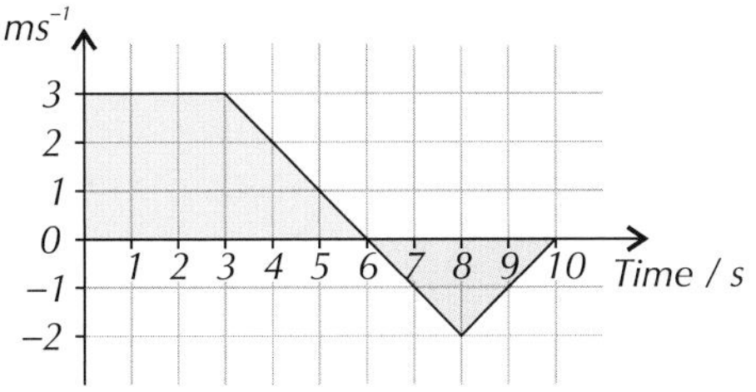

Blue area = 13.5 m, red area = –4 m

So the total displacement (i.e. the displacement of the train from its starting position) = 13.5 – 4 = 9.5 m.

Tip: To find the area between the line and the horizontal axis, you could use the formula for a trapezium and a triangle, or split it up into a square and two triangles. The formulas for calculating the areas of common shapes are over on page 251.

Rates of change

A graph is a plot of how one variable changes with another. The rate of change of the variable on the vertical axis with respect to the variable on the horizontal axis at any point is given by the gradient of the graph.

$$\text{Rate of change of } y \text{ with } x = \frac{\Delta y}{\Delta x} = \text{gradient of a } y\text{-}x \text{ graph.}$$

Often, the gradient represents a useful rate of change that you want to work out. For example, the gradient of a velocity-time graph is rate of change of velocity, which is acceleration.

For a linear graph, the gradient can just be found by calculating the change in y over the change in x between any two points.

Example — Maths Skills

The gradient of a force-extension graph for a spring obeying Hooke's law is equal to the spring constant of the spring.

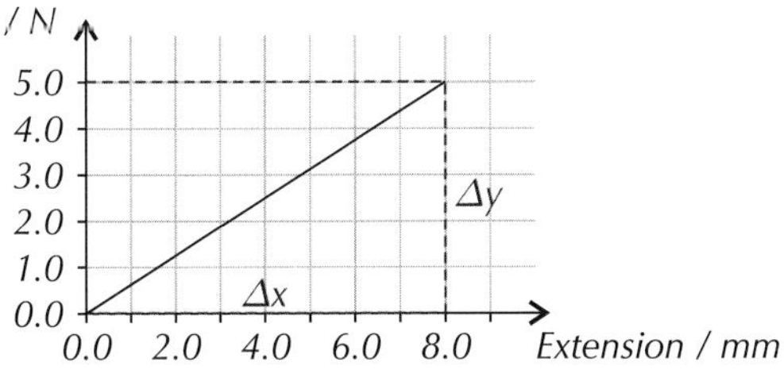

The gradient of this graph is equal to: $\frac{\Delta y}{\Delta x} = \frac{5.0}{8.0 \times 10^{-3}} = 625$

So the spring constant of this spring = 625 Nm^{-1}.

Tip: Don't forget to check the units of the axes before you calculate the gradient. In this case, the extension is given in mm, so the change in x is 8×10^{-3}, not just 8.

Gradients of curved graphs

For a curved graph, the gradient, and so the rate of change, is always changing. So if you use the method on the previous page to calculate the gradient of a curved graph, you get the average gradient, and so the average rate of change.

To find the instantaneous rate of change (at a point), draw a **tangent** to the curve at the point where you want to know the gradient and find the gradient of the tangent.

Tip: When drawing a tangent, it helps to make it long — it will be easier to draw, and the tangent line will be more likely to intersect some grid lines, making the gradient easier to calculate. You should aim to make the hypotenuse of the triangle you use to calculate the gradient at least half as long as the line on the graph.

Example — Maths Skills

The velocity-time graph of a cyclist is shown below.

a) Find the acceleration of the cyclist at 70 s.

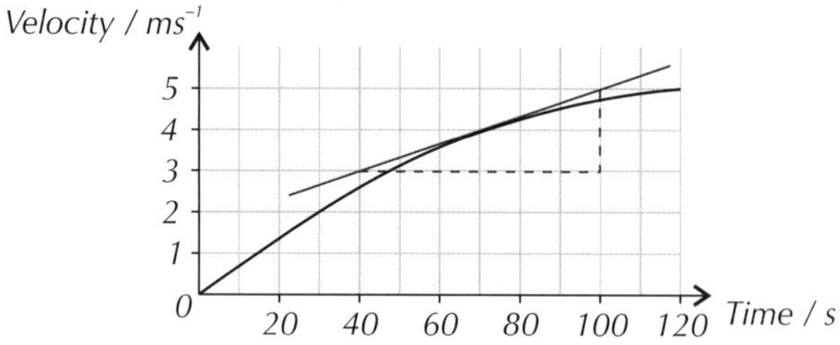

A tangent to the curve at 70 s is drawn on the graph with a gradient of:

$$\frac{\Delta y}{\Delta x} = \frac{5-3}{100-40} = \frac{2}{60} = 0.03333... = 0.03 \text{ (to 1 s.f.)}$$

So the acceleration at 70 s = 0.03 ms^{-2}

b) Find the average acceleration of the cyclist over the 120 s.

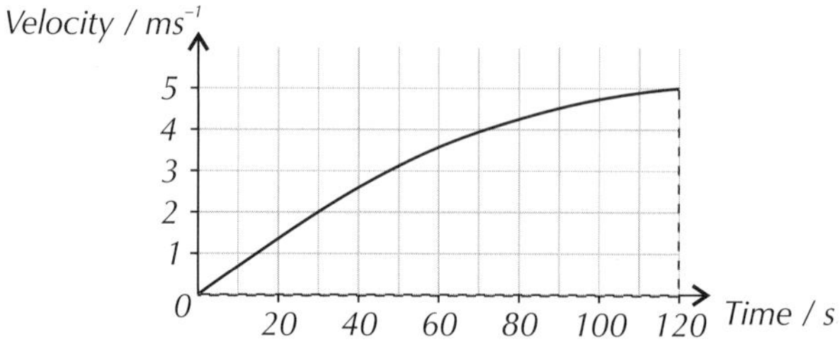

Over the 120 s, the average rate of change is:

$$\frac{\Delta y}{\Delta x} = \frac{5-0}{120-0} = \frac{5}{120} = 0.0416... = 0.04 \text{ (to 1 s.f.)}$$

So the average acceleration over 120 s = 0.04 ms^{-2}

Figure 1: Make sure you use a really sharp pencil and a ruler whenever you're drawing graphs and tangents.

Rate of change of a gradient

The gradient is already a 'rate of change of something', so the rate of change of a gradient is the 'rate of change of the rate of change'. Sometimes these represent useful quantities too.

A common example of this is on a displacement-time graph. The rate of change of its gradient is equal to the acceleration.

Example — Maths Skills

The graph shows a displacement-time graph for an object falling from a height from rest. Its acceleration is due to gravity. You can use this graph to find the value for acceleration due to gravity, $\boldsymbol{g}$ — you just need to find the rate of change of the gradient.

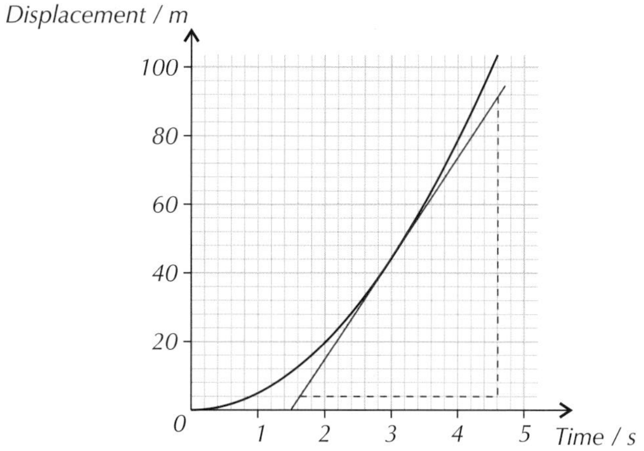

The gradient (velocity) at $t = 0$ is 0 because the object was dropped from rest.

At 3 s, the gradient is found by drawing a tangent:

Gradient at 3 s $= \frac{92-4}{4.6-1.6} = \frac{88}{3} = 29.333...$

Rate of change of gradient between $t = 0$ s and $t = 3$ s:

$$\frac{\text{change in gradient}}{\text{change in } t} = \frac{29.333...-0}{3-0} = \frac{29.333...}{3} = 9.777... = 10 \text{ (to 1 s.f.)}$$

So the value of $\boldsymbol{g} \approx 10$ ms^{-2} (to 1 s.f.).

Tip: The gradient of a displacement-time graph at a particular point is equal to the instantaneous velocity at that point. Finding the change in the gradient over time is the same as finding the change in the velocity over time — which is acceleration (see page 48).

Tip: The actual value of $\boldsymbol{g}$ is 9.81 ms^{-2}. It is found to be 9.777... ms^{-2} here because reading off a graph is not as accurate as calculating the value of $\boldsymbol{g}$ directly.

Modelling rates of change

You can use equations involving rates of change to model quantities with an iterative spreadsheet. If you know the rate of change of something, you can plot a graph for how it changes over time.

For example, acceleration $\boldsymbol{a} = \frac{\Delta \boldsymbol{v}}{\Delta t}$, so $\Delta \boldsymbol{v} = \boldsymbol{a}\Delta t$, where $\boldsymbol{v}$ is velocity and t is time. Consider the situation in which an object is fired vertically upwards with a known initial velocity, $\boldsymbol{v}_{init}$. The acceleration is $-\boldsymbol{g}$ (it's slowing down), so $\Delta \boldsymbol{v} = -\boldsymbol{g}\Delta t$. Since we know $\boldsymbol{v}_{init}$, we can pick a small value of Δt and see how $\boldsymbol{v}$ changes over time. You can also see how displacement ($\boldsymbol{s}$) varies.

- Set up a spreadsheet with column headings for t, $\boldsymbol{v}$ and $\boldsymbol{s}$, as well as a single data input cell for each of Δt, $\boldsymbol{v}_{init}$ and $\Delta \boldsymbol{v}$. $\Delta \boldsymbol{v}$ is calculated using the equation above, $\Delta \boldsymbol{v} = -\boldsymbol{g}\Delta t$.
- Decide on a Δt that you want to use, e.g. 0.1 s — this is the time interval between the values of $\boldsymbol{v}$ (and $\boldsymbol{s}$) that the spreadsheet will calculate.
- You can then enter formulas into the spreadsheet to calculate the new velocity after each time interval. The displacement for each time interval is just the average velocity during the time interval, multiplied by the time interval Δt.

Tip: Make sure you're familiar with your spreadsheet program before you start trying to model anything. You'll need to know how to reference and do calculations involving cells.

Tip: Data input cells are the cells in which you write the variables that aren't changing, e.g. initial velocity, time interval, etc. Make sure the references to them in your formulas are fixed when you autofill the rows (iterations) later.

Tip: If you write the formulas properly, the spreadsheet can automatically fill them in for as many rows (iterations) as you want.

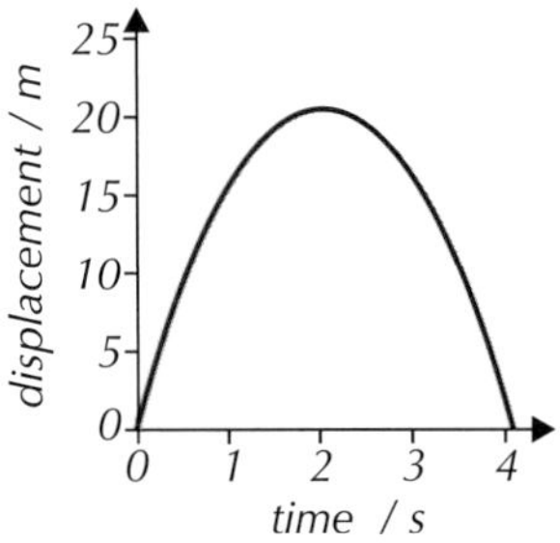

Figure 2: *A graph of* **s** *against t, for an object fired vertically with an initial velocity of 20 ms^{-1}.*

Data input cells		
	Δt	*0.1 s*
	$\mathbf{v}_{init}$	*E.g. 20 ms^{-1}*
	$\Delta \mathbf{v}$	*$-9.81 \times \Delta t$*

t in s	*v in ms^{-1}*	*s in m*
$t_0 = 0$	$\mathbf{v}_0 = \mathbf{v}_{init}$	$\mathbf{s}_0 = 0$
$t_1 = t_0 + \Delta t$	$\mathbf{v}_1 = \mathbf{v}_0 + \Delta \mathbf{v}$	$\mathbf{s}_1 = \mathbf{s}_0 + \left(\frac{\mathbf{v}_1 + \mathbf{v}_0}{2} \times \Delta t\right)$
$t_2 = t_1 + \Delta t$	$\mathbf{v}_2 = \mathbf{v}_1 + \Delta \mathbf{v}$	$\mathbf{s}_2 = \mathbf{s}_1 + \left(\frac{\mathbf{v}_2 + \mathbf{v}_1}{2} \times \Delta t\right)$

Figure 3: *An example of the formulas that can be used to create an iterative spreadsheet of velocity over time for an object with constant acceleration due to gravity.*

- You can then plot a graph of either **v** against *t* or **s** against *t* — see Figure 2.

Sketching graphs

There are some graph shapes that crop up in Physics all the time. The following graphs are examples of the types of graphs you need to know how to recognise and sketch. *k* is constant in all cases.

Tip: $R = \frac{\rho L}{A}$ on p.149 is an example of an equation of the form $y = \frac{k}{x}$, where $y = R$, $x = A$ and $k = \rho L$.

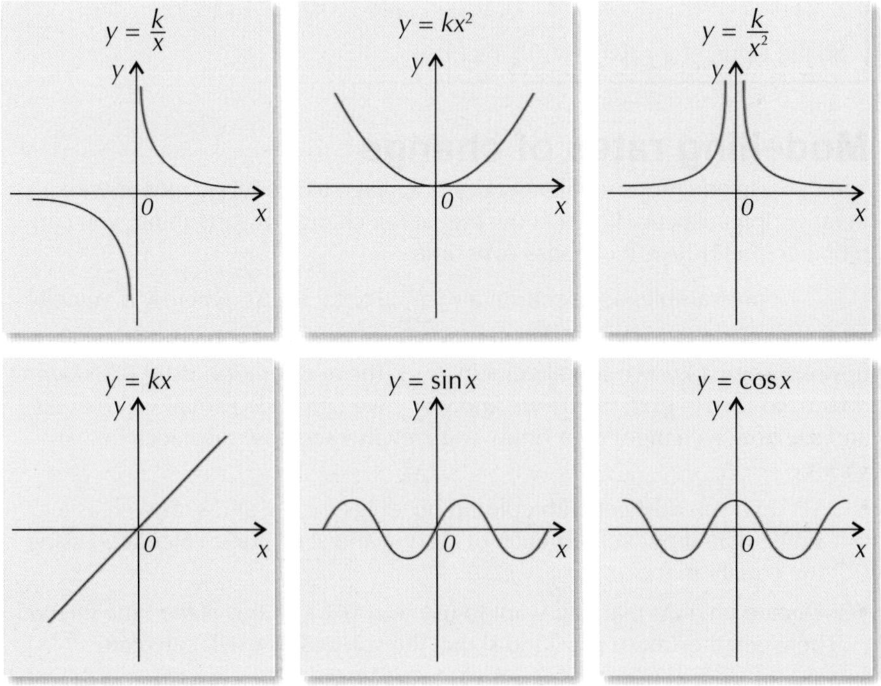

4. Geometry and Trigonometry

You'll often find that you need to deal with different 2D and 3D shapes in Physics. Sometimes you'll need to resolve forces, which could mean using all sorts of angle rules, as well as Pythagoras and trigonometry. Here's a recap on the basics.

Geometry basics

Angle rules

These angle rules should be familiar — make sure you're happy with them.

When two parallel lines are intercepted by the same line:

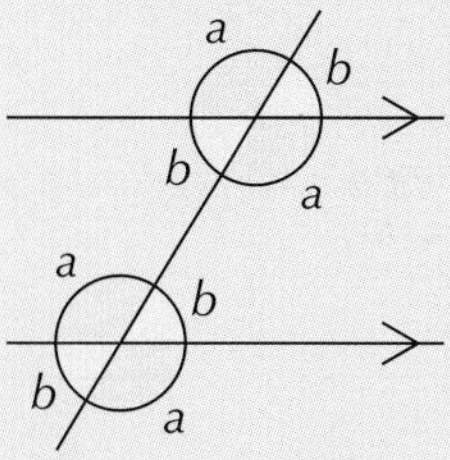

Vertically opposite angles are equal, and
$a + b = 180°$

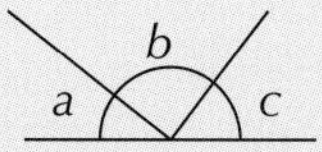

Angles on a straight line add up to 180°.

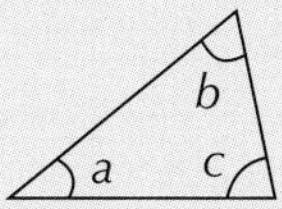

Angles in a triangle add up to 180°.

$a + b + c = 180°$

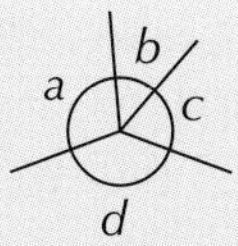

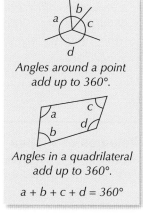

Angles around a point add up to 360°.

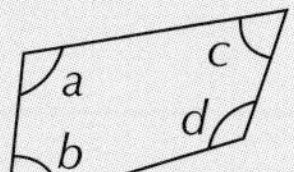

Angles in a quadrilateral add up to 360°.

$a + b + c + d = 360°$

Tip: Remember, the arrows on the lines in the diagram mean that they're parallel.

Angles can be measured in degrees or radians — make sure you know how to convert between them:

- To convert from degrees to radians, multiply by $\frac{\pi}{180°}$.
- To convert from radians to degrees, multiply by $\frac{180°}{\pi}$.

Exam Tip
Don't forget to put your calculator into either degrees or radians mode depending on what you're working in. It's a common mistake that could cost you marks.

Circumference and arc length

You may need to calculate the distance around the edge of a circle (or part of it).

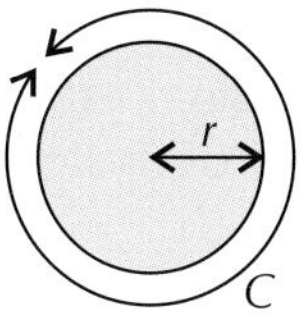

Circumference, $C = 2\pi r$

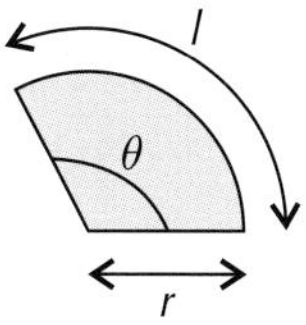

Arc length, $l = r\theta$, θ in radians

Exam Tip
You'll be given these in the data and formulae booklet, just remember that θ is in radians.

Areas of shapes

Make sure you remember how to calculate the areas of these shapes:

Triangle

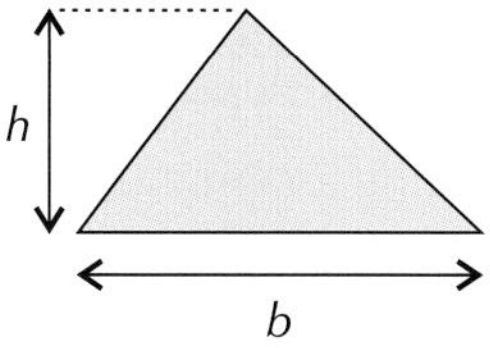

$A = \frac{1}{2} \times b \times h$

Circle

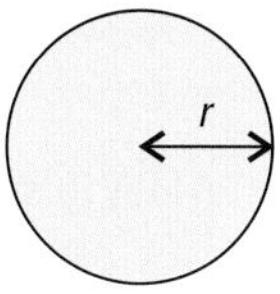

$A = \pi \times r^2$

Rectangle

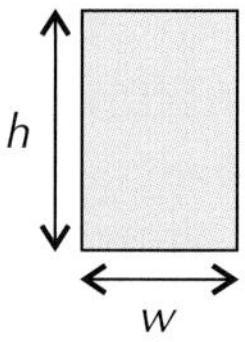

$A = h \times w$

Trapezium

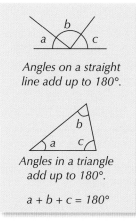

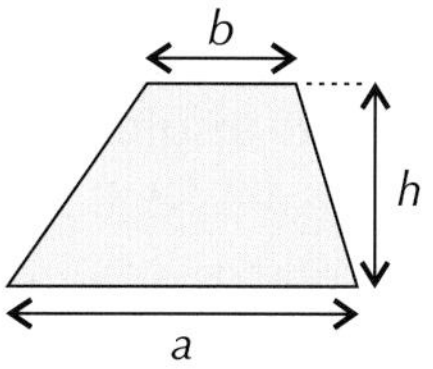

$A = \frac{1}{2} \times (a + b) \times h$

Exam Tip
You'll be given the formulae for the area of a circle and the area of a trapezium in the data and formulae booklet.

Surface areas

If you need to work out the surface area of a 3D shape, you just need to add up the areas of all the 2D faces of the shape. The exception to this is a sphere, where the surface area is given by $A = 4\pi r^2$ — this will be given to you in the data and formulae booklet.

Exam Tip
The curved surface area of a cylinder is given in the data and formulae booklet. This is the surface area of a hollow cylinder, i.e. with no ends. If you need to calculate a closed cylinder, you'll need to add the areas of the two circular ends ($2 \times \pi r^2$).

Example — Maths Skills

A piece of wire has the shape of a cylinder. It has radius 2.0 mm and length 0.020 m. Calculate the surface area of the wire.

The surface of a cylinder is made of two circles (the ends of the wire) and a rectangle with a width equal to the circumference of one of those circles (which is rolled to make the length of the wire).

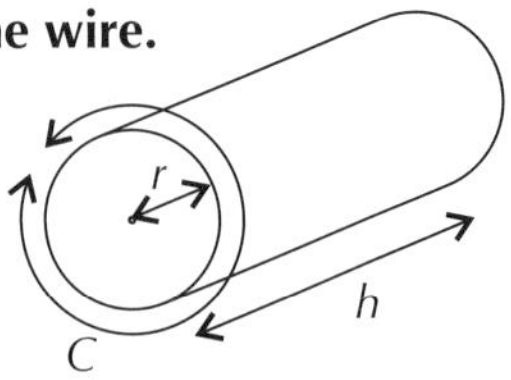

Surface area = (2 × area of the circle) + (area of the rectangle)

$= (2 \times \pi r^2) + (2\pi r \times h)$

$= (2 \times \pi \times (2.0 \times 10^{-3})^2) + (2 \times \pi \times (2.0 \times 10^{-3}) \times 0.020)$

$= 2.7646... \times 10^{-4} = 2.8 \times 10^{-4}$ m^2 (to 2 s.f.)

Volumes of shapes

Make sure you remember how to calculate the volumes of a cuboid, a sphere and a cylinder:

Exam Tip
You'll be given the volume of a sphere and a cylinder in the data and formulae booklet — hoorah.

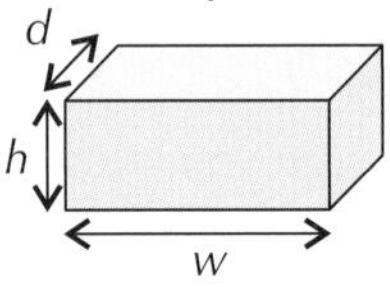

$V = w \times h \times d$

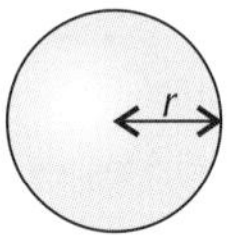

$V = \frac{4}{3}\pi r^3$

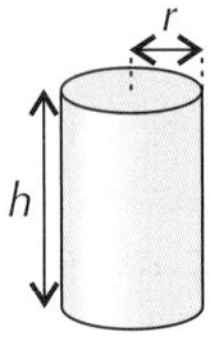

$V = \pi r^2 h$

Figure 1: You can find the buttons for sine (sin) cosine (cos) and tangent (tan) on your calculator as well as their inverse functions ($\sin^{-1}$, $\cos^{-1}$ and $\tan^{-1}$).

Trigonometry basics

Right-angled triangles

You can use Pythagoras' theorem for all right-angled triangles — the square of the hypotenuse is equal to the sum of the squares of the two smaller sides.

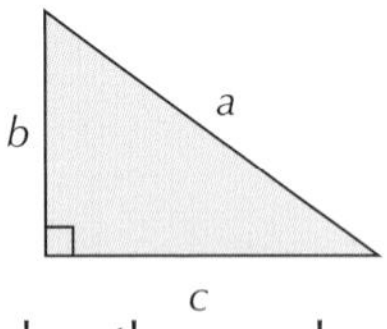

$a^2 = b^2 + c^2$

To work out a length or angle within a right-angled triangle, remember SOH CAH TOA (covered on page 35). There are plenty of examples of this being used to resolve vectors over on page 36. Just remember:

$$\sin\theta = \frac{\text{opposite}}{\text{hypotenuse}} \qquad \cos\theta = \frac{\text{adjacent}}{\text{hypotenuse}} \qquad \tan\theta = \frac{\text{opposite}}{\text{adjacent}}$$

Small-angle approximations

For really small angles in radians, you can make the following assumptions for the values of sin, cos and tan:

$$\sin\theta \approx \theta \qquad \tan\theta \approx \theta \qquad \cos\theta \approx 1$$

This is really useful in Physics as the angles are often small (p.210 and p.214).

Exam Tip
You'll be given these small-angle approximations in the data and formulae booklet.

Sine and cosine rules

If a triangle is not right angled, you need to use the sine and cosine rules to work out angles and side lengths.

Tip: These rules work on any triangle.

The sine rule:

$$\frac{a}{\sin A} = \frac{b}{\sin B} = \frac{c}{\sin C}$$

The cosine rule:

$$a^2 = b^2 + c^2 - 2bc\cos A$$

Tip: You can use any two bits of the sine rule to make a normal equation with just one = sign. The sine rule also works if you flip all the fractions upside down: $\frac{\sin A}{a} = \frac{\sin B}{b} = \frac{\sin C}{c}$.

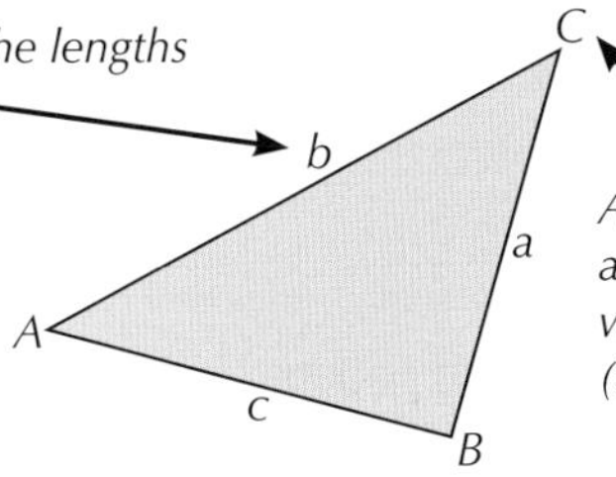

Which rule you can use depends on which sides and angles you already know.

Example — Maths Skills

A cart is pulled by two horses, both pulling at different angles and with different forces, as shown. Calculate the magnitude and direction of the resultant force.

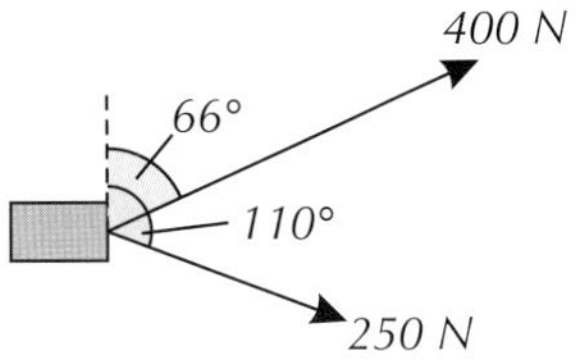

Tip: You'll often be required to represent 3D problems in 2D (e.g. with a force diagram) and solve them using these trigonometry rules.

Draw a vector triangle and work out any angles that you can with angle rules.

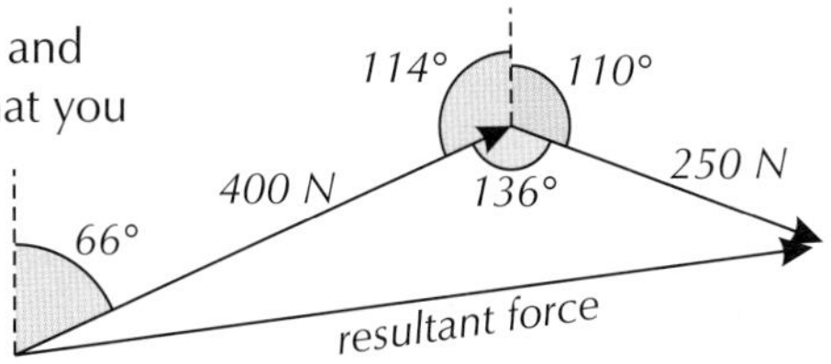

Tip: When working out angles, remember that the angles on a line must add up to 180° and the angles around a point must add up to 360°.

You can use the cosine rule, so label the angle that you know A.

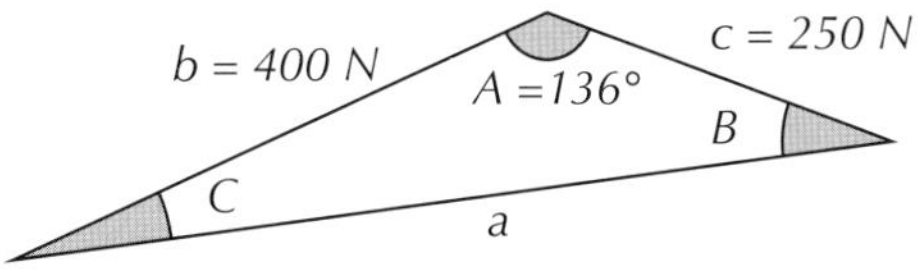

The cosine rule gives: $a = \sqrt{b^2 + c^2 - 2bc\cos A}$

$= \sqrt{400^2 + 250^2 - 2 \times 400 \times 250 \times \cos 136°}$

$= 605.28... = 610\text{ N (to 2 s.f.)}$

You can now use the sine rule in the form $\frac{\sin C}{c} = \frac{\sin A}{a}$ to find C.

$C = \sin^{-1}\left(\frac{\sin A}{a} \times c\right) = \sin^{-1}\left(\frac{\sin 136°}{605.28...} \times 250\right)$

$= 16.673... = 17°\text{ (to 2 s.f.)}$

So the resultant force is 610 N (to 2 s.f.) at a bearing of 083° (to 2 s.f.).

Tip: You could have also re-labelled the triangle so that C was A instead, and used the cosine rule again.

Tip: The angle from north is 66° + 17° = 83°.

Exam Structure and Technique

Passing exams isn't all about revision — it really helps if you know how the exam is structured and have got your exam technique nailed so that you pick up every mark you can.

AS exam structure

For OCR A AS Physics you'll sit two exam papers. Each one will be worth 50% of your overall AS mark, and could cover anything from your AS course.

Paper 1 — Breadth in Physics

This paper will be 1 hour and 30 minutes long and have 70 marks available. The paper is split into 2 sections:

- **Section A (20 marks)**
  There are 20 multiple choice questions, each worth one mark.
- **Section B (50 marks)**
  This section is made up of short answer question parts.

Paper 2 — Depth in Physics

This paper will also be 1 hour 30 minutes long and have 70 marks up for grabs. The questions can be made up of short and/or extended answer question parts. Some extended answer question parts are known as 'quality of extended response' questions — there's more on answering these on the next page.

In each of these papers, make sure you look at how many marks each question part is worth before answering it — generally the more marks there are, the more work you'll need to put in to get them all.

Command words

It sounds obvious, but it's really important you read each question carefully, and give an answer that fits. Look for command words in the question — they'll give you an idea of the kind of answer you should write.

Some command words, like calculate, draw and complete are pretty self-explanatory. But command words for written questions can be a bit trickier. Common command words for these questions are:

- State — give a definition, example or fact.
- Identify — pick out information from data provided in the question, or say what something is.
- Suggest/Predict — use your scientific knowledge to work out what the answer might be.
- Describe — don't waste time explaining <u>why</u> a process happens — that's not what the question is after. It just wants to know <u>what</u> happens.
- Explain — give reasons for why something happens, not just a description.

Exam Tip
Make sure you have a good read through this exam structure. It might not seem important now but you don't want to get any nasty surprises at the start of an exam.

Exam Tip
If you don't know the answer to a multiple choice question, it's always best to make the best guess you can rather than give no answer at all. You might just guess the right answer...

Exam Tip
If you're doing A-level Physics, you won't have to sit any exams at the end of your first year.

Exam Tip
Make sure you read the whole question carefully. Sometimes they specify the details (or the level of detail) they want you to include in your answer. For example, they may ask something like "Describe how the apparatus can be used to accurately and safely determine the *I-V* characteristic of a filament lamp." Make sure you talk about <u>accuracy</u> and <u>safety</u> to get all of the marks.

- Compare — make sure you relate the things you're comparing to each other. It's no good just listing details about each one, you need to say how these things are similar or different.
- Discuss — you'll need to include more detail. Depending on the question you could need to cover what happens, what the effects are, and perhaps include a brief explanation of why it happens.
- Justify — show or prove that something is correct.
- Evaluate — Give the arguments both for and against an issue, or the advantages and disadvantages of something. You also need to give an overall judgement.

Quality of extended responses

For some extended answer questions, you'll be marked on the 'quality of your extended response'. These questions are designed to test how well you can put together a well structured and logical line of reasoning. They'll often require you to give a long answer in full written English, e.g. to explain, analyse or discuss something. To get top marks, you need to make sure that:

- you answer the question and all the information you give is relevant to the question you've been asked,
- you back up your points with clear evidence using the data given to you in the question,
- you organise your answer clearly, coherently and in a sensible order,
- you use specialist scientific vocabulary where it's appropriate.

These questions could also involve other tasks, like a calculation or having to draw an experimental set-up, like a circuit. Make sure any drawings are clear and use correct symbols where appropriate. When doing calculations, make sure your working is laid out logically and it's clear how you've reached your answer. That includes making sure any estimates and assumptions you've made in your working are clearly stated, e.g. assuming air resistance is negligible.

There's usually a lot to think about with this type of question, and it can be easy to write down a lot of great and relevant physics but forget to answer all parts of the question. It's always a good idea to double check you've done everything a question has asked you to do before moving on.

Exam Tip
Questions where you're marked on the quality of your extended response are marked with an asterisk (*) by the question.

Exam Tip
Don't worry too much about quality of extended response questions. Really, you should be looking to give full and coherent explanations for every question.

Exam Tip
Whilst these questions don't test your handwriting, spelling or grammar, if the examiner can't read what you've written or understand the point you're trying to make, it will lose you marks.

Strange questions

You may get some weird questions that seem to have nothing to do with anything you've learnt. DON'T PANIC. Every question will be something you can answer using physics you know, it just may be in a new context.

Check the question for any key words that you recognise. For example, if a question talks about acceleration, think about the rules and equations you know, and whether any of them apply to the situation in the question. Sometimes you might have to pull together ideas from different parts of physics — read the question and try to think about what physics is being used. That way you can list any equations or facts you know to do with that topic and try to use them to answer the question.

Time management

This is one of the most important exam skills to have. How long you spend on each question is really important in an exam — it could make all the difference to your grade.

Everyone has their own method of getting through the exam. Some people find it easier to go through the paper question by question and some people like to do the questions they find easiest first. The most important thing is to find out the way that suits you best before the exam — and that means doing all the practice exams you can before the big day.

Check out the exam timings given by OCR that can be found on page 254 and on the front of your exam paper. These timings give you just over 1 minute per mark.

However, some questions will require lots of work for only a few marks and other questions will be much quicker. So don't spend ages struggling with questions that are only worth a couple of marks — move on. You can come back to them later when you've bagged loads of other marks elsewhere.

Exam Tip
Make sure you read the rest of the information given on the front of the exam paper before you start. It'll help make sure you're well prepared.

Examples

The questions below are both worth the same number of marks but require different amounts of work.

1 a) Define the term 'ultimate tensile strength'.

(2 marks)

3 a) Draw a labelled diagram of a circuit that would be suitable for a student to measure the resistance of component A.

(2 marks)

Question 1 a) only requires you to write down a definition — if you can remember it this shouldn't take you too long.

Question 3 a) requires you to draw a diagram including a number of components — this may take you a lot longer than writing down a definition, especially if you have to add quite a few components and work out whether they should be in parallel or series.

So, if you're running out of time it makes sense to do questions like 1 a) first and come back to 3 a) if you've got time at the end.

Exam Tip
Don't forget to go back and do any questions that you left the first time round — you don't want to miss out on marks because you forgot to do a question.

It's worth keeping in mind that the multiple choice questions in Section A of Paper 1 are all only worth 1 mark, even though some of them could be quite tricky and time-consuming. Don't make the mistake of spending too much time on these. If you're struggling with some of them, move on to the written answer questions where there are more marks available and then go back to the harder multiple choice questions later.

Exam data and formulae booklet

When you sit your exams, you'll be given a data and formulae booklet as an insert within the exam paper. On it you'll find a lot of equations from the course, but not all of them. Make sure you know which equations you'll be given, and which you need to learn off by heart for the exam. There's also some useful data in the booklet to help you with your exam, including...

- the elementary charge, e
- the Planck constant, h
- the number of joules, J, in 1 electronvolt, eV.

Exam Tip
The same data sheet is used in the AS and A Level exams, so if you're sitting AS there'll be some information on the data sheet that you may not be familiar with. Don't be put off by it — it's there for people sitting the A Level exams and you won't need to use it. Phew!

Answers

Module 1

Development of Practical Skills

1. Planning an Experiment

Page 8 — Application Question

Q1 a) Independent variable — angle of the ramp
Dependent variable — the final velocity of trolley
b) Any one from: e.g. the distance the trolley travels / the initial velocity of the trolley.

Page 8 — Fact Recall Questions

Q1 To make sure that it is only the independent variable that is affecting the dependent variable, otherwise the results won't be valid.

Q2 An experiment that is carried out using the same equipment before the real experiment. It is used to roughly work out the effect that changing the independent variable will have on the dependent variable, and to help choose appropriate units, range and increments of measurement.

Q3 Any three from: whether the experiment tests what it was meant to test / if the method is clear enough for someone else to follow / whether all control variables are going to be kept constant / whether the apparatus and techniques are appropriate for the investigation / if the method gives precise results / that the experiment is going to be carried out safely.

2. Recording and Processing Data

Page 10 — Application Questions

Q1 a) $4.53 \times 3.142 = 14.23326 =$ **14.2 (to 3 s.f.)**

The number with the lowest number of significant figures in this calculation is 4.53, which is to 3 significant figures. So the answer must also be to 3 significant figures.

b) $0.315 \div 0.025 = 12.6 =$ **13 (to 2 s.f.)**

The number to the lowest number of significant figures in this calculation is 0.025, which is to 2 significant figures.

Q2 Extension at weight of 2.0 N:
Mean = $(2.9 + 3.2 + 3.1) \div 3 = 3.066... =$ **3.1 cm (to 2 s.f.)**
Extension at weight of 4.0 N:
Mean = $(5.8 + 5.9) \div 2 = 5.85 =$ **5.9 cm (to 2 s.f.)**
Extension at weight of 6.0 N:
Mean = $(8.4 + 8.4 + 8.5) \div 3 = 8.433... =$ **8.4 cm (to 2 s.f.)**

The result for trial 2 of the 4.0 N weight is an anomaly and so should be left out of the calculation for the mean. All the answers should be given to 2 s.f. as the data is only to 2 s.f..

Page 10 — Fact Recall Questions

Q1 Data with a numerical value.

Q2 A result that doesn't fit in with the rest of the results and is likely to be wrong.

3. Presenting Results

Page 12 — Application Question

Q1

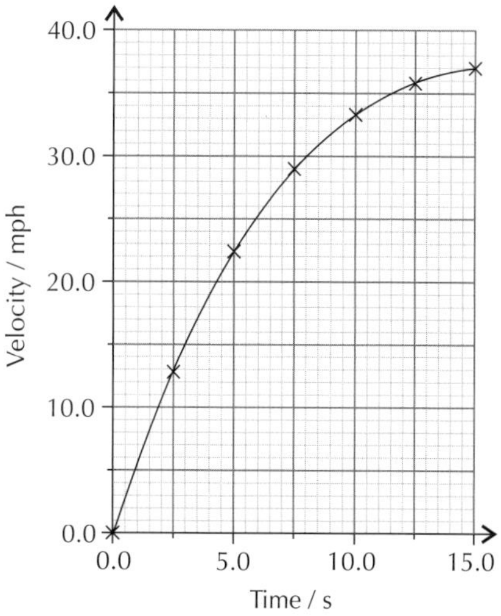

Page 12 — Fact Recall Questions

Q1 You can present categoric data in a pie chart / bar chart.

Q2 The independent variable.

4. Analysing Results

Page 15 — Application Question

Q1 a) Negative correlation.
b) Rearrange the equation to match $y = mx + c$.
$V = -rI + \varepsilon$, so, y-intercept, $c = \varepsilon$
so, $\varepsilon =$ **16 V**
c) $V = -rI + \varepsilon$, so gradient, $m = -r$

$$\text{gradient} = \frac{\Delta y}{\Delta x} = \frac{-16}{20} = -0.8\ \Omega$$

$r = -m = -(-0.8) =$ **0.8 Ω**

5. Evaluating and Drawing Conclusions

Page 20 — Application Questions

Q1 a) **±0.1 g**
b) $(0.1 \div 50) \times 100 =$ **0.2%**

Q2 a) **±0.05 A**

The current is given to 2 significant figures, so the assumed uncertainty is half of 0.1 A.

b) First calculate the mean:
$(3.4 + 3.6 + 4.0 + 3.9 + 3.6) \div 5 = 3.7$ V
Then find the range of the results:
$4.0 - 3.4 = 0.6$ V
So the uncertainty is $0.6 \div 2 = \pm 0.3$ V
So the mean potential difference is **3.7 ± 0.3 V**

Q3 a) The results are not valid as the temperature changed during the experiment.
b) Any two from: e.g. take more repeats for each length / take readings over a greater range of wire lengths / keep the temperature the same throughout the experiment / use more sensitive apparatus to measure the diameter of the wire.

Page 20 — Fact Recall Questions

Q1 The uncertainty given as a percentage of the measurement.

Q2 Any two from: e.g. by taking more repeats / by using more sensitive equipment for recording results / by using more appropriate equipment for recording results.

Q3 Precision depends on the amount of spread of your data from the mean of your results. Accuracy is how close your results are to the true value.

Exam-style Questions — Page 22

1 D *(1 mark)*

2 a) Absolute uncertainty = ± 0.5 °C
As a percentage of 90:
(0.5 ÷ 90) × 100 = 0.555... = **0.6% (to 1 s.f.)**
(2 marks for the correct answer, otherwise 1 mark for giving the absolute uncertainty)

b) Mean of the current:
2.8 A is an anomaly, and so shouldn't be included in the calculation.
(1.9 + 1.8 + 2.0 + 2.0 + 2.1) ÷ 5 = 1.96 = 2.0 A (to 2 s.f.)
Range of values = 2.1 – 1.8 = 0.3 A
So the uncertainty = 0.15 A
So the mean current = **2.0 ± 0.15 A**
(3 marks for the correct answer, otherwise 1 mark for using the correct equation to calculate the mean and 1 mark for using the range of values to calculate the uncertainty)

c) How to grade your answer (pick the description that best matches your answer):
0 marks: There is no relevant information.
1-2 marks: At least one point from evaluation and one point from improvements have been included in the answer. Answer is basic and has lack of structure. Information is missing and there are few backed up arguments.
3-4 marks: Point 1 or 2 and point 3, 4 or 5 from evaluations is included in the answer. At least two points from improvements have been included in the answer. Answer has some structure, and information is presented with a clear line of reasoning, with arguments that are partially backed up.
5-6 marks: Point 1 or 2, point 3 or 4 and point 5 from evaluations is included in the answer. Points 1 or 2 and at least one other point from improvements have been included in the answer. The answer is well structured. There is a clear and logical line of reasoning, with information and arguments that are fully backed up.
Here are some points your answer may include:
Evaluation
1. She took a large number of repeat readings for the current at each temperature, allowing her to calculate a more precise mean.
2. The set of current values for each water temperature are all quite close to the mean, which shows that the results are quite precise/repeatable.
3. One limitation is that the potential difference of the power supply may not be the same as the potential difference across the thermistor, as there will be some resistance in the ammeter and the wires. This means their calculations of the resistance will be inaccurate/ there will be a systematic error in the results.
4. The experiment does not answer the original question of how the resistance of the thermistor varies with temperature as the potential difference across the thermistor was not monitored or controlled.
5. The intervals between the temperatures are quite large, and the student has not investigated a large enough range of temperatures. So it would not be possible to determine the type of mathematical relationship between resistance and temperature (e.g. linear or non-linear).

Improvements
1. To monitor and control the potential difference across the thermistor, a voltmeter could be connected in parallel to the thermistor, and a variable resistor could be connected in series with the thermistor. This would give a more accurate calculation of resistance.
2. The student should take more readings for temperatures between 50 °C and 90 °C, e.g. at 5 °C intervals.
3. The student could use an ammeter with a higher resolution to reduce the uncertainty in each measurement.
4. A thermometer with a higher resolution could be used, or a digital thermometer to reduce any human error in the readings.

Module 2

Foundations of Physics

1. Quantities and Units

Page 26 — Application Questions

Q1 0.3 × (1 × 10^{12}) = **300 000 000 000 Hz** (= 3 × 10^{11} Hz)

Q2 Mass, m, is measured in kilograms, kg
Velocity, $\boldsymbol{v}$ = distance ÷ time
Distance is measured in metres, m, time is measured in seconds, s, so velocity is measured in m ÷ s, or ms^{-1}.
$\boldsymbol{p} = m\boldsymbol{v}$, so the units of momentum = kg × ms^{-1} = $kgms^{-1}$

Page 26 — Fact Recall Questions

Q1 kelvin / K

Q2 Any two from: e.g. J (joule) / Ω (ohm) / V (volt) / N (newton) / ms^{-1} / $kgms^{-1}$

Q3 a) 1 × 10^{-12}
b) 0.01 or 1 × 10^{-2}
c) 1 × 10^{6}

2. Making Estimates

Page 28 — Application Questions

Q1 a) A room is about the height of one-and-a-half people.
A person is around 1.8 m in height.
One room = 1.5 × 1.8 = 2.7 m.
A two-storey house is as tall as 2 rooms, plus the height of the roof and any material between rooms.
So a two-storey house is about as tall as 3 rooms.
3 × 2.7 = 8.1 m.
So a two-storey house is about 8 m tall (to 1 s.f.).

b) The mass of a person is about 70 kg. Mass of a child is about half the mass of an adult, so 70 ÷ 2 = 35 kg.
Gravitational potential energy = 35 × 9.81 × 3
= 1030.05 J
So the gravitational potential energy of the child is about 1000 J (to 1 s.f.).

Q2 The actual value of the change in velocity (over a given time) was larger, so the actual acceleration of the ball would be larger. This means that the actual force on the ball would be larger than the one calculated.

3. Errors and Uncertainties

Page 31 — Application Questions

Q1 $v = f\lambda = 125 \times 2.72 = 340$ ms^{-1}
The uncertainty is found by adding together the percentage uncertainties.
1% + 1.5% = 2.5%
So v = **340 ± 2.5% ms^{-1}**

Q2 volume = $L^3 = 4.0^3 = 64$ cm^3
Now find the percentage uncertainty in L:
(0.05 ÷ 4.0) × 100 = 12.5%
Multiply this by the power to find the uncertainty in L^3:
1.25% × 3 = 3.75%
So volume = **64 ± 3.75% cm^3**

Page 31 — Fact Recall Questions

Q1 a) E.g. taking repeated measurements and averaging the results / using more sensitive apparatus.
b) E.g. calibrating equipment.

Q2 Add together their absolute uncertainties.

Q3 $$\text{percentage difference} = \frac{\text{experimental value} - \text{accepted value}}{\text{accepted value}} \times 100$$
Percentage difference shows the accuracy of an experimental result.

4. Graphical Representations of Uncertainties

Page 33 — Application Question

Q1 a)

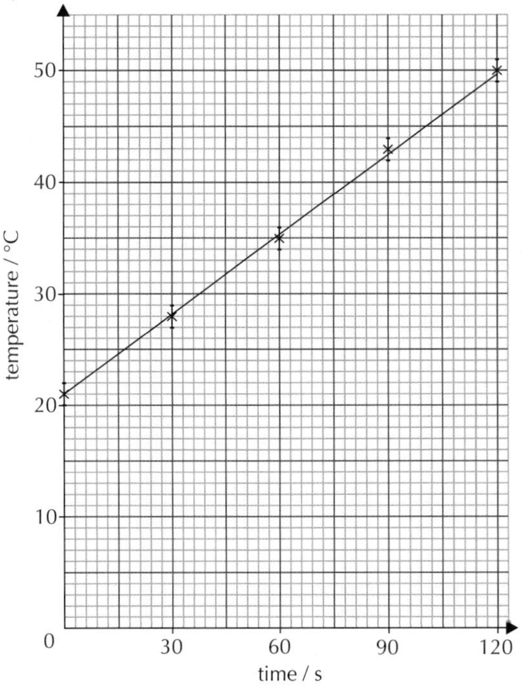

b) Plot the worst lines on the graph:

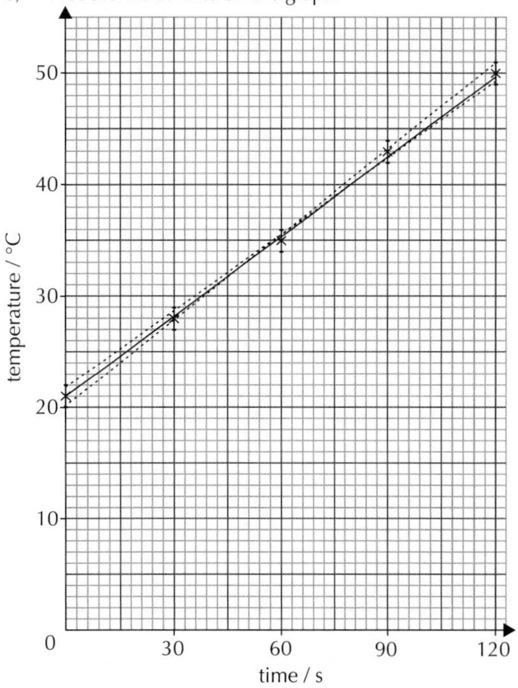

The gradient of the line of best fit
= (49.5 – 21) ÷ 120 = 0.2375
The gradient of the steepest worst line
= (51 – 20) ÷ 120 = 0.2583...
The gradient of the shallowest worst line
= (49 – 222) ÷ 120 = 0.225
The difference between the gradient of the steepest worst line and the line of best fit is 0.2583... – 0.2375 = 0.0208...
The difference between the line of best fit and the gradient of the shallowest worst line is 0.2375 – 0.225 = 0.0125
The result for the steepest worst line is larger, so take this as the uncertainty in the final result.
So the gradient = **0.24 ± 0.02 °C s^{-1} (to 2 s.f.)**

The results in the table are to 2 s.f., so the gradient should be given to 2 s.f. too. You should then quote the uncertainty rounded to the same number of decimal places as the rounded value of the gradient.

5. Scalars and Vectors

Page 38 — Application Questions

Q1 $v = \sqrt{2.0^2 + 0.75^2} = 2.136.... = 2.1$ ms^{-1} (to 2 s.f.)
$\theta = \tan^{-1}\frac{0.75}{2.0} = 20.556... = 21°$ (to 2 s.f.)
So the resultant velocity is **2.1 ms^{-1} at 21° down from the horizontal**.

Once you've found the magnitude of the vector you could use sin or cos to find the angle θ too, but it's safer to use tan as you know the values of the opposite and adjacent sides are correct.

Q2 Horizontal component $\boldsymbol{F}_x = \boldsymbol{F}\cos\theta = 12\cos 56° = 6.710...$
= **6.7 N (to 2 s.f.)**
Vertical component $\boldsymbol{F}_y = \boldsymbol{F}\sin\theta = 12\sin 56° = 9.948...$
= **9.9 N (to 2 s.f.)**

Q3 Start by drawing a scale diagram with an appropriate scale (e.g. 5.0 cm = 1.0 N). Then measure the side and angle:
The resultant force is 5.0 N on a bearing of 055°.

Q4 Start by drawing a diagram to show the forces on the brick:

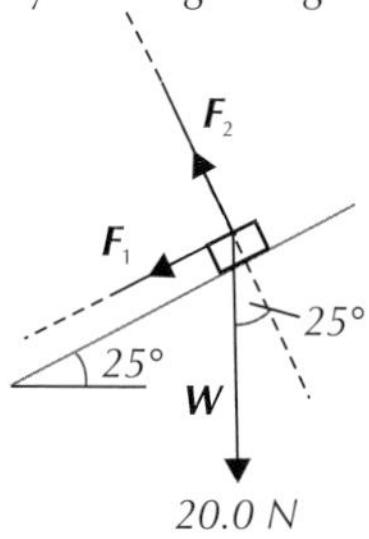

Then use trigonometry to find the size of F_1 and F_2:

a) $F_1 = \sin 25° \times 20.0 = 8.452... =$ **8.5 N (to 2 s.f.)**
b) $F_2 = \cos 25° \times 20.0 = 18.126... =$ **18 N (to 2 s.f.)**

Q5 Let force A be the 22 N force, and force B be the 18 N force.
Resolving force A:
$A_x = 22\cos 40° = 16.85...$
$A_y = 22\sin 40° = 14.14...$
Resolving force B:
$B_x = 18\cos 50° = 11.57...$
$B_y = 18\sin 50° = 13.78...$
Then calculate the resultant horizontal component:
$F_x = A_x - B_x = 16.85... - 11.57... = 5.28...$
Calculate the resultant vertical component:
$F_y = A_y - B_y = 14.41... - 13.78... = 0.35...$
Find the magnitude of the resultant force:
$R = \sqrt{F_x^2 + F_y^2} = \sqrt{5.28...^2 + 0.35...^2} = 5.29...$
Now draw a diagram to help you find the angle of the resultant force on the toy:

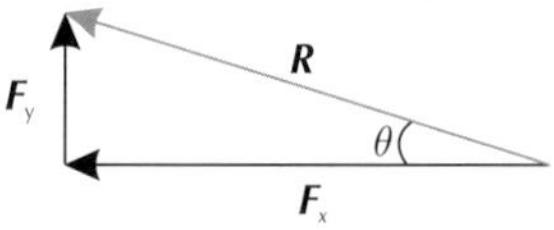

$\tan\theta = \text{opposite} \div \text{adjacent}$, so $\theta = \tan^{-1}\left(\frac{F_y}{F_x}\right)$
$\theta = \tan^{-1}\left(\frac{0.35...}{5.28...}\right) = 3.817...°$

So the resultant force is **5.3 N (to 2 s.f.) to the left at an angle of 3.8° (to 2 s.f.) above the horizontal**.

Page 38 — Fact Recall Questions

Q1 A scalar quantity has only a magnitude (size), while a vector quantity has size and direction.
Q2 The resultant (vector).

Exam-style Questions — Page 40

1 D ***(1 mark)***
The error bar for the measurement of 0.4 V shows an absolute uncertainty of ± 0.05 V. (0.05 ÷ 0.4) × 100 = 12.5%.

2 a) Start by drawing a diagram to show the forces:

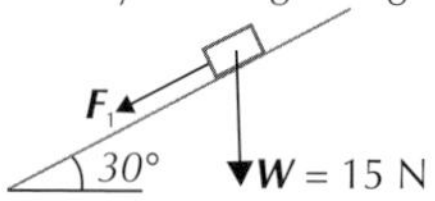

Component down the slope, $F_1 = W\sin\theta$
$= 15\sin 30 = 7.5$ N
The percentage uncertainty in the weight is:
(0.5 ÷ 15) × 100 = 3.33...%
This is equal to the percentage uncertainty in the component of the box's weight that acts down the slope.
So the component = **7.5 ± 3.3% N (to 2 s.f.)**
(3 marks for correct answer and uncertainty, otherwise 1 mark for correct answer without uncertainty, and 1 mark for correct method of calculation)

b) Start by drawing a diagram to show the forces:

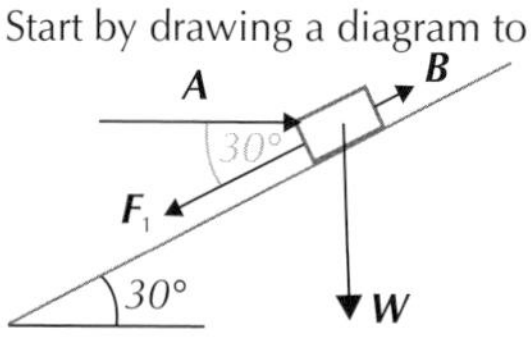

For the box to have a resultant force of 3.0 N up the slope, the component of A up the slope minus F_1 must equal B.
The component of A up the slope = 23 cos 30°
The angle between A and the slope is 30° because for two parallel lines that are being intersected, the alternate angles are equal.
$F_1 = W\sin\theta = W\sin 30°$,
$B = 3.0$ N
so $23\cos 30° - W\sin 30° = 3.0$
$W = (23\cos 30° - 3.0) \div \sin 30°$
$= 33.83...$ N = **34 N (to 2 s.f.)**
(3 marks for correct answer, otherwise 1 mark for correct resolution of force A up the slope and 1 mark for correct calculation of W)

3 a) It is a systematic error ***(1 mark)***. Random errors cannot be predicted and cause results to change in unpredictable ways. Systematic errors usually shift all of the measurements by the same amount ***(1 mark)***.
b) 3 cm = 0.03 m
force constant = force ÷ extension = 60 ÷ 0.03
= 2000 Nm^{-1}
Now find the percentage uncertainties in both force and extension:
% uncertainty in force = (5 ÷ 60) × 100 = 8.33... %
% uncertainty in extension = (0.05 ÷ 3) × 100 = 1.66...%
Add the percentage uncertainties to find the uncertainty in the force constant:
8.33...% + 1.66...% = 10 %
So force constant = **2000 ± 10% Nm^{-1}**
(4 marks for correct answer, otherwise 1 mark for correct force constant, 1 mark for correct percentage uncertainties of force and extension and 1 mark for correct method used to combine uncertainties)

Module 3

Section 1 — Motion

1. Constant Acceleration

Page 42 — Application Questions

Q1 $u = 0\ \text{ms}^{-1}$ $v = 10\ \text{ms}^{-1}$ $t = 20$ s $a = ?$ $s = ?$
so use $s = \frac{1}{2}(u + v)t \Rightarrow s = \frac{1}{2}(0 + 10) \times 20 =$ **100 m**

Q2 $u = 25\ \text{ms}^{-1}$ $v = 0\ \text{ms}^{-1}$ $t = 18$ s $a = ?$ $s = ?$
$v = u + at \Rightarrow a = \frac{v - u}{t} = \frac{0 - 25}{18} = -1.3888...$
So the deceleration is **1.4 ms^{-2} (to 2 s.f)**.

Q3 $s = 103$ m $u = 0\ \text{ms}^{-1}$ $t = 9.2$ s $v = ?$ $a = ?$
$s = ut + \frac{1}{2}at^2 \Rightarrow a = \frac{s - ut}{\frac{1}{2}t^2} = \frac{103 - (0 \times 9.2)}{\frac{1}{2} \times 9.2^2}$
$= 2.4338... =$ **2.4 ms^{-2} (to 2 s.f.)**

Page 42 — Fact Recall Questions

Q1 a) The velocity of an object is its rate of change of displacement.
b) The acceleration of an object is its rate of change of velocity.

Q2 The equations are:

$v = u + at$

$s = \frac{1}{2}(u + v)t$

$s = ut + \frac{1}{2}at^2$

$v^2 = u^2 + 2as$

2. Acceleration Due To Gravity

Page 45 — Application Questions

Q1 $s = \frac{1}{2}gt^2 = \frac{1}{2} \times -9.81 \times 6.19^2 = -187.940...$

So height = **188 m (to 3 s.f.)**

Height is a scalar quantity so you don't need to worry about the minus signs here.

Q2 $v^2 = u^2 + 2as \Rightarrow v = \sqrt{0^2 + (2 \times -9.81 \times -6.83)}$
$= (-)11.576...\ ms^{-1}$

So it's travelling at **11.6 ms⁻¹ (to 3 s.f.)**.

Q3 E.g. use a small, heavy ball to negate the effect of air resistance and use a mechanism to automatically release and time the ball bearing's fall.

Page 45 — Fact Recall Questions

Q1 The only force present in free fall motion is weight.

Q2 a) E.g. Measure the length of time it takes for a metal ball bearing to fall a known distance using a switch to release the ball bearing from an electromagnet and start a timer, and a trap door to catch the ball bearing and stop the timer. Measure the height h from the bottom of the ball bearing to the trapdoor. Flick the switch to simultaneously start the timer and disconnect the electromagnet, releasing the ball bearing. The ball bearing will fall, knocking the trapdoor down and breaking the circuit — which stops the timer. Record the time t shown on the timer. Repeat this experiment three times and average the time taken to fall from this height. Repeat this experiment but drop the ball bearing from several different heights.

b) For each height, rearrange $h = \frac{1}{2}gt^2$ to get $g = 2h \div t^2$ then substitute in the height and average time that you have measured.

3. Projectile Motion

Page 47 — Application Questions

Q1 First find how long it's in the air by considering only the vertical velocity:

$$s = \frac{1}{2}gt^2 \Rightarrow t = \sqrt{\frac{2s}{g}} = \sqrt{\frac{2 \times -1.61}{-9.81}} = 0.5729...\ s$$

Then find out how far it travels in this time:

$s = ut = 502 \times 0.5729... = 287.60... =$ **288 m (to 3 s.f.)**

Remember there's no acceleration in the horizontal direction.

Q2 a) Consider only the vertical velocity:

$u_v = \sin 60.0° \times 25 = 21.65...\ ms^{-1}$

$v_v^2 = u_v^2 + 2gs$

$\Rightarrow v_v = \sqrt{21.65...^2 + 2 \times (-9.81) \times (0)} = -21.65...\ ms^{-1}$

The rock will be moving towards the ground, so it will have a negative final velocity.

$$v_v = u_v + at \Rightarrow t = \frac{v_v - u_v}{a} = \frac{-21.65... - 21.65...}{-9.81}$$

$= 4.413... =$ **4.4 s (to 2 s.f)**

b) Consider the horizontal velocity:

$u_h = \cos 60.0° \times 25 = 12.5\ ms^{-1}$

So $s = u_h t = 12.5 \times 4.413... = 55.174... =$ **55 m (to 2 s.f.)**

Q3 The vertical velocity, $u_v = \sin 31.5° \times 12.1 = 6.322...\ ms^{-1}$

At the highest point, the ball's vertical velocity will be 0 ms⁻¹.

$v_v = 0\ ms^{-1}$, $a = -9.81\ ms^{-2}$.

$$v_v^2 = u_v^2 + 2as, \text{ so } s = \frac{v_v^2 - u_v^2}{2a} = \frac{0^2 - 6.322...^2}{2 \times -9.81} = 2.0372...\ m$$

Total height above ground = 2.0372... + 4.20 = 6.2372...
= **6.24 m (to 3 s.f.)**

Page 47 — Fact Recall Questions

Q1 Free fall motion with an initial velocity is called projectile motion.

Q2 Resolve the initial velocity into horizontal and vertical components, then use the vertical component to work out how long it's in the air and/or how high it goes. Then use the horizontal component to work out how far it goes in the horizontal direction while it's in the air.

4. Displacement-Time Graphs

Page 51 — Application Questions

Q1

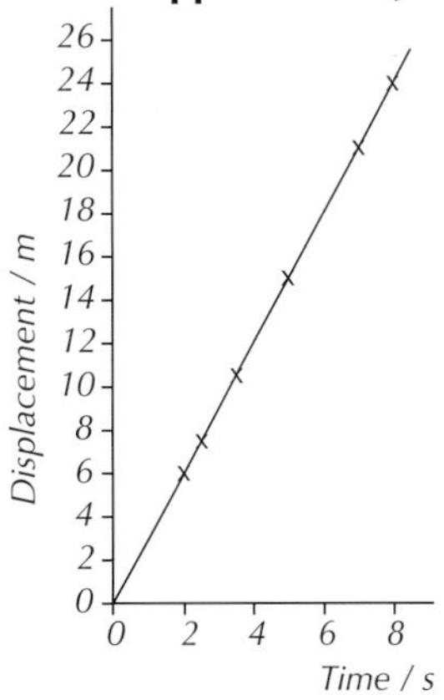

Q2 a) The cyclist is moving forwards at a constant velocity.

b) The cyclist is moving forwards but decelerating.

c) The cyclist isn't moving.

d) The cyclist is moving back towards the starting point at a constant velocity.

Q3 First find the rocket's acceleration:

$\boldsymbol{v} = \boldsymbol{u} + \boldsymbol{at} \Rightarrow \boldsymbol{a} = \frac{\boldsymbol{v} - \boldsymbol{u}}{t} = \frac{100.0 - 0}{5.0} = 20\ \text{ms}^{-2}$

Then work out the rocket's displacement at intervals with $\boldsymbol{s} = \boldsymbol{u}t + \frac{1}{2}\boldsymbol{a}t^2$:

t (s)	s (m)
0	0
1	10
2	40
3	90
4	160
5	250

Then plot the graph:

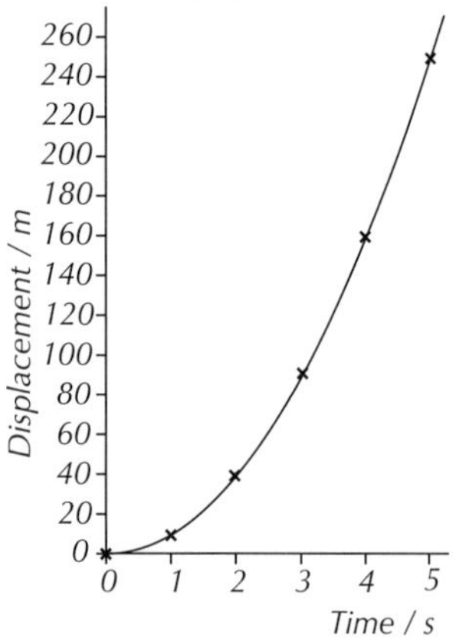

Q4 a)

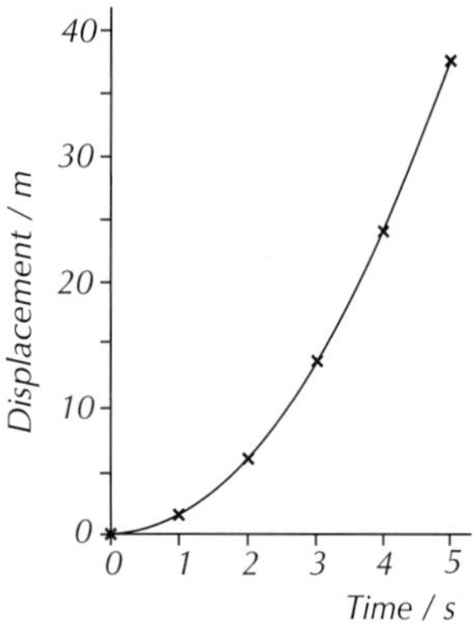

b) Draw a tangent at $t = 3.0$ and measure its gradient:

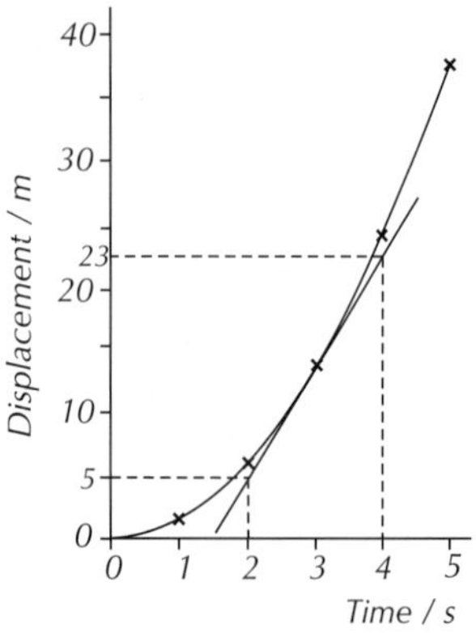

$v = \frac{\Delta y}{\Delta x} = \frac{23.0 - 5.0}{4.0 - 2.0} = \frac{18.0}{2.0} = \mathbf{9.0\ ms^{-1}}$

Page 52 — Fact Recall Questions

Q1 A curved line on a displacement-time graph shows acceleration (or deceleration).

Q2 A straight line on a displacement-time graph shows constant velocity.

Q3 Acceleration.

Q4 Instantaneous velocity.

Q5 Instantaneous velocity is an object's velocity at a particular moment in time, average velocity is the overall displacement divided by time taken.

Q6 Divide the overall change in displacement by time taken.

5. Velocity-Time Graphs

Page 56 — Application Question

Q1 Find the displacement by finding the area under the graph. To do this, split it into a triangle and a rectangle:

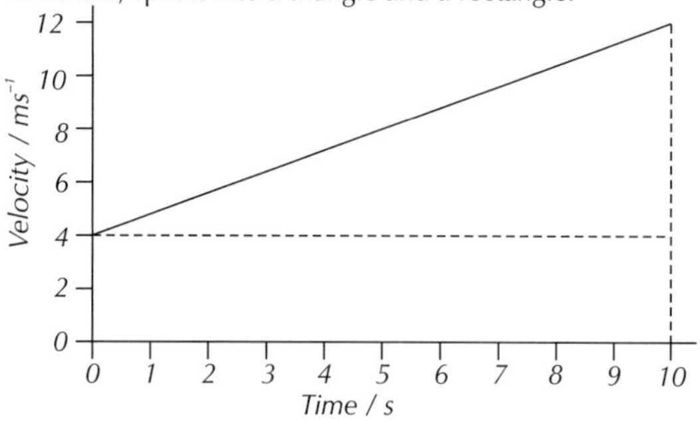

Area of triangle = ½ × base × height = ½ × 10 × 8 = 40

Area of rectangle = base × height = 10 × 4 = 40

So displacement = 40 + 40 = **80 m**

You could also treat it as a trapezium and work out the area directly using the formula for the area of a trapezium: area = ½(a + b) × h

Page 58 — Application Questions

Q1 a)

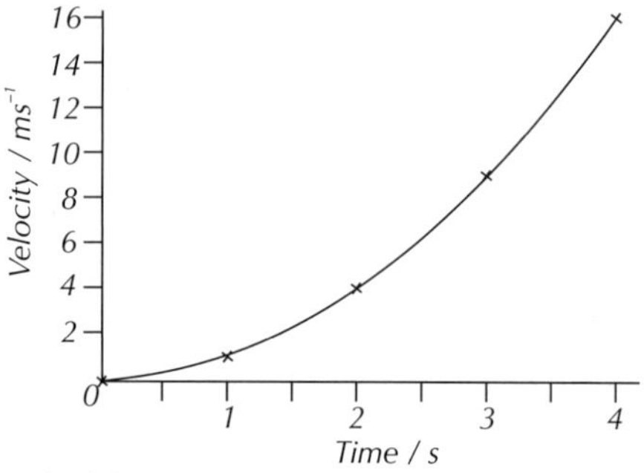

b) To find the acceleration, draw a tangent at $t = 2$ and find its gradient:

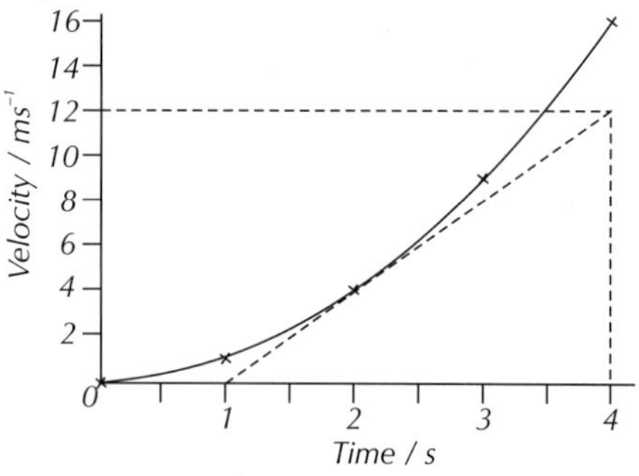

Acceleration $= \frac{\Delta y}{\Delta x} = \frac{12 - 0}{4 - 1} = \frac{12}{3} = \mathbf{4\ ms^{-2}}$

Q2

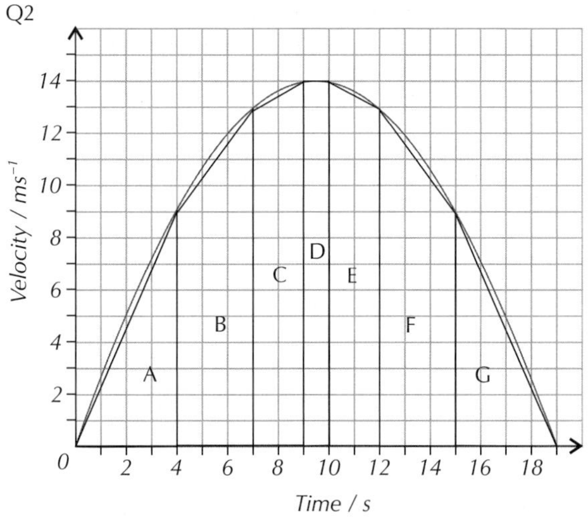

Area of first triangle (A) = ½(4 × 9) = 18 m
Area of first trapezium (B) = ½(9 + 13) × 3
= 33 m
Area of second trapezium (C) = ½(13 + 14) × 2
= 27 m
Area of rectangle (D) = 14 × 1 = 14 m
Area of third trapezium (E) = ½(14 + 13) × 2
= 27 m
Area of fourth trapezium (F) = ½(13 + 9) × 3
= 33 m
Area of second triangle (G) = ½((19 – 15) × 9) = 18 m
Total area = 18 + 33 + 27 + 14 + 27 + 33 + 18
= **170 m (accept 168 – 172 m)**

You'd still get the marks if you got the correct answer using a different method, for example if you counted the squares.

Page 58 — Fact Recall Questions

Q1 The gradient of a velocity-time graph tells you the acceleration.

Q2 Uniform acceleration on a velocity-time graph is shown by a straight line.

Q3 The area under a velocity-time graph tells you the displacement.

Q4 Non-uniform acceleration is shown on a velocity-time graph by a curved line.

6. Investigating Motion

Page 62 — Application Question

Q1 The ticker timer makes dots at a rate of 2 dots per second, so time between dots = 1 ÷ 2 = 0.5 s
Distance between dots = 7 cm = 0.07 m
$v = \frac{s}{t} = \frac{0.07}{0.5} = \mathbf{0.14\ ms^{-1}}$

Page 62 — Fact Recall Questions

Q1 E.g. light gates have a lower uncertainty than stopwatches because they do not depend on human reaction times.

Q2 E.g. Place a smooth ramp 1 m away from a wall. Place a metre rule along the 1 m flat stretch between the wall and the ramp. Set up a video camera to film the set-up from the side. Measure the length of a trolley, hold it in place on the ramp and begin filming. Let go of the trolley and let it roll down the ramp and hit the wall. Once the trolley has come to a stop, stop the recording. Use video analysis software to go through the video frame-by-frame, and count how many frames it takes for the trolley to completely pass a reference point on the meter rule before the collision. Use the frame rate of the video to find the time taken for the trolley to pass the reference point. Use this time and the length of the trolley to calculate the speed of the trolley. Repeat this video analysis for after the collision.

7. Stopping Distances

Page 64 — Application Questions

Q1 Stopping distance = 15 + 38 = **53 m**

Q2 Dahlia travels 14 m during her reaction time.
$s = vt$, so:
$t = s \div v$
= 14 ÷ 25
= **0.56 s**

Page 64 — Fact Recall Questions

Q1 The stopping distance is the distance covered by the vehicle in the time between the driver first spotting a hazard and the vehicle coming to a complete stop. It's the sum of the thinking distance and the braking distance.
The thinking distance is the distance the vehicle travels during the driver's reaction time.
The braking distance is the distance the vehicle travels after the brakes are applied until it comes to a complete stop.

Q2 Any three from: e.g. mass of the vehicle, ice (or water, oil, leaves etc.) on the road, quality of the tyres, quality of the vehicle's brakes, weather conditions.

Q3 a) Braking
b) Thinking
c) Thinking
d) Braking

Exam-style Questions — Page 66-68

1 C ***(1 mark)***
The equation of motion you would use is $s = \frac{1}{2}gt^2$ *as you know that the ball's initial velocity (*u*) is zero. So you need a value for* s *(distance from the starting point to the light gate) and* t *(time taken for the ball bearing to travel this distance).*

2 D ***(1 mark)***
Use thinking distance = speed × reaction time and stopping distance = thinking distance + braking distance.

3 B ***(1 mark)***
Use $v^2 = 2gs$*, where* $g = 9.81\ ms^{-2}$*, as initial velocity is zero.*

4 D ***(1 mark)***
The horizontal component of the velocity is 2.50 cos 60°.
The horizontal distance travelled is 3.00 × 2.50 cos 60°.

5 a) E.g. the student accelerates for the first 50 s. She then walks at a constant speed for 100 s, before decelerating to a stop in the next 75 s. ***(1 mark for correct description of motion and 1 mark for stating the correct times)***

b) total displacement = 250 m
total time taken = 225 s
average velocity = total displacement ÷ total time taken
= 250 ÷ 225
= 1.111... ms^{-1} = **1.1 ms^{-1} (to 2 s.f.)**
(2 marks for correct answer, otherwise 1 mark for correct working if answer incorrect)

6 a)

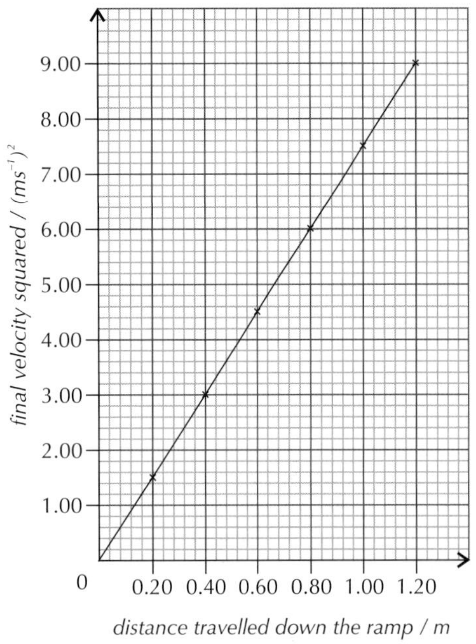

(1 mark for all points correctly plotted, 1 mark for line of best fit drawn correctly)

b) $\mathbf{v}^2 = \mathbf{u}^2 + 2\mathbf{as}$ and $\mathbf{u} = 0$, so $\mathbf{v}^2 = 2\mathbf{as}$
Equation of a straight line through the origin is $y = mx$.
Comparing $\mathbf{v}^2 = 2\mathbf{as}$ and $y = mx$, you can see that
$y = \mathbf{v}^2$, $x = \mathbf{s}$ and $m = 2\mathbf{a}$
so $\mathbf{a} = 0.5 \times m$
change in $y = 9.00 - 0 = 9.00\ (ms^{-1})^2$
change in $x = 1.20 - 0 = 1.20$ m
so $\mathbf{a} = 0.5 \times (9.00 \div 1.20)$
= **3.75 ms^{-2} (to 3 s.f.)**
(3 marks for correct answer, otherwise 1 mark for stating that gradient = 2a and 1 mark for correct working if answer incorrect)

Since the graph is a straight line, the acceleration is constant.

7 a) The cyclist's displacement is given by the area under the graph. To find this, split the area up:

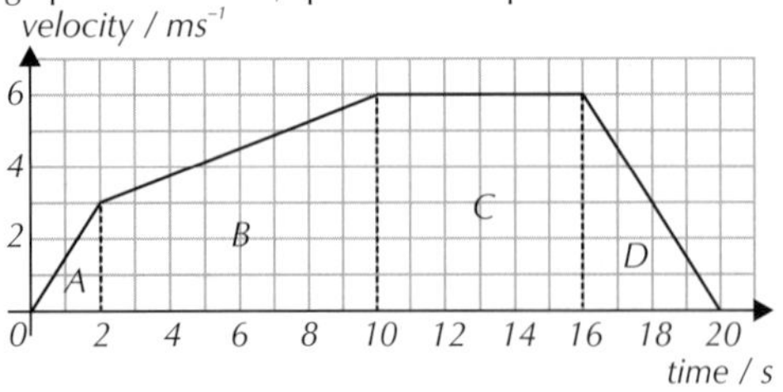

A: $\frac{1}{2} \times 2 \times 3 = 3$ m

B: $8 \times \frac{6+3}{2} = 36$ m

C: $6 \times 6 = 36$ m

D: $\frac{1}{2} \times 4 \times 6 = 12$ m

So displacement = 3 + 36 + 36 + 12 = **87 m**
(2 marks for correct answer, otherwise 1 mark for correct working if answer incorrect)

b) change in $y = 0 - 6 = -6\ ms^{-1}$
change in $x = 20 - 16 = 4$ s
gradient = change in y ÷ change in x
$= -6 \div 4 = -1.5\ ms^{-2}$
so acceleration = **–1.5 ms^{-2}**
(2 marks for correct answer, otherwise 1 mark for correct working if answer incorrect)

Remember, deceleration is just a negative acceleration.

c) $\mathbf{v}^2 = \mathbf{u}^2 + 2\mathbf{as}$
$\Rightarrow \mathbf{v} = \sqrt{(0)^2 + (2 \times 3.40 \times 22.5)}$
= 12.369... ms^{-1}
= **12.4 ms^{-1}(to 3 s.f.)**
(2 marks for correct answer, otherwise 1 mark for correct working if answer incorrect)

d) $\mathbf{v}^2 = \mathbf{u}^2 + 2\mathbf{as}$
$\Rightarrow \mathbf{v} = -\sqrt{(\sin 29.0° \times 6.50)^2 + (2 \times -9.81 \times -1.31)}$
= –5.969... ms^{-1} = **–5.97 ms^{-1} (to 3 s.f.)**
(2 marks for correct answer, otherwise 1 mark for correct working if answer incorrect)

Use the negative solution for **v** as it's travelling downwards when it hits the ground.

e) $\mathbf{v} = \mathbf{u} + \mathbf{a}t \Rightarrow t = \frac{\mathbf{v} - \mathbf{u}}{\mathbf{a}} = \frac{-5.969... - (\sin 29.0° \times 6.50)}{-9.81}$
= 0.9297... = **0.930 s (to 3 s.f.)**
(2 marks for correct answer, otherwise 1 mark for correct working if answer incorrect)

Section 2 — Forces in Action

1. Mass, Weight and Force Basics

Page 71 — Application Questions

Q1 $\mathbf{W} = m\mathbf{g}$, so:
$m = \mathbf{W} \div \mathbf{g}$
$= 7.75 \div 0.620$
= **12.5 kg**

Q2

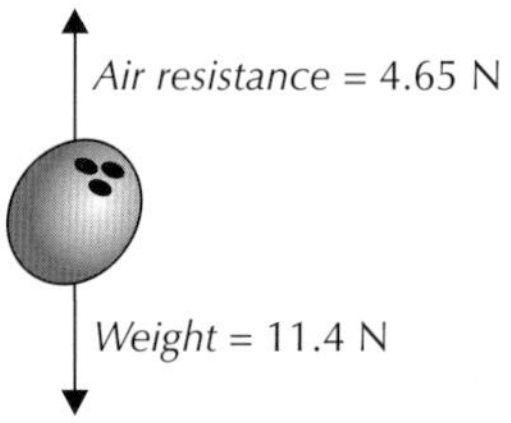

Page 71 — Fact Recall Questions

Q1 $\mathbf{W} = m\mathbf{g}$ / weight = mass × gravitational field strength
Q2 The centre of mass of an object is the single point that you can consider its whole weight to act through.
Q3 At the centre of the object.
Q4 upthrust
Q5 free-body diagram

2. Net Forces

Page 74 — Application Questions

Q1 $\mathbf{F} = m\mathbf{a} \Rightarrow \mathbf{F} = 24.1 \times 3.5 = 84.35$ N = **84 N (to 2 s.f.)**
Q2 $\mathbf{F} = m\mathbf{a} \Rightarrow m = \frac{\mathbf{F}}{\mathbf{a}} = \frac{18}{29} = 0.6206...$ kg = **0.62 kg (to 2 s.f.)**

Q3 a) First, find the net force in the north-south direction. Let north be positive and south be negative.
North-south force = 20.0 – 60.0 = –40.0 N
Next, draw a triangle of forces:

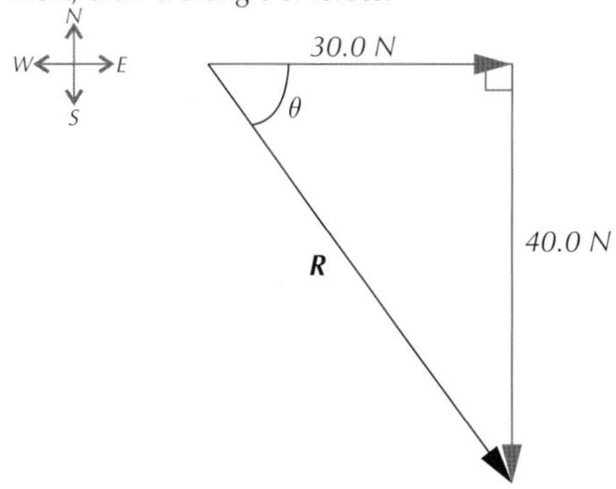

By Pythagoras' theorem:
$\boldsymbol{R} = \sqrt{30.0^2 + 40.0^2} = 50.0$ N
Find the direction of $\boldsymbol{R}$ as a clockwise angle from east.
$\theta = \tan^{-1}\left(\frac{40.0}{30.0}\right) = 53.13...° = 53.1°$ (to 3 s.f.)
So the net force is **50.0 N at 53.1° clockwise from east.**

b) $\boldsymbol{F} = m\boldsymbol{a}$
$\Rightarrow \boldsymbol{a} = \frac{50.0}{89.0} = 0.56179...\text{ms}^{-2} = \mathbf{0.562\ ms^{-2}}$ **(to 3 s.f.)**

Page 74 — Fact Recall Questions

Q1 The net force is the sum of all the forces acting on the object, accounting for their relative directions.

Q2 $\boldsymbol{F}$ = net force (N), m = mass (kg) and $\boldsymbol{a}$ = acceleration (ms^{-2}).

3. Equilibrium

Page 77 — Application Questions

Q1 Draw a scale diagram of the forces (e.g. using a scale of 1.0 cm = 1.0 N), joined up tip-to tail:

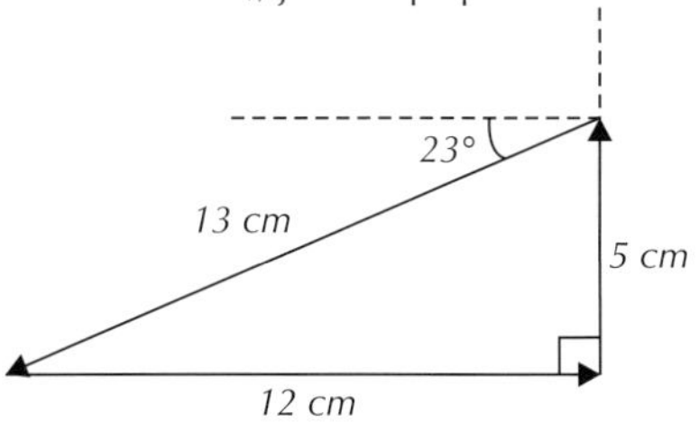

They form a closed triangle, so the object's in equilibrium.
This diagram has been shrunk to fit in the column — but you should draw it full-size.

Q2 Either:
Start by drawing the forces in a closed triangle:

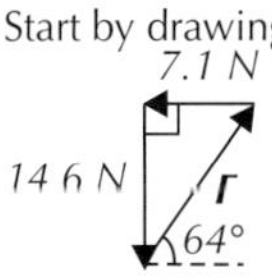

$\boldsymbol{F} = \sqrt{7.1^2 + 14.6^2} = 16.234...$ N = **16 N (to 2 s.f.)**
Or:
Use the horizontal components:
$(\cos 64° \times \boldsymbol{F}) - 7.1 = 0 \Rightarrow \boldsymbol{F} = \frac{7.1}{\cos 64°} = 16.196...$ N
= **16 N (to 2 s.f.)**
You could have also used vertical components, in which case you'd use Fsin 64° and 14.6 N instead.

Q3 Since the box is in equilibrium, the force $\boldsymbol{F}$ must have the same magnitude as the component of the 16 N force parallel to force $\boldsymbol{F}$.
So:
$\boldsymbol{F} = \sin 39° \times 16 = 10.069...$ N = **10 N (to 2 s.f.)**
You could also have used a triangle of forces to answer this question.

Page 77 — Fact Recall Questions

Q1 0 N

Q2 Splitting a force into two perpendicular components (usually horizontal and vertical).

4. Moments and Torques

Page 82 — Application Questions

Q1 $M = Fx = 73.1 \times 0.25 = 18.275$ Nm = **18 Nm (to 2 s.f.)**

Q2 Anticlockwise moment applied by child on left:
$M = Fx = 450.0 \times 1.50 = 675$ Nm
So clockwise moment applied by child on right = 675 Nm
$M = Fx \Rightarrow x = \frac{M}{F} = \frac{675}{500.0} = \mathbf{1.35\ m}$

Q3 a) weight $\boldsymbol{W} = m\boldsymbol{g} = 24\ 000 \times 9.81 = 235\ 440$ N
moment = $Fx = 235\ 440 \times 3.5 = 824\ 040$ kN m
= **820 kN m anticlockwise (to 2 s.f.)**
Don't forget to convert the mass in kg to weight in N before you calculate the moment.

b) clockwise moment about support =
$(55\ 000 \times 7.5) + (X \times 6.5) = 412\ 500 + 6.5X$
anticlockwise moment about support = 824 040 (you worked this out in part a)).
clockwise moments = anticlockwise moments, so
$412\ 500 + 6.5X = 824\ 040$
$X = \frac{824\ 040 - 412\ 500}{6.5} = 63\ 313.8...$ kN
= **63 kN (to 2 s.f.)**

Q4 $T = Fd \Rightarrow F = \frac{T}{d} = \frac{50.0}{0.35} = 142.85...$ N = **143 N (to 2 s.f.)**

Page 82 — Fact Recall Questions

Q1 A moment is the turning effect of a force around a turning point. It's the force × the perpendicular distance from the pivot to the line of action of the force.

Q2 A pair of forces of equal size which act parallel to each other but in opposite directions is called a couple.

5. Drag and Terminal Velocity

Page 86 — Application Questions

Q1 a) The ball starts with a large (positive) acceleration as it falls through the air. The acceleration is decreasing slightly (due to air resistance). After it hits the water it experiences a sudden deceleration, which decreases until the ball has reached terminal velocity (3.9 ms^{-1}). It then falls at a constant velocity until it hits the bottom of the cylinder.

b)

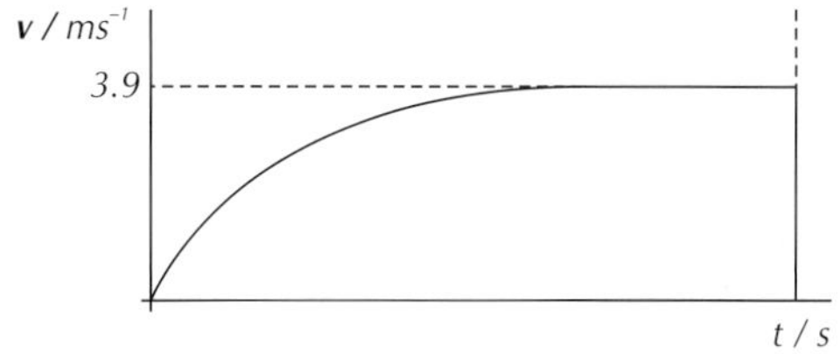

Q2 Air resistance on a car will increase with the car's speed until the frictional force balances the driving force. The larger the air resistance on the car, the lower the speed it will reach before the driving and frictional forces become balanced.

Page 86 — Fact Recall Questions

Q1 Friction is a force that opposes motion. Drag is the name given to friction caused by a fluid.

Q2 Friction acts in the opposite direction to the motion.

Q3 When an object reaches terminal velocity, the frictional forces are equal in size to the driving force(s) and in the opposite direction.

Q4 The correct graph is a).

Q5 Skydivers reduce their terminal velocity by using a parachute to increase the drag they experience.

Q6

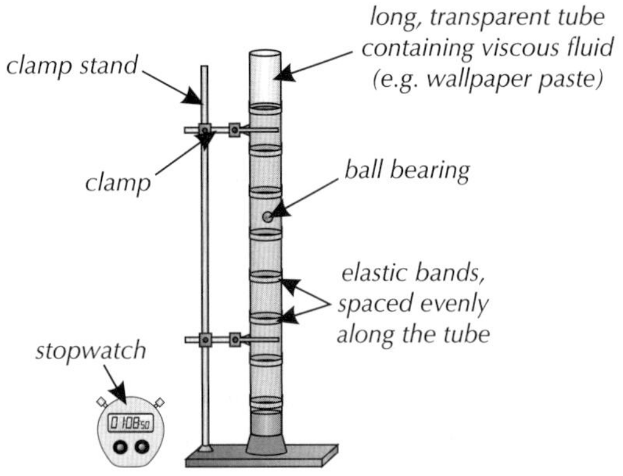

6. Density, Pressure and Upthrust

Page 89 — Application Questions

Q1 $\rho = \frac{m}{V} = \frac{360}{0.45} = \mathbf{800\ kg\,m^{-3}}$

Q2 $p = \frac{F}{A}$

so, $A = \frac{F}{p} = \frac{26\,500}{159\,000} = 0.1666...\ m^2 = \mathbf{0.167\ m^2\ (to\ 3\ s.f.)}$

Q3 $\rho = \frac{m}{V}$, so $m = \rho \times V$

$m = 2700 \times 9.1 \times 10^{-4} = 2.457\ kg = \mathbf{2.5\ kg\ (to\ 2\ s.f.)}$

Q4 $V = \frac{4}{3}\pi r^3 = \frac{4}{3}\pi(0.040)^3 = 2.68... \times 10^{-4}\ m^3$

$\rho = \frac{m}{V} = \frac{0.15}{2.68... \times 10^{-4}} = 559.52...\ kg\,m^{-3}$

$= \mathbf{560\ kg\,m^{-3}\ (to\ 2\ s.f.)}$

Q5 upthrust = $(h_2 - h_1)\rho g A$

Convert cm to m and g cm^{-3} to kg m^{-3}:

$h_2 = 0.760$ m, $h_1 = 0.650$ m, $r = 0.0500$ m,

$\rho = 1.00 \times 1000 = 1000$ kg m^{-3}

$A = \pi r^2 = \pi \times 0.0500^2$

upthrust = $(0.760 - 0.650) \times 1000 \times 9.81 \times (\pi \times 0.0500^2)$

= 8.47523... N

= **8.48 N (to 3 s.f.)**

Page 89 — Fact Recall Questions

Q1 $\rho = \frac{m}{V}$, where ρ = density, m = mass and V = volume.

Q2 The weight of the amount of water displaced by the object.

Q3 For the object to float in the fluid, the density of the object must be lower than the density of the fluid.

Exam-style Questions — Pages 91-93

1 C ***(1 mark)***

Calculate the mass of the object by dividing the weight on Earth by 9.81 ms^{-2}. Then divide the weight on Venus by the mass you calculated to find the gravitational field strength.

2 A ***(1 mark)***

3 B ***(1 mark)***

4 C ***(1 mark)***

Since the diagrams are to scale, you can just measure the distance between the forces for each couple, and use your measurements and the forces to calculate the torques.

5 a) E.g. Fill a glass tube that has been marked at regular intervals (e.g. with rubber bands) with liquid X. Drop a ball bearing into the tube ***(1 mark)***. Use a stopwatch to record the time at which it reaches each mark on the tube. Calculate the time taken by the ball to move between consecutive markings ***(1 mark)***. Use this and the distance between markings to calculate the velocity of the ball between each pair of markings. When the velocity becomes constant, the ball has reached its terminal velocity ***(1 mark)***.

b) mass of liquid = mass of full beaker – mass of empty beaker

= 862 – 250 = 612 g

$\rho = \frac{m}{V} = \frac{612}{450} = 1.36\ g\,cm^{-3} = \mathbf{1.4\ g\,cm^{-3}\ (to\ 2\ s.f.)}$

(2 mark for correct answer, 1 mark for correct method if answer incorrect)

c) Convert density into kgm^{-3} and height into m:

$\rho = 1360$ kgm^{-3}, $h = 0.040$ m

$p = h\rho g$

$= 0.040 \times 1360 \times 9.81$

$= 533.664$ Pa = **530 Pa (to 2 s.f.)**

(2 mark for correct answer, 1 mark for correct method if answer incorrect)

d) Apple floats, so upthrust is equal to the apple's weight.

mass of apple = 185 ÷ 1000 = 0.185 kg

upthrust = $\mathbf{W} = mg$

$= 0.185 \times 9.81$

= 1.8148... N = **1.81 N (to 3 s.f.)**

(2 marks for correct answer, 1 mark for correct method if answer incorrect)

6 a) The constant pulling forces on the dinghy cause it to accelerate. As the dinghy's velocity increases, the resistive force on the dinghy increases ***(1 mark)***. This causes the resultant force on the dinghy to decrease, so its acceleration decreases ***(1 mark)***. Eventually, the resistive force will equal the forwards components of the pulling forces, and the resultant force is 0. At this point, the dinghy stops accelerating, the velocity becomes constant, and the dinghy has reached terminal velocity ***(1 mark)***.

b)

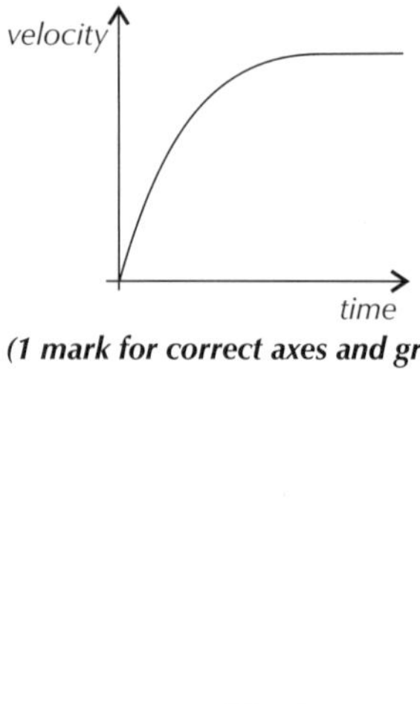

(1 mark for correct axes and graph shape)

c) At terminal velocity, the resultant force on the dingy is 0. So $\boldsymbol{F}$ must be equal to the sum of the forwards components of the 80.0 N forces.
forwards component of one 80.0 N force
$= \cos 15.0° \times 80.0$
So $\boldsymbol{F} = (\cos 15.0° \times 80.0) + (\cos 15.0° \times 80.0)$
$= 154.548...$ N = **155 N (to 3 s.f.)**
(2 marks for correct answer, 1 mark for correct method if answer incorrect)

d) $\boldsymbol{F} = m\boldsymbol{a}$
$\boldsymbol{a} = \boldsymbol{F} \div m = 154.548... \div 83.2$
$= 1.85754...$ ms^{-2} = **1.86 ms^{-2} (to 3 s.f.)**
(2 marks for correct answer, 1 mark for correct method if answer incorrect)

7 a) The moment of a force about a point/pivot is equal to the force × the perpendicular distance between the line of action of the force and the point/pivot ***(1 mark)***.

b) The front wheels will exert a greater force on the truck ***(1 mark)***. The distance between the front wheels and the centre of mass is shorter than between the rear wheels and the centre of mass, so the force exerted by the front wheels must be larger in order for moments to be balanced ***(1 mark)***.

c) If the front wheels feel no force, the clockwise moments must balance the anticlockwise moments about the pivot (rear wheels).
anticlockwise moments = clockwise moments
$\Rightarrow \boldsymbol{W} \times 0.65 = 21\,000 \times 2.4$
$\Rightarrow \boldsymbol{W} = \dfrac{21000 \times 2.4}{0.65} = 77538.4...$ N
= 78 000 N (to 2 s.f.)

(2 marks for correct answer, 1 mark for anticlockwise moments = clockwise moments if answer incorrect)

8 a) The centre of gravity is the single point through which all of an object's weight can be considered to act ***(1 mark)***.

b) Suspend the parrot from the edge by a string, and draw a straight line directly downwards from the string across the parrot, using a plumb bob to help ***(1 mark)***. Then move the string to a different position on the edge of the parrot, and repeat the previous step ***(1 mark)***. The parrot's centre of gravity is at the point where the two lines drawn intersect ***(1 mark)***.

c) Because cranes are tall they have a naturally high centre of mass. The base must therefore be heavy to lower the centre of mass ***(1 mark)*** and wide ***(1 mark)*** so that the centre of mass stays within the base area of the crane ***(1 mark)***.

Section 3 — Work, Energy and Power

1. Work and Power

Page 97 — Application Questions

Q1 $W = \boldsymbol{Fx} = 203 \times 2.81 = 570.43$ = **570 J (to 3 s.f.)**

Q2 $P = \boldsymbol{Fv} \Rightarrow \boldsymbol{F} = \dfrac{P}{\boldsymbol{v}} = \dfrac{60\,100}{34.7} = 1731.98...$ = **1730 N (to 3 s.f.)**

Q3 $W = \boldsymbol{Fx}\cos\theta = 371 \times 1.39 \times \cos 13.1° = 502.26...$
= **502 J (to 3 s.f.)**

Q4 Look at only the horizontal component of the force:
$P = \boldsymbol{Fv}\cos\theta = 83.1 \times 2.99 \times \cos 15.2° = 239.77...$
= **240 W (to 3 s.f.)**

Q5 a) $P = \dfrac{W}{t} = \dfrac{980\,000}{22} = 44\,545.4...$ = **45 kW (to 2 s.f.)**

b) $W = \boldsymbol{Fx}\cos\theta \Rightarrow \boldsymbol{x} = W \div (\boldsymbol{F}\cos\theta)$
$= 980\,000 \div (9500\cos 15°)$
$= 106.79...$
= **110 m (to 2 s.f.)**

Page 97 — Fact Recall Questions

Q1 Energy is transferred when work is done.

Q2 One joule is the work done when a force of 1 newton moves an object through a distance of 1 metre.

Q3 Power is the rate of doing work (or transferring energy).

Q4 Power = force × velocity (or $P = \boldsymbol{Fv}$)

2. Kinetic Energy and Gravitational Potential Energy

Page 99 — Application Questions

Q1 $E_p = mgh = 32.4 \times 9.81 \times 0.285 = 90.585...$
= **90.6 J (to 3 s.f.)**

Q2 $E_p = mgh$ where h is change in height.
Change in height = 890 – 760 = 130 m
So $E_p = 770 \times 9.81 \times 130 = 981\,981$
= **980 000 J** or **980 kJ (to 2 s.f.)**

Q3 $E_k = \frac{1}{2}mv^2 \Rightarrow m = \dfrac{2E_k}{v^2} = \dfrac{2 \times 150\,000}{16^2} = 1171.875$
= **1200 kg (to 2 s.f.)**

Page 99 — Fact Recall Questions

Q1 An object has kinetic energy when it is moving.

Q2 An object gains gravitational energy when it's lifted up in a gravitational field.

3. Conservation of Energy

Page 103 — Application Questions

Q1 $\text{efficiency} = \dfrac{\text{useful output energy}}{\text{total input energy}} \times 100$

$\Rightarrow \text{useful output energy} = \dfrac{\text{efficiency}}{100} \times \text{total input energy}$

$= \dfrac{20.0}{100} \times 2900 =$ **580 J**

Q2 $\frac{1}{2}mv^2 = mgh \Rightarrow h = \dfrac{v^2}{2g}$
$h = \dfrac{7.8^2}{2 \times 9.81} = 3.1009...$ = **3.1 m (to 2 s.f.)**

Q3 a) $E_p = mgh = 0.65 \times 9.81 \times 103 = 656.7...$
= **660 J (to 2 s.f.)**

b) $\frac{1}{2}mv^2 = 0.95 \times E_p \Rightarrow v = \sqrt{\dfrac{2 \times 0.95 \times 656.7...}{0.65}}$
$= 43.81...$ = **44 ms^{-1} (to 2 s.f.)**

c) $mgh = 0.800 \times \frac{1}{2}mv^2 \Rightarrow h = \dfrac{0.400v^2}{g}$
$= \dfrac{0.400 \times 43.81...^2}{9.81}$
$= 78.28$
= **78 m (to 2 s.f.)**

Even though the falcon has just converted gravitational potential energy into kinetic energy and back again, it's lost some height because some of the energy has been transferred to heat energy, sound, etc.

Page 103 — Fact Recall Questions

Q1 Energy cannot be created or destroyed. Energy can be transferred from one form to another but the total amount of energy in a closed system will not change.

Q2 How much of the input energy is transferred usefully by a system.

Exam-style Questions — Page 105

1 C *(1 mark)*

2 a) Gravity *(1 mark)*

b) $W = \mathbf{F}x\cos\theta = 660 \times 95 \times \cos 11°$
$= 61\ 548.02... = \mathbf{62\ kJ\ (to\ 2\ s.f.)}$
(2 marks — 1 mark for correct answer, 1 mark for correct substitutions.)

3 a) $E_k = \frac{1}{2}mv^2 = \frac{1}{2} \times 74.8 \times 6.5^2 = 1580.15$
$= \mathbf{1600\ J\ (to\ 2\ s.f.)}$
(2 marks for correct answer, 1 mark for correct working if answer incorrect)

b) The brakes do work against friction to convert all the E_k to other types of energy.
So energy transferred = $W = E_k = 1580.15$ J
$P = \frac{W}{t} = \frac{1580.15}{3.0} = 526.71...$
$= \mathbf{530\ W\ (to\ 2\ s.f.)}$
(2 marks for correct answer, 1 mark for correct working if answer incorrect)

c) $mgh = \frac{1}{2}mv^2 \Rightarrow gh = \frac{1}{2}v^2$
$\Rightarrow v = \sqrt{2 \times 9.81 \times 22.5}$
$= 21.010... = \mathbf{21.0\ ms^{-1}\ (to\ 3\ s.f.)}$
(2 marks for correct answer, 1 mark for correct working if answer incorrect)

Section 4 — Materials

1. Hooke's Law

Page 110 — Application Questions

Q1 1.60 cm = 0.0160 m
$\mathbf{F} = k\mathbf{x} = 1250 \times 0.0160 = \mathbf{20.0\ N}$

Q2 0.80 mm = 0.00080 m (= 8.0×10^{-4} m)
Rearrange $\mathbf{F} = k\mathbf{x}$ to get $k = \frac{\mathbf{F}}{\mathbf{x}}$

$$k = \frac{20}{8.0 \times 10^{-4}} = \mathbf{25\ 000\ Nm^{-1}}$$

Q3 a) extension = new length – original length
= 22.0 – 20.0 = 2.0 cm = **0.020 m**

b) Rearrange $\mathbf{F} = k\mathbf{x}$ to get $k = \frac{\mathbf{F}}{\mathbf{x}}$
$$k = \frac{55.0}{0.020} = \mathbf{2750\ Nm^{-1}}$$

Q4 First add the top, k_t, and bottom, k_b, spring constants for both sets of springs in series:
$$\frac{1}{k_s} = \frac{1}{k_t} + \frac{1}{k_b} = \frac{1}{80} + \frac{1}{60}$$
$$\Rightarrow k_s = 1 \div \left(\frac{1}{80} + \frac{1}{60}\right) = 34.285...\text{Nm}^{-1}$$

Add the combined spring constants for the left, k_l, and right, k_r, sides in parallel to get the overall combined spring constant:
$k_{combined} = k_l + k_r = 2 \times k_s = 2 \times 34.285... = 68.571...\ \text{Nm}^{-1}$
$= \mathbf{70\ Nm^{-1}\ (to\ 1\ s.f.)}$

Page 110 — Fact Recall Questions

Q1 $\mathbf{F} = k\mathbf{x}$. Where $\mathbf{F}$ is the force applied, k is the force constant and $\mathbf{x}$ is the extension.

Q2 The point beyond which force is no longer proportional to extension.

Q3 You would need to measure the original length before adding the weight, and the extended length once the weight has been added. Calculate the extension by subtracting the original length of the spring from its extended length.

2. Elastic and Plastic Deformation

Page 114 — Application Questions

Q1 $E = \frac{1}{2}\mathbf{F}\mathbf{x} = \frac{1}{2} \times 30 \times 1.2 \times 10^{-2} = \mathbf{0.18\ J}$

Q2 Work done = area under force-time graph
$= \frac{1}{2} \times 26 \times 10^{-3} \times 12 = 0.156\ \text{J} = \mathbf{0.16\ J\ (to\ 2\ s.f.)}$

Q3

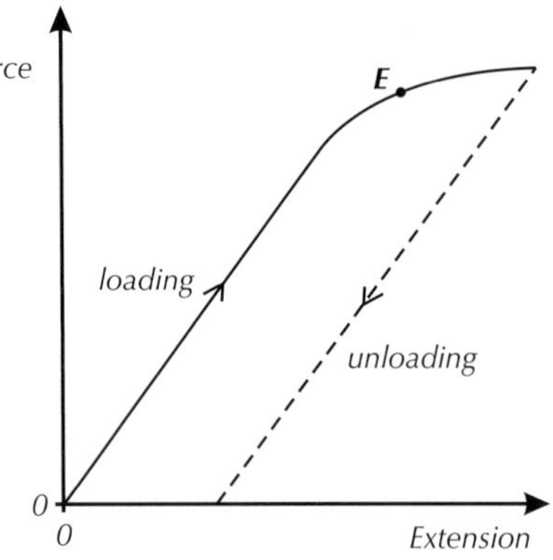

Q4 The band is elastic, because it returns to its original length (i.e. its extension is zero) after all the load has been removed.

Page 114 — Fact Recall Questions

Q1 The force (or load) beyond which a material will be permanently stretched.

Q2 A material that is deforming elastically returns to its original shape/length once the forces acting on it are removed.

Q3 A material that is deforming plastically is permanently stretched once the forces acting on it are removed.

Q4 The area between the two lines is the work done to permanently deform the material.

3. Stress and Strain

Page 116 — Application Questions

Q1 $\sigma = \frac{\mathbf{F}}{A} = \frac{50.0}{3.1 \times 10^{-6}} = 1.6129... \times 10^7$
$= \mathbf{1.6 \times 10^7\ Pa\ (or\ Nm^{-2})\ (to\ 2\ s.f.)}$

Q2 extension = new length – original length
= 12.3 – 12.0 = 0.3 cm
$\varepsilon = \frac{\mathbf{x}}{L} = \frac{0.3}{12.0} = \mathbf{0.025}$
Remember, there are no units for strain, as it is a ratio. Just make sure when working it out that the extension and original length are in the same units.

Q3 $\sigma = \frac{\mathbf{F}}{A}$
so $\mathbf{F} = \sigma \times A = (3.8 \times 10^8) \times (1.2 \times 10^{-7})$
$= 45.6 = \mathbf{46\ N\ (to\ 2\ s.f.)}$

Page 116 — Fact Recall Questions

Q1 a) The force applied to a material divided by its cross-sectional area.
b) The change in length divided by the original length of a material.
c) The stress that a material experiences when it breaks.
d) The maximum stress that a material can withstand before breaking.

4. The Young Modulus

Page 119 — Application Questions

Q1 a) 1.1 mm = 1.1×10^{-3} m

$$A = \pi\left(\frac{\text{diameter}}{2}\right)^2$$

$$= \pi\left(\frac{1.1 \times 10^{-3}}{2}\right)^2 = 9.503... \times 10^{-7}$$

$$= \mathbf{9.5 \times 10^{-7}\ m^2\ (to\ 2\ s.f.)}$$

b) $\boldsymbol{x}$ = 0.20 mm = 2.0×10^{-4} m

$\boldsymbol{F}$ = 23 N, L = 1.0 m, $A = 9.503... \times 10^{-7}$ m^2

$$E = \frac{FL}{Ax} = \frac{23 \times 1.0}{(9.503... \times 10^{-7}) \times (2.0 \times 10^{-4})}$$

$= 1.2101... \times 10^{11} =$ **1.2×10^{11} Pa (or Nm^{-2}) (to 2 s.f.)**

Q2 a) $\sigma = \frac{F}{A} = \frac{100}{8.0 \times 10^{-7}} = 1.25 \times 10^8$

= **1.3×10^8 Pa (to 2 s.f.)**

b) $E = \frac{\sigma}{\varepsilon}$ so $\varepsilon = \frac{1.25 \times 10^8}{3.5 \times 10^8} = 0.3571...$ = **0.36 (to 2 s.f.)**

Q3 energy per unit volume $= \frac{1}{2} \times 4\,200\,000 \times \frac{0.11}{254}$

= 909.44... = **910 Jm^{-3} (to 2 s.f.)**

Page 119 — Fact Recall Questions

Q1 Nm^{-2} or Pa.

Q2 Original length, extension, weights/load, diameter of wire (to find cross-sectional area).

Q3 E.g. wear safety goggles while carrying out the experiment / stand up so can move out of the way of falling weights.

Q4 The Young modulus of a material.

5. Stress-Strain Graphs

Page 124 — Application Questions

Q1 a) The elastic limit

b) The material is obeying Hooke's law.

c) Point C

d) The Young modulus is the gradient of the graph up to point A, so:

Young modulus = $(150 \times 10^6) \div 0.002$ = **7.5×10^{10} Pa**

Watch out for units — here the graph gives stress in MPa. You need to convert this into a value in Pa before you can calculate the Young modulus for the material.

e) Point A is the limit of proportionality. The energy stored per unit volume is given by the area under the graph up to Point A, which is $0.5 \times 0.002 \times 150$ = **0.15 MPa.**

Q2 Graph B shows a brittle material, as it is just a straight line. Graph A shows a material reaching its elastic limit and undergoing plastic deformation. Brittle materials don't deform plastically.

Page 124 — Fact Recall Questions

Q1 The stress at which a large amount of plastic deformation takes place with a constant or reduced load.

Q2 Any one of: e.g. polythene, rubber.

Q3 Yes. The stress-strain graph for a brittle material is a straight line through the origin, which shows it obeys Hooke's law.

Exam-style Questions — Pages 126-127

1 D ***(1 mark)***

$E = \sigma \div \varepsilon = FL \div Ax$

Read F from graph to be 10 N.

$\boldsymbol{F}$ = 10 N, L = 0.80 m, $\boldsymbol{x}$ = 0.080 m, $A = 5.0 \times 10^{-6}$ m^2

$E = (10 \times 0.80) \div (5 \times 10^{-6} \times 0.080)$

$= 2.0 \times 10^7$ Pa

2 A ***(1 mark)***

$F = kx \Rightarrow k = F \div x = 1.1 \div (5 \times 10^{-3})$

= 220 Nm^{-1}

$E = \frac{1}{2}kx^2 = \frac{1}{2} \times 220... \times 0.018^2$

= 0.0356... = 0.036 J (to 2 s.f.)

3 a) How to grade your answer (pick the description that best matches your answer):

0 marks: There is no relevant information.

1-2 marks: A diagram has been drawn, and method points 5, 7, 8 and 9 have been covered. Answer is basic and has lack of structure. Information is missing and there are few backed up arguments.

3-4 marks: A diagram has been drawn and most of the method points have been covered. Answer has some structure, and information is presented with a clear line of reasoning, with arguments that are partially backed up.

5-6 marks: A diagram has been drawn, all of the method points have been covered, and at least one point from the accuracy points have been covered. The answer is well structured. There is a clear and logical line of reasoning, with information and arguments that are fully backed up.

Here are some points your answer may include:

Apparatus

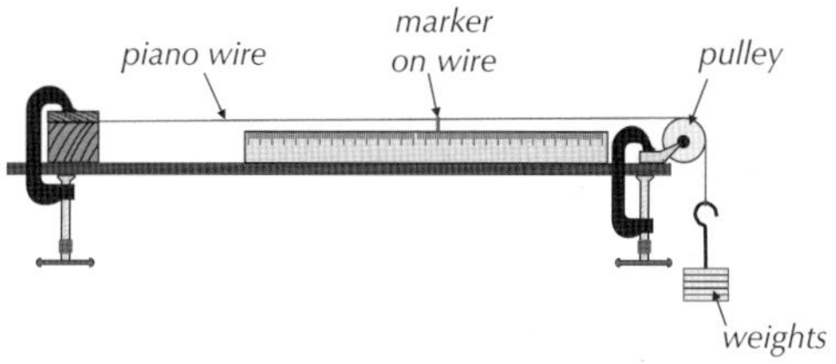

Method

1. Add just enough weight to the end of the wire to straighten it.
2. Measure the starting position of the marker on the wire.
3. Use a micrometer or vernier callipers to measure the diameter of wire.
4. Use $A = \pi r^2$ to calculate its cross-sectional area.
5. Add weights to the end of the wire in steps, recording the weight and the marker reading each time.
6. Calculate the extension of the wire after each weight is added by subtracting the original marker position from the current marker reading.
7. Calculate the stress on the wire at each step using $\sigma = \frac{F}{A}$ and the strain using $\varepsilon = \frac{x}{L}$.
8. Plot a stress-strain graph for the wire.
9. The Young modulus is equal to the gradient of the linear graph.

Reducing Error

1. Use a mass meter/digital scales to measure the weight of each weight used.
2. Measure the wire's diameter in at least three different places and take an average.
3. Use a long piece of wire to give a large extension and reduce uncertainty.
4. Use a thin marker on the wire to reduce random errors.
5. Keep the marker and ruler at eye level when measuring the extension.
6. Use a travelling microscope to view the position of the marker when measuring extension.
7. As wire is unloaded, re-measure the extension for each weight, and average your results (as long as you haven't gone past the elastic limit).

b) Young modulus $= \text{gradient} = \dfrac{\Delta\text{stress}}{\Delta\text{strain}}$

$$= \frac{5.0 \times 10^{8}}{3.0 \times 10^{-3}}$$
$$= 1.666... \times 10^{11}\,\text{Pa}$$
$$= \mathbf{1.7 \times 10^{11}\,Pa\ (to\ 2\ s.f.)}$$

(2 marks for the correct answer, otherwise 1 mark for the correct working.)

You could also give your answer in MPa, GPa, or Nm^{-2}.

c) Elastic potential energy per unit volume
$= \text{area under graph} = \frac{1}{2} \times 1.8 \times 10^{-3} \times 3.0 \times 10^{8}$
$= 270\,000\ Jm^{-3}$
Volume of wire $= 1.0 \times 10^{-7} \times 1.6 = 1.6 \times 10^{-7}\ m^3$
So elastic potential energy stored in wire
$= 270\,000 \times 1.6 \times 10^{-7} = 0.0432$ J = **0.043 J (to 2 s.f.)**
(3 marks for the correct answer, otherwise 1 mark for correctly calculating the area under the graph, and 1 mark for correctly calculating the volume of the wire.)

4 a) $E = \frac{\sigma}{\varepsilon} = \frac{FL}{Ax} \Rightarrow A = \frac{FL}{Ex}$
$F = 2.0$ kN $= 2000$ N, $L = 2.0$ m, $E = 2.10 \times 10^{11}$ Pa,
$x = 0.20$ mm $= 2.0 \times 10^{-4}$ m
$$A = \frac{2000 \times 2.0}{(2.10 \times 10^{11}) \times (2.0 \times 10^{-4})} = 9.523... \times 10^{-5}$$
$$= \mathbf{9.5 \times 10^{-5}\,m^2\ (to\ 2\ s.f.)}$$
(2 marks for correct answer, otherwise 1 mark for correct working)

b) E.g.

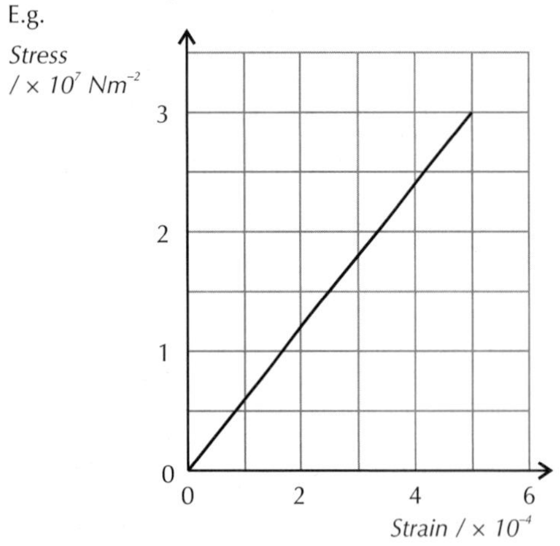

(1 mark for graph showing straight line passing through origin, 1 mark for graph ending at breaking stress, 1 mark for gradient equal to Young modulus)

Section 5 — Newton's Laws of Motion and Momentum

1. Newton's Laws of Motion

Page 130 — Application Questions

Q1

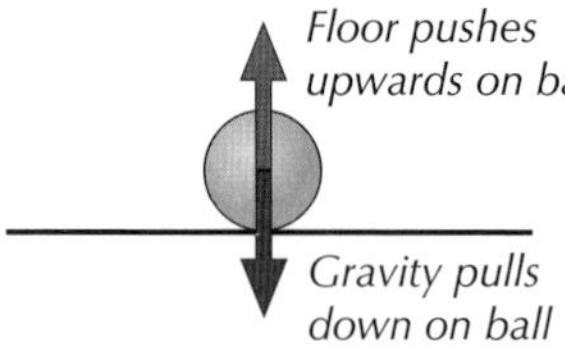

Q2 The rocket is burning through its fuel stores, so is losing mass in the form of fuel. $F = ma$ cannot be used since it requires the mass of the object to remain constant.

Q3 When a bird flaps its wings it pushes down on the air. The air then pushes back up on the bird's wings with the same force, which causes it to lift.

Q4 Rearranging $F = ma$:
$m = \frac{F}{a} = \frac{780}{0.41} = 1902.439... =$ **1900 kg (to 2 s.f.)**

Q5 First find the force they push each other with:
$\mathbf{F} = m \times \mathbf{a} = 60.0 \times 2.3 = 138$ N
Then find the acceleration of the other skater:
$\mathbf{F} = m \times \mathbf{a} \Rightarrow \mathbf{a} = \frac{F}{m} = \frac{138}{55.0} = 2.5090...$ = **2.5 ms⁻² (to 2 s.f.)**

Page 130 — Fact Recall Question

Q1 Newton's 1st law: The velocity of an object won't change unless a resultant force acts on it. This means a body will stay still or move in a straight line at a constant speed unless there's a resultant force acting on it.
Newton's 2nd law: Net force = change in momentum ÷ change in time. This means a larger force acting on an object over a given time causes a larger change in the momentum of the object.
Newton's 3rd law: If object A exerts a force on object B, then object B exerts an equal but opposite force on object A. This means every action has an equal and opposite reaction.

2. Momentum

Page 134 — Application Questions

Q1 Momentum before = Momentum after
$0 = (125 \times \mathbf{v}) + (1.0 \times 10) = 125\mathbf{v} + 10$
$\mathbf{v} = -10 \div 125 = -0.08\ ms^{-1}$
So the boat moves at **$0.08\ ms^{-1}$** in the opposite direction to the rock.

Q2 Momentum before = Momentum after
$(0.165 \times 2.25) + (0.165 \times -4.75) = (0.165 \times -4.25) + (0.165 \times \mathbf{v})$
$-0.4125 = -0.70125 + 0.165\mathbf{v}$
So $\mathbf{v} = \mathbf{1.75\ ms^{-1}}$
Kinetic energy before:
$= (0.5 \times 0.165 \times 2.25^2) + (0.5 \times 0.165 \times (-4.75)^2)$
$= 2.2790...$ J
Kinetic energy after:
$= (0.5 \times 0.165 \times (-4.25)^2) + (0.5 \times 0.165 \times (1.75)^2)$
$= 1.7428...$ J
Kinetic energy is not conserved, so this is an inelastic collision.

Q3 Mass (per second) = density × volume (per second)
= 1000 × (8.4 × 10^{-3})
= 8.4 kg

To find the velocity of the water, consider the length of the cylinder of water shot out of the hose per second. This gives you the distance travelled per second.

$$\text{Velocity} = \frac{\text{volume of water (per second)}}{\text{cross–sectional area of hose}}$$
$$= \frac{8.4 \times 10^{-3}}{5.6 \times 10^{-4}}$$
$$= 15\ \text{ms}^{-1}$$

Linear momentum = mass × velocity
= 8.4 × 15
= 126 = **130 kgms^{-1} (to 2 s.f.)**

Page 134 — Fact Recall Questions

Q1 Linear momentum = mass × velocity / $\boldsymbol{p} = m\boldsymbol{v}$

Q2 Linear momentum is always conserved — i.e. the total linear momentum is the same before and after a collision (provided no external forces act).

Q3 A perfectly elastic collision is one where linear momentum and kinetic energy are conserved. An inelastic collision is one where linear momentum is conserved, but kinetic energy is not.
Some kinetic energy is lost to the surroundings and/or converted to other forms (such as heat and sound).

3. Impulse and Vehicle Safety

Page 138 — Application Questions

Q1 Impulse = area under force–time graph
= ½ × 10 × 10^{-3} × 300 = **1.5 Ns**

Q2 Rigid materials don't deform very easily, so a large proportion of the energy involved in the crash is transferred elsewhere instead of being absorbed.

Q3 a) The seat belt increases the time that the dummy takes to come to a stop by stretching. Since force is equal to change in momentum over time taken, this reduces the overall force. It also slows the dummy down so that it hits the airbag with less force.

b) Air bags inflate very rapidly, with a lot of force. Without a seat belt, the passenger can keep moving forwards quickly as the car slows down. They could hit the air bag as it is inflating with a force big enough to cause injury.

Q4 Velocity in ms^{-1} = (125 × 1000) ÷ 3600 = 34.7222... ms^{-1}
There are 1000 m in a km and 3600 seconds in an hour.

$$\boldsymbol{F} = \frac{\Delta \boldsymbol{p}}{\Delta t} = \frac{\Delta(m\boldsymbol{v})}{\Delta t}$$
$$\Delta t = \frac{m\boldsymbol{v} - m\boldsymbol{u}}{\boldsymbol{F}}$$
$$= \frac{(18\,000 \times 0) - (18\,000 \times 34.7222...)}{-62\,000}$$
$$= 10.080... = \mathbf{10\ s\ (to\ 2\ s.f.)}$$

Page 138 — Fact Recall Questions

Q1 The product of average force and time / the change in momentum of a body.

Q2 Air bags rapidly inflate on collision, providing a cushion which increases the time it takes for the passenger to slow down, and so reduces the force on the passenger. It also prevents them from hitting hard surfaces inside the car.

Q3 Seat belts can cause bruising during a crash, and can be dangerous for small children if booster seats aren't used.

Q4 E.g. crumple zones at the front and back of cars crumple up on impact. This causes the car to take longer to stop, increasing the impact time and decreasing the force on the passengers.

Exam-style Questions — Pages 140-141

1 C ***(1 mark)***
When the ball is fired, the cannon moves backwards and the ball is shot forwards, conserving momentum. Before the ball is fired, the kinetic energy is 0 J as neither object is moving, so point 1 cannot be correct. The cannon has a much larger mass than the ball, so for a given force it has a smaller acceleration than the ball (using F = ma) so point 3 cannot be correct.

2 C ***(1 mark)***
For a scenario to show Newton's Third Law, it has to show a pair of identical forces that act on two separate objects.

3 B ***(1 mark)***
Take the direction that the first ball, of mass 0.25 kg, is travelling in to be the positive direction.
Momentum of first ball = mv = 0.25 × 1.2 = 0.3 kg ms^{-1}.
Mass of second ball = 0.25 ÷ 2 = 0.125 kg.
Momentum of second ball = 0.125 × −0.3 = −0.0375 kg ms^{-1}.
So total momentum before collision
= 0.3 − 0.0375 = 0.2625 kg ms^{-1}.
After the collision, the balls move together so the mass is 0.25 + 0.125 = 0.375 kg.
$p = mv$ so $v = p \div m = 0.2625 \div 0.375 = 0.7$ ms^{-1}.

4 a) The rate of change of momentum of an object is equal to the net force which acts on the object.
$\boldsymbol{F} = \dfrac{\Delta \boldsymbol{p}}{\Delta t}$ ***(1 mark)***

b) $\boldsymbol{F} = \dfrac{\Delta \boldsymbol{p}}{\Delta t} = \dfrac{\Delta(m\boldsymbol{v})}{\Delta t}$

So, $\boldsymbol{F}\Delta t = \Delta(m\boldsymbol{v})$
$\boldsymbol{F}\Delta t$ is constant for both cases, so:
$\Delta(m\boldsymbol{v})_1 = \Delta(m\boldsymbol{v})_2$
$\Rightarrow m_1 \Delta \boldsymbol{v}_1 = m_2 \Delta \boldsymbol{v}_2$
m_1 = 1000 kg, $\Delta \boldsymbol{v}_1$ = 31 − 26.5 = 4.5 ms^{-1} ,
m_2 = 1000 − 50 = 950 kg
So, $\Delta \boldsymbol{v}_2 = \dfrac{m_1 \Delta \boldsymbol{v}_1}{m_2} = \dfrac{1000 \times 4.5}{950}$ = 4.7368... ms^{-1}
So, final velocity = 26.5 + 4.7368...
= 31.2368...
= **31.2 ms^{-1} (to 3 s.f.)**
(2 marks for correct answer, otherwise 1 mark for correct working)

5 a) E.g. this is an inelastic collision ***(1 mark)*** because kinetic energy is not conserved — some is converted to sound energy ***(1 mark)***.

b) Impulse is equal to the change in momentum.
Momentum before = (325 × 2.40) = 780 kgms^{-1}
Momentum after = 0
So magnitude of impulse = **780 kgms^{-1}**
(2 marks for correct answer, otherwise 1 mark for correct working.)

c) If the dodgem's initial speed was doubled, its initial momentum would be doubled, and therefore the impulse would be doubled:
Impulse = 780 × 2 = **1560 kgms^{-1}** ***(1 mark)***

For parts b) and c), you could also give your answer in units of Ns.

d) Say right is positive direction.
Horizontal momentum before collision
= horizontal momentum after collision.
$m \times (5.1 \sin 42° + 0) = m \times (-1.5 \sin 25° + v_B \sin 59°)$
Cancelling m:
$5.1 \sin 42° = -1.5 \sin 25° + v_B \sin 59°$
$\Rightarrow v_B = \frac{5.1 \sin 42° + 1.5 \sin 25°}{\sin 59°} = 4.720...$
$= \mathbf{4.7\ ms^{-1}}$ **(to 2 s.f.)**
(2 marks for correct answer, otherwise 1 mark for correct working.)
You could also work this out using vertical momentum conservation.

6 a) Divide into three sections:

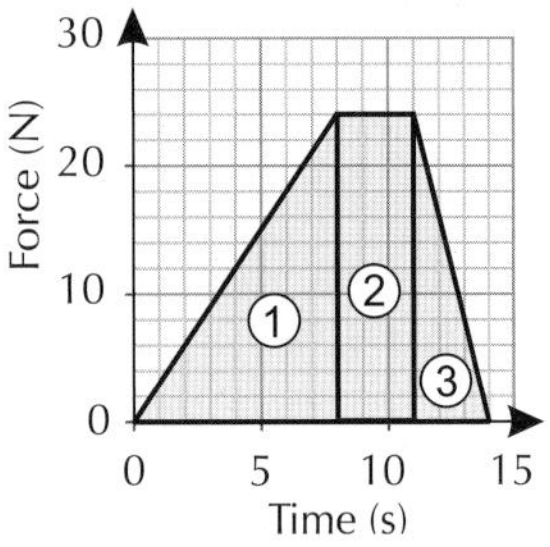

So the total area under the graph
= area 1 + area 2 + area 3
= (½ × 8 × 24) + (3 × 24) + (½ × 3 × 24) = **204 Ns**
(2 marks for correct answer, otherwise 1 mark for calculating the area under the graph)

b) $\Delta \mathbf{p} = \Delta(m\mathbf{v}) = \mathbf{F}\Delta t$
Rearranging:
$m = \frac{F\Delta t}{\Delta v} = \frac{204}{2.2} = 92.727... =$ **93 kg (to 2 s.f.)**
(2 marks for correct answer, otherwise 1 mark for correct working)

c) E.g. There is no resultant force acting on it, as friction is assumed to be negligible, so Newton's First Law states that the velocity of the trolley will not change ***(1 mark)***.

Module 4

Section 1 — Electricity

1. Circuit Diagrams

Page 142 — Application Questions

Q1

Q2 E.g.

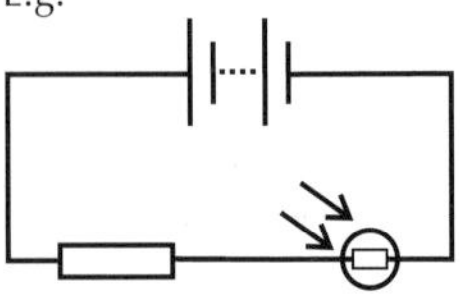

2. Current

Page 145 — Application Questions

Q1 $4e = 4 \times 1.60 \times 10^{-19} = \mathbf{6.4 \times 10^{-19}\ C}$

Q2 $I = \Delta Q \div \Delta t = 91 \div 32 = 2.84375 =$ **2.8 A (to 2 s.f.)**

Q3 $v = I \div Ane$
$= 12 \div (0.50 \times 10^{-6} \times 8.5 \times 10^{28} \times 1.60 \times 10^{-19})$
$= 0.00176... = \mathbf{0.0018\ ms^{-1}}$ **(to 2 s.f.)**

Page 145 — Fact Recall Questions

Q1 Current is the rate of flow of charge.

Q2 From positive to negative.

Q3 An electrically charged particle that is free to move in an object.

Q4 1.60×10^{-19} C

Q5 Zero

Q6 Any one from: e.g. increase the cross-sectional area of the wire, increase the number density of charge carriers/electrons in the wire, increase the mean drift velocity of the charge carriers/electrons (by increasing the p.d. across the wire).

3. Potential Difference

Page 147 — Application Questions

Q1 $V = W \div Q = 114 \div 56.0 = 2.035... =$ **2.04 V (to 3 s.f.)**

Q2 $VQ = ½mv^2$ so $V = mv^2 \div 2Q$
$V = (6.64 \times 10^{-27} \times (2.20 \times 10^4)^2) \div (2 \times 2 \times 1.60 \times 10^{-19})$
= 5.0215 V = **5.02 V (to 3 s.f.)**

Page 147 — Fact Recall Questions

Q1 The potential difference between two points is the work done to move a unit charge between those two points.

Q2 In parallel across the component.

Q3 $eV = ½mv^2$ where e = elementary charge, V = potential difference, m = mass of the electron and v = final velocity of the electron.

4. Resistance and Resistivity

Page 151 — Application Questions

Q1 $V = I \times R = 2.10 \times 8.62 = 18.102 =$ **18.1 V (to 3 s.f.)**

Q2 $R = V \div I = 13.4 \div 1.21 = 11.074... =$ **11.1 Ω (to 3 s.f.)**

Q3 $R = \rho L \div A = (1.72 \times 10^{-8} \times 0.40) \div (2.8 \times 10^{-5})$
$= 2.457... \times 10^{-4}\ \Omega = \mathbf{2.5 \times 10^{-4}\ \Omega}$ **(to 2 s.f.)**

Q4 Gradient = $\Delta y \div \Delta x = (0.10 \times 10^{-3}) \div 0.30 = 0.00033...$
Cross-sectional area = $\pi r^2 = \pi \times 0.004^2 = 0.0000502...$
Resistivity = gradient × cross-sectional area
= 0.00033... × 0.0000502...
$= 1.675... \times 10^{-8} = \mathbf{1.7 \times 10^{-8}\ \Omega m}$ **(to 2 s.f.)**

Page 151 — Fact Recall Questions

Q1 The resistance of something is a measure of how difficult it is to get a current to flow through it.
It is defined as $R = V \div I$.

Q2 Area = πr^2, assuming the wire is cylindrical, so that the cross-section of the wire is circular.

Q3 Use a test wire of the metal to be investigated, with a known cross-sectional area. Clamp the test wire to a ruler so that one end is aligned with the zero-mark. Connect this wire in a circuit with a power supply, an ammeter and a voltmeter. Use a flying lead to connect the test wire, so the length of test wire connected in the circuit can be varied. Connect the flying lead to the wire and record the length of the wire in the circuit. Measure the current through and potential difference across the wire and use these to calculate the resistance of that particular length of wire. Repeat this process at least once more for the same length of wire and use the values to calculate an average resistance for this length of wire. Repeat this process for different lengths of wire and plot a graph of average resistance against length. Use this graph to calculate the resistivity of the wire material by finding the gradient and multiplying it by the cross-sectional area of the wire.

Q4 Resistivity is dependent on temperature, so the temperature must be kept constant so that it doesn't affect the results of the experiment (it can cause errors). As current flows through a wire, it causes the temperature of the wire to increase. The temperature could be kept constant by ensuring only a small current is used. A switch can also be used to ensure that current is only flowing through the wire in short bursts.

5. Types of Conductor

Page 154 — Fact Recall Questions

Q1 Nothing — the resistance of an ohmic conductor is constant (if the physical conditions it's under are constant).

Q2 Temperature.

Q3

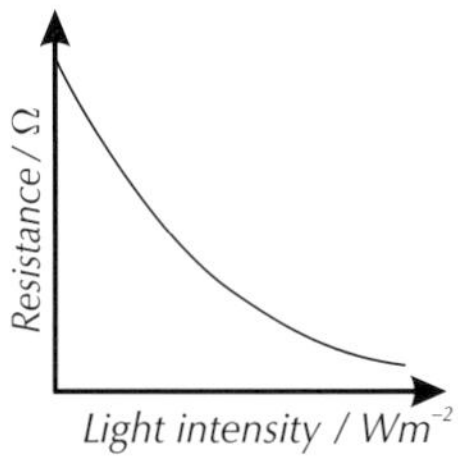

6. *I-V* Characteristics

Page 157 — Application Question

Q1 a) a diode / LED

b) The diode requires a voltage of about 0.6 V in the forward bias before it will conduct, so there is no current flow until about 0.6 V on the diagram. After 0.6 V, the current is allowed to flow, and increases with an increase in potential difference.

c) In reverse bias, the resistance of the diode is very high.

Page 157 — Fact Recall Questions

Q1 A voltmeter is assumed to have infinite resistance and an ammeter is assumed to have zero resistance.

Q2 a)

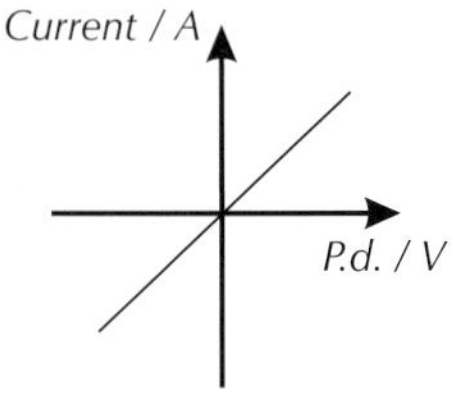

b)

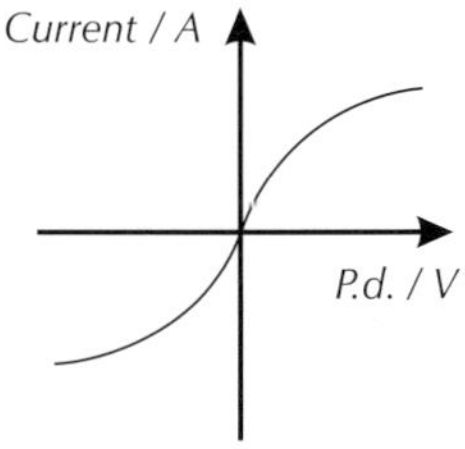

Q3 A filament lamp is not an ohmic conductor. Its *I-V* characteristic is not a straight line — so current is not proportional to potential difference.

7. Power and Electrical Energy

Page 160 — Application Questions

Q1 **3400 W** (3.4 kW)

Power is defined as the energy transfer per second. It's measured in watts, where 1 watt is equal to 1 joule per second.

Q2 a) $P = \frac{W}{t} = \frac{12\,500}{2.00} = \mathbf{6250\ W}$

b) $I = \frac{P}{V} = \frac{6250}{8.00} = 781.25 = \mathbf{781\ A\ (to\ 3\ s.f.)}$

Q3 $P = \frac{V^2}{R}$, so rearranging: $R = \frac{V^2}{P}$

$R = \frac{230^2}{5200} = 10.173... = \mathbf{10\ \Omega\ (to\ 2\ s.f.)}$

Q4 $W = VIt = 230 \times 1.2 \times 45 = 12\,420 = \mathbf{12\,000\ J\ (to\ 2\ s.f.)}$

Q5 $P = 1250$ W

$P = I^2R$, so rearranging: $I = \sqrt{\frac{P}{R}}$

$I = \sqrt{\frac{1250}{54.2}} = 4.8023... = \mathbf{4.80\ A\ (to\ 3\ s.f.)}$

Page 160 — Fact Recall Questions

Q1 Power is the rate of transfer of energy (or doing work). It's measured in watts (W), where 1 watt is equivalent to 1 joule per second.

Q2 E.g. $P = VI$, $P = \frac{V^2}{R}$, $P = I^2R$

Q3 $W = VIt$

8. Domestic Electricity

Page 162 — Application Questions

Q1 1 kWh = 3.6×10^6 J

So, energy transferred in kWh,

$W = 72\,000 \div (3.6 \times 10^6) = \mathbf{0.02\ kWh}$

Q2 Cost = number of units × price per unit

So, number of units = cost ÷ price per unit

£28.24 = 2824p

number of units = 2824 ÷ 12.2

= 231.47... = **231 units (to 3 s.f.)**

9. E.m.f. and Internal Resistance

Page 167 — Application Questions

Q1 $\varepsilon = V + v$, so $v = \varepsilon - V = 2.50 - 2.24 = \mathbf{0.26\ V}$

Q2 $\varepsilon = V + Ir = 4.68 + (0.63 \times 0.89) = 5.2407$

$= \mathbf{5.2\ V\ (to\ 2\ s.f.)}$

Q3 $\varepsilon = I(R + r)$, so $\varepsilon \div I = R + r$ and so $R = (\varepsilon \div I) - r$

$R = (15.0 \div 26.1) - 8.28 \times 10^{-3} = 0.566432...$

$= \mathbf{0.566\ \Omega\ (to\ 3\ s.f.)}$

Q4 $P = I^2R = (1.2)^2 \times 0.50 = 0.72$ W

So **0.72 J** is dissipated each second.

Q5 a) $\varepsilon = \mathbf{5.0\ V}$

The e.m.f. is the intercept on the vertical axis.

b) internal resistance = –gradient of the graph

$= -(\Delta y \div \Delta x)$

e.g. internal resistance = –(–5.0 ÷ 0.6)

= 8.333...

= **8.3 Ω (to 2 s.f.)**

c) The straight line would still have the same *y*-intercept at 5.0 V. The gradient = $-r$, so the gradient would be half as steep as that for the original power supply, so it would intercept the *x*-axis at 1.2 A.

Page 167 — Fact Recall Questions

Q1 The load resistance is the total resistance of all the components in the external part of the circuit.
The load resistance doesn't include the internal resistance of the power source.

Q2 volts (V)

Q3 The energy wasted per coulomb overcoming an internal resistance.

Q4 The gradient is $-r$ (where r is the internal resistance) and the vertical intercept is ε (the electromotive force).

10. Conservation of Energy and Charge in Circuits

Page 171 — Application Questions

Q1 a) $R = R_1 + R_2 + R_3$
$40\ \Omega = R_1 + 20\ \Omega + 10\ \Omega$
$R_1 = 40 - 20 - 10 =$ **10 Ω**

b) 0.4 A
The current flowing through a series circuit is the same at all points of the circuit.

Q2 a) First calculate the total resistance of the 3 Ω and 6 Ω resistors in parallel, using $\frac{1}{R} = \frac{1}{R_1} + \frac{1}{R_2}$

$\frac{1}{R} = \frac{1}{3} + \frac{1}{6} = \frac{1}{2}$, so $R = 2\ \Omega$

Resistors in series add up and the total resistance is 10 Ω, so the total resistance of the 12 Ω and R_1 resistors in parallel is equal to: $10\ \Omega - 2\ \Omega - 5\ \Omega = 3\ \Omega$
The 5 Ω here is the resistance of the resistor in between the two sets of parallel resistors.

So for the R_1 resistor and the 12 Ω resistor in parallel, the total resistance is 3 Ω. So:

$\frac{1}{3} = \frac{1}{R_1} + \frac{1}{12}$

$\frac{1}{R_1} = \frac{1}{3} - \frac{1}{12} = \frac{1}{4}$, so $R_1 =$ **4 Ω**

b) First find the total current through the circuit, using the total resistance and the source p.d.
$I = V \div R$
$I = 12 \div 10 = 1.2$ A
This current flows through the 5 Ω resistor, so find the p.d. across this resistor using:
$V = I \times R = 1.2 \times 5 =$ **6 V**

c) The p.d. across the resistors in parallel (3 Ω and 6 Ω) is:
$V = I \times R = 1.2 \times 2 = 2.4$ V
So the current through the 6 Ω is:
$I = V \div R = 2.4 \div 6 =$ **0.4 A**
Remember, current splits depending on the resistance — it doesn't just split equally between resistors (unless the resistors have equal resistance).

Page 171 — Fact Recall Questions

Q1 The total current entering a junction = the total current leaving it.

Q2 The total e.m.f. around a series circuit = the sum of the p.d.s across each component.

Q3 They are in series.

Q4 parallel

11. The Potential Divider

Page 174 — Application Questions

Q1 a) $V_{out} = \frac{R_2}{R_1 + R_2} V_{in} = \frac{3.0}{12 + 3.0} \times 16 =$ **3.2 V**

b) $V_{out} = \frac{R_2}{R_1 + R_2} V_{in}$, so $5.0 = \frac{R_2}{12 + R_2} \times 16$
$5.0(12 + R_2) = 16R_2 \Rightarrow 60 + 5.0R_2 = 16R_2 \Rightarrow 60 = 11R_2$
$R_2 = \frac{60}{11} = 5.4545... =$ **5.5 Ω (to 2 s.f.)**

Q2 $V_{out} = \frac{R_2}{R_1 + R_2} V_{in}$ so $\frac{V_{out}}{V_{in}} = \frac{R_2}{R_1 + R_2} = \frac{4}{16} = \frac{1}{4}$
$4R_2 = R_1 + R_2$ so $3R_2 = R_1$
So, for example, you could have $R_1 = 9\ \Omega$ and $R_2 = 3\ \Omega$.
Here, you can have any values that $3R_2 = R_1$ is true for.

Q3 a) $V_{out} = \frac{R_2}{R_1 + R_2} V_{in}$ so $V_{out} = \frac{1.5}{3.0 + 1.5} \times 1.5 =$ **0.5 V**

b) $V_{out} = \frac{R_2}{R_1 + R_2} V_{in}$ so $0.30 = \frac{R_2}{3.0 + R_2} \times 1.5$
$0.30(3.0 + R_2) = 1.5R_2 \Rightarrow 0.90 + 0.30R_2 = 1.5R_2$
$0.90 = 1.2R_2$
$R_2 =$ **0.75 Ω**

Page 174 — Fact Recall Questions

Q1 A potential divider is a circuit containing a voltage source and a couple of resistors in series. The voltage across one of the resistors is used as an output voltage. If the resistors aren't fixed, the circuit will be capable of producing a variable output voltage.

Q2 $V_{out} = \frac{R_2}{R_1 + R_2} V_{in}$, where V_{out} = the output potential difference, R_2 = the resistance of the resistor connected across the voltage output, R_1 = the resistance of the other resistor in the potential divider and V_{in} = the potential difference of the power supply.

Q3 You can make a light sensor using a potential divider by using an LDR as one of the resistors.

Q4 A potential divider containing a variable resistor instead of two resistors in series. E.g. they are used in a volume control on a stereo.

Exam-style Questions — Pages 176-178

1 B ***(1 mark)***

2 C ***(1 mark)***

3 D ***(1 mark)***

4 C ***(1 mark)***

5 a) $P = VI = 3.00 \times 0.724 = 2.172 =$ **2.17 W (to 3 s.f.)**
(2 marks for correct answer, 1 mark for correct working if answer incorrect)

b) 5 minutes = 300 seconds
$\Delta Q = I \times \Delta t = 0.724 \times 300 = 217.2 =$ **217 C (to 3 s.f.)**
(2 marks for correct answer, 1 mark for correct working if answer incorrect)

c) $V = W \div Q = 56.5 \div 217.2 = 0.26012...$
$=$ **0.260 V (to 3 s.f.)**
(2 marks for correct answer, 1 mark for correct working if answer incorrect)

d) p.d. across the filament lamp $= I \times R$
$= 0.724 \times 2.00$
$= 1.448$ V

$V = V_1 + V_2 + V_{bulb}$
$3.00 = 0.26012... + V_2 + 1.448$
$V_2 = 1.2918... =$ **1.29 V (to 3 s.f.)**
(2 marks for correct answer, 1 mark for correct working if answer incorrect)

e) No, the filament lamp is not an ohmic conductor as I is not directly proportional to V ***(1 mark)***.

6 a) As the electrons move through the battery, they collide with atoms inside the battery and transfer some of their energy ***(1 mark)***. (The small amount of resistance that causes this energy loss inside the battery is called internal resistance.)

b) E.g.

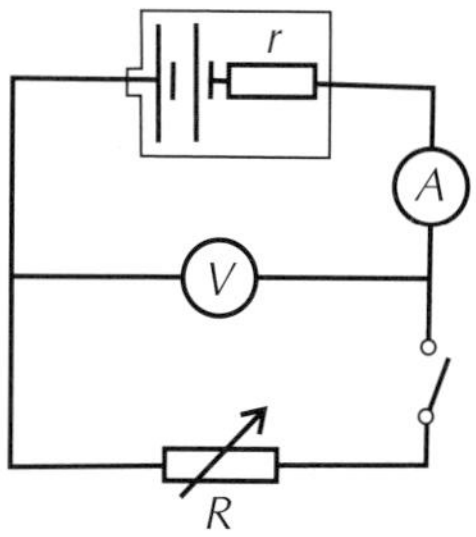

(1 mark for a sensible circuit that could be used in this experiment. It should contain a battery, a variable resistor, a voltmeter and an ammeter.)

E.g. Set the variable resistor (the load resistance) to its highest resistance. Close the switch and record the current (I) through and potential difference (V) across the circuit ***(1 mark)***. Open the switch and close it again to get another set of current and potential difference readings for this load resistance. Repeat this to get a third set of readings. Calculate the mean current and potential difference for this resistance from your results ***(1 mark)***. Decrease the resistance of the variable resistor by a small amount and repeat the above process for this resistance. Continue until you have a set of mean currents and potential differences for 10 different load resistances ***(1 mark)***. Plot a V-I graph of the mean current and potential difference values. This will give you a straight-line graph whose gradient is $-r$, where r is the internal resistance of the battery ***(1 mark)***.

c)

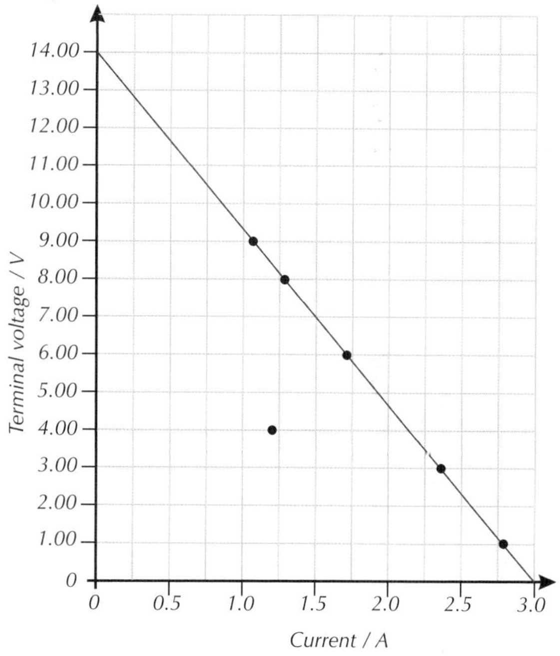

(1 mark for all points correctly plotted, 1 mark for line of best fit drawn)

d) e.m.f. = y-intercept = **14 V** ***(1 mark)***

e) internal resistance = –gradient = $-\Delta y \div \Delta x$

(E.g. = 14.00 ÷ 3.0) = 4.666... = **4.67 Ω (to 3 s.f.)**

(2 marks for correct answer, 1 mark for correct working if answer incorrect)

7 a) For the parallel resistors:

$$\frac{1}{R} = \frac{1}{R_1} + \frac{1}{R_2}$$

$$\frac{1}{R} = \frac{1}{10.0} + \frac{1}{10.0}$$

$$\frac{1}{R} = \frac{1}{5.00}$$

$R = 5.00\ \Omega$

For the whole circuit:

$R = 10.0 + 5.00 =$ **15.0 Ω**

(2 marks for the correct answer, 1 mark for correct working if answer incorrect)

b) Resistance of component A, $R_A = 10.0\ \Omega$

Potential difference splits according to the ratio of resistance of the component to the total resistance, so:

$$V_A = \frac{R_A}{R}V$$

$$= \frac{10.0}{15.0} \times 12$$

= **8.0 V**

(2 marks for the correct answer, 1 mark for correct working if answer incorrect)

c) $R = 3.21 \times 10^{-3} + 5.00 = 5.00321\ \Omega$

$I = V \div R$

$I = 12 \div 5.00321 = 2.3984... =$ **2.4 A (to 2 s.f.)**

(2 marks for the correct answer, 1 mark for correct working if answer incorrect)

d) $\rho = (R \times A) \div L = (3.21 \times 10^{-3} \times 3.05 \times 10^{-6}) \div 0.0300$

$= 3.2635 \times 10^{-7}$

$=$ **3.26×10^{-7} Ωm (to 3 s.f.)**

(2 marks for the correct answer, 1 mark for correct working if answer incorrect)

8 a) E.g.

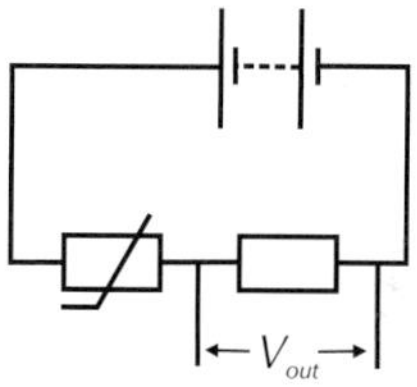

(1 mark for drawing the cells, thermistor and resistor in series, 1 mark for correctly drawing the circuit such that the output voltage is across the resistor)

b) $$V_{out} = \frac{R_2}{R_1 + R_2}V_{in}$$

$$= \frac{6.0}{9.2 + 6.0} \times 22 = 8.6842... =$$ **8.7 V (to 2 s.f.)**

(1 mark)

c) $$W = \frac{V^2}{R}t = \frac{V_{out}^2}{R_2}t$$

$t = 12 \times 60 = 720$ s

$$W = \frac{(8.6842...)^2}{6.0} \times 720$$

= 9049.861... J

= **9000 J (to 2 s.f.)**

(2 marks for the correct answer, 1 mark for correct working if answer incorrect)

d) $V_{out} = \frac{R_2}{R_1 + R_2} V_{in}$

Rearrange for R_1:

$V_{out}(R_1 + R_2) = R_2 V_{in}$

$R_1 + R_2 = \frac{R_2 V_{in}}{V_{out}}$

$R_1 = \frac{R_2 V_{in}}{V_{out}} - R_2$

$= \frac{6.0 \times 22}{13} - 6.0$

$= 4.1538...$

$=$ **4.2 Ω (to 2 s.f.)**

(2 marks for the correct answer, 1 mark for correct working if answer incorrect)

Section 2 — Waves

1. Progressive Waves

Page 182 — Application Questions

Q1 The wave is travelling to the left / from right to left.

The point at X is moving upwards, so the higher point of the wave must be moving towards X. So the wave must be moving to the left.

Q2 a) −0.2 m

b) 0.2 m

For displacement the direction matters (it can be negative), but for amplitude you only need a magnitude.

c) 1.6 m

Page 182 — Fact Recall Questions

Q1 By causing particles or fields in the region to oscillate.

Q2 *A* shows the amplitude of the wave.

B shows a crest of the wave.

C shows the wavelength of the wave.

Q3 E.g. the amount by which one wave lags behind another / the difference between a point on one wave and the next identical point on the second wave.

Q4 In longitudinal waves, the direction of oscillations are along the same line as the direction of energy propagation. In transverse waves, the direction of oscillations are perpendicular to the direction of energy propagation.

Q5 E.g.

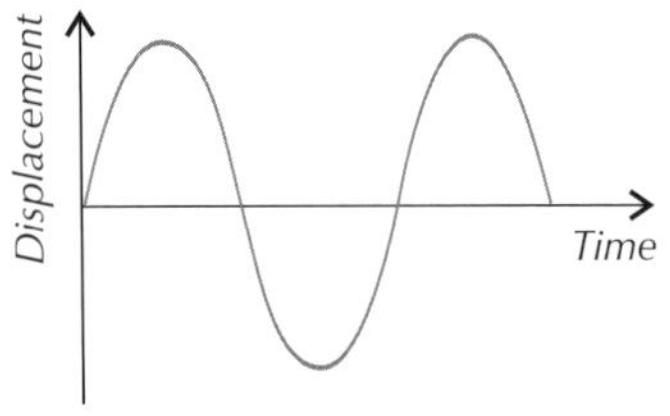

The displacement-time graph for a longitudinal wave looks just like the one for a transverse wave.

2. Frequency, Speed and Intensity

Page 186 — Application Questions

Q1 a) Rearrange $I = \frac{P}{A}$ for power:

$P = IA$

$= 5 \times 0.2$

$=$ **1 W**

b) intensity $\propto$ (amplitude)^2

So, $\frac{\text{intensity}}{(\text{amplitude})^2} = \text{constant}$

$\frac{\text{final intensity}}{(\text{final amplitude})^2} = \frac{\text{initial intensity}}{(\text{initial amplitude})^2}$

$\text{final intensity} = \text{initial intensity} \times \left(\frac{\text{final amplitude}}{\text{initial amplitude}}\right)^2$

Amplitude is doubled, so

final amplitude ÷ initial amplitude = 2

So, final intensity $= 5 \times (2)^2$

$=$ **20 Wm^{-2}**

Q2 a) The length of 1.5 oscillations is 0.15 m, so the length of one oscillation is $\frac{0.15}{1.5} = 0.10$ m.

So wavelength, $\lambda =$ **0.10 m**.

b) $v = f\lambda$, and $v = \frac{d}{t}$

Rearrange $v = \frac{d}{t}$ for t, and substitute in $v = f\lambda$:

$t = \frac{d}{f\lambda} = \frac{1.0}{30.0 \times 0.10} = 0.33...\text{s}$

So the time taken to travel 1.0 m is **0.33 s (to 2 s.f.)**

Page 186 — Fact Recall Questions

Q1 frequency $= \frac{1}{\text{period}}$ / $f = \frac{1}{T}$

Q2 The vertical axis shows voltage.

The horizontal axis shows time.

Q3 Calculate the period of the wave from the oscilloscope display, by counting the number of divisions for one full cycle and multiplying this by the value of one division. Use this value of the period to calculate the frequency using $f = \frac{1}{T}$.

Q4 wave speed = frequency × wavelength / $v = f\lambda$

Q5 The intensity of a progressive wave is the rate of flow of energy per unit area at right angles to the direction of travel of the wave.

Q6 intensity $\propto$ (amplitude)^2

3. Electromagnetic Waves

Page 188 — Application Question

Q1 Speed of EM waves in a vacuum, $v = 3.00 \times 10^8$ ms^{-1}

rearrange $v = f\lambda$ for f:

$f = v \div \lambda$

$= 3.00 \times 10^8 \div 2.40 \times 10^5$

$=$ **1250 Hz**

Page 188 — Fact Recall Questions

Q1 Transverse waves.

Q2 Gamma rays

Q3 a) 10^{-3} — 10^{-1} m

b) 10^{-8} — 4×10^{-7} m

c) 10^{-13} — 10^{-8} m

Q4 Infrared light, visible light and ultraviolet light.

4. Polarisation

Page 191 — Application Question

Q1 a) This wave must be transverse because it can be polarised.

b) C represents the transmission axis. It must be the same as the first polarising filter, because all the waves that pass through the first one also gets through the second one.

c) The transmission axis would now be at right angles to the waves that passed through the first filter, so no waves would get through the second filter.

5. Reflection and Refraction

Page 194 — Application Questions

Q1 The angle of incidence is measured from the normal, so:
angle of incidence = 90 – 30 = 60°
angle of incidence = angle of reflection, so:
angle of reflection = **60°**

Q2 Side B is deeper. The wave has bent away from the normal and has a longer wavelength in side B, so must be travelling faster here. Water waves travel faster in deeper water so B must be deeper.

Page 194 — Fact Recall Questions

Q1 angle of incidence = angle of reflection

Q2 a) The wave bends towards the normal.
b) The wavelength of the wave decreases, but its frequency stays the same.

6. Refractive Index and Total Internal Reflection

Page 199 — Application Questions

Q1 a) $n = \frac{c}{v} = \frac{3.00 \times 10^8}{1.94 \times 10^8} = 1.546... = \mathbf{1.55}$ **(to 3 s.f.)**

b) The light will bend towards the normal — $n_{air} = 1$, so air is less optically dense than the material, so light slows down as it crosses the boundary.

c) $\sin C = \frac{1}{n} \Rightarrow C = \sin^{-1}\left(\frac{1}{n}\right) = \sin^{-1}\left(\frac{1}{1.546...}\right) = 40.290...$
$= \mathbf{40.3°}$ **(to 3 s.f.)**

Q2 So that the ray won't refract as it enters the block.

Q3 a) When light travelling from the cage meets the water-air boundary, it's refracted (away from the normal). This makes it look like the light is coming from a different point to where the cage actually is.

b) You know: $n_1 = 1.38$, $n_2 = 1.49$, $\theta_1 = 37.2°$, $\theta_2 = ?$
So rearrange the law of refraction to find θ_2:

$$n_1 \sin\theta_1 = n_2 \sin\theta_2 \Rightarrow \theta_2 = \sin^{-1}\left(\frac{n_1 \sin\theta_1}{n_2}\right)$$
$$= \sin^{-1}\left(\frac{1.38 \times \sin 37.2°}{1.49}\right)$$
$$= 34.053... = \mathbf{34.1°} \textbf{ (to 3 s.f.)}$$

Page 199 — Fact Recall Questions

Q1 It's a measure of the optical density of the material, given by the ratio of the speed of light in a vacuum to the speed of light in the material.

Q2 It will bend towards the normal.

Q3 $n_2 < n_1$ and the angle of incidence must be greater than the critical angle.

7. Superposition and Interference

Page 203 — Application Questions

Q1 E.g. 90°

Q2 Two waves 180° out of phase, e.g.

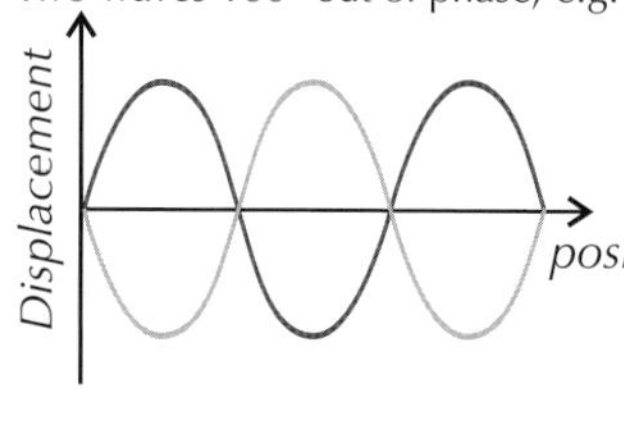

Q3 a) i) Point G
ii) No points.
iii) Point E
b) Two points (C and E).

Page 203 — Fact Recall Questions

Q1 When two or more waves meet, the resultant displacement equals the vector sum of the individual displacements.

Q2 When two waves pass through each other and their displacements combine to make a displacement with greater magnitude.

Q3 The phase difference of two points on a wave is the difference in their positions in the wave's cycle.

Q4 Phase difference can be measured in degrees, radians or fractions of a cycle.

Q5 When their phase difference is an odd multiple of 180° (π radians or half a cycle).

Q6 Two wave sources are coherent if the waves have the same wavelength and frequency and a fixed phase difference between them.

Q7 Two waves are in phase if they have a phase difference of 0° (or a multiple of 360°).
You could have said 2π radians or 1 full cycle instead of 360° here.

8. Diffraction

Page 205 — Application Question

Q1 No, the gap is much smaller than the waves, so the waves are mostly reflected back.

Page 205 — Fact Recall Questions

Q1 All waves.

Q2 Diffraction effects are strongest when the gap size is similar in size to the wavelength. The size of the doorway and the wavelength of sound waves are roughly equal, so the sound waves diffract through the doorway and can be heard around the corner. Light has a much smaller wavelength than the doorway, so diffraction effects aren't noticeable and the person cannot be seen around the corner.

Q3 Monochromatic light is light made up of only one wavelength (and so frequency).

Q4 A bright central fringe with alternating dark and bright fringes on either side of it.

9. Two-Source Interference

Page 208 — Application Questions

Q1 a) E.g.

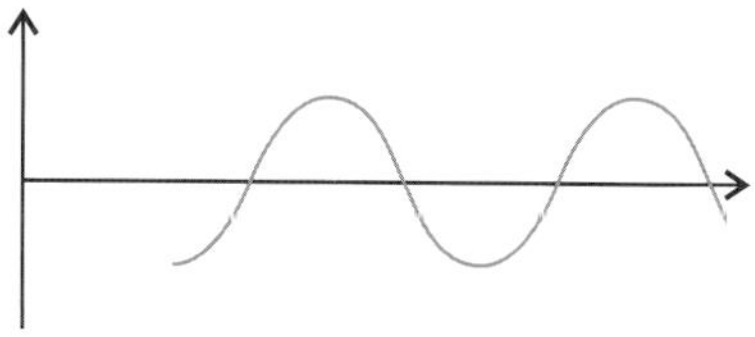

b) E.g.

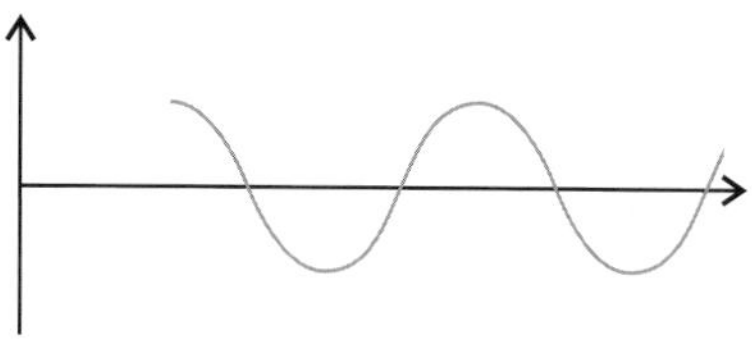

Q2 p.d. = $x\lambda$, so $x = 0.42 \div 0.12 = 3.5$
As x is in the form $n + \frac{1}{2}$ (where $n = 3$), there will be destructive interference.

Page 208 — Fact Recall Questions

Q1 They must be coherent.

Q2 The path difference is the amount by which the path travelled by one wave is longer than the path travelled by the other wave.

Q3 You see constructive interference when the path difference equals $n\lambda$ (n is an integer).

Q4 E.g. Have one amplifier attached to two loudspeakers.

Q5 E.g. Attach two loudspeakers to an amplifier and create sound waves at a set frequency. Walk along a straight line parallel to the line of the speakers. Mark down points of maximum loudness and quietness, which show the position of constructive and destructive interference.

Q6 The probe would detect alternating areas of maximum and minimum signal strength.

10. Young's Double-Slit Experiment

Page 212 — Application Questions

Q1 a) Laser light is coherent/monochromatic, so the pattern is clearer.

b) Light fringes are produced where there is constructive interference and dark fringes are produced where there is destructive interference.

c) $x = \frac{\lambda D}{a} = \frac{(4.5 \times 10^{-7}) \times 12.0}{0.00030} = \mathbf{0.018\ m}$

d) There are 10 maxima with a gap of 0.018 m between each one, so the total width is 9 × 0.018 = 0.162 m. So y = **0.16 (to 2 s.f.)**.

Even though there are 10 maxima, there are only 9 fringe spacings (the gaps between them).

Q2 Rearrange the double-slit formula: $D = \frac{ax}{\lambda}$

So $D = \frac{(1.29 \times 10^{-2}) \times (0.11 \times 10^{-3})}{615 \times 10^{-9}}$

$= 2.307... =$ **2.3 m (to 2 s.f.)**

Page 212 — Fact Recall Questions

Q1 By shining light through a double-slit system.

Q2 E.g. Mount a card with two thin slits, with spacing a, a distance D from an observation screen. Shine the laser beam through the slits to create an interference pattern on the screen, then find the fringe spacing, x, by measuring across several fringes with a ruler then dividing by the number of fringe widths between them. Use the double-slit formula $\lambda = \frac{ax}{D}$ to calculate the wavelength of the light.

Q3 Young's double-slit experiment showed that light could diffract and interfere. Both of these qualities are wave properties, which suggested that light was a wave.

11. Diffraction Gratings

Page 215 — Application Question

Q1 a) First work out the slit spacing. It has 4.5×10^5 slits per metre, so the slit spacing $d = \frac{1}{4.5 \times 10^5}$

$= 2.222... \times 10^{-6}$ m

Use the diffraction grating equation, rearranged for θ, and using $n = 3$:

$\theta = \sin^{-1}\left(\frac{n\lambda}{d}\right) = \sin^{-1}\left(\frac{3 \times (5.9 \times 10^{-7})}{2.222... \times 10^{-6}}\right)$

$= 52.797... =$ **53° (to 2 s.f.)**

b) No, because $\frac{n\lambda}{d} = \frac{4 \times (5.9 \times 10^{-7})}{2.222... \times 10^{-6}} = 1.1$ (to 2 s.f.).

The sin function is only defined between –1 and 1, so $\sin^{-1} 1.1$ is impossible.

c) The pattern will be more spread out, because the angle is related to n, d and λ. If n and d remain constant, θ will become larger and so each order of maximum will be further from the zero order.

Page 215 — Fact Recall Questions

Q1 E.g. Measure the distance D between the diffraction grating and an observation screen. Shine a laser through the diffraction grating onto the screen, and using a ruler measure the spacing to the nth order maximum (choose a value of n). Calculate the angle to the normal made by the maximum using $\theta \approx \frac{x}{D}$.
Rearrange the diffraction grating equation to $\lambda = \frac{d \sin\theta}{n}$ and use it to calculate the wavelength.

Q2 White light is made up of a range of different wavelengths. These diffract by different amounts when they pass through the diffraction grating, forming a spectrum.

12. Stationary Waves

Page 220 — Application Questions

Q1 This wave is at the third harmonic so 1.5 wavelengths fit on the string, so $1.5\lambda = 6$, so λ = **4 m**.

Q2 a) The wave is vibrating at the fundamental frequency, so the length of the string is half a wavelength. So λ = 5 m.
$v = f\lambda = 100 \times 5 =$ **500 ms^{-1}**

b) $v = f\lambda$ so $\lambda = \frac{v}{f} = \frac{500}{200} = 2.5$ m
So one wavelength (or two half wavelengths) would fit on the string at this frequency. This resonant frequency is called the second harmonic.

You could also just look at the frequency — it's twice the frequency of the first harmonic, so 2 × ½ wavelengths fit on the string.

Q3 The length of the pipe is equal to $\frac{\lambda}{4}$.

Q4 At fundamental frequency, length of open pipe is half a wavelength.
So length of open pipe $= \frac{1}{2} \times 3.2 = 1.6$ m
Length of closed pipe = 1.6 – 0.2 = 1.4 m
At fundamental frequency, length of closed pipe is one quarter of the wavelength.
So wavelength = 4 × length of closed pipe
= 4 × 1.4 = **5.6 m**

Page 220 — Fact Recall Questions

Q1 The superposition of two progressive waves with the same wavelength and frequency, moving in opposite directions.

Q2 Unlike progressive waves, no energy is transmitted by a stationary wave.

Q3 A resonant frequency of a string is a frequency at which a stationary wave is formed because an exact number of waves are produced in the time it takes for a wave to get to the end of the string and back again.

Q4 $\frac{\lambda}{2}$

Q5 The lowest possible resonant frequency.

Q6 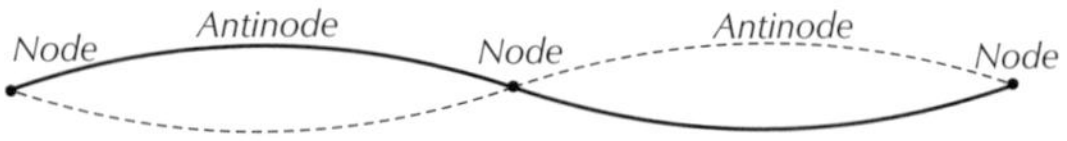

Q7 E.g. Use a metal plate to reflect microwaves and a probe to observe nodes and antinodes.

Exam-style Questions — Pages 222-224

1 D ***(1 mark)***

Constructive interference occurs when the path difference is a whole number of wavelengths.

2 C ***(1 mark)***

3 A ***(1 mark)***

1.7×10^{-16} ms = 1.7×10^{-19} s

$f = 1 \div T = 1 \div (1.7 \times 10^{-19}) = 5.88... \times 10^{18}$ Hz

All electromagnetic waves travel at the same speed in a vacuum: $v = 3.00 \times 10^8$ ms^{-1}.

Rearrange $v = f\lambda$ to $\lambda = v \div f = 3 \times 10^8 \div 5.88... \times 10^{18}$

$= 5.1 \times 10^{-11}$ m

4 D ***(1 mark)***

Intensity ÷ amplitude^2 = constant, so:

initial intensity (I_i) ÷ (initial amplitude (x_i))^2 = final intensity (I_f) ÷ (final amplitude (x_f))^2

Rearranging: $x_f = x_i\sqrt{\frac{I_f}{I_i}} = 0.78 \times \sqrt{0.11 \div 0.42}$

$= 0.399...$ m = 40 cm (to 2 s.f.)

5 a) The third harmonic ***(1 mark)***

b) Tube length = $3 \times \frac{\lambda}{2}$

Rearranging:

$\lambda = \frac{2}{3} \times \text{tube length} = \frac{2}{3} \times 1.25$

= 0.8333... = **0.833 m (to 3 s.f.)** ***(1 mark)***

c) How to grade your answer (pick the description that best matches your answer):

0 marks: There is no relevant information.

1-2 marks: A diagram has been drawn, and method points 2, 6, and 8 have been covered. Answer is basic and has lack of structure. Information is missing and there are few backed up arguments.

3-4 marks: A labelled diagram has been drawn and method points 1, 2, 4, 6, and 8 have been covered. At least one accuracy point is covered. Answer has some structure, and information is presented with a clear line of reasoning, with arguments that are partially backed up.

5-6 marks: A labelled diagram has been drawn, all of the method points have been covered, and at least one point from the accuracy points has been covered. The answer is well structured. There is a clear and logical line of reasoning, with information and arguments that are fully backed up.

Here are some points your answer may include:

Diagram

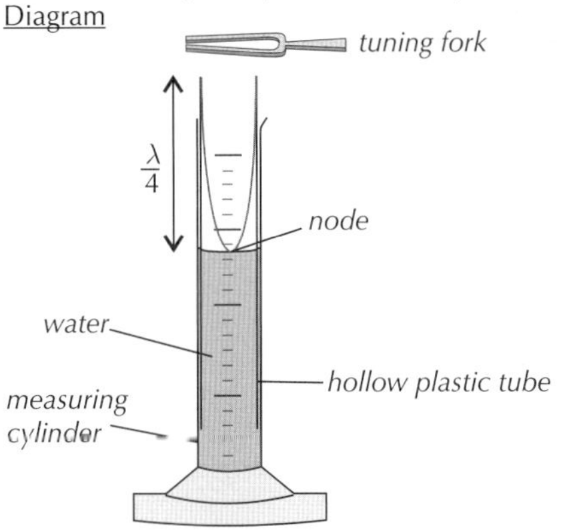

Method

1. Suspend the tube in water in a measuring cylinder to create a closed-end pipe.
2. Note down the frequency of the sound produced by the tuning fork.
3. Gently tap tuning fork to generate sound waves.
4. Hold tuning fork just above tube to direct sound waves into the tube.
5. Move the tube up and down in the water until you find the shortest distance between the top of the tube and the water level at which the sound from the fork is loudest.
6. Measure the distance between the top of the tube and the water level.
7. Multiply this distance by four to get the wavelength of the wave.
8. Plug f and λ into $v = f\lambda$ to calculate v.

Improving accuracy

1. Repeat the experiment with different tuning forks and take an average for the value of v.
2. Repeat for each tuning fork to find average λ.

6 a) Each division is 0.500 μs and one cycle is 6 divisions wide, so one cycle takes 6 × 0.500 = 3.00 μs

3.00 μs = 3.00×10^{-6} s

$f = \frac{1}{T} = \frac{1}{3.00 \times 10^{-6}} = 3.33... \times 10^5$ Hz

Rearrange $v = f\lambda$ to $\lambda = \frac{v}{f}$

So $\lambda = \frac{3.00 \times 10^8}{3.33... \times 10^5} = \mathbf{900\ m}$

(3 marks for correct answer, otherwise 1 mark for calculating the frequency and 1 mark for correct working.)

b) Radio ***(1 mark)***

c)

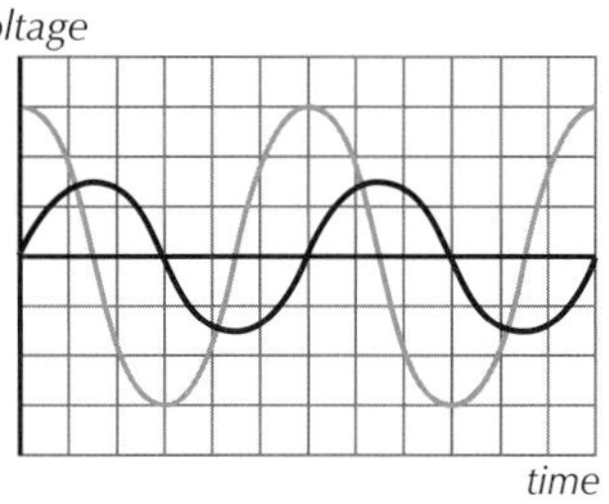

(1 mark for second wave of equal wavelength and frequency and half the amplitude, and 1 mark for second wave drawn 90° out of phase ahead of 1st wave.)

d) $I = \frac{P}{A} \Rightarrow P = IA$ for a given A

and $I \propto$ (amplitude)^2, so $P \propto$ (amplitude)^2

$\frac{P}{(\text{amplitude})^2} = \text{constant}$

So $\frac{P_1}{(\text{amplitude of 1st wave})^2} = \frac{P_2}{(\text{amplitude of 2nd wave})^2}$

$P_2 = P_1\left(\frac{\text{amplitude of 2nd wave}}{\text{amplitude of 1st wave}}\right)^2$

$= 15.2 \times \left(\frac{1}{2}\right)^2 = \mathbf{3.8\ W}$

(2 marks for correct answer, otherwise 1 mark for correct working.)

7 a) There are 9 maxima, so 8 fringes.

So fringe spacing $x = \frac{0.24}{8} = 0.030$ m.

To find λ use the double-slit formula:

$\lambda = \frac{ax}{D} = \frac{0.030 \times 0.15 \times 10^{-3}}{7.5}$

= **6.0 × 10^{-7} m (= 600 nm)**

(3 marks for correct answer, otherwise 1 mark for finding fringe spacing and 1 mark for attempting to use double-slit formula.)

b) Lasers are coherent ***(1 mark)*** and monochromatic, so the diffraction patterns are clearer ***(1 mark)***.

c) Distance between slits $= \dfrac{1}{2.55 \times 10^5}$

$= 3.921... \times 10^{-6}$ m

$d\sin\theta = n\lambda \Rightarrow \theta = \sin^{-1}\left(\dfrac{n\lambda}{d}\right)$

$= \sin^{-1}\left(\dfrac{1 \times (6 \times 10^{-7})}{3.921... \times 10^{-6}}\right)$

$= 8.800... =$ **8.8° (to 2 s.f.)**

(4 marks for correct answer. Otherwise 1 mark for finding the space between slits, 1 mark for rearranging formula to find θ, and 1 mark for correct calculations.)

d) The maxima would become much clearer / better defined. ***(1 mark)***

8 a) $n = \frac{c}{v} = \dfrac{3.00 \times 10^8}{2.03 \times 10^8} = 1.477... =$ **1.48 (to 3 s.f.)**

(2 marks for correct answer, otherwise 1 mark for correct working if answer incorrect.)

b) Use the law of refraction at the air-core boundary: $n_1 \sin\theta_1 = n_2 \sin\theta_2$ with $n_1 = 1$, $\theta_1 = 34°$, $\theta_2 = 21°$.

Rearrange: $n_2 = \dfrac{n_1 \sin\theta_1}{\sin\theta_2} = \dfrac{1 \times \sin 34°}{\sin 21°} = 1.56...$

$=$ **1.6 (to 2 s.f.)**

(3 marks for correct answer, otherwise 1 mark for substituting into the correct formula and 1 mark for correct rearrangement if answer incorrect.)

c) $n = \frac{c}{v}$ and $v = f\lambda$.

When a wave travels through a boundary, its wavelength changes and its frequency remains constant. So n becomes:

$n = \dfrac{c}{f\lambda}$ so $\lambda = \dfrac{c}{fn} = \dfrac{3.00 \times 10^8}{5.00 \times 10^{14} \times 1.56...}$

$= 3.845... \times 10^{-7} =$ **380 nm (to 2 s.f.)**

(3 marks for correct answer, otherwise 1 mark for knowing f is constant and 1 mark for substituting into correct formula.)

d) $\sin C = \dfrac{n_2}{n_1} = \dfrac{1.47...}{1.56...} = 0.9470...$

so $C = \sin^{-1}(0.9470...) = 71.2... =$ **71° (to 2 s.f.)**

(2 marks for correct answer, 1 mark for correct working if answer incorrect.)

e) The light ray enters the cladding at an angle of 90° – 21° = 69° (the angle has to add to the angle between the cladding and the normal), which is less than the critical angle, so total internal reflection cannot happen and it enters the cladding instead.

(1 mark for θ < C, 1 mark for mention of total internal reflection.)

f) Ray B has been totally internally reflected because it hits the core-cladding boundary at an angle greater than the critical angle. ***(1 mark for total internal reflection, 1 mark for critical angle.)***

Section 3 — Quantum Physics

1. The Photon Model

Page 226 — Application Questions

Q1 $2.20 \times 1.60 \times 10^{-19} =$ **3.52×10^{-19} J**

Q2 $E = hf = (6.63 \times 10^{-34}) \times (6.0 \times 10^{13})$

$= 3.978 \times 10^{-20}$

$=$ **4.0×10^{-20} J (to 2 s.f.)**

Q3 $E = \dfrac{hc}{\lambda}$ so $\lambda = \dfrac{hc}{E}$

$= ((6.63 \times 10^{-34}) \times (3.00 \times 10^8)) \div (8.2 \times 10^{-20})$

$= 2.425... \times 10^{-6}$

$=$ **2.4×10^{-6} m (to 2 s.f.)**

Page 226 — Fact Recall Questions

Q1 A photon is a quantum of energy of EM radiation.

Q2 $E = \dfrac{hc}{\lambda}$

Q3 energy

2. The Planck Constant

Page 229 — Application Questions

Q1 $eV_0 = \dfrac{hc}{\lambda}$

so $V_0 = \dfrac{hc}{e\lambda} = \dfrac{6.63 \times 10^{-34} \times 3.00 \times 10^8}{1.60 \times 10^{-19} \times 600 \times 10^{-9}}$

$= 2.071... =$ **2.1 V (to 2 s.f.)**

Q2 Gradient of graph $= (2.0 - 1.3) \div [(2.1 \times 10^6) - (1.58 \times 10^6)]$

$= 0.7 \div (0.52 \times 10^6) = 1.34... \times 10^{-6}$ Vm

$h = \dfrac{e \times \text{gradient}}{c} = \dfrac{1.60 \times 10^{-19} \times 1.34... \times 10^{-6}}{3.00 \times 10^8}$

$= 7.179... \times 10^{-34} =$ **7.2×10^{-34} Js (to 2 s.f.)**

Page 229 — Fact Recall Questions

Q1 The minimum voltage needed for a current to flow through an LED / The voltage needed to give electrons in the circuit the same energy as a photon emitted by the LED.

Q2 $eV_0 = \dfrac{hc}{\lambda}$

Q3 a) E.g.

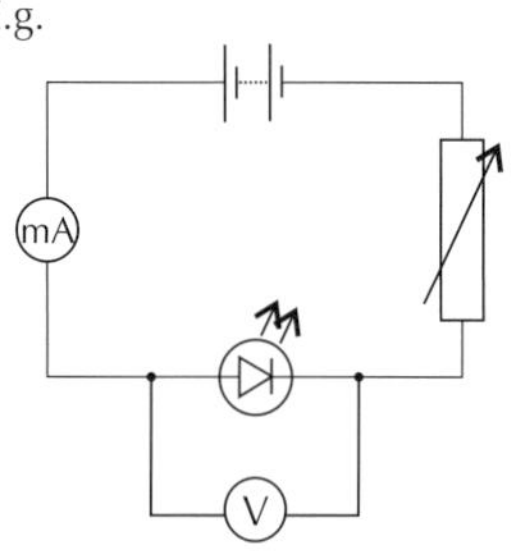

b) The currents through the circuit will be very small.

3. The Photoelectric Effect

Page 233 — Application Questions

Q1 The work function is the minimum amount of energy required for an electron to be emitted from the zinc's surface. The energy of each photon is greater than this value, and so they will be able to transfer enough energy to release electrons from the zinc sheet.

Q2 a) The maximum kinetic energy of the electrons increases as the frequency of the incident radiation increases. Increasing the frequency of the radiation increases the energy of each photon ($E = hf$), and so more energy can be transferred to the free electrons in the metal.

The maximum kinetic energy of the photoelectrons emitted is the energy transferred by a photon minus the work function energy. The work function energy remains the same, so as the energy of the incident photons increases, the maximum kinetic energy of the emitted electrons also increases.

b) $E = hf$, $h = 6.63 \times 10^{-34}$ Js, $f = 1.20 \times 10^{16}$ Hz,

so $E = (6.63 \times 10^{-34}) \times (1.20 \times 10^{16})$

$= 7.956 \times 10^{-18} =$ **7.96×10^{-18} J (to 3 s.f.)**

c) $hf = \phi + KE_{max}$

$KE_{max} = 7.26 \times 10^{-18}$ J, $hf = 7.956 \times 10^{-18}$ J,

so the work function of the metal (ϕ) is

$\phi = hf - KE_{max} = (7.956 \times 10^{-18}) - (7.26 \times 10^{-18})$

$=$ **6.96×10^{-19} J**

Page 233 — Fact Recall Questions

Q1 The photoelectric effect is when electrons are emitted from the surface of a metal when radiation of a high enough frequency (usually ultraviolet light) is shone on it.

Q2 Initially, the gold leaf in the electroscope is repelled from the negatively charged metal. The UV radiation releases photoelectrons from the zinc plate, which removes negative charge from the zinc plate. The gold leaf falls as the charge on the plate is reduced, reducing the repulsion between the leaf and the metal it's attached to.

Q3 More electrons will be emitted, but their maximum kinetic energy will remain the same.

Q4 Before an electron can be emitted by a metal, it needs enough energy to break the bonds holding it there. This means there is a minimum amount of energy an electron needs before it can escape the metal surface. The threshold frequency is the minimum frequency of radiation that has photons with this energy.

Q5 The maximum amount of energy that can be transferred to an electron is the energy of one photon. There is a minimum amount of energy needed to free the electron from the metal (the work function energy). Therefore the maximum amount of kinetic energy an electron can have is the energy of one photon minus the work function energy.

4. Wave-Particle Duality

Page 237 — Application Questions

Q1 $\lambda = \frac{h}{p}$, where p (momentum) = mass × velocity, so the de Broglie wavelength is inversely proportional to the velocity of a particle. Therefore increasing the velocity will decrease the de Broglie wavelength of a particle.

Q2 a) $\lambda = \frac{h}{p}$, so $p = h \div \lambda$

$h = 6.63 \times 10^{-34}$ Js, $\lambda = 0.162$ nm,

$\lambda = 0.162 \times 10^{-9}$ m $= 1.62 \times 10^{-10}$ m,

$p = (6.63 \times 10^{-34}) \div (1.62 \times 10^{-10})$

$= 4.09259... \times 10^{-24}$ kg ms^{-1}

= 4.09 × 10^{-24} kg ms^{-1} (to 3 s.f.)

Make sure you always include units with your answer — it could get you some precious extra marks in the exam.

b) $m_e = 9.11 \times 10^{-31}$ kg,

$\mathbf{v = p \div m_e}$

$= (4.09259... \times 10^{-24}) \div (9.11 \times 10^{-31})$

$= 4.4924... \times 10^{6}$ ms^{-1}

$E_k = \frac{1}{2}mv^2 = \frac{1}{2} \times (9.11 \times 10^{-31}) \times (4.4924... \times 10^{6})^2$

= 9.19 × 10^{-18} J (to 3 s.f.)

Q3 a) $\lambda = \frac{h}{p} = \frac{6.63 \times 10^{-34}}{6.646 \times 10^{-27} \times 60.0}$

$= 1.662... \times 10^{-9}$ = **1.66 × 10^{-9} m (to 3 s.f.)**

b) $\lambda = \frac{h}{p}$, so $v = h \div \lambda m$

$v = \frac{6.63 \times 10^{-34}}{9.11 \times 10^{-31} \times 1.662... \times 10^{-9}}$

= 437716.7... ms^{-1} = **4.38 × 10^{5} ms^{-1} (to 3 s.f.)**

Page 237 — Fact Recall Questions

Q1 Diffraction shows electromagnetic waves have wave properties, and the photoelectric effect shows electromagnetic waves have particle properties.

Q2 All particles have both particle and wave properties. Waves can also show particle properties.

Q3 Electron diffraction

Exam-style Questions — Pages 239-240

1 C *(1 mark)*

2 GeV = $2 \times 10^{9} \times 1.60 \times 10^{-19} = 3.2 \times 10^{-10}$ J.

$E = hf$, so $f = E \div h = (3.2 \times 10^{-10}) \div (6.63 \times 10^{-34})$

$= 4.826... \times 10^{23}$ Hz

2 B *(1 mark)*

4.33 eV $= 4.33 \times 1.60 \times 10^{-19} = 6.928 \times 10^{-19}$ J.

$\phi = hf_0 = hc \div \lambda$

so $\lambda = hc \div \phi$

$= (6.63 \times 10^{-34} \times 3.00 \times 10^{8}) \div (6.928 \times 10^{-19})$

$= 2.870... \times 10^{-7}$ m

3 D *(1 mark)*

$c = f\lambda$ so $\lambda = c \div f = 5.172... \times 10^{-7}$ m.

$V_0 = \frac{hc}{e\lambda} = (6.63 \times 10^{-34} \times 3.00 \times 10^{8})$

$\div (1.60 \times 10^{-19} \times 5.172... \times 10^{-7}) = 2.40...$ V

4 D *(1 mark)*

The spacing of the grating is 2×10^{-6} m. Diffraction only occurs when the de Broglie wavelength is roughly equal to this spacing.

The momentum of the neutrons is $p = mv$

$= 1.675 \times 10^{-27} \times 3200 = 5.36 \times 10^{-24}$ kg ms^{-1}.

So the de Broglie wavelength is

$(6.63 \times 10^{-34}) \div (5.36 \times 10^{-24}) = 1.23... \times 10^{-10}$.

This is a lot smaller than the spacing of the grating, so diffraction does not occur.

5 a) $E = hc \div \lambda = (6.63 \times 10^{-34} \times 3.00 \times 10^{8}) \div (5.00 \times 10^{-7})$

$= 3.978 \times 10^{-19}$ J

$(3.978 \times 10^{-19}) \div (1.60 \times 10^{-19}) = 2.48625$

= 2.49 eV (to 3 s.f.)

(2 marks for correct answer, otherwise 1 mark for correct calculation of energy in joules)

b) eV_0 = energy of one photon, E,

so $V_0 = \frac{E}{e} = \frac{3.978 \times 10^{-19}}{1.60 \times 10^{-19}}$

= 2.486... V *(1 mark)*

So the LED will not light up, as the potential difference across it is smaller than its threshold voltage *(1 mark)*.

6 a) All particles have both particle and wave properties. Waves can also show particle properties *(1 mark)*.

b) i) $m_e = 9.11 \times 10^{-31}$ kg, $E_k = 1.02 \times 10^{-26}$ J

Rearrange $E_k = \frac{1}{2}mv^2$ to give $v = \sqrt{\frac{2E_k}{m}}$

$v = \sqrt{\frac{2 \times 1.02 \times 10^{-26}}{9.11 \times 10^{-31}}} = 149.64...$ ms^{-1}

= 150 ms^{-1} (to 3 s.f.)

(2 marks for correct answer, otherwise 1 mark for correct working)

ii) $\lambda = \frac{h}{p} = (6.63 \times 10^{-34}) \div (9.11 \times 10^{-31} \times 149.64...)$

$= 4.863... \times 10^{-6}$ = **4.86 × 10^{-6} m (to 3 s.f.)**

(2 marks for correct answer, otherwise 1 mark for correct working)

iii) The kinetic energy of each electron = $\frac{1}{2}mv^2 = eV$, so if the potential difference is halved, the speed of each electron decreases by a factor of $\sqrt{2}$. This means that the de Broglie wavelength will increase by a factor of $\sqrt{2}$ *(1 mark)*.

7 a) The work function of a metal is the minimum energy an electron needs to escape the surface of the metal *(1 mark)*.

b) The energy of photons depends on the frequency of the light *(1 mark)*. Below a certain frequency (the threshold frequency), the photons don't have enough energy to release an electron from the metal's surface *(1 mark)*.

c) A zinc plate is attached to the top of an electroscope ***(1 mark)***. The zinc plate is negatively charged, which causes the gold leaf in the electroscope to rise up as it is repelled from the metal ***(1 mark)***. The zinc plate is then irradiated with UV radiation ***(1 mark)***. Electrons are lost from the zinc plate due to the photoelectric effect ***(1 mark)***. The zinc plate and electroscope therefore lose their negative charge and so the gold leaf falls back down as it is no longer repelled ***(1 mark)***.

d) $\phi = hf_0$
$f_0 = 1.03 \times 10^{15}$ Hz, $h = 6.63 \times 10^{-34}$ Js
So $\phi = hf_0 = (6.63 \times 10^{-34}) \times (1.03 \times 10^{15})$
$= 6.8289 \times 10^{-19}$ J
$hf = \phi + KE_{max}$
$hf = 3.0 \times 10^{-18}$ J, $\phi = 6.8289 \times 10^{-19}$ J,
substituting into $hf = \phi + KE_{max}$ gives:
$3.0 \times 10^{-18} = 6.8289 \times 10^{-19} + KE_{max}$
$KE_{max} = (3.0 \times 10^{-18}) - (6.8289 \times 10^{-19})$
$= 2.317... \times 10^{-18} =$ **2.3×10^{-18} J (to 2 s.f.)**
(3 marks for correct answer, otherwise 1 mark for correct calculation of work function and 1 mark for correct working to calculate KE_{max})

e) i) If the intensity of the incident radiation is increased, this increases the number of photons hitting an area in a given time, but not the energy of each photon (as this depends on the frequency of the radiation) ***(1 mark)***. As the electrons can only absorb one photon at a time, their kinetic energy and therefore their speed is unaffected by the increase in intensity ***(1 mark)***.

ii) The rate at which photoelectrons are emitted increases, as there are more photons hitting an area in a given time, so more electrons can be liberated in a given time ***(1 mark)***.

Glossary

A

Absolute uncertainty
The total uncertainty of a measurement.

Acceleration
The rate of change of velocity.

Accurate result
A result that is really close to the true answer.

Air bag
Safety devices used in vehicles that inflate quickly on collision to 'cushion' passengers.

Ammeter
A component used to measure the current flowing through a circuit.

Amplitude
The maximum magnitude of the displacement of a wave, i.e. the distance from the undisturbed position to a crest or trough.

Angle of incidence
The angle that incoming light makes with the normal of a boundary.

Angle of refraction
The angle that refracted light makes with the normal of a boundary.

Anomalous result
A result that doesn't fit in with the pattern of the other results in a set of data.

Antinode
A point of maximum amplitude on a stationary wave.

Archimedes' principle
When an object is fully or partially immersed in a fluid, it experiences an upthrust equal to the weight of the fluid it has displaced.

Average speed
The total distance covered by an object divided by the total time elapsed.

B

Base unit
A fundamental unit that cannot be derived from other units.

Braking distance
The distance travelled by a vehicle after the brakes are applied until it comes to a complete stop.

Breaking stress
The stress experienced by a material at the point that it breaks.

Brittle
A brittle material doesn't deform plastically, but snaps when the stress on it reaches a certain point.

C

Calibration
Checking a scale on a measuring instrument by measuring a known value.

Centre of mass (centre of gravity)
The point which you can consider all of an object's weight to act through.

Charge carrier
An electrically charged particle that is free to move within a material.

Coherent
Sources (or waves) that have the same wavelength and frequency and a fixed phase difference between them are coherent.

Compressive deformation
Deformation of an object caused by balanced inwards forces, which leads to compression (squashing).

Compressive force
A force which squashes something.

Constructive interference
When two waves interfere to make a wave with a larger displacement.

Control variable
A variable that is kept constant in an experiment.

Conventional current
Standard current that is said to flow from a positive terminal to a negative terminal.

Correlation
A relationship between two variables.

Coulomb
A unit of charge. One coulomb (C) is the amount of charge that passes in 1 second when the current is 1 ampere.

Couple
A pair of forces of equal size which act parallel to each other but in opposite directions.

Critical angle
The angle of incidence at which the angle of refraction is 90°.

Crumple zone
Part of a car or other vehicle designed to crumple on impact.

Current
The rate of flow of charge in a circuit. Measured in amperes (A).

D

Density
The mass per unit volume of a material or object.

Dependent variable
The variable that you measure in an experiment.

Destructive interference
When two waves interfere to make a wave with a reduced displacement.

Diffraction
When waves spread out as they pass through a narrow gap or go round obstacles.

Diffraction grating
A slide or other thin object that contains lots of equally spaced slits very close together, used to show diffraction patterns of waves.

Diode
A component designed to allow current flow in one direction only.

Directly proportional
Two variables that are directly proportional will produce a straight line that goes through the origin when plotted against each other.

Displacement
How far an object has travelled from its starting point in a given direction.

Displacement (waves)
The distance a point on a wave has moved from its undisturbed position.

Displacement-time graph
A graph showing how the displacement of an object changes over a period of time.

Drag
Friction caused by a fluid (gas or liquid).

Ductile
A material that can be drawn into wires or other shapes without losing its strength.

E

Efficiency
The ratio of useful energy given out by a mechanical system to the amount of energy put into the system.

Elastic collision
A collision in which momentum and kinetic energy are conserved.

Elastic deformation
If a deformation is elastic, the material returns to its original shape once the forces are removed.

Elastic limit
The force (or stress) beyond which a material will be permanently stretched.

Elastic potential energy
The energy stored in a stretched material.

Electromagnetic spectrum
A continuous spectrum of all the possible frequencies of electromagnetic radiation.

Electromotive force (e.m.f.)
The amount of electrical energy a power supply transfers to each coulomb of charge.

Elementary charge, e
The smallest unit of charge, equal to 1.60×10^{-19} C.

Equilibrium
An object is in equilibrium if all the forces acting on it cancel each other out.

F

Force constant
The force needed to extend an object per unit extension. The units are Nm^{-1}. Each object has its own force constant.

Free-body diagram
A diagram showing all the forces acting on an object, but none of the forces the object exerts on its surroundings.

Free fall
The motion of an object undergoing an acceleration of $\boldsymbol{g}$.

Frequency
The number of whole wave cycles (oscillations) per second passing a given point.

Friction
A force that opposes motion. It acts in the opposite direction to the motion. It arises when two objects are moving past each other, or an object is moving through a fluid.

Fundamental mode of vibration
The lowest frequency at which a stationary wave is formed.

G

Gravitational potential energy
The energy an object gains when lifted up in a gravitational field, due to its position.

H

Homogeneity of units
When both sides of an equation have the same units.

Hooke's law
The extension of a stretched object is proportional to the load or force applied to it. This applies up to the limit of proportionality.

Hooke's law limit
See limit of proportionality.

Hypothesis
A specific testable statement, based on a theory, about what will happen in a test situation.

I

Impulse
The impulse of a force acting on an object is the product of average force and time.

Independent variable
The variable you change in an experiment.

Inelastic collision
A collision in which momentum is conserved but kinetic energy is not.

Instantaneous speed
The speed of an object at a given point in time.

Insulator
A substance which does not conduct electricity. Perfect insulators contain no charge carriers.

Intensity (of a wave)
The rate of flow of energy per unit area at right angles to the direction of travel of a wave.

Interference
The superposition of two or more waves.

Internal resistance
The resistance created in a power source when electrons collide with atoms inside the power source and lose energy.

Ionisation
Ionisation occurs when electromagnetic waves transfer enough energy to an atomic electron to remove the electron from the atom.

***I-V* characteristic**
A graph which shows how the current (I) flowing through a component changes as the potential difference (V) across it is increased.

J

Joule
One joule is the work done when a force of 1 newton moves an object through a distance of 1 metre.

K

Kinetic energy
The energy possessed by a moving object due to its movement.

Kirchhoff's first law
The total current entering a junction in a circuit must equal the total current leaving the junction.

Kirchhoff's second law
The total e.m.f. around a series circuit is equal to the sum of the potential differences across each component in the circuit.

L

Laser
A source of coherent, monochromatic light.

Lever
A structure made of a rigid object rotating around a pivot, in which an effort force works against a load force.

Light-dependent resistor (LDR)
A resistor with a resistance that depends on the intensity of light falling on it. The resistance decreases with increasing light intensity.

Limit of proportionality
The point beyond which force is no longer proportional to extension.

Linear momentum
The linear momentum of an object is the product of its mass and velocity.

Longitudinal wave
A wave in which the oscillations of the particles/fields (i.e. the displacement) is in the direction of energy propagation.

Lost volts
The energy wasted per coulomb overcoming the internal resistance of a power source.

M

Margin of error
The maximum difference between a recorded data value and the true value.

Mass
The amount of matter in an object.

Maxima
Constructive interference that occurs at any point where the path difference is a whole number of wavelengths.

Mean
The average of the values collected in repeated measurements, obtained by adding all the values together and dividing by the total number of values.

Mean drift velocity
The average velocity of the net movement of charge carriers towards a terminal of the power supply.

Minima
Destructive interference that occurs at points where the path difference is half a wavelength, one and a half wavelengths, two and a half wavelengths, etc.

Model
A simplified picture of what's physically going on.

Moment
The turning effect of a force around a turning point.

Momentum
See linear momentum.

Monochromatic
A light source that is all of the same wavelength (or frequency).

N

Net force
A single force that is equivalent to all the other forces acting on an object added together.

Newton's 1st law of motion
The velocity of an object will not change unless a resultant force acts on it.

Newton's 2nd law of motion
The rate of change of momentum of an object is equal to the net force which acts on the object.

Newton's 3rd law of motion
If object A exerts a force on object B, then object B exerts an equal but opposite force on object A.

Node
A point of zero amplitude on a stationary wave.

Non-ohmic conductor
A conductor that doesn't obey Ohm's law — under constant physical conditions, the resistance of the conductor changes as the current through it changes.

Normal contact force
The perpendicular force that a surface exerts on an object in contact with that surface. The force is equal and opposite to the force applied to the surface by the object.

O

Ohm
A unit of resistance. A component has a resistance of 1 Ω if a potential difference of 1 V makes a current of 1 A flow through it.

Ohmic conductor
A conductor that obeys Ohm's law — under constant physical conditions, the resistance of an ohmic conductor is constant for any current passing through it.

One-to-one interaction
Where a particle interacts with a single other particle.

Optical density
The property of a medium that describes how fast light travels through it. The more optically dense a material is, the more light slows down when it enters it. The optical density of a material is measured by its refractive index.

Oscilloscope
Displays waves from a signal generator as a function of voltage over time.

P

Path difference
The amount by which the path travelled by one wave is longer than the path travelled by another wave.

Peer review
Where a scientific report is sent out to peers (other scientists) who examine the methods, data and results before publication.

Percentage difference
The difference between a measured value and its true value, as a percentage of the true value.

Percentage error
The uncertainty given as a percentage of the measurement taken.

Period (waves)
The time taken for one whole wave cycle to pass a given point.

Phase
A measurement of the position of a certain point on a wave cycle, measured as an angle (in degrees or radians) or in fractions of a cycle.

Phase difference
The amount by which one wave lags behind another, or the difference in phase between two points on a wave. It is measured as an angle (in degrees or radians) or in fractions of a cycle.

Photoelectric effect
The emission of electrons from a metal when light of a high enough frequency is shone on it.

Photoelectron
An electron released through the photoelectric effect.

Photon
A quantum of energy of electromagnetic radiation.

Physical quantity
A quantity that can be measured, that has both a numerical value and a unit.

Pilot experiment
An experiment carried out before the actual experiment. The same set-up as the actual experiment is used to vary the independent variable to see (roughly) how much the dependent variable changes.

Pivot
The point about which an object will turn when it experiences a moment.

Plane polarised wave
A wave in which all the vibrations are in one direction or plane.

Plastic deformation
If a deformation is plastic, the material is permanently deformed.

Polarised wave
See plane polarised wave.

Polarising filter
A filter that only transmits vibrations of a wave in one direction or plane, called the plane of transmission.

Polymeric
A polymeric material is made up of molecules that are arranged in long chains.

Potential difference
The work done moving a unit charge between two points in a circuit.

Potential divider
A circuit containing a voltage source and a pair of resistors. The voltage across one of the resistors is used as an output voltage. If the resistors aren't fixed, the circuit will be capable of producing a variable output voltage.

Power
The rate of transfer of energy or the rate of doing work. It's measured in watts (W), where 1 watt is equivalent to 1 joule per second.

Precise result
The smaller the amount of spread of your data from the mean, the more precise it is.

Prediction
See hypothesis.

Prefix
A scaling factor used before a unit.

Pressure
The force applied to a surface per unit area.

Principle of conservation of energy
Energy cannot be created or destroyed. Energy can be transferred from one form to another but the total amount of energy in a closed system will not change.

Principle of conservation of momentum
Assuming no external forces act, the total linear momentum before a collision is equal to the total linear momentum after a collision.

Principle of moments
For a body to be in equilibrium, the sum of the clockwise moments acting about any point must equal the sum of the anticlockwise moments about the same point.

Progressive wave
A moving wave that carries energy from one place to another without transferring any material.

Projectile motion
Motion with a constant horizontal velocity and a vertical velocity affected by acceleration due to gravity.

Q

Qualitative data
Non-numerical data.

Quantitative data
Numerical data.

R

Random error
An error that occurs by chance. Its effect on experimental results cannot be predicted.

Reaction force
See normal contact force.

Reaction time
The time taken for a person to react after an event (e.g. seeing a hazard).

Reflection
When a wave is bounced back when it hits a boundary.

Refraction
The way a wave changes direction as it enters a different medium.

Refractive index
The ratio between the speed of light in a vacuum and the speed of light in a material.

Repeatable result
A result that can be repeated by the same person using the same method and equipment.

Reproducible result
A result that can be consistently reproduced in an independent experiment.

Resistance
A component has a resistance of 1 Ω if a potential difference of 1 V across it makes a current of 1 A flow through it. Resistance is measured in ohms (Ω).

Resistivity
The resistance of a 1 m length of a material with a 1 m^2 cross-sectional area. It is measured in ohm-metres (Ωm).

Resolution
The smallest change in what's being measured that can be detected by the equipment.

Resonant frequency
A frequency at which a stationary wave is formed because an exact number of waves are produced in the time it takes for a wave to get to the end of the vibrating medium and back again.

Resultant force
See net force.

Resultant vector
The vector that's formed when two or more vectors are added together.

Ripple tank
A shallow tank of water in which water waves are created by a vibrating dipper.

S

Scalar
A quantity with a size but no direction.

Scale drawing
A drawing that is proportional to the real-life situation it represents.

Seat belt
A belt used in vehicles that is designed to stretch slightly to protect the wearer in a crash.

Semiconductor
A material which conducts electricity (but not as well as a metal). When the temperature of a semiconductor rises, it can release more charge carriers and its resistance decreases.

S.I. derived units
Units that can be derived from the S.I. base units.

Speed
How fast something is moving, regardless of direction.

Standard form
A number written in the form $A \times 10^n$, where A is a number between 1 and 10 and n is a whole number.

Stationary (standing) wave
A wave created by the superposition of two progressive waves with the same frequency (or wavelength), moving in opposite directions.

Stiffness
Stiffness is a measure of the extent to which a material resists deformation in response to stress.

Stiffness constant
See force constant.

Stopping distance
The distance covered by a vehicle in the time between the driver spotting a hazard and the vehicle coming to a complete stop. It's the sum of the thinking distance and the braking distance.

Strain
The change in length divided by the original length of the material.

Strength
The strength of a material is a measure of its ability to withstand stress without breaking.

Stress
The force applied divided by the cross-sectional area.

Superposition
When two or more waves cross, the resultant displacement equals the vector sum of the individual displacements.

Systematic error
An error that usually causes measurements to be shifted from their true value by a fixed amount.

T

Tangent
A line drawn on a graph that is parallel to the curve at the point that it meets it. Used to calculate the gradient of a curve at a point.

Tensile deformation
Deformation of an object caused by balanced outwards forces, which leads to extension (stretching).

Tensile force
A force which stretches something.

Tensile strain
See strain.

Tensile stress
See stress.

Tension
The force that acts equally on either end of an object that is pulled tight.

Terminal potential difference
The potential difference between the two terminals of a power supply. This is equal to e.m.f. when there is no internal resistance.

Terminal velocity
The velocity at which the driving force(s) match the frictional force(s).

Theory
A possible explanation for an observation.

Thermistor
A resistor with a resistance that depends on its temperature — it is a type of semiconductor.

Thinking distance
The distance travelled by a vehicle between the driver seeing a hazard and applying the brakes.

Threshold frequency
The lowest frequency of light that when shone on a metal will cause electrons to be released from it (by the photoelectric effect).

Threshold voltage (of an LED)
The lowest voltage that will cause a current to flow through a light-emitting diode (LED).

Torque
The turning effect caused by a force couple.

Total internal reflection (TIR)
When all light is completely reflected back into a medium at a boundary with another less optically dense medium, instead of being refracted. It only happens at angles of incidence greater than the critical angle.

Transverse wave
A wave in which the oscillations of the particles/fields (i.e. the displacement) is at right angles to the direction of energy propagation.

U

Ultimate tensile strength
The maximum stress that a material can withstand before breaking.

Upthrust
The upwards force experienced by an object partially or fully immersed in a fluid.

V

Valid result
A valid result is a result that is precise and answers the original question.

Validation (of a theory)
The process of testing a theory by repeating experiments, or by using the theory to make new predictions and then testing these new predictions with new experiments.

Variable
A quantity that has the potential to change, e.g. weight, temperature, concentration.

Vector
A quantity with a size and a direction.

Velocity
The rate of change of displacement.

Velocity-time graph
A graph showing how the velocity of an object changes over a period of time.

Viscosity
A measure of how thick a fluid is.

Volt
The unit of potential difference. The potential difference across a component is 1 volt when you convert 1 joule of energy moving 1 coulomb of charge through the component.

Voltmeter
A component used to measure the potential difference across another component in a circuit.

W

Watt
A rate of energy transfer equal to 1 joule per second.

Wave-particle duality
All particles have both particle and wave properties. Waves can also show particle properties.

Wave speed
The speed that a wave travels at.

Wavelength
The length of one whole wave oscillation or wave cycle, e.g. the distance between two crests (or troughs) of a wave.

Weight
The force experienced by a mass due to a gravitational field.

Work
The amount of energy transferred from one form to another when a force moves an object through a distance or when a charged particle moves through a potential difference.

Work function
The minimum amount of energy required for an electron to escape a metal's surface.

Worst line
A line of best fit which has either the maximum or minimum possible slope for the data and goes through all of the error bars.

Y

Yield point (or yield stress)
The stress at which a large amount of plastic deformation takes place with a constant or reduced load.

Young modulus
The stress divided by strain for a material, up to its limit of proportionality.

Z

Zero error
When a measuring instrument falsely reads a non-zero value when the true value being measured is zero.

Zero order line
The line of maximum brightness at the centre of a diffraction pattern.

Acknowledgements

OCR Specification statements throughout the book are adapted and reproduced by permission of OCR.

OCR, A level Specification Physics A, H556, 2017 and OCR AS Level Specification Physics A, H156, 2017

Data acknowledgements

Data used to construct stopping distances diagram on page 64 from the Highway Code.
Contains public sector information licensed under the Open Government Licence v3.0.
http://www.nationalarchives.gov.uk/doc/open-government-licence/version/3/

Photograph acknowledgements

Cover Image **Russell Kightley**/Science Photo Library, p 1 Science Photo Library, p 6 **Daniel Sambraus**/Science Photo Library, p 8 Science Photo Library, p 9 (left) **Andrew Lambert Photography**/Science Photo Library, p 9 (right) **Andrew Lambert Photography**/Science Photo Library, p 11 **GIPhotoStock**/Science Photo Library, p 13 **Edward Kinsman**/Science Photo Library, p 17 © **Simon Whiteley**, p 18 Science Photo Library, p 24 Science Photo Library, p 25 **Martyn F. Chillmaid**/Science Photo Library, p 35 **Adam Jones**/Science Photo Library, p 41 **Mehau Kulyk**/Science Photo Library, p 47 **Edward Kinsman**/Science Photo Library, p 48 **Ted Kinsman**/Science Photo Library, p 56 **Michael Donne**/Science Photo Library, p 59 **Martyn F. Chillmaid**/Science Photo Library, p 60 **Martyn F. Chillmaid**/Science Photo Library, p 61 **Ted Kinsman**/Science Photo Library, p 62 **James Cavallini**/Science Photo Library, p 64 (top) **Ton Kinsbergen**/Science Photo Library, p 64 (bottom) **David Woodfall Images**/Science Photo Library, p 72 **Erich Schrempp**/Science Photo Library, p 73 **GIPhotoStock**/Science Photo Library, p 79 (bottom) **Peter Menzel**/Science Photo Library, p 81 **Chris Sattlberger**/Science Photo Library, p 84 **Martyn F. Chillmaid**/Science Photo Library, p 85 **Paul Rapson**/Science Photo Library, p 88 Science Photo Library, p 89 (top) **David Woodfall Images**/Science Photo Library, p 96 **David Scharf**/Science Photo Library, p 99 **NASA**/Science Photo Library, p 111 (top) Science Photo Library, p 111 (bottom) **Edward Kinsman**/Science Photo Library, p 115 **Langley Research Center/NASA**/Science Photo Library, p 116 **Martyn F. Chillmaid**/Science Photo Library, p 118 **Alex Bartel**/Science Photo Library, p 120 **Ton Kinsbergen**/Science Photo Library, p 121 **Ted Kinsman**/Science Photo Library, p 122 (bottom) **Trl Ltd.**/Science Photo Library, p 128 **Middle Temple Library**/Science Photo Library, p 133 **Ted Kinsman**/Science Photo Library, p 142 **Tek Image**/Science Photo Library, p 146 **Trevor Clifford Photography**/Science Photo Library, p 148 **Science Source**/Science Photo Library, p 153 **Martyn F. Chillmaid**/Science Photo Library, p 155 **Trevor Clifford Photography**/Science Photo Library, p 156 **Bildagentur-Online/Ohde**/Science Photo Library, p 158 **Martyn F. Chillmaid**/Science Photo Library, p 165 **Doug Martin**/Science Photo Library, p 168 **Library of Congress**/Science Photo Library, p 173 **Trevor Clifford Photography**/Science Photo Library, p 181 Science Photo Library, p 182 Science Photo Library, p 183 **Leonard Lessin**/Science Photo Library, p 184 **GIPhotoStock**/Science Photo Library, p 187 **H. S. Photos**/Science Photo Library, p 188 (top) **Sputnik**/Science Photo Library, p 188 (bottom) Science Photo Library, p 189 **Jerome Wexler**/Science Photo Library, p 190 **Carlos Dominguez**/Science Photo Library, p 191 **Martyn F. Chillmaid**/Science Photo Library, p 192 (top) **GIPhotoStock**/Science Photo Library, p 193 **Andrew Lambert Photography**/Science Photo Library, p 197 (top) **GIPhotoStock**/Science Photo Library, p 197 (bottom) **GIPhotoStock**/Science Photo Library, p 198 **GIPhotoStock**/Science Photo Library, p 201 **Andrew Lambert Photography**/Science Photo Library, p 204 **Andrew Lambert Photography**/Science Photo Library, p 205 **Edward Kinsman**/Science Photo Library, p 207 **Berenice Abbott**/Science Photo Library, p 209 **GIPhotoStock**/Science Photo Library, p 210 **GIPhotoStock**/Science Photo Library, p 213 **GIPhotoStock**/Science Photo Library, p 214 **GIPhotoStock**/Science Photo Library, p 217 **Edward Kinsman**/Science Photo Library, p 227 **Martyn F. Chillmaid**/Science Photo Library, p 230 © **Charlotte Whiteley**, p 231 **US Library of Congress**/Science Photo Library, p 235 (top) Science Photo Library, p 235 (bottom) **Andrew Lambert Photography**/Science Photo Library, p 237 **Gustoimages**/Science Photo Library, p 241 © **David Maliphant**, p 252 © **David Maliphant**

Index

E

F

G

H

I

Data Tables

This list summarises some of the constants and values that you might need to refer to when answering questions in this book. Everything here will be provided in your exam data and formulae booklet somewhere... so you need to get used to looking them up and using them correctly. If a number isn't given on this sheet — unlucky... you'll need to remember it as it won't be given to you in the exam.

Physical constants

Quantity	Value
acceleration of free fall, g	$9.81\ ms^{-2}$
elementary charge e	1.60×10^{-19} C
speed of light in a vacuum, c	$3.00 \times 10^{8}\ ms^{-1}$
Planck constant, h	6.63×10^{-34} Js
electron rest mass, m_e	9.11×10^{-31} kg
proton rest mass, m_p	1.673×10^{-27} kg
neutron rest mass, m_n	1.675×10^{-27} kg
alpha particle rest mass, m_α	6.646×10^{-27} kg

Conversion factors

unit	conversion
electronvolt	$1\ eV = 1.60 \times 10^{-19}$ J
day	$1\ day = 8.64 \times 10^{4}$ s
year	$1\ year \approx 3.16 \times 10^{7}$ s

PRATB51